ELECTRONICS

Devices, Discrete and Integrated Circuits

ARTHUR H. SEIDMAN
Pratt Institute

JACK L. WAINTRAUB
Middlesex County College

CHARLES E. MERRILL PUBLISHING COMPANY
A Bell and Howell Company
Columbus Toronto London Sydney

Merrill's International Series in
Electrical and Electronics Technology

Samuel L. Oppenheimer, *Consulting Editor*

For their understanding and patience, to our families—

Lee, Ben, and Rebecca Seidman
Betty, Adrienne, and Michael Waintraub

Cover photo courtesy Western Electric.

Published by
CHARLES E. MERRILL PUBLISHING COMPANY
A Bell & Howell Company
Columbus, Ohio 43216

This book was set in Times Roman.
The production editor was Linda Johnstone.
The cover was prepared by Will Chenoweth.

International Standard Book Number: 0-675-8494-6

Library of Congress Catalog Card Number: 76-54056

3 4 5 6 7 8 9 10 — 82 81 80 79 78

Printed in the United States of America

PREFACE

The field of electronics is vast and rapidly changing. New devices and applications are being developed constantly. It is the intent of the text to prepare the student to understand and to cope with these new developments in electronics.

In writing the text, the authors had four objectives:

1. To state material clearly.
2. To include numerous examples that demonstrate the application of the concepts covered.
3. To provide a solid foundation in electronics, stressing practical applications.
4. To emphasize the integrated circuit in analog and digital applications.

The text is written for the basic course in electronics for the electrical technology student. It is also suitable for the nonelectrical major in engineering and science and can serve as a reference for practicing technicians and engineers. Because of the organization of material in the text, the instructor has the flexibility of designing a course to satisfy his or her needs.

The prerequisites are high school algebra and a basic knowledge of ac and dc circuits. The numerous practical examples throughout the text and chapter problems are carefully designed to clarify concepts and introduce the student to standard industrial practices.

The primary goal in educating a technologist is to prepare him or her for industry. To achieve this goal, industrial data are used extensively throughout the book. The modern electrical technologist must be versatile and must be able to service various branches of the electronics industry. In keeping with this philosophy, Chapter 10, for example, is devoted to monolithic and hybrid IC fabrication.

The authors are indebted to many individuals for their constructive criticism and suggestions in shaping the text. First, to our students for their keen questions which helped us see things that often were taken for granted. To our colleagues for their valuable suggestions. To the reviewers, especially Sam Oppenheimer, whose comments helped improve immeasurably our presentation. To Mr.

Leonard Stern and Mrs. Eileen Q. Noonan of Western Electric for the use of their photographic library. Finally, to Andrea Posner and Linda Johnstone of Charles E. Merrill for their cooperation and valuable suggestions in the production of the book.

Arthur H. Seidman

Jack L. Waintraub

CONTENTS

part ii SMALL-SIGNAL OPERATION

9

Feedback 155

10

Integrated Circuit Technology 179

11

The Operational Amplifier 215

12

Using the Op Amp 239

part iii LARGE-SIGNAL OPERATION

13

Power Amplifiers 265

19

Diodes and Transistors as Switches 413

20

Integrated (IC) Logic 437

21

Multivibrators 459

22

Counters, Registers, and Memories 487

23

Displays, Converters, and the Microprocessor 523

1

Introduction

The field of electronics has an exciting past that dates back to the late nineteenth century. The first significant discovery occurred in 1883 when Thomas Edison, in one of his many attempts to improve the performance of the incandescent lamp, placed an electrode, called the *plate*, inside a lamp (Fig. 1–1). He then connected one terminal of a galvanometer, used for detecting the flow of direct current, to the plate. When the other galvanometer terminal was returned to the positive side of the battery, the galvanometer indicated current flow from the plate. Conversely, when the galvanometer was connected to the negative side of the battery, no current flowed. The observed phenomenon is called the *Edison effect*. (In 1883, the electron was not as yet identified. This had to wait unil 1897, when J. J. Thomson discovered the electron and determined its charge-to-mass ratio.)

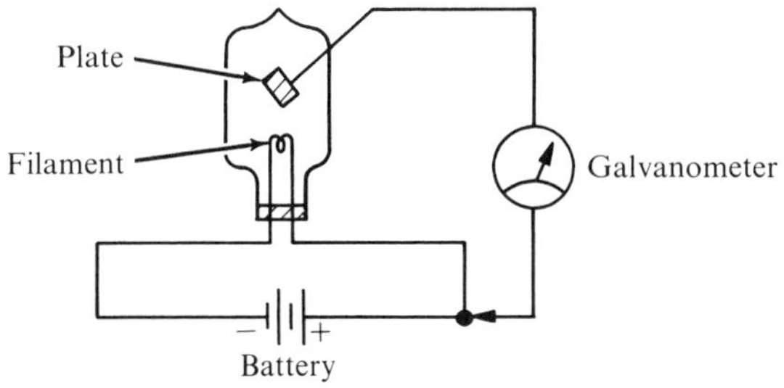

Fig. 1–1. *The Edison effect.*

The Edison effect is easily explained in terms of the electron theory. The heated filament "boils off" electrons. When the plate is connected to the positive side of the battery, electrons having a negative charge are attracted to the plate (unlike charges attract), and current flows. Because like charges repel, when the plate is connected to the negative side, the electrons are repelled, and no current flows. Edison dutifully recorded his observations but failed to recognize the importance of the discovery.

At the turn of the century, the great interest in electronics was centered about wireless telegraphy. One problem was the detection of wireless signals. A number of detectors were in use, but each suffered from various shortcomings. An improved detector, the *vacuum-tube diode*, was patented by

John Ambrose Fleming in 1905. The device was an application of the Edison effect. Using modern symbols, the vacuum-tube diode is shown in Fig. 1–2. Instead of the filament itself as a source of electrons, most tubes have a sleeve of metal, called a *cathode* (*K*), surrounding the filament. The cathode now becomes the source of electrons. Surrounding the cathode is the plate, or *anode* (*A*), of the tube.

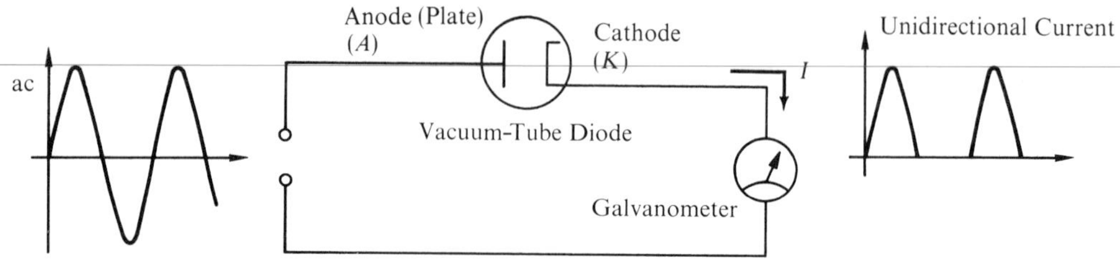

Fig. 1–2. *A vacuum-tube diode used to convert an ac signal to a unidirectional current.*

The basic operation of a vacuum-tube diode is illustrated in Fig. 1–2. An ac signal is applied in series with the tube and galvanometer. During the positive half-cycle, the plate becomes positive with respect to the cathode; the diode, therefore, conducts current. During the negative half-cycle, the plate is negative with respect to the cathode, and no current flows. Thus, an ac signal has been converted into a unidirectional current which can be detected by a galvanometer.

In 1906, General Dunwoody found that carborundum (silicon carbide) can be made to behave like Fleming's diode. It was called a *crystal detector*. This device became very popular in the early days of radio and is still widely used today. In today's terminology, the crystal detector is referred to as a *semiconductor*, or *solid-state, diode*. Its electrical symbol is shown in Fig. 1–3. Much will be said about this device later in the text.

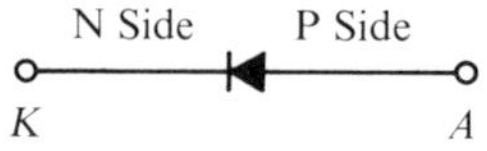

Fig. 1–3. *Electrical symbol for a semiconductor diode.*

1.1 First Electronics Revolution

Another worker seeking a good detector for wireless signals was Lee DeForest. His research was directed to the flame detector and, in 1907, he developed the *triode vacuum tube*, or *audion*, as he called it. The modern symbol for a triode vacuum tube is given in Fig. 1–4. The key to the operation of the triode is the *grid*, which is located between the cathode and the plate. Because of its close proximity to the cathode, the grid exerts an extremely strong influence over electrons streaming away from the cathode.

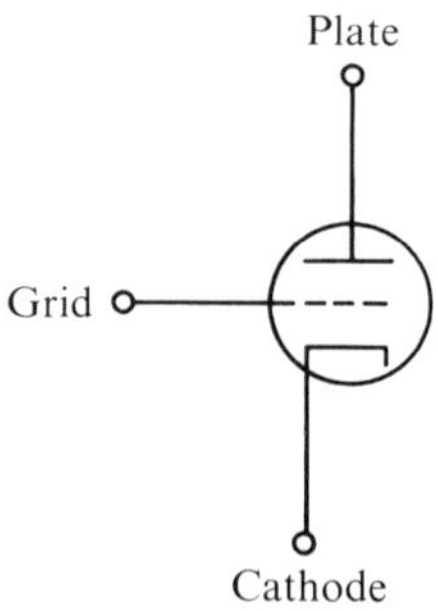

Fig. 1–4. *Electrical symbol for a triode vacuum tube.*

If a small signal is impressed across the grid and the cathode of the triode (which is connected to a suitable dc power supply), a much larger ("magnified") and faithful replica of the signal appears across the plate and cathode of the tube. This behavior is referred to as *amplification*, and the circuit is called an *amplifier*. In addition, if the plate, through a suitable circuit, is connected to the grid, the circuit generates sinusoidal waves of constant amplitude and frequency without the presence of an external signal. This circuit is called an *oscillator*.

With these two vacuum-tube circuits, the amplifier and oscillator, radio and television broadcasting as we know them today were made possible. Other applications, such as radar, automatic pilots, stereo amplifiers, and computers, all owe their existence to the invention of the vacuum tube. The impact of this invention created a great technical and social revolution, transforming our life styles and thinking in ways that are not yet fully appreciated.

Since 1907, the audion has undergone many changes, all dedicated to the improvement of its operation and reliability. The vacuum tube, however, has inherent weaknesses. The tube's filament must be heated to a temperature sufficient to allow the cathode to "boil off" electrons. To accomplish this, the filament is supplied with voltage and current, typically 6.3 volts (V) and 0.3 ampere (A), respectively. If the voltage is multiplied by the current, we obtain the supplied power to the filament. This turns out to be approximately 2 watts (W) (6.3 V $\times$ 0.3 A). The first electronic digital computer contained some 18,000 vacuum tubes. Assuming each tube required 2 W for heating its filament, a total of 36,000 W of power had to be supplied. This is an exhorbitant amount and waste of power.

The vacuum tube has other shortcomings. For one, it is rather large in size and bulky. Its useful life, although good, is not as good as that of resistors and capacitors found in amplifiers and oscillators. This is the reason tubes are made to plug in or out of a circuit so easily.

Today's computer would be unknown, and devices such as the pacemaker virtually impossible, if they depended for their operation on vacuum tubes. What was needed was a device which did all the things a vacuum tube does without requiring filament power, was small in size, and was highly reliable. This need was fulfilled with the invention of the transistor, a device which created a second revolution in the electronics field.

1.2 Second Electronics Revolution

The transistor was invented by John Bardeen, Walter Brattain, and William Shockley in 1947. Because of its importance, these men shared the Nobel Prize in physics in

1956. A page from their laboratory notebook is reproduced in Fig. 1–5. The entry describes the event and adds that, “This circuit was actually spoken over and by switching the device in and out a distinct gain in speech level could be heard and seen on the scope presentation with no noticeable change in quality.”

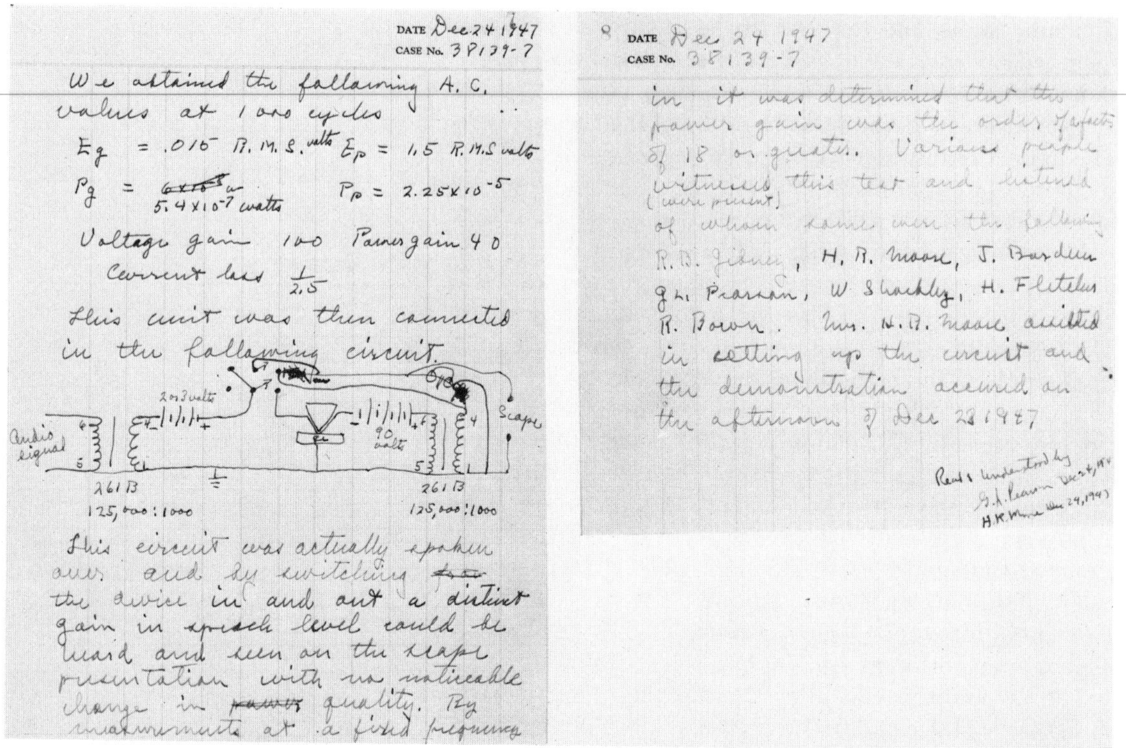

DATE Dec 24 1947
CASE No. 38139-7

We obtained the following A.C. values at 1000 cycles

Eg = .015 R.M.S. volts   Ep = 1.5 R.M.S volts

Pg = 5.4 × 10-7 watts   Pp = 2.25 × 10-5

Voltage gain 100   Power gain 40

Current loss 1/2.5

This unit was then connected in the following circuit.

This circuit was actually spoken over and by switching the device in and out a distinct gain in speech level could be heard and seen on the scope presentation with no noticeable change in quality. By measurements at a fixed frequency

DATE Dec 24 1947
CASE No. 38139-7

in it was determined that the power gain was the order of a factor of 18 or greater. Various people witnessed this test and listened (were present) of whom some were the following R. B. Gibney, H. R. Moore, J. Bardeen, G. L. Pearson, W. Shockley, H. Fletcher, R. Bown. Mr. H. R. Moore assisted in setting up the circuit and the demonstration occurred on the afternoon of Dec 23 1947

Read & understood by
G. L. Pearson Dec 24, 1947
H. R. Moore Dec 24, 1947

Fig. 1–5. *Laboratory notebook entry records the events of December 24, 1947, when the transistor effect was discovered. (Courtesy Bell Telephone Laboratories.)*

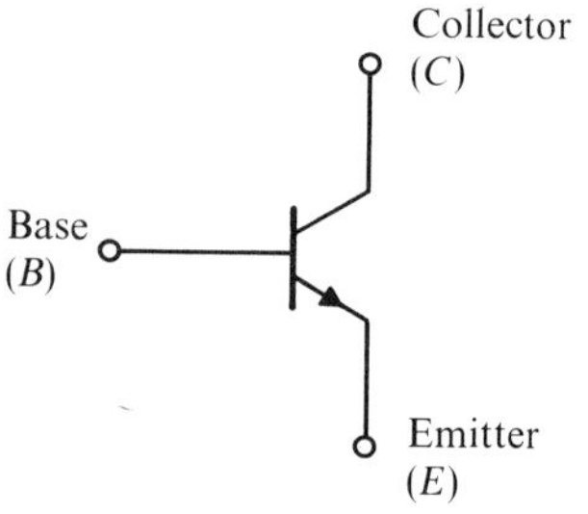

Fig. 1–6. *Electrical symbol for an NPN bipolar junction transistor (BJT).*

The first transistor device made was the point-contact transistor. Like the vacuum tube, the point-contact transistor was able to amplify signals and could be made to oscillate. Its operation, however, was often erratic and not well understood. Based on Shockley’s theoretical studies, the *bipolar junction transistor* (BJT) was developed a few years later. The BJT is superior in performance and does not suffer from the limitations of the point-contact transistor. This transistor is in widespread use today.

The electrical symbol of an NPN bipolar junction transistor is shown in Fig. 1–6. The base is roughly analogous to the grid of a vacuum tube, the collector to the plate, and the emitter to the cathode. This transistor is an example of a group of devices called *solid-state* devices. A detailed discussion of its operation, as well as of other solid-state devices, is given in the next few chapters.

Another solid-state device of importance is the *field-effect transistor* (FET). The electrical symbol for one version, the

N-channel FET, is illustrated in Fig. 1–7. The gate corresponds to the grid, the drain to the plate, and the source to the cathode. In fact, the FET is more like the vacuum tube than is the junction transistor.

The transistor proved to be a boon for the electronics industry. Overcoming the objections to the vacuum tube, the transistor has helped to accelerate the growth and development of electronics. It has made possible sophisticated digital computers, the electronic hand-held calculator, inexpensive transistor radios, and so on.

As progress was made in improving transistor performance, other solid-state devices evolved. These include the silicon-controlled rectifier (SCR), the light-emitting diode (LED), and the unijunction transistor (UJT). These and other devices will be explored later in the text.

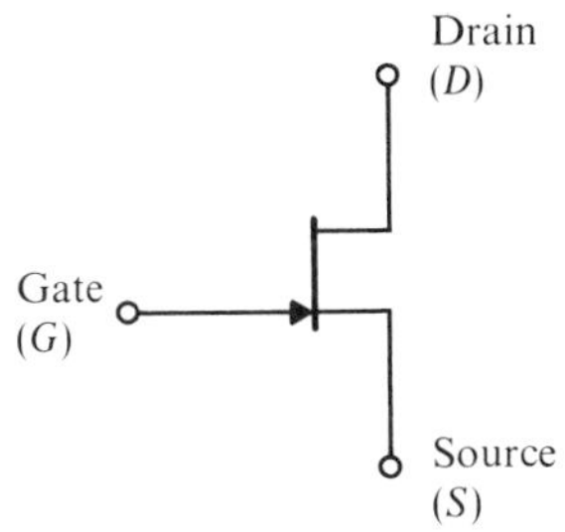

Fig. 1–7. *Electrical symbol for an N-channel field-effect transistor (FET).*

1.3 The Integrated Circuit

As methods for manufacturing transistors developed, a point in the technology was reached at which it became feasible to manufacture a complete circuit by the same methods used to make an individual transistor. As a result, the *integrated circuit* (IC) was invented by Dr. Robert Noyce.

For example, an amplifier or a shift register found in computers can be made in a chip of silicon not much larger than a single transistor. Because the various components are interconnected in the chip, one serious source of circuit failure, poor connections, is minimized. Added to these advantages of smaller size and greater reliability is the factor of reduced cost.

Where more than one hundred circuits are integrated in the same chip, we have *large-scale integration* (LSI). Many sections in a digital computer, such as the memory, are examples of large-scale integration.

1.4 Preview of Text

Because of their importance, solid-state and integrated circuits will be our prime concerns. More and more, the integrated circuit is replacing functions that were carried out by *discrete circuits*, in which individual transistors and other components are wired together. With few exceptions, the vacuum tube has become extinct as an element in the design of new circuits.

In part i of the text, we shall learn how diodes, transistors, and other solid-state devices are made and operate. Part ii covers small-signal operation of amplifiers, the making of integrated circuits, and the operational amplifier. In

Part iii, our concern will be with the operation of amplifiers that handle large signals, such as the power amplifier in a stereo. Part iv covers the application of diodes in power supplies. Part v discusses switching and logic circuits, as well as memories, found in the digital computer.

Further Reading

Aitken, Hugh G. J. *Syntony and Spark: The Origins of Radio.* New York: John Wiley and Sons, Inc., 1976.

Asimov, I. "Happy Birthday Transistor." *Saturday Review,* Dec. 23, 1972, pp. 45–51.

Chipman, Robert A. "DeForest and the Triode Detector." *Scientific American,* May 1965, pp. 92–100.

Seidman, Arthur H. "Evolving Transistor." *Electronics World,* March 1965, pp. 30–33.

Sharlin, Harold I. *The Making of the Electrical Age.* New York: Abelard-Schuman, Ltd., 1963.

Sparks, Morgan. "The Junction Transistor." *Scientific American,* July 1952, pp. 29–32.

Suran, J. J. "A Perspective on Integrated Electronics." *IEEE Spectrum,* January 1970, pp. 67–79.

Susskind, Charles. "The Early History of Electronics." *IEEE Spectrum* (four-part series), August 1968, pp. 90–98; December 1968, pp. 57–60; April 1969, pp. 69–74; and August 1969, pp. 66–70.

part i

DEVICE OPERATION

The text is concerned primarily with solid-state (semiconductor) devices as circuit elements in amplifier and switching circuits. To gain an appreciation of the properties and limitations of these devices, it is valuable to have an understanding of their operation. In this part, operation of diodes, transistors, the silicon-controlled rectifier, the unijunction transistor, and other semiconductor devices is explained.

2

Semiconductor Theory and Diode Operation

Since 1900, the concepts of atomic structure have undergone a revolution. The classical picture of an atom composed of electrons revolving in an infinite number of possible orbits around a nucleus, similar to planets orbiting around the sun, led to a serious difficulty. Theoretical considerations demonstrated that all atoms with such a structure should annihilate themselves.

To overcome this objection, Niels Bohr advanced a *quantized* picture of the atom. Limiting himself to the hydrogen atom, Bohr stated that an electron revolving around a nucleus can exist in only certain specified orbits having defined energies. The contribution made by Bohr was monumental and earned him a Nobel Prize in physics.

To extend the quantized picture to atoms of greater complexity than hydrogen, in 1926 Erwin Schrödinger developed the theory of *wave mechanics*. In wave mechanics, electrons are considered as waves with specific wavelengths. Furthermore, according to Heisenberg's uncertainty principle, we can never be absolutely sure of the exact location or velocity of an electron. These concepts, however strange they may seem, have helped the physicist and engineer to better understand and predict the behavior of atoms. This greater understanding has led to the development of transistors and other solid-state devices.

In this chapter, we shall consider those concepts of modern atomic physics that are vital for understanding the operation of solid-state devices. These concepts will then be applied to the operation of the junction diode. In Chapters 3 and 4, we shall consider the operation of transistors and other devices, such as the silicon-controlled rectifier and the unijunction transistor.

2.1 Atomic Structure

The electron may be viewed as a particle having a negative charge of 1.6×10^{-19} coulomb (C), a mass of 9.1×10^{-31} kilogram (kg), and a diameter of 6×10^{-14} centimeter (cm). It may also be viewed as a wave having a wavelength that varies inversely with its speed. An electron, therefore, has a *dual nature*. For understanding the operation of most solid-state devices, the particle picture of the electron is adequate and is used in the text.

Hydrogen has the simplest atomic structure. It has a single electron, which orbits around a nucleus containing a single proton. The *atomic number* of an atom, Z, is equal to the number of protons. Therefore, for hydrogen, $Z = 1$.

The charge of a proton is positive and equal to the negative charge of the electron. Most of the weight of an atom is that of its protons, their mass being approximately 2000 times as great as an electron. In addition to protons, *neutrons* also occupy the nucleus of many elements. The neutron is electrically neutral (has no electric charge), and its mass is slightly greater than that of a proton. A two-dimensional representation, or *model*, of a hydrogen atom is illustrated in Fig. 2–1.

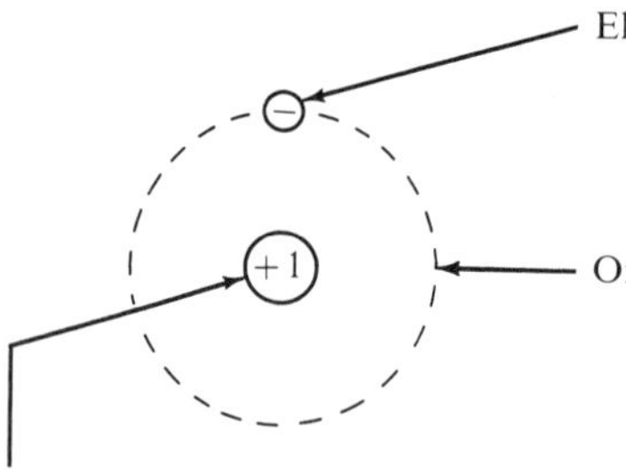

Fig. 2–1. *Model of a hydrogen atom ($Z = 1$).*

An important rule in modern atomic physics is *Pauli's exclusion principle*, which states that no more than two electrons can have the same energy state. Any orbit contains only a single electron. The electron orbits, in turn, are confined to *shells* and *subshells*. As a consequence of Pauli's exclusion principle, no more than two electrons can occupy the shell closest to the nucleus of an atom (called the K shell).

Extending outward from the K shell, the next shell is called the L shell. The L shell contains up to eight electrons in two subshells. The first subshell has a maximum of two electrons, and the second, six electrons. Eighteen electrons is the maximum number for the M shell, which surrounds the L shell. The M shell is split into three subshells containing up to two, six, and ten electrons in each. To account for all known chemical elements, four shells in addition to the K, L, and M shells are required.

An element whose shell or subshell is completely filled is chemically *inert*. An example of an inert element is helium (He), whose K shell is completely filled ($Z = 2$). Another example is argon (Ar) ($Z = 18$). In addition to filled K

and L shells, argon has the first two M subshells of two and six electrons each filled.

A two-dimensional view of a silicon (Si) atom, the basic material used in solid-state devices, is shown in Fig. 2–2. The atomic number of silicon is $Z = 14$. The K and L shells are completely filled with two and eight electrons, respectively. The first subshell of the M shell is filled with two electrons; the second subshell, however, contains only two electrons and is therefore unfilled. The four electrons in the M shell are called *valence electrons*. Because silicon has four valence electrons, it is referred to as a *tetravalent element*. Another tetravalent element used for solid-state devices is germanium (Ge).

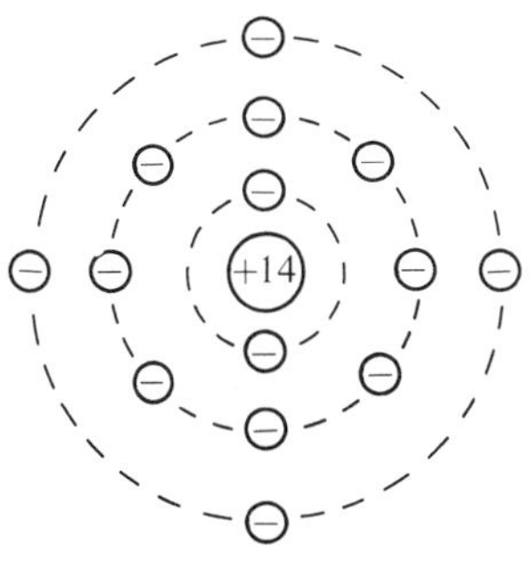

Fig. 2–2. *Model of a silicon atom ($Z = 14$).*

Elements having three valence electrons are called *trivalent elements*. Examples of trivalent elements are boron (B), indium (In), and aluminum (Al). *Pentavalent elements* have five valence electrons. Phosphorus (P), antimony (Sb), and arsenic (As) are examples of pentavalent elements.

Single Crystal

Atoms of silicon and germanium are arranged in an orderly fashion in their crystals. Such a structure with each atom part of a geometric pattern repeated throughout the crystal is called a *single crystal*. Atoms of a *polycrystalline* substance, such as sugar, are not arranged in an orderly pattern.

Covalent Bonds

Atoms of silicon and germanium form *covalent bonds*, as illustrated in Fig. 2–3. Each valence electron of an atom is shared with a valence electron of its neighboring atom. Because only four valence electrons of an atom are involved in the bond, for simplicity the nucleus is shown with a +4 charge for electrical neutrality.

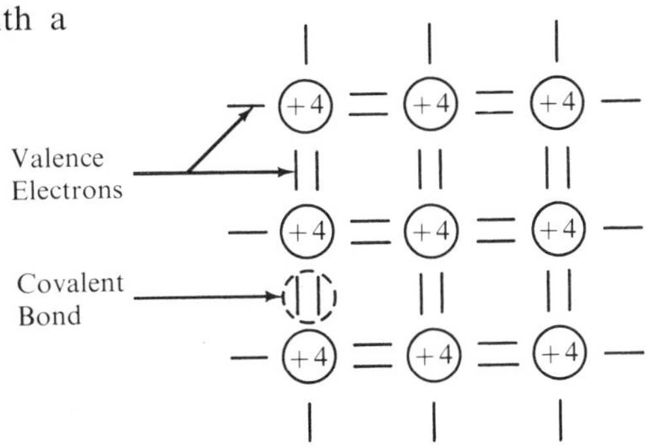

Fig. 2–3. *Two-dimensional representation of covalent bonding.*

Energy Bands

As mentioned earlier, electrons in an atom can occupy only certain orbits. In a cubic centimeter of silicon, there are some 10^{22} atoms. There are as many energy states as there are atoms. Because of such a huge number of atoms, interaction occurs between the many energy states of electrons in a solid. As a result, the individual energy level of a single atom appears as continuous bands of energies.

A typical *energy band diagram* of silicon or an insulator is illustrated in Fig. 2–4. The *valence band* of energies corresponds to the energy of valence electrons in covalent bonds, as illustrated in Fig. 2–3. Before electrons can serve as carriers of current, they must gain sufficient energy to be located in the *conduction band* of energies.

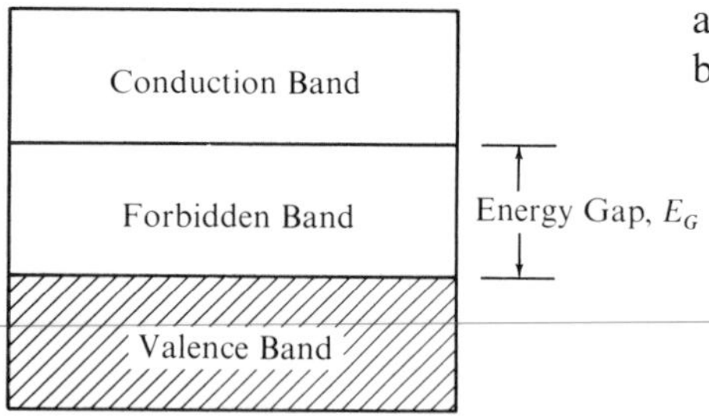

Fig. 2–4. *An energy band diagram of a semiconductor or insulator.*

According to modern atomic theory, an electron in the valence band of energies must acquire a minimum energy before it can occupy the conduction band of energies. The minimum energy is equal to the *energy gap*, E_G, of the material (Fig. 2–4). Furthermore, an electron can never find itself located in the *forbidden band* of energies, which separates the valence and conduction bands.

A comparison of energy gap values for different materials is provided in Table 2–1. Energy is expressed in *electron-volts* (eV). An electron-volt is the amount of kinetic energy acquired by an electron when accelerated by a potential difference of one volt (V).

TABLE 2–1. Energy gap values for some materials.

Material	E_G (eV)
Germanium, Ge	0.7
Silicon, Si	1.1
Diamond, C	6

The energy gaps for germanium and silicon are much less than that for diamond. Because of the large energy gap in diamond (6 eV), hardly an electron in the valence band can leap across the forbidden band to occupy the conduction band. Therefore, diamond is classified as an *insulator*.

The energy gaps of pure germanium and silicon are sufficiently small that, at room temperature (27°C), some electrons in the valence band acquire enough energy to occupy the conduction band. For germanium, the energy required is approximately 0.7 eV, and for silicon, 1.1 eV. Because germanium and silicon have resistivities greater than those for conductors, but less than those for insulators, they are referred to as *semiconductors*. A semiconductor that is absolutely pure is said to be *intrinsic*.

For every electron that lands in the conduction band, a vacancy (*hole*) is created in the valence band (Fig. 2–5). The hole is regarded as a particle with a positive charge equal to the negative charge of an electron. The process that results in a hole in the valence band for every electron that reaches the conduction band is called the *intrinsic generation of electron-hole pairs.*

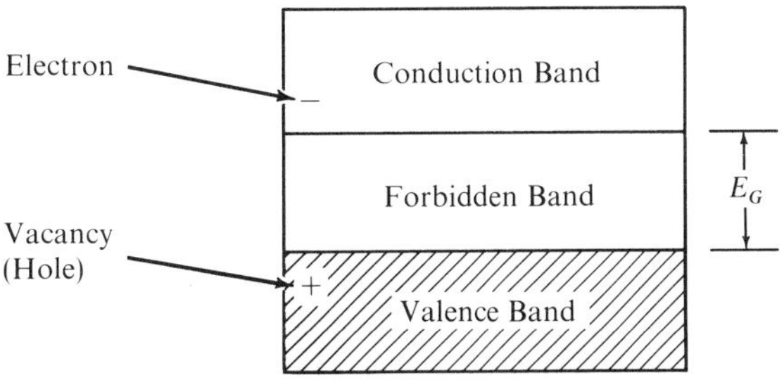

Fig. 2–5. *The intrinsic generation of an electron-hole pair.*

When a voltage is impressed across a semiconductor, both electrons and holes contribute to the total current flow. The electrons are attracted toward the positive terminal, and the holes toward the negative terminal, of the source. Holes, however, move more slowly than electrons.

As greater energy is acquired by electrons in the valence band, the generation of electron-hole pairs increases rapidly. Sources of energy include heat (*thermal*), light, x-rays, gamma rays, and fast-moving neutrons. Since germanium has a lower energy gap than silicon, germanium devices are limited to 85°C operation. A silicon device, because of its greater energy gap, can operate at temperatures as high as 150°C.

At a sufficiently low temperature, no electron-hole pairs are generated. An intrinsic semiconductor then behaves like an insulator. Because of the large number of electron-hole pairs generated at elevated temperatures, however, an intrinsic semiconductor then acts like a conductor.

For metallic conductors, the valence and conduction bands overlap (Fig. 2–6). A supply of electrons is therefore always available in the conduction band. Because no forbidden band has to be traversed, electron-hole pairs are not generated. Current flow in conductors is solely by electrons.

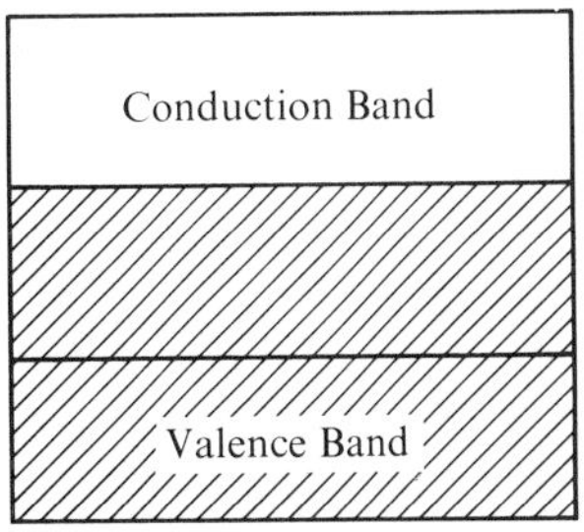

Fig. 2–6. *For a conductor, the valence and conduction bands of energy overlap.*

2.2 Doping Semiconductors

Intrinsic silicon (or germanium) is not useful for the fabrication of semiconductor devices. To make these elements useful, selected impurities as minute as one impurity atom for 100 million (10^8) silicon or germanium atoms are introduced in the material. The process is called *doping*, and the doped semiconductor is said to be *extrinsic.*

Consider first the addition of a pentavalent impurity, such as phosphorus. Because of its small concentration (one impurity atom for 10^8 silicon or germanium atoms), it is reasonable to expect that the impurity atom will be surrounded by *host* (silicon or germanium) atoms in the crystal lattice. This condition is illustrated in Fig. 2–7A.

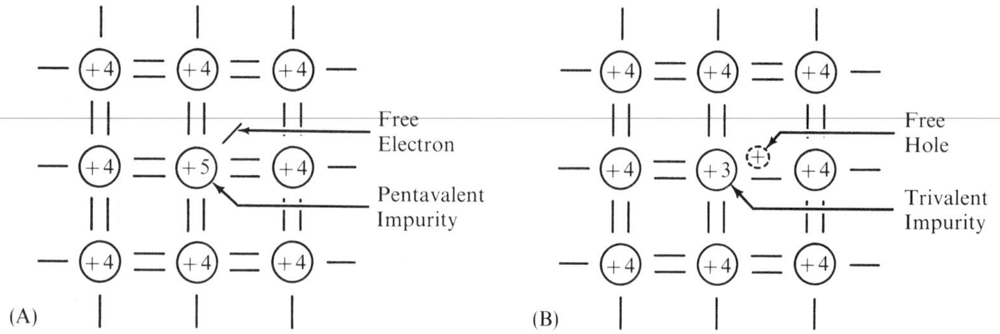

Fig. 2–7. *Doped (extrinsic) semiconductors. (A) N-type. (B) P-type.*

The pentavalent impurity is represented by a nucleus having a +5 charge. Four of its valence electrons form covalent bonds with electrons of its four neighboring host atoms. The fifth valence electron, however, cannot form a covalent bond and becomes a *free* electron. A pentavalent impurity is referred to as a *donor* and the doped material as *N-type*, because it has an excess of free electrons.

Figure 2–7B provides a picture of a semiconductor doped with a trivalent impurity, such as boron. Its three valence electrons share electrons only with three neighboring host atoms. The fourth neighbor "sees" a vacancy. Because of thermal agitation, an electron from another covalent bond fills the vacancy, and a new vacancy is created elsewhere. The movement of the vacancy is equivalent to the movement of a hole. A trivalent impurity is referred to as an *acceptor* and the doped material as *P-type*, because it has an excess of free holes.

In a doped semiconductor, the intrinsic generation of electron-hole pairs still continues. The impurity concentration, however, is sufficient to predominate. In an N-type semiconductor, therefore, electrons are the *majority carriers*. The few holes present because of the generation of electron-hole pairs are the *minority carriers*. For a P-type semiconductor, the reverse is true. Holes are now the majority carriers and electrons the minority carriers.

2.3 Fermi Level

Another result of modern atomic theory is the concept of the *Fermi level*. Consider the energy band diagram of an intrinsic semiconductor in Fig. 2–8A. Drawn in the center

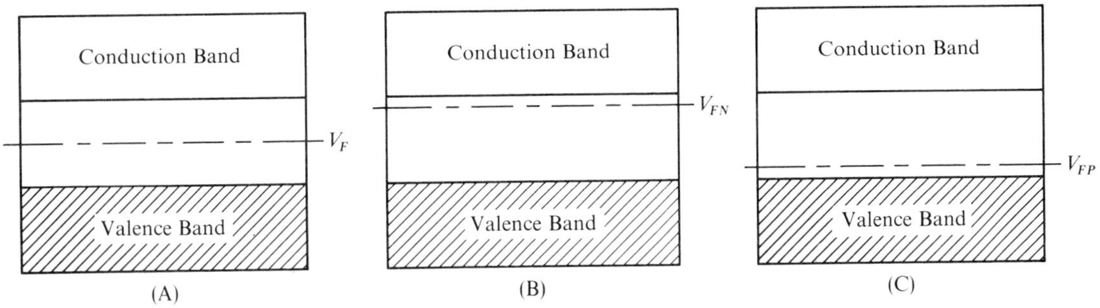

Fig. 2–8. *Location of the Fermi level for (A) an intrinsic semiconductor, (B) an N-type semiconductor, and (C) a P-type semiconductor.*

of the forbidden band of energies is a dashed line labeled V_F, the Fermi level expressed as a voltage. In simplified terms, it denotes that the *probability* of finding an electron in the conduction band is equal to the probability of finding a hole in the valence band.

In an N-type semiconductor, electrons are the majority carriers and holes the minority carriers. The Fermi level, V_{FN}, is therefore close to the bottom of the conduction band (Fig. 2–8B). The probability of finding an electron in the conduction band is now much greater than the chance of finding a hole in the valence band of energies.

For a P-type semiconductor, the Fermi level, V_{FP}, is close to the top of the valence band (Fig. 2–8C). In this case, holes are majority carriers and electrons minority carriers. The probability of finding holes in the valence band is now greater than the probability of finding electrons in the conduction band of energies.

2.4 Operation of the Junction Diode

The basic structure of a junction diode, and its electrical symbol, are illustrated in Fig. 2–9. One-half of intrinsic silicon (or germanium) is doped with a P-type impurity, and the other half with an N-type impurity. At the interface of the P and N regions, a *PN junction* is formed. The basic operation of a junction diode is dependent on the flow of electrons and holes across the PN junction.

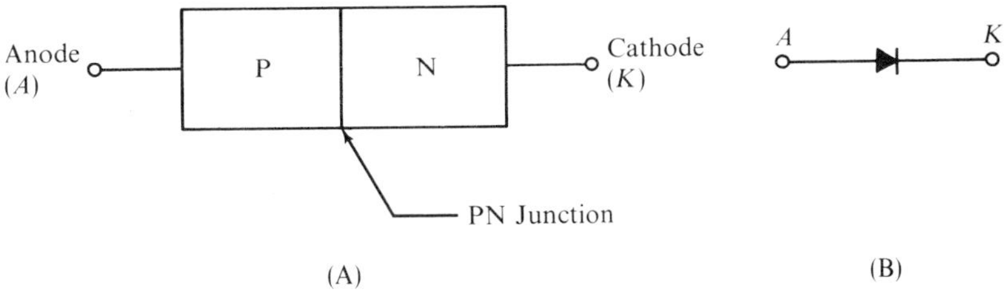

Fig. 2–9. *The junction diode. (A) Cross-section of its basic structure. (B) Electrical symbol.*

There are three modes of diode operation, as illustrated in Fig. 2–10. These are the following:

1. *Unbiased.* The anode (P region) is connected directly to the cathode (N region). No current flows.
2. *Forward bias.* The anode is connected to the positive terminal of bias source *V* and the cathode to the negative terminal. Current flows and is limited primarily by the resistance present in the circuit to which the diode is connected.
3. *Reverse (back) bias.* The anode is connected to the negative terminal of *V* and the cathode to the positive terminal. A very minute current in the order of nanoamperes (10^{-9} A, or nA) or microamperes (10^{-6} A, or μA) flows.

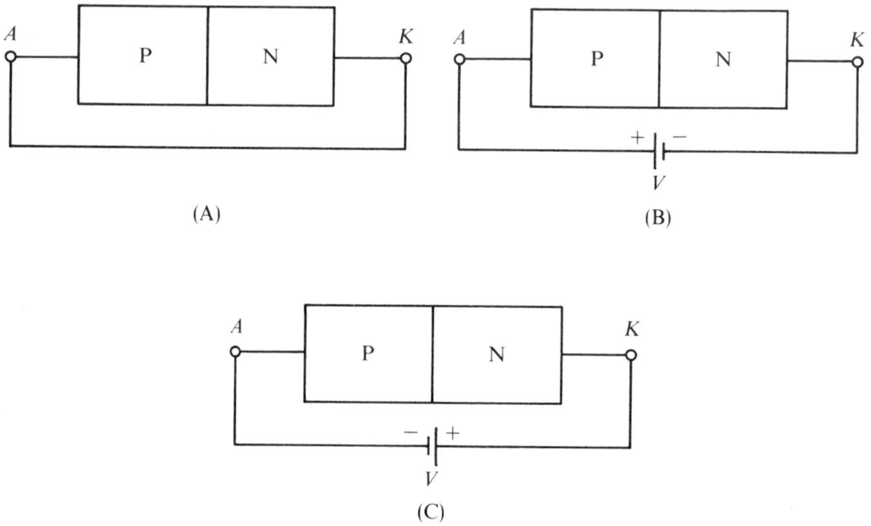

Fig. 2–10. *Three modes of operation for a junction diode. (A) Unbiased. (B) Forward biased. (C) Reverse biased.*

Unbiased Operation

In the P region of the diode, there are many holes and few electrons. In the N region, the reverse is true: there are many electrons and few holes. Because of the unequal concentrations of current carriers, holes from the P region cross the PN junction and flow into the N region. Similarly, electrons from the N region cross the junction and flow into the P region.

The process of current flow from a high concentration of electrons (or holes) to a low concentration of electrons (or holes) in the absence of an electric field is called *diffusion.* As we shall see in Chapter 3, diffusion is also an important mechanism in the operation of transistors.

Because of the initial diffusion of electrons and holes across the PN junction, no free electrons or holes exist on either side of the junction. Instead, there are *uncovered* negative acceptor and positive donor ions on each side of the junction (Fig. 2–11). This region, because it is depleted of free electrons or holes, is called the *depletion region.* Because of the presence of positive and negative ions, a *contact potential* is developed across the junction. The contact potential inhibits the further flow of electrons or holes.

To gain further insight into diode action, we refer to the energy diagram of Fig. 2–12 for an unbiased junction diode. Because there is no external bias and both regions are at the same temperature, the Fermi level V_{FP} for the P region lines up with the Fermi level V_{FN} for the N region. As a result, a steep sloping of the energy bands occurs in the vicinity of the junction. The slopes are called *energy hills.* Contact potential, V_C, is equal to the difference in the Fermi levels of the N and P regions: $V_C = V_{FN} - V_{FP}$.

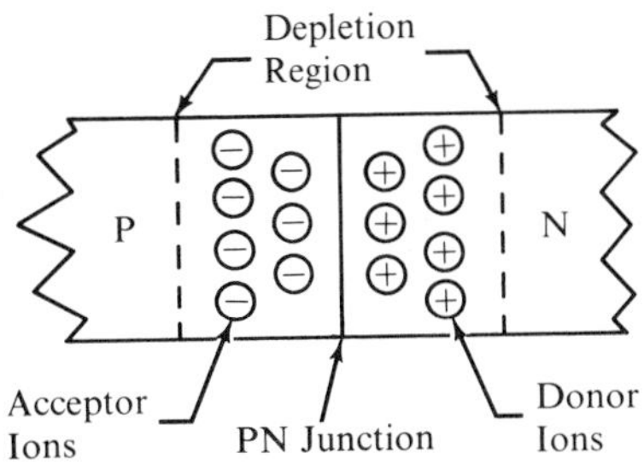

Fig. 2–11. *The depletion region of a junction diode contains uncovered acceptor and donor ions. No free electrons or holes are present in the depletion region.*

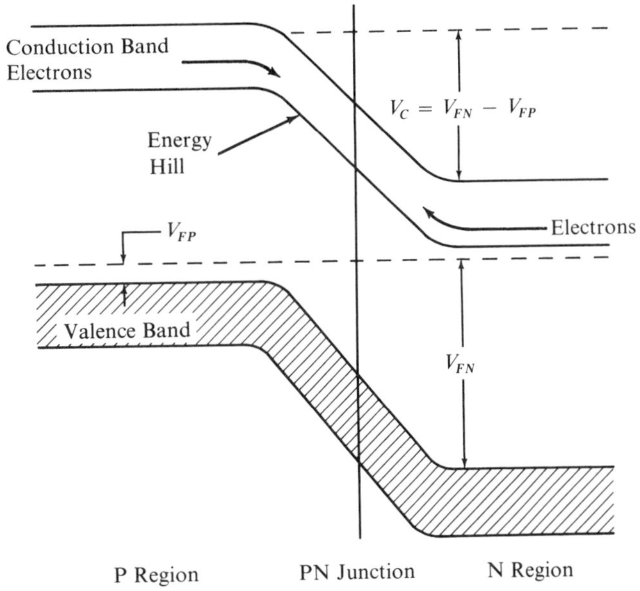

Fig. 2–12. *Energy diagram of an unbiased junction diode.*

Electrons, which are minority carriers in the P region, can easily "slide down" the energy hill, as indicated in Fig. 2–12. Because the bias voltage across the diode is zero, the net current flow in the diode must also be zero. For this to be true, some electrons in the N region have sufficient energy to "climb" the energy hill and oppose electrons "sliding down" the hill. The result is a net current of zero. A similar argument can be advanced for the flow of holes.

Forward-Bias Operation

When the diode is forward biased, the contact potential is reduced in the amount equal to the bias voltage, V (Fig. 2–13). The energy hill is thereby lowered, and electrons and holes have sufficient energy to "climb" the hill and cross the junction. For this condition, the current flow is limited primarily by the external resistance in the circuit.

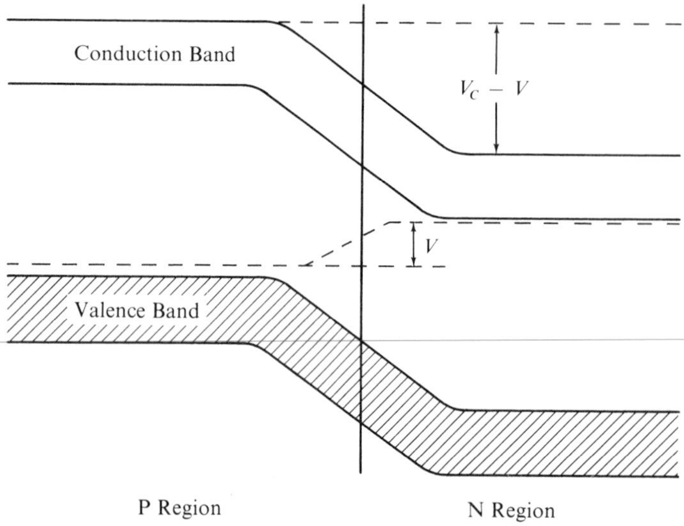

Fig. 2–13. *Energy diagram of a forward-biased junction diode.*

Reverse-Bias Operation

If a diode is reverse biased, the contact potential is raised by an amount equal to the reverse-bias voltage (Fig. 2–14). The energy hill now becomes very steep. No majority carriers, electrons in the N region or holes in the P region, have sufficient energy to "climb" the hills. As a result, only minority electrons and holes "slide down" the energy hills. A minute reverse current, in the order of nanoamperes or microamperes, flows. This minute current, because of the intrinsic generation of electron-hole pairs, is called the *reverse saturation current.* The reverse saturation current increases at elevated temperatures.

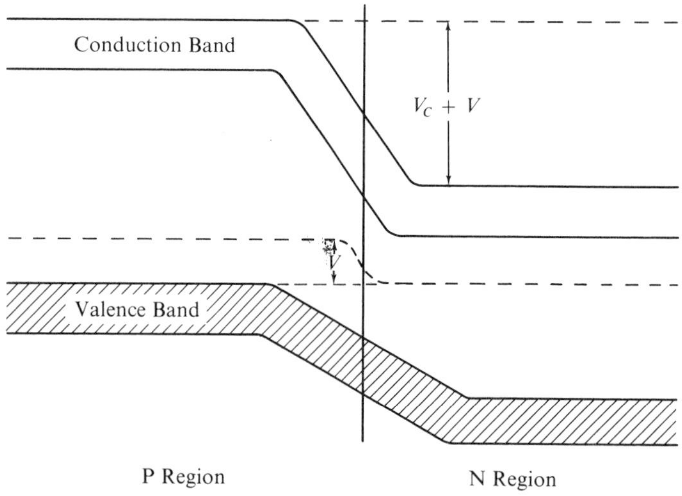

Fig. 2–14. *Energy diagram of a reverse-biased junction diode.*

2.5 Diode Characteristics

Based on the discussion of its operation, the volt-ampere (VA) characteristics of a junction diode should appear as illustrated in Fig. 2–15A. Mathematically, the characteristics are represented by the *rectifier equation*:

$$I = I_s(\epsilon^{qV/kT} - 1) \qquad \textbf{(2–1)}$$

where I = diode current.
I_s = reverse saturation current.
ϵ = 2.718, base of natural logs.
V = voltage across diode.
q = charge of electron, 1.6×10^{-19} coulomb (C).
k = Boltzmann's constant, 1.38×10^{-23} joule (J) per kelvin (K). One kelvin = 273° + °C.
T = temperature, in kelvins.

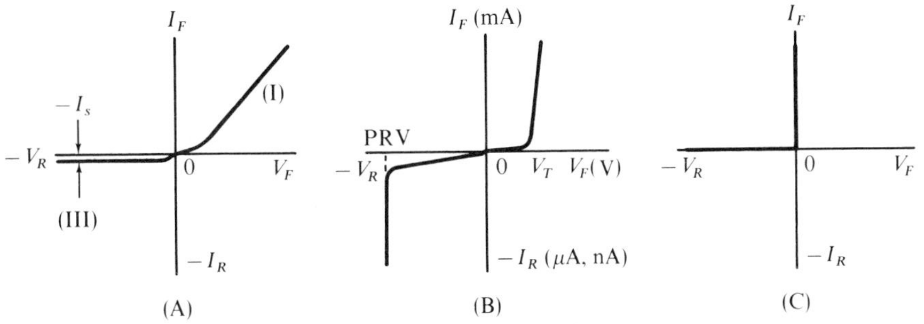

Fig. 2–15. *Volt-ampere characteristics of junction diodes. (A) Based on the rectifier equation. (B) Physical diode. (C) Ideal diode.*

Room temperature (approximately 27°C) = 273 + 27 = 300 K. Evaluation of q/kT in Eq. (2–1) yields

$$\frac{q}{kT} = \frac{1.6 \times 10^{-19}}{1.38 \times 10^{-23} \times 300} \simeq 39$$

Hence, at room temperature, Eq. (2–1) may be expressed by

$$I = I_s(\epsilon^{39V} - 1) \qquad \textbf{(2–2)}$$

For forward-bias operation, let voltage V equal the forward-bias voltage, V_F. If V_F is greater than a few tenths of a volt, Eq. (2–2) for the forward current, $I = I_F$, reduces to

$$I_F \simeq I_s \epsilon^{39V_F} \qquad \textbf{(2–3a)}$$

If the reverse-bias voltage, $V = V_R$, is more negative by a few tenths of a volt, Eq. (2–2) for the reverse current, $I = I_R$, may be approximated by

$$I_R \simeq -I_s \qquad \textbf{(2–3b)}$$

EXAMPLE 2–1.

Show that Eq. (2–2) may be approximated by Eq. (2–3a) and Eq. (2–3b), respectively, if

(a) $V_F = 0.2\,\text{V}$.

(b) $V_R = -0.2\,\text{V}$.

Solutions:

(a) Substitution of $V_F = 0.2$ in Eq. (2–2) yields

$$\begin{aligned} I &= I_s(\epsilon^{39(0.2)} - 1) \\ &= I_s(\epsilon^{7.8} - 1) \\ &= I_s(2441 - 1) \end{aligned}$$

Because $2441 \gg 1$, $I \simeq I_s\epsilon^{39V_F}$.

(b) $$\begin{aligned} I &= I_s(\epsilon^{39(-0.2)} - 1) \\ &= I_s(\epsilon^{-7.8} - 1) \\ &= I_s(0.0004 - 1) \simeq -I_s \end{aligned}$$

When forward biased (quadrant I in Fig. 2–15A), current in the diode increases nonlinearly with increasing forward voltage. In reverse-bias operation (quadrant III), reverse saturation current I_s is constant for reverse voltages more negative than a few tenths of a volt.

Because of mechanisms neglected in the explanation of the basic operation of diodes, the actual characteristics of a *physical diode* appear as in Fig. 2–15B. For a range of forward voltage from zero to V_T volts, little forward current flows. Voltage V_T is the *threshold, cut-in,* or *offset voltage* of a junction diode. At voltages less than V_T, electrons recombine with holes, thereby limiting the forward current. As the forward voltage is raised, more electrons and holes become available, and the effect of recombination is minimized.

At room temperature, V_T is approximately 0.6 V for silicon and 0.2 V for germanium. The threshold voltage decreases at the rate of 2 mV per degree Celsius rise in temperature. When conducting current, the typical voltage at room temperature across a diode is 0.7 V for silicon and 0.3 V for germanium.

When reverse biased, the reverse current in a physical diode is not independent of reverse voltage, as indicated in Fig. 2–15A. Instead, as the reverse voltage is raised, the magnitude of the reverse current increases. Further, if the reverse voltage reaches the *peak reverse,* or *inverse, voltage* (PRV, or PIV), the reverse current increases rapidly.

The P and N regions of a diode, like other materials, have an ohmic resistance (*bulk resistance*). According to Ohm's law, current I is equal to the voltage V divided by the resistance R: $I = V/R$. Consequently, a current obeying Ohm's law is superimposed on the reverse saturation current. The total reverse current, therefore, rises with increasing reverse bias.

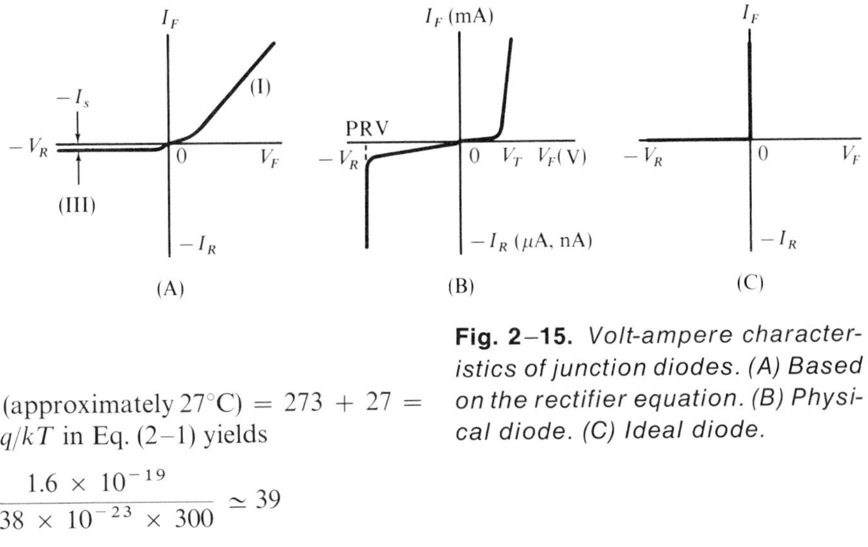

When the reverse voltage equals the PRV, electrons and holes have acquired an appreciable amount of energy. If a high-energy electron or hole collides with an atom in the crystal lattice, an electron is released from its covalent bond. As a result, an electron-hole pair is produced. This process is repeated many times. A rapid multiplication of electrons and holes and a corresponding increase in current occur. For this condition (*voltage breakdown*), the voltage across the reverse-biased diode is essentially constant. As pointed out in Chapter 4, this mechanism is a basis for the zener diode, used in the regulation of voltages.

A model for a forward-biased (conducting) physical diode is shown in Fig. 2–16A. It is represented by a *foward resistance*, R_F, in series with a battery equal to the threshold voltage, V_T. In reverse bias, the diode may be represented by a *reverse resistance*, R_R, shown in Fig. 2–16B. Because R_R is in the order of megohms (MΩ), it is usually assumed to be infinite.

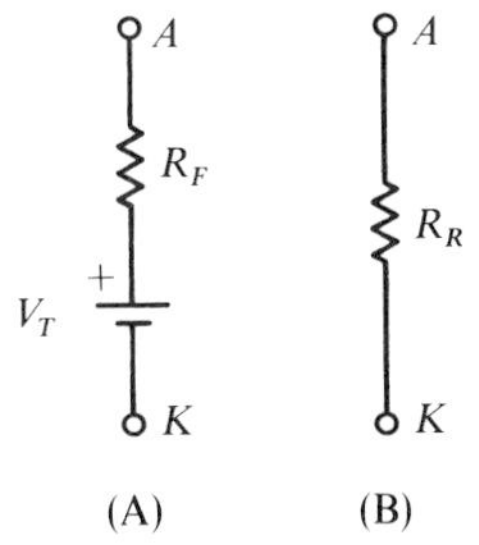

Fig. 2–16. *Model of a physical diode. (A) Forward-biased condition. (B) Reverse-biased condition.*

EXAMPLE 2–2.

For the diode circuit of Fig. 2–17, assume that $R_F = 50\,\Omega$, $R_R = \infty$, and $V_T = 0\,\text{V}$. Determine the current and dissipated power in the diode and load resistance, R_L, when

(a) Point A is positive with respect to B.

(b) Point A is negative with respect to B.

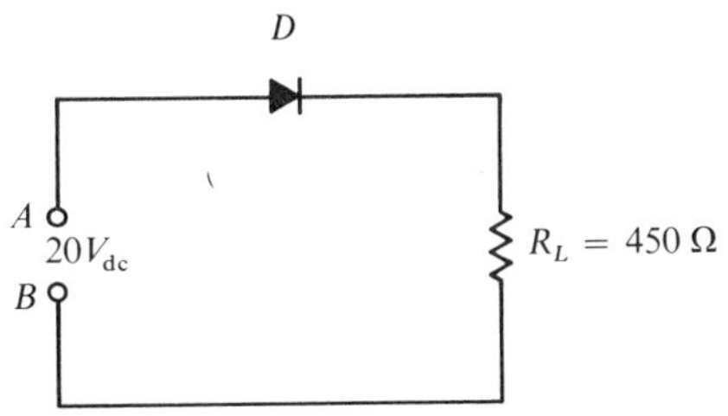

Fig. 2–17. *Analysis of a diode circuit. (See Example 2–2.)*

Solutions:

(a) When A is positive with respect to B, the diode is forward biased. Representing the diode by the model of Fig. 2–16A with $V_T = 0$, the circuit appears as in Fig. 2–18A. Current I is $20/(50 + 450) = 20/500 = 0.04\,\text{A}$. The power dissipated in the diode is $P_D = I^2R_F = (0.04)^2 \times 50 = 0.08\,\text{W} = 80\,\text{mW}$. In R_L, the power dissipated is $(0.04)^2 \times 450 = 0.72\,\text{W} = 720\,\text{mW}$.

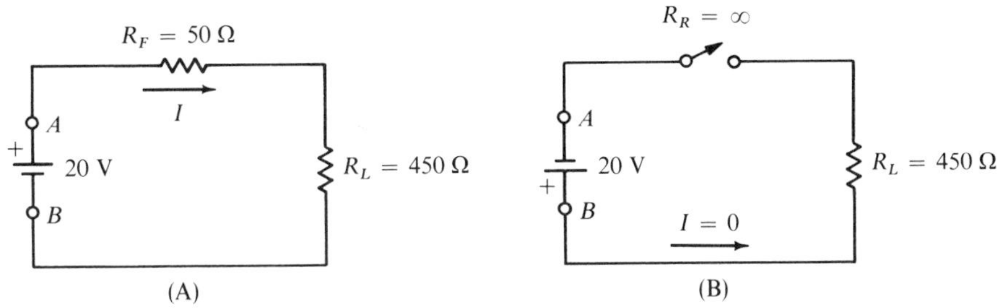

Fig. 2–18. *Models for the circuit of Fig. 2–17 when the diode is (A) forward biased and (B) reverse biased.*

(b) When A is negative with respect to B, the diode is reverse biased. Because $R_R = \infty$, it is represented by an open switch in Fig. 2–18B. Current $I = 0$, and the dissipated power in the diode and load resistance is also equal to zero.

Ideal Diode Characteristics

In many applications, it is convenient to assume that the junction diode acts like an *ideal diode* exhibiting the ideal volt-ampere characteristics of Fig. 2–15C. A useful fiction, the voltage across an ideal diode is zero, regardless of the magnitude of forward current. In its reverse-biased state, the reverse current is zero, independent of the value of the reverse voltage. An ideal diode, therefore, may be represented by a closed switch when forward biased and by an open switch when reverse biased.

Depletion Capacitance

The depletion region of a junction diode is devoid of free electrons and holes. It may be regarded, therefore, as an insulator. The P and N regions surrounding the depletion region may be viewed as conductors. This combination acts like a capacitor. The depletion region serves as the dielectric and the P and N regions as the plates of a capacitor. The capacitance is referred to as *depletion*, or *barrier*, *capacitance*.

The capacitance varies inversely with the width of the dielectric. The width of the depletion region (dielectric) depends on the magnitude and polarity of the voltage across the diode. For forward-biased voltages, the depletion width is relatively narrow; for reverse-biased voltages, the depletion width is wide. Consequently, a forward-biased diode has greater depletion capacitance than a reverse-biased diode. The change in depletion capacitance with the impressed voltage across a diode is the basis for the *varactor*, considered in Chapter 4.

2.6 Diode Applications

The junction diode, either as a discrete or integrated element, enjoys a wide spectrum of applications. Three common applications, as a rectifier, clipper, and logic gate, are illustrated in the following examples. *In each example, it is assumed that the diode is ideal.*

EXAMPLE 2–3.

A circuit for converting a sine wave into a unidirectional current or voltage is called a *rectifier*. Explain the operation of the *half-wave rectifier* of Fig. 2–19A.

Solution:

Referring to Fig. 2–19B, we see that during the positive half-cycle (0°—180°) of input voltage v_i, the diode is forward biased, and current flows. The diode acts like a closed switch, and output voltage, v_o, equals the input voltage for the positive half-cycle.

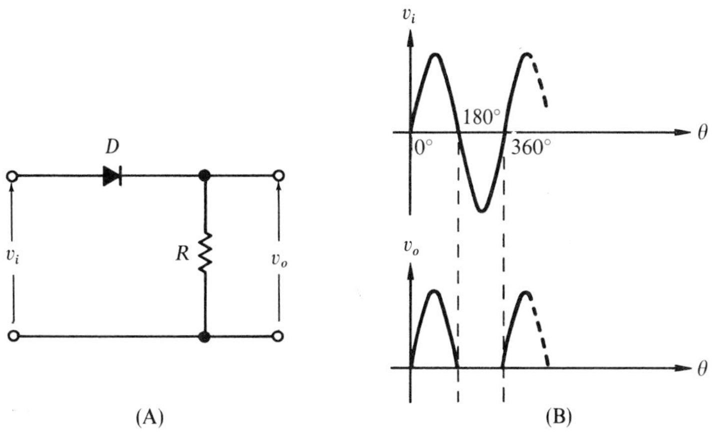

Fig. 2–19. *Half-wave rectifier. (A) Circuit. (B) Input and output waveforms. (See Example 2–3.)*

During the negative half-cycle (180°–360°), the diode is reverse biased, and no current flows. The diode acts like an open switch, and v_o is zero during the negative half-cycle.

The output voltage is always positive (unidirectional). Methods for smoothing out, or filtering, the unidirectional waveform so it appears as a dc voltage is the subject of Chapter 15.

EXAMPLE 2–4.

An example of a *symmetrical clipper* is shown in Fig. 2–20A. It clips the positive and negative portions of the input sine wave, v_i, so the output, v_o, approximates a trapezoidal waveform. Explain the operation of the circuit.

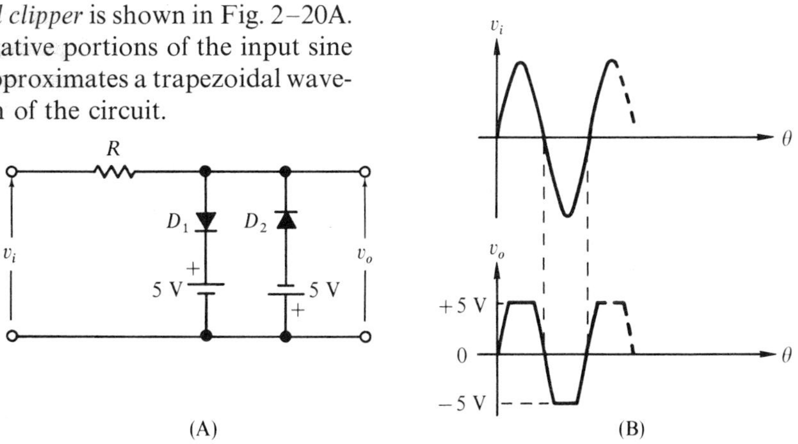

Fig. 2–20. *Symmetrical clipper. (A) Circuit. (B) Input and output waveforms. (See Example 2–4.)*

Solution:

In Fig. 2–20B, when v_i is less than 5 V, both diodes are reverse biased, and $v_o = v_i$. As soon as v_i is slightly more positive than 5 V, diode D_1 is forward biased (diode D_2 remains reverse biased). The output is clamped (maintained) at +5 V and remains clamped at that value until v_i becomes less than 5 V.

When v_i is between +5 V and −5 V, both diodes are reverse biased again, and $v_o = v_i$. As soon as v_i becomes more negative than −5 V, D_2 conducts (D_1 is reverse biased), and the output is now clamped to −5 V. It remains clamped at this value until v_i is less negative than −5 V.

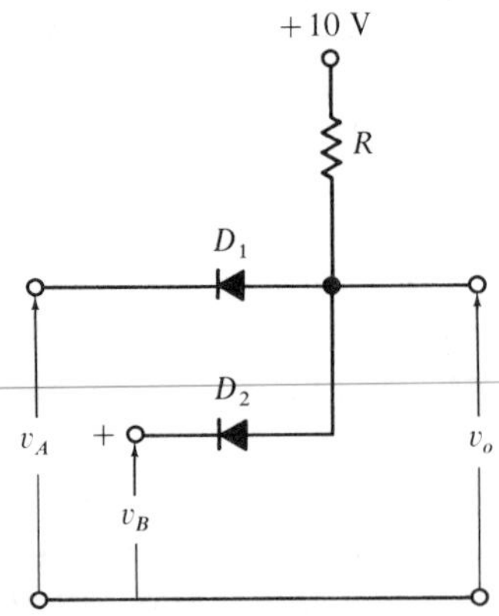

Fig. 2–21. *Example of a two-input AND gate. (See Example 2–5.)*

EXAMPLE 2–5.

An important logic element used in digital computers is the *AND gate.* An example of a two-input AND gate is illustrated in Fig. 2–21. Output voltage $v_o = 10\text{ V}$ only when v_A *and* v_B are present simultaneously; otherwise, $v_o = 0\text{ V}$. Assume that v_A and v_B are each equal to 10.1 V. Explain the operation of the circuit.

Solution:

When v_A and v_B are present simultaneously, both diodes are reverse biased because their cathode voltage (10.1 V) is more positive than their anode voltage (10 V). Output voltage $v_o = 10\text{ V}$.

If either v_A or v_B is zero, then diode D_1 (or D_2) is forward biased and acts like a closed switch. For this condition, $v_o = 0\text{ V}$.

SUMMARY

The concept of atomic structure developed in the first quarter of the twentieth century paved the way for the invention of the transistor and other solid-state devices. In this chapter, we saw that modern atomic concepts help to explain the operation of the junction diode. Basically, a junction diode is a two-terminal device having a P and an N region. At the interface of the two regions, a PN junction is formed. A lead connected to the P region is called the anode; a lead connected to the N region is the cathode.

If the anode is made positive with respect to the cathode, the diode conducts and is said to be forward biased. Its behavior can often be approximated by a closed switch. When reverse biased, the anode is negative with respect to the cathode. No current flows, and in this condition, it may be represented by an open switch.

The junction diode has many applications. Some examples considered in the chapter included rectification, clipping, and logic. Because of its other properties, the junction diode also may be used as a variable capacitor (varactor) and as a voltage regulator (zener diode).

Further Reading

Kaufman, M., and A. H. Seidman, eds. *Handbook for Electronics Engineering Technicians.* New York: McGraw-Hill Book Company, 1976, Chapter 8.

Lenert, Louis H. *Semiconductor Physics, Devices, and Circuits.* Columbus, Ohio: Charles E. Merrill Publishing Company, 1968, Chapters 1, 2, and 4.

Matthews, John I. *Solid-State Electronics Concepts.* New York: McGraw-Hill Book Company, 1972, Chapters 5 and 6.

Seidman, A. H., and S. L. Marshall. *Semiconductor Fundamentals: Devices and Circuits.* New York: John Wiley and Sons, Inc., 1963, Chapters 1–3.

Shive, John N. *Physics of Solid-State Electronics.* Columbus, Ohio: Charles E. Merrill Publishing Company, 1966.

Tocci, Ronald J. *Fundamentals of Electronic Devices.* 2nd ed. Columbus, Ohio: Charles E. Merrill Publishing Company, 1975, Chapters 1–5.

REVIEW QUESTIONS

2.1 Describe briefly Bohr's quantized picture of the hydrogen atom.

2.2 How is an electron viewed from the point of view of wave mechanics?

2.3 What is the meaning of Heisenberg's uncertainty principle?

2.4 What is the dual nature of an electron?

2.5 Define the atomic number, Z, of an atom.

2.6 Discuss the differences between an electron, a proton, and a neutron.

2.7 State Pauli's exclusion principle. What is the significance of the principle?

2.8 What distinguishes an inert element?

2.9 Define valence electron.

2.10 What are the differences between a trivalent, tetravalent, and pentavalent element? Provide an example of each type of element.

2.11 What is the difference between a single crystal and polycrystalline substance?

2.12 Define covalent bond.

2.13 Explain the difference between the valence and conduction bands of energy.

2.14 What is meant by the energy gap of a material? How does the energy gap of silicon compare with that of germanium and the diamond form of carbon?

2.15 What is the significance of the forbidden band of energies?

2.16 Define electron-volt.

2.17 In what important characteristic does a semiconductor differ from an insulator and a conductor?

2.18 Define hole.

2.19 What is meant by intrinsic generation of electron-hole pairs?

2.20 Explain what occurs when a voltage is impressed across a semiconductor.

2.21 Define intrinsic, extrinsic, and doping.

2.22 What is meant by N-type and P-type material?

2.23 Define donor and acceptor atoms. Provide an example of each type.

2.24 What is the difference between majority and minority carriers?

2.25 What is the meaning of Fermi level? Draw energy diagrams illustrating the location of the Fermi level for
(a) Intrinsic semiconductors.
(b) N-type semiconductors.
(c) P-type semiconductors.

2.26 What is a PN junction?

2.27 Explain the three modes of diode operation.

2.28 Define current flow by diffusion.

2.29 Define depletion region.

2.30 How is contact potential developed?

2.31 Define reverse saturation current.

2.32 What is the meaning of the threshold voltage of a diode?

2.33 What occurs when the reverse voltage across a diode reaches its peak reverse (or inverse) value?

2.34 Explain why the current in a reverse-biased diode rises with increasing reverse voltage.

2.35 Draw the voltage-current (V-I) characteristics of
(a) A physical diode.
(b) An ideal diode.

2.36 Represent a physical diode by a suitable model when it is
(a) Forward biased.
(b) Reverse biased.

2.37 Define depletion (barrier) capacitance of a junction diode.

PROBLEMS

P2–1 At room temperature, $I_s = 10\,\text{nA}$ (nanoamperes) for a particular junction diode.
(a) If the diode is forward biased by 0.2 V, what is the diode current?
(b) What is the approximate diode current if the diode is reverse biased by $-1\,\text{V}$?

P2–2 Repeat prob. P2–1 for
(a) $V_F = 0.3\,\text{V}$.
(b) $V_R = -0.3\,\text{V}$.

P2–3 At 25°C, the voltage across a forward-biased silicon diode is 0.7 V. What is its voltage at
(a) 75°C?
(b) 125°C?

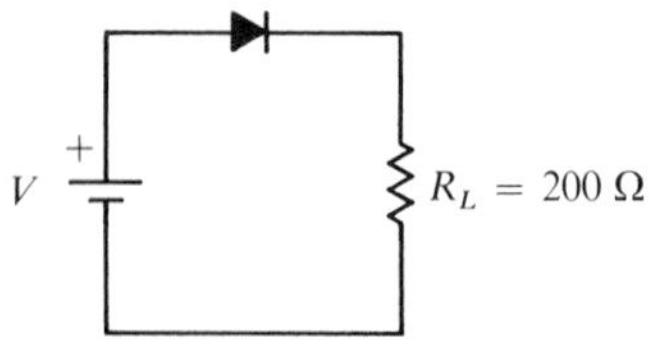

Fig. 2–22.

P2–4 For the diode in the circuit of Fig. 2–22, $R_F = 20\,\Omega$, $R_R = \infty$, and $V_T = 0\,\text{V}$. Calculate the current and dissipated power in the diode and load resistor R_L if
(a) $V = 10\,\text{V}$.
(b) $V = 50\,\text{V}$.

P2–5 Repeat prob. P2–4 assuming an ideal diode.

P2–6 In prob. P2–4, the diode is reverse biased. What is the current flow? Why?

P2–7 Assume that the diode in Fig. 2–19 is ideal. Carefully draw and dimension v_o for the input waveforms of Fig. 2–23.

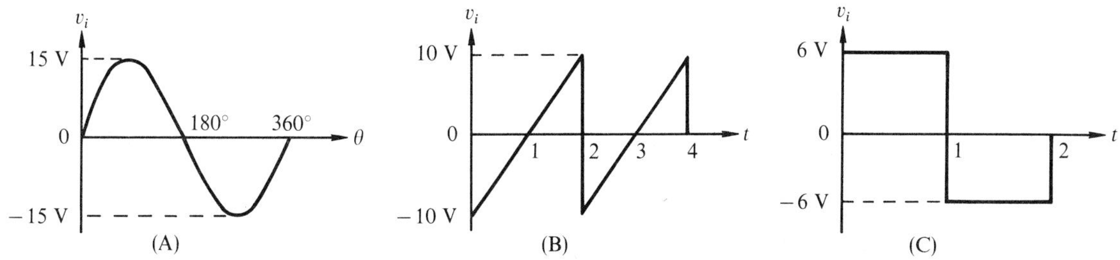

Fig. 2–23.

P2–8 A clipping circuit is illustrated in Fig. 2–24. The input to the circuit, v_i, is a sine wave. Assuming ideal diodes, carefully draw and dimension v_o if

(a) $V_1 = V_2 = 10\,\text{V}$.
(b) $V_1 = 10\,\text{V}$, $V_2 = 20\,\text{V}$.
(c) $V_1 = 20\,\text{V}$, $V_2 = 10\,\text{V}$.

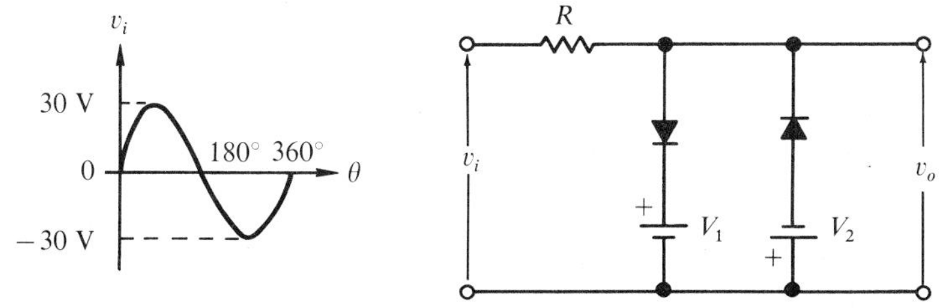

Fig. 2–24.

P2–9 Repeat prob. P2–8 for the input waveform of Fig. 2–25.

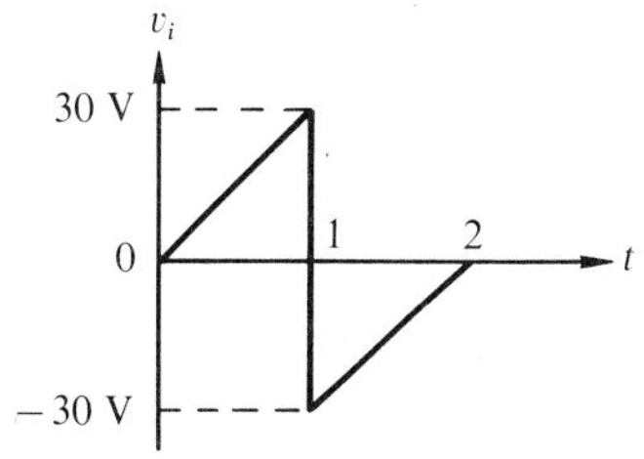

Fig. 2–25.

P2–10 Repeat prob. P2–8 for the input waveform of Fig. 2–26. What is the waveform called?

P2–11 For the two-input AND gate of Fig. 2–21, assuming ideal diodes, determine v_o if

(a) $v_A = v_B = 0\,\text{V}$.
(b) $v_A = 10\,\text{V}$, $v_B = 0\,\text{V}$.
(c) $v_A = 0\,\text{V}$, $v_B = 10\,\text{V}$.
(d) $v_A = v_B = 10\,\text{V}$.
(e) $v_A = 5\,\text{V}$, $v_B = 10\,\text{V}$.

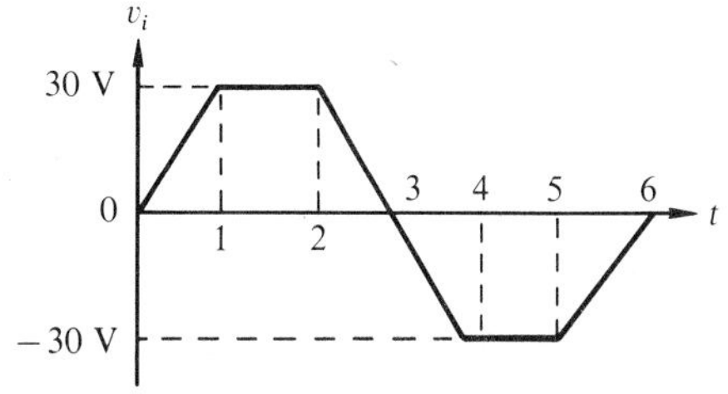

Fig. 2–26.

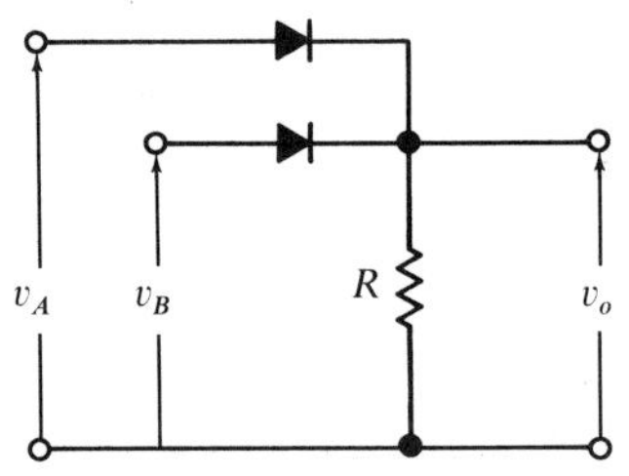

Fig. 2–27.

P2–12 Another important logic element used in digital computers is the OR gate. An example of a two-input OR gate is provided in Fig. 2–27. An output voltage is present if input v_A, input v_B, *or* both are present. Assuming ideal diodes, determine v_o for conditions (a) through (e) of prob. P2–11.

3

Transistor Operation

The *transistor*, a semiconductor element having three terminals and capable of providing power gain, is an *active* device. Elements such as the resistor, capacitor, and transformer are *passive* because they do not provide power gain. In addition to its use as an amplifier, the transistor is employed in the generation of sinusoidal and nonsinusoidal waveforms (e.g., square waves) and in switching circuits.

There are two families of transistors: the bipolar junction transistor (BJT) and the field-effect transistor (FET). When just *transistor* or *junction transistor* is used, it refers to the BJT. Each family contains different types of transistors, each of which exhibits specific characteristics. The operation of these devices and their characteristics are explained in this chapter.

3.1 The Bipolar Junction Transistor

There are two types of bipolar junction transistors: the NPN and PNP (Fig. 3–1). Each device has *two* PN junctions in a "sandwich-type" structure. In the NPN transistor, shown in elementary form in Fig. 3–2A, a thin P-type region is sandwiched between two thicker N-type regions. For the PNP transistor, the reverse is true; in Fig. 3–2B, an N-type region is sandwiched between two P-type regions. Electrical symbols for NPN and PNP transistors are provided in Fig. 3–3.

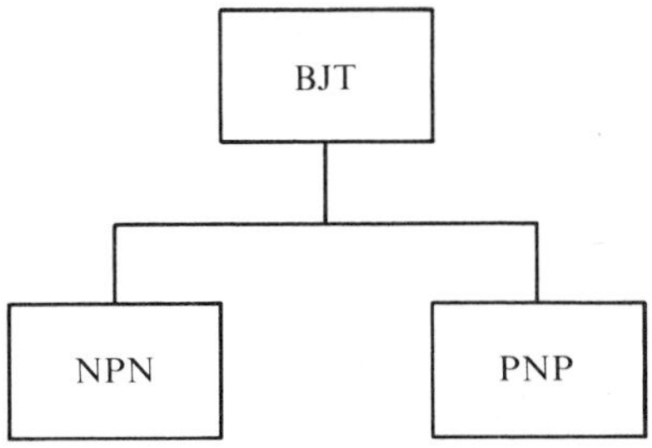

Fig. 3–1. *Two types of junction transistors: NPN and PNP.*

For each type of transistor, the region sandwiched between the two outer regions is called the *base*, *B*. One outer region is referred to as the *emitter*, *E*, and the other as the *collector*, *C*. PN junction J_1 is called the *emitter-base* (*E-B*) (or *base-emitter*, *B-E*) junction and J_2 the *collector-base* (*C-B*) junction.

The diffusion process is invariably used in manufacturing a BJT. A cross-section of a diffused NPN transistor is illustrated in Fig. 3–4. In the diffusion process, impurity atoms such as boron for P-type material and phosphorus for N-type material flow from a source of high concentration to a low concentration. (This subject is treated in detail in Chapter 10.)

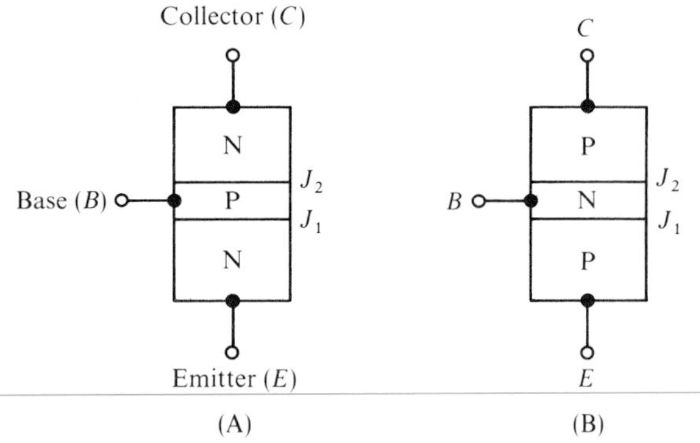

Fig. 3–2. *Cross-section of elementary (A) NPN and (B) PNP transistors. Each device has two PN junctions in a "sandwich-type" structure.*

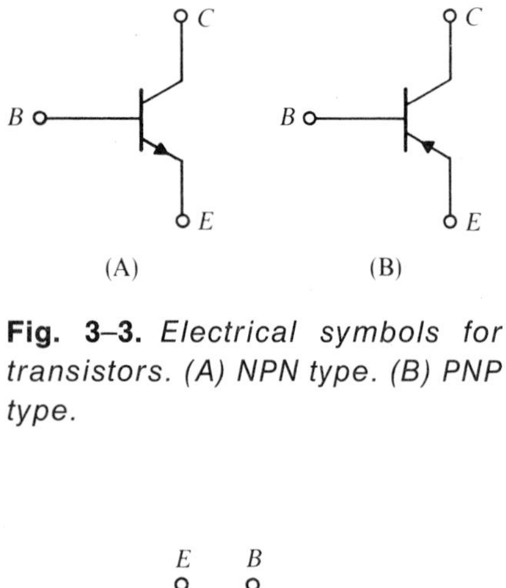

Fig. 3–3. *Electrical symbols for transistors. (A) NPN type. (B) PNP type.*

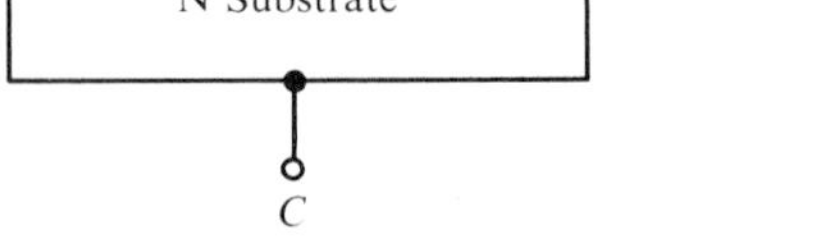

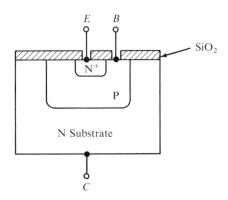

Fig. 3–4. *Cross-section of a diffused NPN transistor.*

The beginning material is an N-type silicon substrate, or chip, in the order of 5 mils (1 mil = 0.001 in.) thick. A thin layer of silicon dioxide, SiO_2, is formed over the transistor substrate. The SiO_2 layer is necessary in the diffusion process. It is used to open an area, or "window," for the base and emitter diffusions. In addition, it also helps to protect the transistor against contamination.

In a selected region, a P-type impurity is diffused into the substrate for the base. A relatively large concentration of an N-type impurity is then diffused in for the emitter. Because of the heavy doping, the emitter region is denoted by N^+. Leads are connected to the three regions for the collector, emitter, and base terminals. The chip is packaged and tested.

The behavior of the emitter-base and collector-base junctions is similar to the diode considered in Chapter 2. For normal amplifier operation, the emitter-base junction is always forward biased and the collector-base junction reverse biased. This is illustrated in Fig. 3–5 for an NPN transistor and in Fig. 3–6 for a PNP transistor. For each device, two bias sources, V_{BB} and V_{CC}, are shown. Resistors R_E and R_C limit the emitter and collector currents, respectively, to safe values.

For the NPN transistor of Fig. 3–5, V_{BB} maintains the base positive with respect to the emitter; hence, the emitter-base junction is forward biased. Source V_{CC} holds the collector positive with respect to the base. The collector-base junction, therefore, is reverse biased. Similar conclusions are drawn for the PNP transistor of Fig. 3–6.

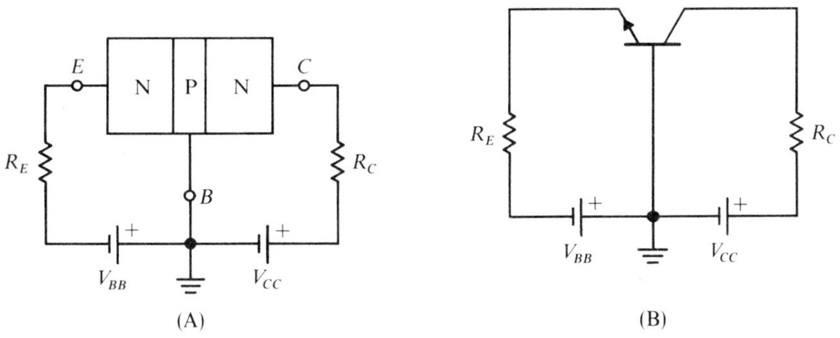

Fig. 3–5. *Biasing an NPN transistor for amplifier operation. (A) Pictorial. (B) Schematic.*

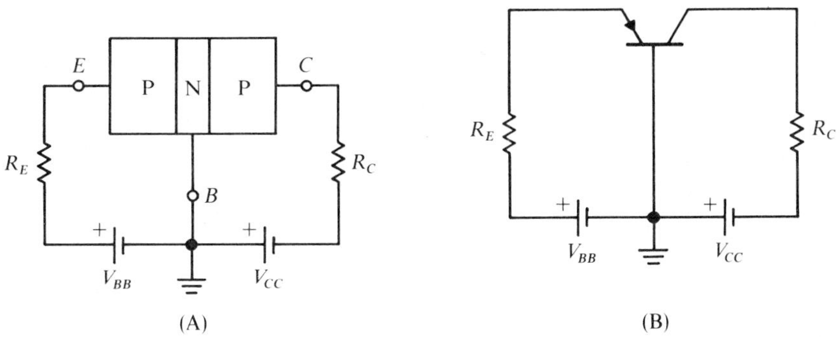

Fig. 3–6. *Biasing a PNP transistor for amplifier operation. (A) Pictorial. (B) Schematic.*

3.2 Operation of the BJT

Figure 3–7A shows how a transistor is capable of amplification with a signal source, V_s, placed in series with V_{BB}. The purpose of bias sources V_{BB} and V_{CC} is to ensure that the transistor is biased for normal amplifier operation. Because we are concerned now only with the signal operation of the transistor, the bias sources are set to zero in Fig. 3–7B. Also, for simplicity, resistance R_E has been set to zero. A similar circuit is obtained if a PNP transistor is used instead of an NPN transistor.

Emitter current, I_e, is the input signal current flowing into the emitter. Collector current, I_c, is the output (collector) current flowing in R_C. The signal voltage across R_C is the output voltage, V_o. *Note*: Lowercase subscripts generally refer to signal (ac) quantities, and uppercase subscripts refer to dc quantities.

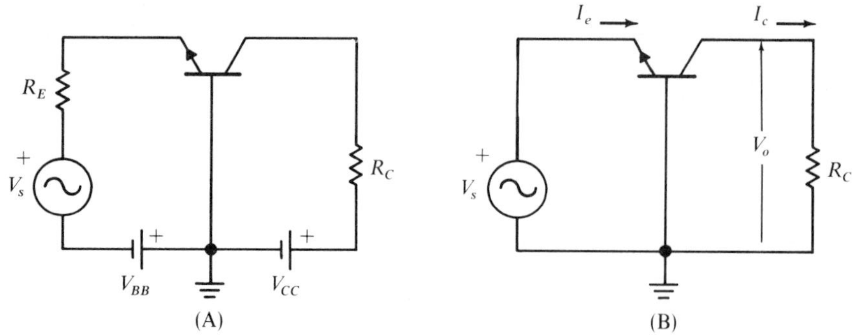

Fig. 3–7. *A transistor operating as an amplifier. (A) Circuit where V_s is the signal source. (B) Circuit simplified by setting biasing sources, V_{BB} and V_{CC}, to zero.*

An energy diagram for electron flow in the circuit of Fig. 3–7B is shown in Fig. 3–8. Because the emitter-base junction is forward biased, the energy hill (see Chapter 2) is small. Consequently, virtually every electron emitted by the emitter "climbs" the hill and finds itself in the base region. Electrons, which are minority carriers in the P-type base region, flow by diffusion. The base width (a small fraction of a mil) is much less than the diffusion length for electrons. Very few electrons, therefore, are lost by recombination in the base.

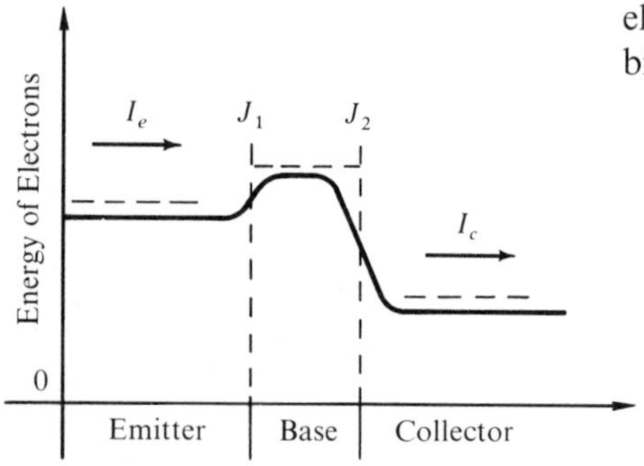

Fig. 3–8. *Energy hill diagram for electrons in the amplifier of Fig. 3–7.*

Because the collector-base junction is reverse biased, its energy hill is steep. Electrons in the base region may be thought of as "sliding down" the hill and are collected by the collector. Since few electrons are lost by recombination in the base, the collector and emitter currents are approximately equal: $I_c \simeq I_e$.

The *voltage gain* of an amplifier, A_v, is defined as the ratio of its output voltage, V_o, to its input voltage, V_s:

$$A_v = \frac{V_o}{V_s} \quad \textbf{(3–1)}$$

Input voltage V_s is equal to the product of input current, I_e, and the resistance between the emitter and base presented to an ac signal. This resistance is referred to as *input resistance*, or *impedance*, R_i. Hence,

$$V_s = I_e R_i \quad \textbf{(3–2a)}$$

Output voltage, V_o, is equal to the product of collector current, I_c, and load resistance, R_C:

$$V_o = I_c R_C \quad \textbf{(3–2b)}$$

Substitution of Eq. (3–2a) and Eq. (3–2b) in Eq. (3–1) yields

$$A_v = \frac{I_c R_C}{I_e R_i} \qquad \textbf{(3–3)}$$

Because R_C is chosen to be greater than R_i and $I_c \simeq I_e$, the voltage gain is greater than one ($A_v > 1$).

The ratio of the collector to emitter current for the amplifier of Fig. 3–7 is the *current gain*, A_i:

$$A_i = \frac{I_c}{I_e} \qquad \textbf{(3–4)}$$

For very small values of I_c and I_e, with R_C equal to zero, the *short-circuit current gain* of the transistor, denoted by the Greek letter alpha (α) or by h_{fb}, is defined. It is also equal to the ratio of the collector to emitter current. To a good approximation, alpha is often equal to A_i:

$$\alpha \simeq A_i \qquad \textbf{(3–5)}$$

If A_i is substituted for I_c/I_e in Eq. (3–3), we obtain

$$A_v = \frac{A_i R_C}{R_i} \qquad \textbf{(3–6)}$$

which states that the voltage gain is equal to the product of the current gain and the ratio of the load to input resistances.

The *power gain*, A_p, is the ratio of the output (load) power to the input power. It may be expressed by the product of the voltage and current gains:

$$A_p = A_v A_i \qquad \textbf{(3–7)}$$

EXAMPLE 3–1.

For the transistor amplifier of Fig. 3–7, assume that $R_C = 10\,\text{k}\Omega$ and $R_i = 100\,\Omega$. For a sinusoidal input signal, $I_e = 1$ mA and $I_c = 0.95$ mA. Determine the magnitude of

(a) A_i.
(b) A_v.
(c) A_p.

Solutions:

(a) By Eq. (3–4), $A_i = 0.95/1 = 0.95$.
(b) By Eq. (3–6), $A_v = 0.95 \times 10{,}000/100 = 95$.
(c) By Eq. (3–7), $A_p = 95 \times 0.95 = 90.25$.

(Although the current gain is less than one, both the voltage and power gain are considerably greater than one.)

3.3 Transistor Configurations

In the transistor amplifier of Fig. 3–7, the base terminal is common to the input (emitter) circuit containing V_s and to the output (collector) circuit containing R_C. For this reason,

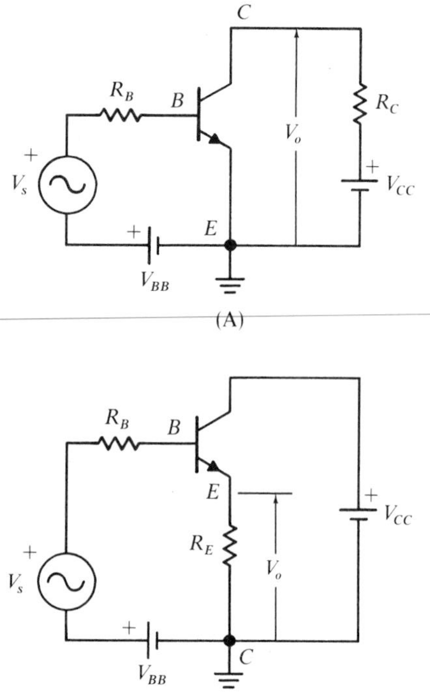

(B)

Fig. 3–9. *Two other useful transistor configurations are (A) the common-emitter (C-E) and (B) the common-collector (C-C) amplifiers. The common-collector amplifier is generally called an emitter follower.*

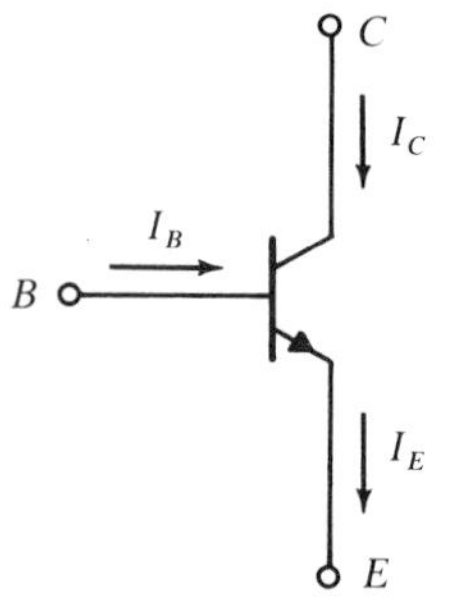

Fig. 3–10. *The dc emitter current (I_E) in a junction transistor always equals the sum of the dc base (I_B) and collector (I_C) currents: $I_C + I_B = I_E$.*

the circuit is called the *common-base* (*C-B*) configuration. Two other useful configurations, illustrated in Fig. 3–9, are the *common-emitter* (*C-E*) and *common-collector* (*C-C*) configurations. The common-collector amplifier is generally called the *emitter follower*.

In the common-emitter amplifier, the input signal is between the base and emitter, and the output signal is developed between the collector and emitter terminals. For the emitter follower, the signal is between the base and collector, and the output is developed between the emitter and collector terminals. (This may be seen by setting the dc biasing sources, V_{CC} and V_{BB}, to zero.) Because it provides the greatest power gain, the common-emitter amplifier is the most widely used configuration. The characteristics of the three transistor amplifiers are examined in Chapter 5.

Regardless of the configuration, the dc emitter current, I_E, always equals the sum of the dc base (I_B) and collector (I_C) currents (Fig. 3–10):

$$I_E = I_B + I_C \tag{3–8}$$

Because the collector-base junction is reverse biased, as for a junction diode, a reverse saturation current flows. Designated for the transistor by I_{CO}, this quantity adds to the collector current, I_C.

As the signal collector current I_c is less than the signal emitter current I_e for a transistor in the *C-B* configuration, the dc collector current is also less than the dc emitter current. Neglecting I_{CO}, we may define the dc current gain, denoted by h_{FB} or by α_{dc}, as the ratio I_C/I_E. The total dc collector current, including I_{CO}, for a common-base amplifier is, therefore,

$$I_C = h_{FB} I_E + I_{CO} \tag{3–9}$$

Substitution of Eq. (3–8) for I_E in Eq. (3–9) and solving for I_C yields

$$I_C = \frac{h_{FB} I_B}{1 - h_{FB}} + \frac{I_{CO}}{1 - h_{FB}} \tag{3–10}$$

The ratio I_C/I_B with $I_{CO} = 0$ is defined by h_{FE}, the dc current gain of a transistor in the *C-E* configuration, where

$$h_{FE} = \frac{h_{FB}}{1 - h_{FB}} \tag{3–11}$$

Current gain h_{FE} is also denoted by β_{dc} (β is the Greek letter beta). Also,

$$1 + h_{FE} = \frac{1}{1 - h_{FB}} \tag{3–12}$$

Substituting Eq. (3–11) and Eq. (3–12) in Eq. (3–10), we have

$$I_C = h_{FE} I_B + (1 + h_{FE}) I_{CO} \tag{3–13}$$

Because I_C is a function of I_B, Eq. (3–13) relates the dc collector and base currents in a transistor in the common-emitter configuration. The value of h_{FB} is close to one; hence, $1 - h_{FB}$ is close to zero, making h_{FE} large. We may conclude that the dc current gain of a transistor in the common-emitter configuration is much greater than unity. Therefore, the reverse saturation current $(1 + h_{FE})I_{CO}$ is much greater than I_{CO} in a transistor connected as a common-base amplifier.

EXAMPLE 3–2.

For a transistor, $h_{FB} = 0.99$ and $I_{CO} = 2\,\text{nA}$. Determine the values of h_{FE} and the reverse saturation current for a transistor in the common-emitter configuration.

Solution:

By Eq. (3–11), $h_{FE} = 0.99/(1 - 0.99) = 99$. The reverse saturation current, by Eq. (3–13), is $(1 + 99) \times 2 = 200\,\text{nA}$.

EXAMPLE 3–3.

For the NPN silicon transistor in the common-emitter configuration of Fig. 3–11, $h_{FE} = 50$ and $I_{CO} = 2\,\text{nA}$.

(a) Determine the values of the dc base and collector currents.
(b) Find the collector-emitter voltage, V_{CE}.
(c) Calculate the collector-base voltage, V_{CB}.
(d) Is the transistor properly biased for amplifier operation?

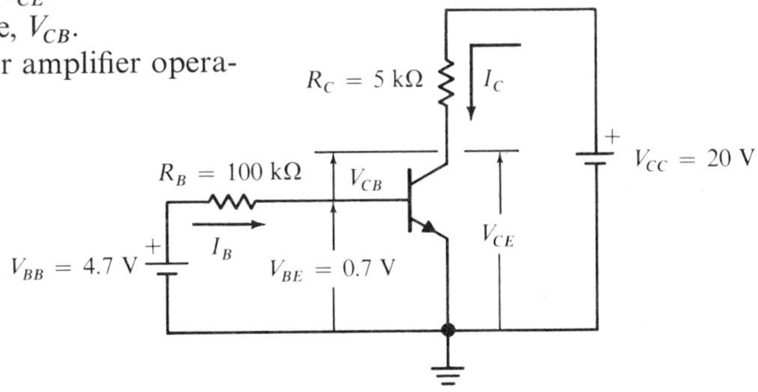

Fig. 3–11. *Biasing a common-emitter amplifier. (See Example 3–3.)*

Solutions:

(a) The emitter-base junction is forward biased. Assuming room-temperature operation, the emitter-base voltage equals 0.7 V, as for a silicon junction diode. Writing a voltage equation for the base circuit, we have

$$4.7 = 100I_B + 0.7$$

Solving for I_B,

$$I_B = \frac{4.7 - 0.7}{100} = 0.04\,\text{mA}$$

Because

$$I_B = 0.04\,\text{mA} \gg I_{CO} = 2\,\text{nA}$$

then

$$I_C \simeq h_{FE} I_B = 50 \times 0.04 = 2\,\text{mA}$$

(b) Writing a voltage equation for the collector circuit,

$$20 = 5I_C + V_{CE} = 5 \times 2 + V_{CE} = 10 + V_{CE}$$

Solving for V_{CE},

$$V_{CE} = 20 - 10 = 10\,\text{V}$$

(c) The collector-base voltage is equal to the difference in the collector-emitter and emitter-base voltages:

$$V_{CB} = V_{CE} - V_{EB}$$

Hence,

$$V_{CB} = 10 - 0.7 = 9.3\,\text{V}$$

(d) From (c), the collector is positive with respect to the base by $+9.3$ V; hence, the collector-base junction is reverse biased. From (a), the emitter-base junction is forward biased. The transistor is biased for amplifier operation.

3.4 Transistor Characteristics

The most useful set of characteristics is the collector family of curves for a BJT in the common-emitter configuration. Such a family of curves is illustrated in Fig. 3–12 for an NPN transistor. For different values of dc base current, I_B, dc collector current, i_C, is plotted along the y-axis and dc collector-emitter voltage, v_{CE}, along the x-axis. The characteristics of a PNP transistor are similar to those of an NPN device, except that minus signs precede the current and voltage quantities.

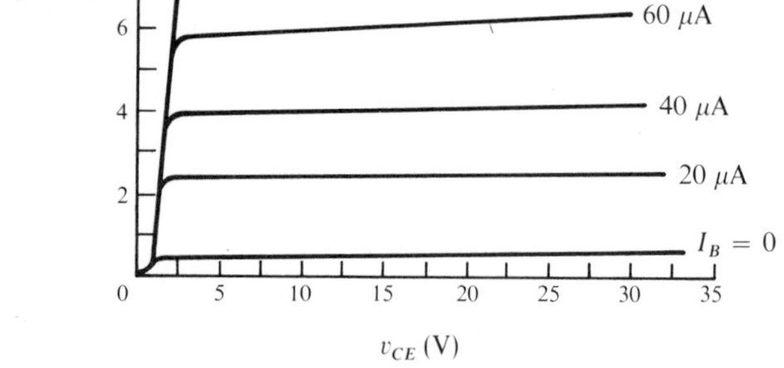

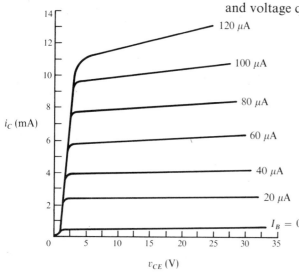

Fig. 3–12. *Typical collector characteristics for an NPN transistor in the C-E configuration.*

The common-emitter collector characteristics may also be used for the emitter follower. For this configuration, the quantity of interest is the ratio of emitter to base currents.

By Eq. (3–8), the emitter current is equal to the sum of the base and collector currents ($I_E = I_B + I_C$). Dividing this quantity by I_B yields the dc current gain for the emitter follower, h_{FC}:

$$h_{FC} = \frac{I_B + I_C}{I_B} = 1 + \frac{I_C}{I_B} = 1 + h_{FE} \quad (3\text{–}14)$$

Because $h_{FE} \gg 1$, $h_{FC} \simeq h_{FE} = I_C/I_B$. Therefore, the characteristics of Fig. 3–12 may also be used for the emitter follower.

In the common-base configuration, $I_C \simeq I_E$. The collector characteristics may therefore be approximated by equidistant lines parallel to the x-axis for different values of emitter current, I_E (Fig. 3–13). For this reason, manufacturers seldom provide the common-base characteristics on their data sheets.

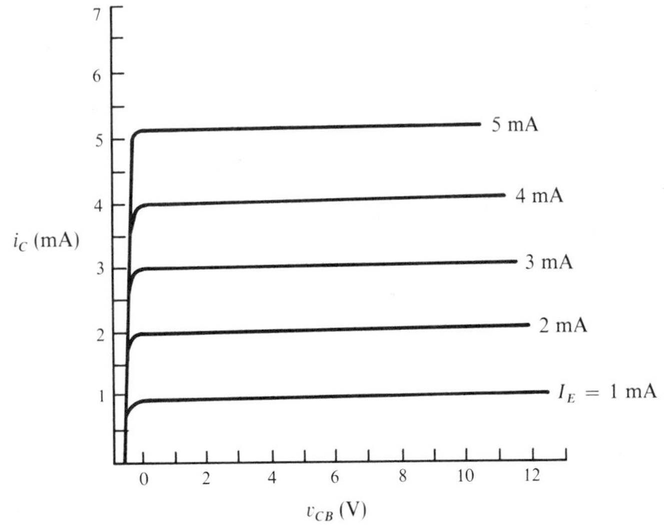

Fig. 3–13. *Typical collector characteristics for an NPN transistor in the C-B configuration.*

3.5 The Field-Effect Transistor

Both majority and minority carriers are involved in the operation of the bipolar junction transistor. For example, in the operation of an NPN transistor in the common-base configuration, electrons are injected into the base region. Because the base is P-type, holes are majority carriers. Electrons in the base are therefore minority carriers. As a result of recombination of some holes with electrons in the base, the collector current is always less than the emitter current.

The operation of the field-effect transistor (FET) depends on majority carriers, either electrons or holes. (For this reason, the FET is sometimes called a *unipolar transistor*.)

In the family tree of Fig. 3–14, there are two basic types of field-effect transistors. These are the *junction* FET (JFET) and the *metal-oxide semiconductor* FET (MOSFET). The MOSFET also is called the *insulated-gate* FET (IGFET). Two types of MOSFETs are available: the depletion- and enhancement-types.

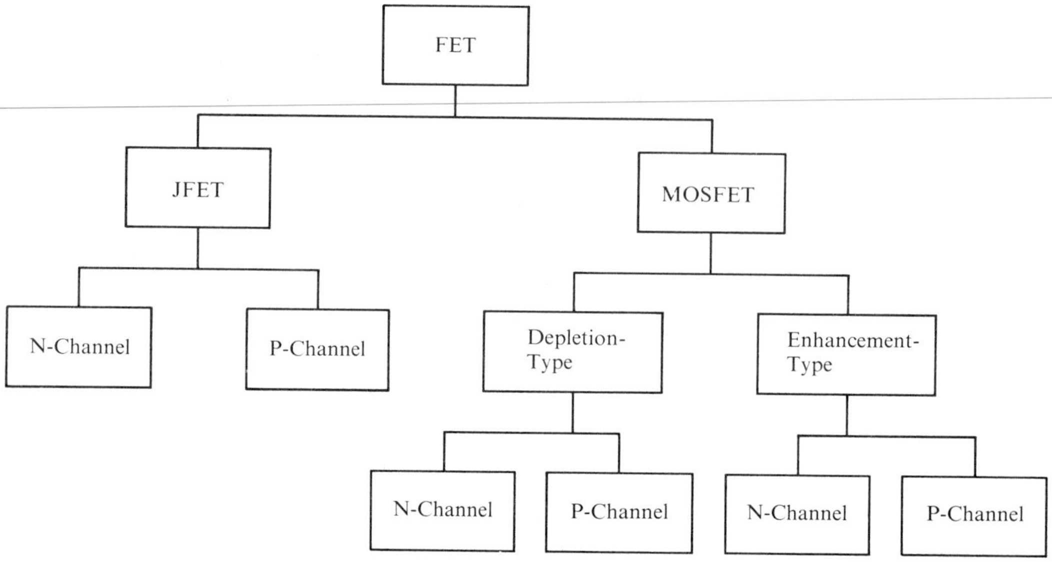

Fig. 3–14. *Family tree for field-effect transistors.*

Regardless of the type of FET, it is either N- or P-channel. In the N-channel device, electrons are the majority carriers; in the P-channel FET, holes are majority carriers.

3.6 Operation of the JFET

A cross-section of an N-channel JFET and its electrical symbol are illustrated in Fig. 3–15. A P-type region is diffused into an N-type silicon chip. Connected to the P region is the *gate* (*G*) terminal. For the *source* (*S*) and *drain*

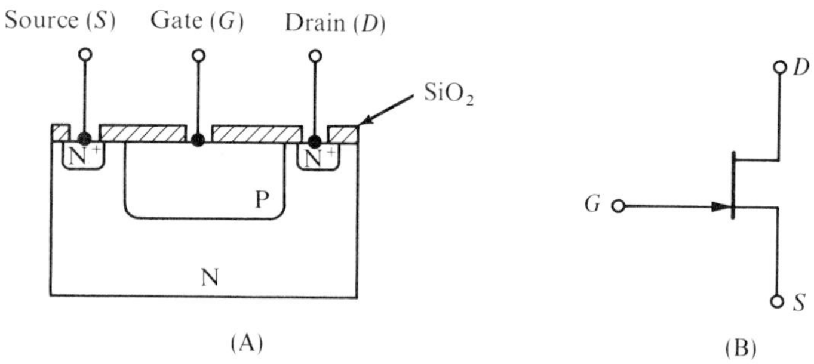

Fig. 3–15. *An N-channel JFET. (A) Cross-section. (B) Electrical symbol.*

(D) terminals, small N^+ regions are diffused in the chip. The N-type chip below the diffused P region serves as the N channel.

A cross-section of a P-channel JFET and its electrical symbol are shown in Fig. 3–16. The substrate is P-type silicon. An N-type diffused region serves as the gate and the two P^+ regions as the drain and source terminals.

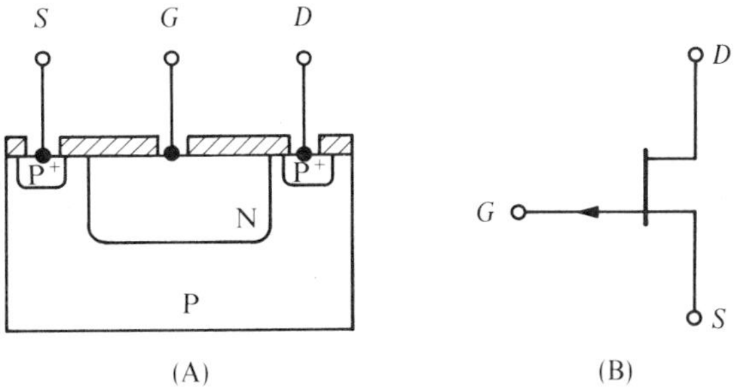

Fig. 3–16. *A P-channel JFET. (A) Cross-section. (B) Electrical symbol.*

As the N-channel JFET is biased, the drain is made positive, and the gate negative, with respect to the source as illustrated in Fig. 3–17. For a P-channel JFET (Fig. 3–16), the reverse is true: the drain is negative, and the gate positive, with respect to the source.

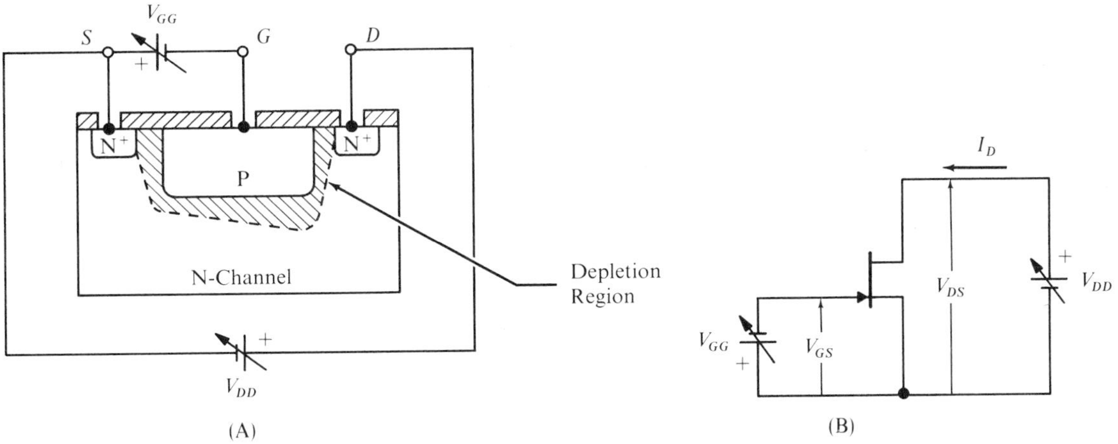

Fig. 3–17. *In biasing an N-channel JFET, the gate is generally negative, and the drain positive, with respect to the source (the reverse is true for a P-channel device). (A) Pictorial view illustrating the formation of the depletion region. (B) Schematic.*

The gate, source, and drain of a FET are analogous to the base, emitter, and collector, respectively, of a BJT. The emitter-base junction of a BJT is forward biased for amplifier operation. Current, therefore, flows in the emitter-base junction. For this reason, the BJT is referred to as a *current-controlled* device. In the FET, however, the junction formed by the gate and source is reverse biased, and no current flows. The FET is therefore called a *voltage-controlled* device.

As an aid in understanding the operation of the JFET, assume that initially $V_{GG} = 0$ in Fig. 3–17. As V_{DD} is increased from zero volts, a voltage gradient is formed in the

N channel. The voltage is V_{DD} volts at the drain terminal and zero volts at the source terminal. Because of the gradient, the PN junction formed by the P-type gate and the N channel is more reverse biased at the drain end than at the source. As in the operation of a junction diode, a depletion region is established and penetrates the N channel. Because of the gradient, the penetration of the depletion region is greater at the drain end than at the source.

As voltage V_{DD} is raised, the drain current, I_D, increases to a point, then levels off (Fig. 3–18A). At a value of $V_{DD} = V_P$ (the *pinchoff voltage*), the channel is saturated with electrons. As V_{DD} is raised beyond V_P, little increase in drain current occurs. The value of drain current at a drain-source voltage of V_P volts and $V_{GG} = 0$ is designated by I_{DSS}.

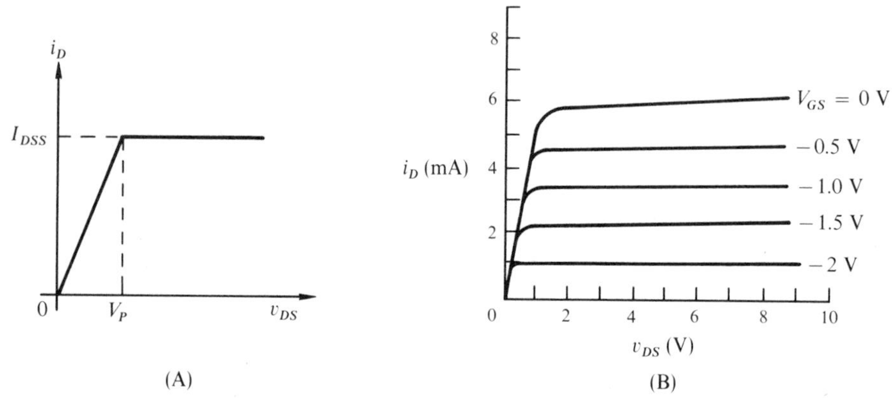

Fig. 3–18. *Current-voltage characteristics of an N-channel JFET. (A) For drain voltages greater than the pinchoff voltage, V_P, the drain current is essentially constant. (B) Typical drain characteristics.*

As the gate-source voltage is made negative, the penetration of the depletion region in the N channel increases. Consequently, the channel becomes saturated with electrons at a lower value of pinchoff voltage. A family of curves where dc drain current, i_D, is plotted as a function of dc drain-source voltage, v_{DS}, for different values of gate-source voltage, V_{GS}, is shown in Fig. 3–18B. The curves are similar to collector characteristics for a BJT and are called the *drain characteristics*. When V_{GS} is equal to the negative of V_P, the drain current is zero, and the device is said to be *cut off*.

EXAMPLE 3–4.

The circuit of Fig. 3–19, where the source is common to the gate and drain circuits, is called a *common-source* (*C-S*) configuration. Determine the values of

(a) V_{GS}.
(b) V_{DS} for $I_D = 2\,\text{mA}$.

Solutions:

(a) Because the gate-source junction is reverse biased, the gate current is zero. Hence, using voltage division,

$$V_{GS} = \frac{-4 \times 100}{100 + 100} = -2\,\text{V}$$

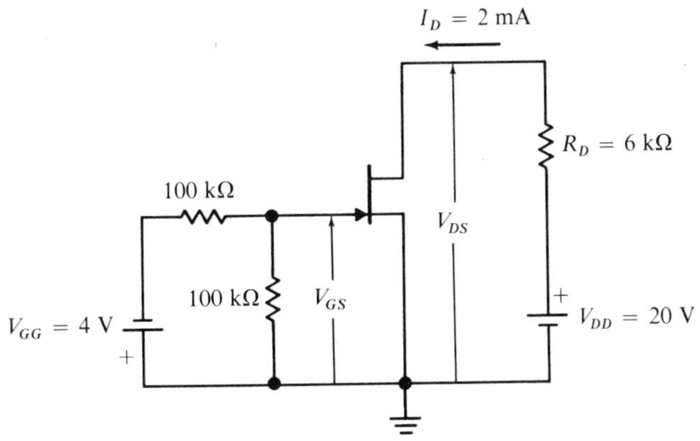

Fig. 3–19. *Biasing a common-source FET amplifier. (See Example 3–4.)*

(b) Writing a voltage equation for the drain circuit,

$$20 = 6 \times 2 + V_{DS}$$

Solving, $V_{DS} = 20 - 12 = 8$ V.

In addition to the common-source configuration, two other useful connections are the *common-gate* (*C-G*) and the *source follower*, or *common-drain* (*C-D*) amplifier, shown in Fig. 3–20. For simplicity, biasing sources have been omitted. The performance of these circuits is considered in later chapters.

3.7 Transfer Characteristics

To understand how a FET provides amplification, consider the *transfer characteristics* of a typical FET in Fig. 3–21. The transfer characteristics are shown as a plot of drain current as a function of gate-source voltage for a given drain-source voltage. In Fig. 3–21, $V_{DS} = 10$ V is shown.

A useful parameter for defining the amplifying properties of a FET is the *forward transconductance*, denoted by g_{fs} or by g_m. It is defined as the ratio of a small change in drain current, ΔI_D, to a small change in gate-source voltage, ΔV_{GS}, with V_{DS} constant:

$$g_{fs} = \left.\frac{\Delta I_D}{\Delta V_{GS}}\right|_{V_{DS}\text{ (constant)}} \qquad \textbf{(3–15)}$$

where Δ is the Greek letter delta and denotes a "small change in." Because the ratio is a current divided by a voltage, the unit for forward transconductance is the *mho* (℧), as for conductance.

If g_{fs} is multiplied by the load resistance R_D in a common-source amplifier, we obtain

$$g_{fs}R_D = \frac{\Delta I_D R_D}{\Delta V_{GS}}$$

But $\Delta I_D R_D$ is equal to the output voltage, V_o, across R_D. Voltage ΔV_{GS} is the signal voltage across the gate-source

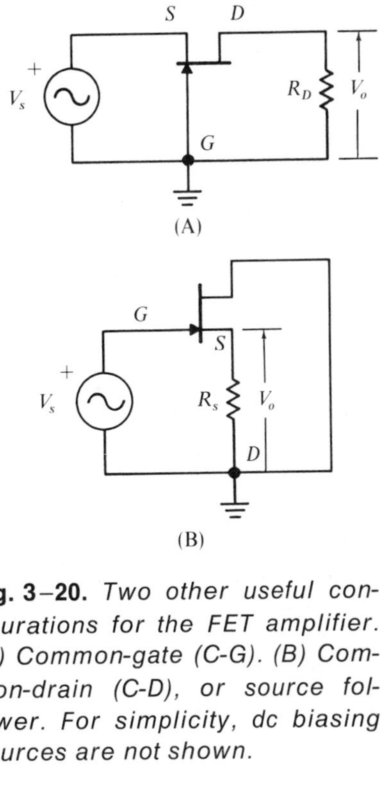

Fig. 3–20. *Two other useful configurations for the FET amplifier. (A) Common-gate (C-G). (B) Common-drain (C-D), or source follower. For simplicity, dc biasing sources are not shown.*

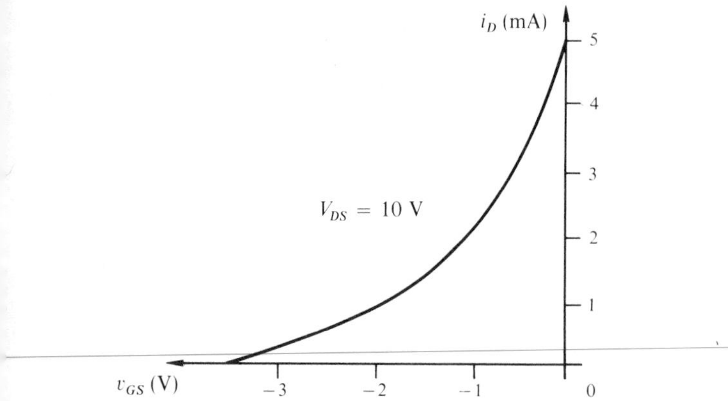

Fig. 3–21. *Transfer characteristics for a typical field-effect transistor. Plotted is drain current, i_D, as a function of gate-source voltage, v_{GS}, for a given drain-source voltage, V_{DS}.*

terminals. Letting ΔV_{GS} equal the signal voltage, V_s, the magnitude of the voltage gain, $|A_v|$, is therefore

$$|A_v| = g_{fs}R_D \quad \textbf{(3–16)}$$

EXAMPLE 3–5.

Figure 3–22A illustrates a common-source amplifier with a 1-V signal impressed across the input. If $R_D = 10\,\text{k}\Omega$ and $V_o = 20$ V, determine

(a) The magnitude of the voltage gain.
(b) g_{fs}.

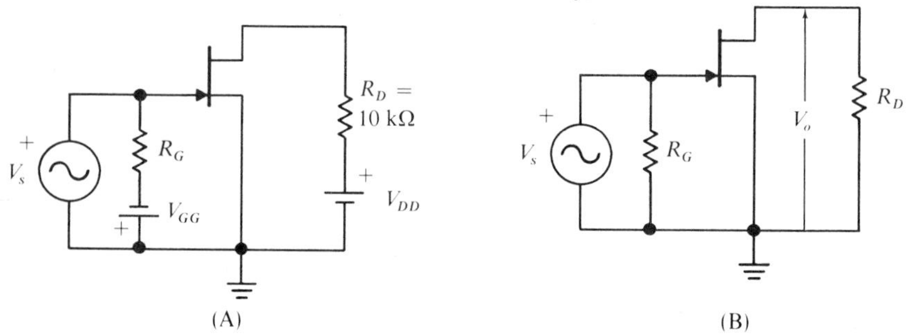

Fig. 3–22. *Determining the voltage gain of a FET amplifier. (A) Circuit. (B) Simplified circuit obtained by setting the dc biasing sources to zero. (See Example 3–5.)*

Solutions:

(a) The circuit of Fig. 3–22A is simplified in Fig. 3–22B by setting bias sources V_{GG} and V_{DD} to zero. By definition, $|A_v| = V_o/V_s = 20/1 = 20$.
(b) By Eq. (3–16), $g_{fs} = |A_v|/R_D$. Hence, $g_{fs} = 20/(10 \times 10^3) = 2 \times 10^{-3}\,℧ = 2$ millimhos (m℧).

3.8 Depletion-Type MOSFET

A cross-section of an N-channel depletion-type MOSFET and its electrical symbol are shown in Fig. 3–23. Diffused in a P-type substrate are two N^+ regions for the source and drain terminals. An N-type region is also diffused between the two N^+ regions for the channel. The substrate terminal, Sub, is often connected internally to the source terminal, *S*. Except for openings for the drain and source terminals, a thin dielectric, such as SiO_2, covers the top of the chip.

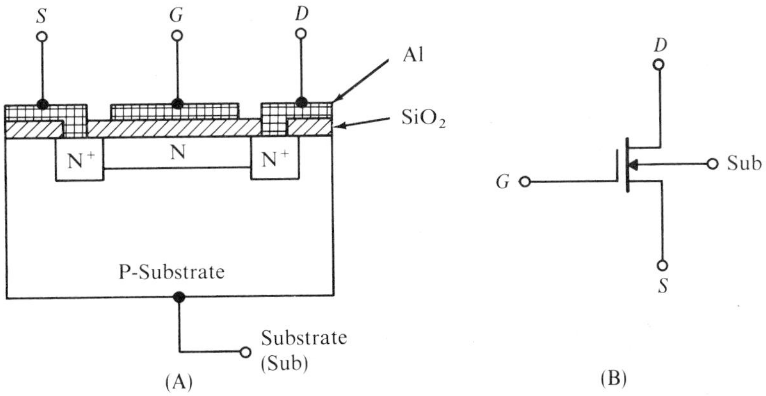

Fig. 3–23. *An N-channel depletion-type MOSFET. (A) Cross-section. (B) Electrical symbol.*

A distinguishing feature of the MOSFET is its gate. The gate in a JFET is a diffused P- or N-type region in the substrate. For a MOSFET, the gate is a metallic electrode (usually aluminum) separated from the channel by the dielectric.

The gate electrode and channel may be thought of as being the top and bottom plates of a capacitor separated by the thin SiO_2 dielectric. If the top plate has a negative charge, for electrical neutrality, the bottom plate must have an equal positive charge. Likewise, if the top plate is positively charged, the bottom plate must be equally negatively charged.

When the gate electrode is made negative with respect to the source, positive charges are induced in the N channel, as shown in Fig. 3–24A. This is similar to the top plate of a capacitor (gate) having a negative charge and the bottom plate (channel) a positive charge. Because a field-effect transistor is a majority-carrier device, electrons are the carriers of current in the N channel. Consequently, the induced positive charges reduce, or deplete, the electrons in the channel, and the drain current is reduced.

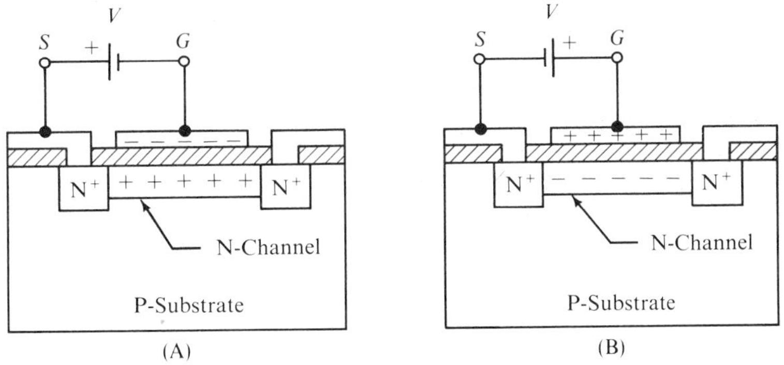

Fig. 3–24. *Operation of an N-channel depletion-type MOSFET. (A) Gate negative with respect to source: electrons are depleted. (B) Gate positive with respect to source: electrons are enhanced.*

This behavior is illustrated in the drain characteristics for an N-channel depletion-type MOSFET in Fig. 3–25. The characteristics are similar to those for the JFET. As the gate-source bias is made more negative, less drain current flows.

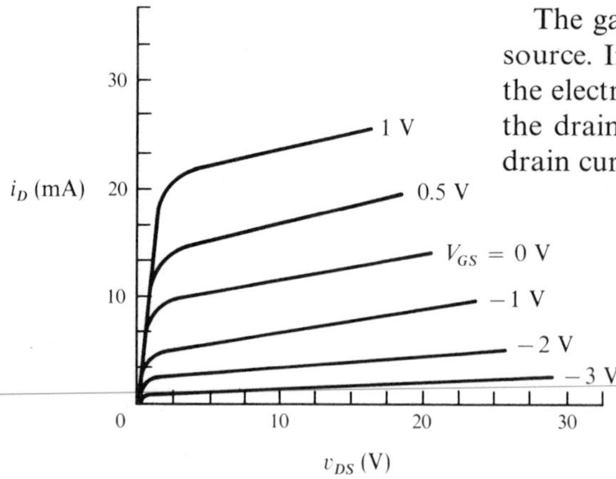

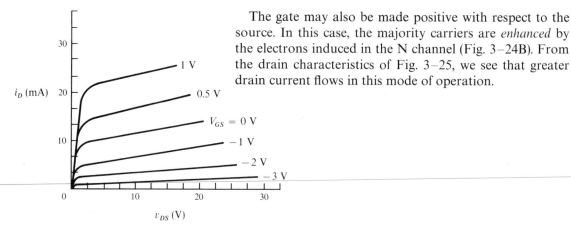

Fig. 3–25. *Typical drain characteristics for an N-channel depletion-type MOSFET.*

The gate may also be made positive with respect to the source. In this case, the majority carriers are *enhanced* by the electrons induced in the N channel (Fig. 3–24B). From the drain characteristics of Fig. 3–25, we see that greater drain current flows in this mode of operation.

3.9 Enhancement-Type MOSFET

The depletion-type MOSFET is a *normally ON* device. The reason for this description is that for $V_{GS} = 0$, a large value of drain current flows (Fig. 3–25). In many applications, such as in digital switching circuits, it is advantageous to use a *normally OFF* device. For $V_{GS} = 0$, the drain current is approximately zero. The enhancement-type MOSFET is normally OFF.

A cross-section and electrical symbol of an N-channel enhancement-type MOSFET are illustrated in Fig. 3–26. The structure of the enhancement-type MOSFET is similar to the depletion-type MOSFET, except no N channel is present. Instead, an N channel is *induced*, as shown in Fig. 3–27.

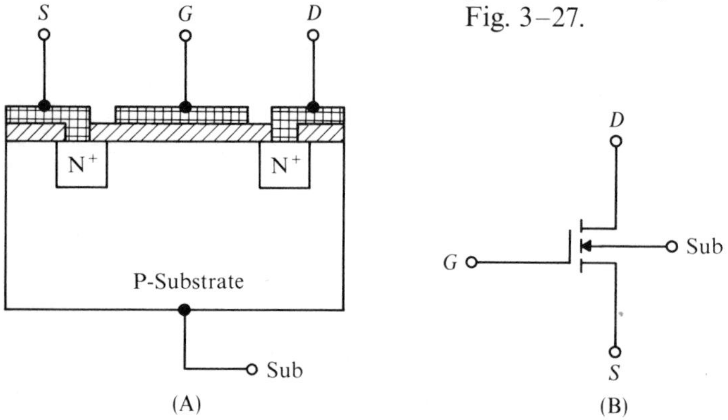

Fig. 3–26. *An N-channel enhancement-type MOSFET. (A) Cross-section. (B) Electrical symbol.*

When the gate is made positive with respect to the source, electrons are induced in the region between the drain and source terminals. An N channel is thereby established. As

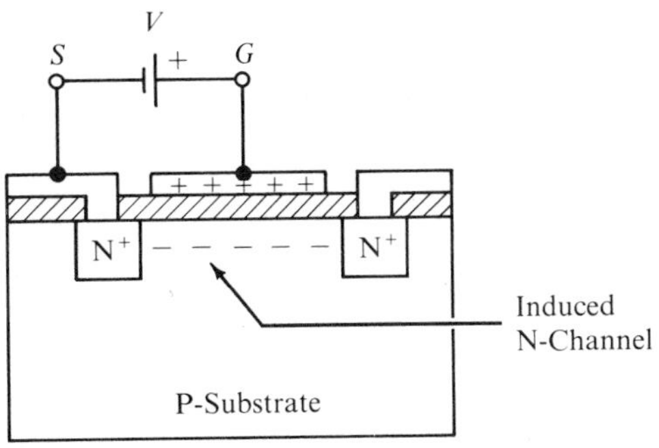

Fig. 3–27. *Inducing an N channel in an enhancement-type MOSFET. The gate is positive with respect to the source.*

the gate voltage is made more positive with respect to the source, the drain current increases. This is indicated in the typical drain characteristics of Fig. 3–28 for an enhancement-type MOSFET.

A cross-section of a P-channel enhancement-type MOSFET and its electrical symbol are provided in Fig. 3–29. In an N-type substrate, two P^+ regions are diffused for the drain and source terminals. As in the N-channel enhancement-type MOSFET, no channel is present. A P-channel is induced by making the gate negative with respect to the source. The drain characteristics are similar to those of Fig. 3–28, except the current and voltage quantities have negative signs.

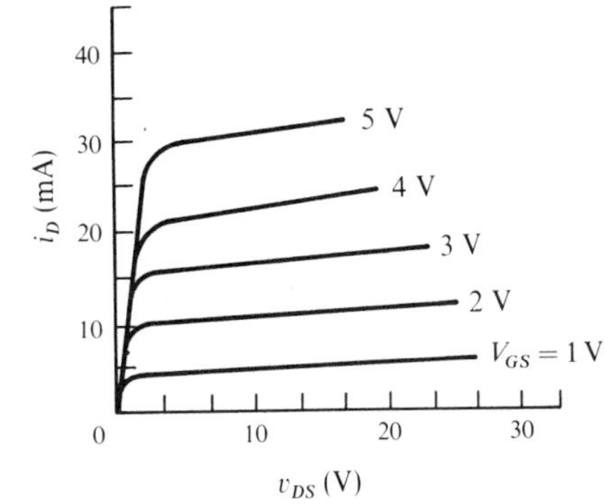

Fig. 3–28. *Typical drain characteristics for an N-channel enhancement-type MOSFET.*

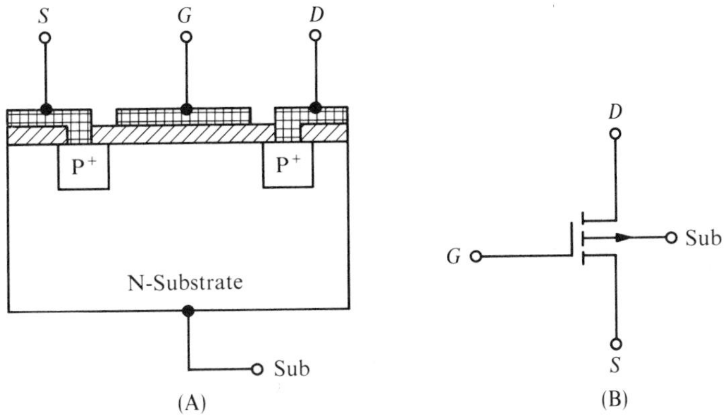

Fig. 3–29. *A P-channel enhancement-type MOSFET. (A) Cross-section. (B) Electrical symbol.*

3.10 The MOSFET as a Circuit Element

As for the JFET, either type of MOSFET may be connected in the common-source, common-gate, or source-follower configuration. Also, the MOSFET is a voltage-controlled device; no dc gate current ever flows. The input resistance of a MOSFET is virtually infinite. In biasing a MOSFET, the drain is positive with respect to the source for an N-channel, and negative for a P-channel, device.

SUMMARY

The different types of bipolar junction and field-effect transistors are classified as active devices because they provide power gain. In biasing a BJT for amplifier operation, the emitter-base junction is forward biased and the collector-base junction reverse biased. Because current flows in a forward-biased junction, the BJT is referred to as a current-controlled device.

For a FET, the drain is positive with respect to the source for an N-channel device and negative for a P-channel device. The gate is biased with respect to the source so that no gate current flows. For this reason, the FET is called a voltage-controlled device.

The base, emitter, and collector of a BJT are analogous, respectively, to the gate, source, and drain terminals of a FET. If the base is common to the emitter and collector circuits, the transistor is said to be in the common-base (*C-B*) configuration. Two other useful configurations are the common-emitter (*C-E*) and the common-collector (*C-C*), or emitter follower. In the *C-E* configuration, the emitter is common to the base and collector circuits. The collector is common for the base and emitter circuits in the emitter follower.

The three useful configurations for the FET are the common-source (*C-S*), common-gate (*C-G*), and common-drain (*C-D*), or source follower. In the *C-S* configuration, the source is common to the gate and drain circuits. For the *C-G* connection, the gate is common to the source and drain circuits. The drain is common for the gate and source circuits in the source follower.

Further Reading

Kaufman, M., and A. H. Seidman, eds. *Handbook for Electronics Engineering Technicians.* New York: McGraw-Hill Book Company, 1976, Chapter 8.

Lenert, Louis H. *Semiconductor Physics, Devices, and Circuits.* Columbus, Ohio: Charles E. Merrill Publishing Company, 1968, Chapter 5.

Matthews, John I. *Solid-State Electronics Concepts.* New York: McGraw-Hill Book Company, 1972, Chapter 7.

Seidman, A. H., and S. L. Marshall. *Semiconductor Fundamentals: Devices and Circuits*. New York: John Wiley and Sons, Inc., 1963, Chapters 4 and 5.

Sowa, W. A., and J. M. Toole. *Special Semiconductor Devices*. New York: Holt, Rinehart and Winston, 1968, Chapter 8.

Tocci, Ronald J. *Fundamentals of Electronic Devices*. 2nd ed. Columbus, Ohio: Charles E. Merrill Publishing Company, 1975, Chapters 9 and 16.

REVIEW QUESTIONS

3.1 What is the principal difference between an active and a passive device?

3.2 Draw cross-sections of an NPN and a PNP transistor. Identify their base, collector, and emitter regions.

3.3 Draw electrical symbols for NPN and PNP transistors.

3.4 For normal amplifier operation, how are the emitter-base and collector-base junctions biased? Illustrate your answer by drawing schematic diagrams showing the biasing of NPN and PNP transistors.

3.5 Explain the differences between the *C-B*, *C-E*, and *C-C* transistor amplifier configurations.

3.6 Why is the common-emitter collector characteristic useful?

3.7 What are two significant differences between the BJT and FET?

3.8 Draw the electrical symbols for the P- and N-channel JFETs.

3.9 The gate, drain, and source of a FET are analogous to what terminals of a BJT?

3.10 What is the difference between a voltage-controlled (FET) and current-controlled (BJT) device?

3.11 Define pinchoff voltage, V_P.

3.12 How do the drain characteristics of a JFET differ from the collector characteristics of a BJT?

3.13 What are some features of the *C-D*, *C-G*, and *C-S* amplifiers?

3.14 Draw the transfer characteristics of a FET in the *C-S* configuration.

3.15 Define transconductance of a FET. What is its unit?

3.16 Draw the electrical symbols for an N-channel and a P-channel depletion-type MOSFET.

3.17 What is the difference between a normally ON and normally OFF MOSFET device?

3.18 How is the channel produced in an enhancement-type MOSFET?

3.19 Draw the electrical symbols for the N- and P-channel enhancement-type MOSFETs.

3.20 What are two major differences between an enhancement- and a depletion-type MOSFET?

PROBLEMS

P3–1 In Fig. 3–7A, $R_C = 12\,k\Omega$, $R_i = 0.1\,k\Omega$, $I_e = 2\,mA$, and $I_c = 1.95\,mA$. Calculate
(a) A_i.
(b) A_v.
(c) A_p.

P3–2 Repeat prob. P3–1 for $R_C = 10\,k\Omega$ and $R_i = 50\,\Omega$. Assume that I_e and I_c have the values given in prob. P3–1.

P3–3 For a transistor in the *C-B* configuration, $h_{FB} = 0.98$ and $I_{CO} = 3\,nA$. Determine
(a) h_{FE}.
(b) The reverse saturation current for the transistor used in the *C-E* configuration.

P3–4 A transistor in the *C-E* configuration has a value of $h_{FE} = 60$. What is the value of h_{FB}?

P3–5 Assume that $h_{FE} = 60$ for the transistor in Fig. 3–30. If $R_C = 4\,k\Omega$, $R_B = 50\,k\Omega$, and $V_{BB} = 2.7\,V$,
(a) Determine I_C, I_B, and V_{CE}.
(b) Is the transistor biased for normal amplifier operation? Why?

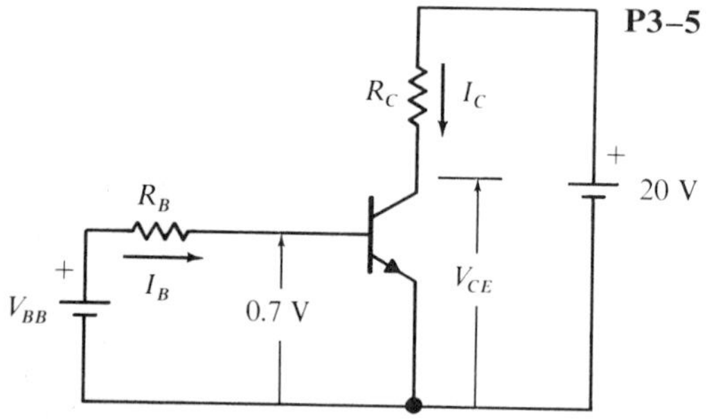

Fig. 3–30.

P3–6 Repeat prob. P3–5 for $R_C = 2\,k\Omega$, $R_B = 50\,k\Omega$, and $V_{BB} = 3.7\,V$.

P3–7 If $h_{FE} = 50$, what is the dc current gain, h_{FC}, for a transistor used as an emitter follower?

P3–8 If in Fig. 3–19, $V_{GG} = 2\,V$ and $V_{DD} = 24\,V$, what are the values of
(a) V_{GS}?
(b) V_{DS}?

P3–9 Assume that in Fig. 3–22A, $R_D = 20\,k\Omega$, $V_o = 10\,V$, and $V_s = 0.5\,V$. Calculate
(a) $|A_v|$.
(b) g_{fs}.

P3–10 A P-channel enhancement-type MOSFET is connected in *C-S* configuration illustrated in Fig. 3–31. Resistance $R_D = 10\,k\Omega$, $g_{fs} = 10\,m℧$, $-V_{DD} = -20\,V$, and $V_{GG} = 2\,V$. Determine
(a) $|A_v|$.
(b) V_{GS}.
(c) V_{DS} if $I_D = 1\,mA$.

P3–11 If in Fig. 3–31, $V_{GS} = -2\,V$, $V_{DS} = -6\,V$, $R_D = 10\,k\Omega$, and $I_D = 2\,mA$, calculate
(a) V_{GG}.
(b) V_{DD}.

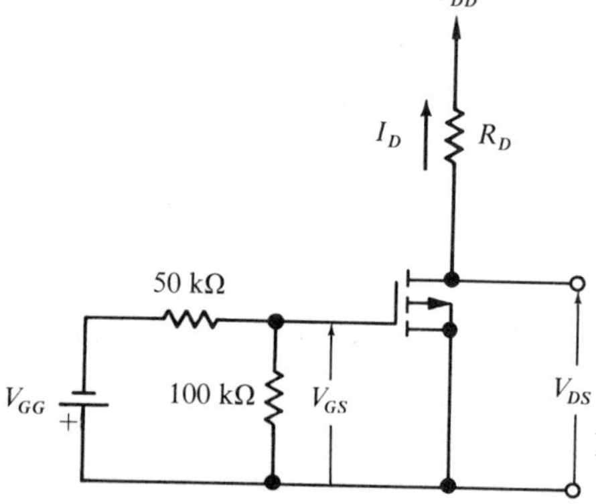

Fig. 3–31.

4

Other Semiconductor Devices and Applications

Diodes, bipolar and field-effect transistors, account for more than 90 percent of semiconductor devices used in discrete and integrated circuits. A number of other devices, however, are of importance. These include the zener diode, the silicon-controlled rectifier, and the unijunction transistor. Such components are employed in voltage regulating circuits and in the control of power. In this chapter, the operation of these as well as other semiconductor devices, and their characteristics, are considered.

4.1 The Zener Diode

The reverse current characteristics of a junction diode (see Chapter 2) are illustrated in detail in Fig. 4–1. For reverse voltages more negative than the peak-reverse voltage (PRV), the diode breaks down, and its reverse current, I_R, increases very rapidly. In the range of reverse current between $-I_{ZK}$ and $-I_{ZM}$, the voltage across the diode is essentially constant and equal to V_Z volts. This nearly constant voltage is called the *zener voltage*.

A diode designed to operate in the reverse-biased region at a specific zener voltage is called a *zener diode*. Its electrical symbol is provided in Fig. 4–2. This device is useful because of its characteristic of nearly constant (zener) voltage over a large range of reverse (zener) current. Because of these properties, an important application for the device is in the regulation of voltage. Zener diodes are available with voltage ratings from approximately 2 to 200 V.

In Fig. 4–1, I_{ZK} is the *zener knee current*. It represents the *minimum* operating current at which the diode regulates. Current I_{ZM} is the *maximum* operating zener current and is limited by power dissipation in the device. Current I_Z is the *operating* current corresponding to zener voltage, V_Z. Maximum zener currents range from a few milliamperes to tens of amperes.

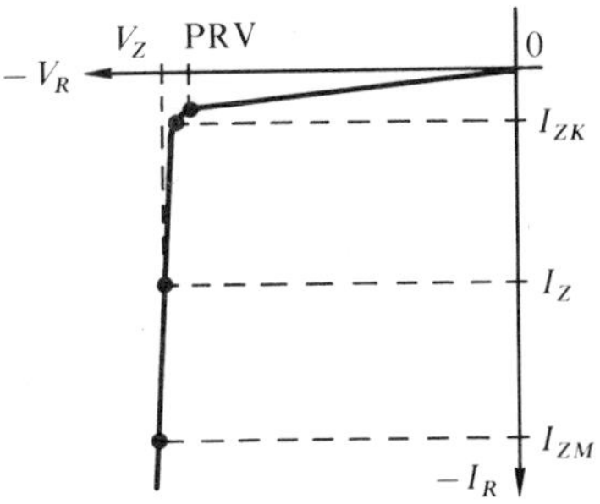

Fig. 4–1. *The reverse characteristics of a junction diode are the basis for the zener diode.*

Fig. 4–2. *Electrical symbol for a zener diode.*

4.2 Avalanche Breakdown and Zener Breakdown

Two mechanisms may explain the operation of a zener diode. One is called *avalanche breakdown* and the other *zener breakdown.* A zener diode, therefore, is sometimes called an avalanche diode.

In a reverse-biased diode, an electric field spreads across the PN junction. If the field reaches sufficient magnitude, electrons and holes acquire appreciable kinetic energy as they move in the crystal. When they collide with atoms in the lattice, electron-hole pairs are released after the collision. The released carriers, in turn, collide with other atoms, resulting in more electrons and holes. Thus, there is a "snowballing" of carriers, and the reverse current increases rapidly. The "snowballing" mechanism is called avalanche breakdown.

In zener breakdown, electron-hole pairs are released by the rupturing of covalent bonds. For zener voltages less than approximately 6 V, the mechanism appears to be zener breakdown. Avalanche breakdown occurs for voltages greater than 6 V.

Another characteristic of zener breakdown is that the zener voltage exhibits a negative temperature coefficient (V_Z decreases with increasing temperature). In avalanche breakdown, however, the zener voltage has a positive temperature coefficient (V_Z increases with increasing temperature). Regardless of the breakdown mechanism, the device is commonly called a zener diode.

4.3 Zener Voltage Regulator

An *ideal* voltage source is one whose voltage is constant, regardless of the magnitude of load current flowing. This behavior is illustrated in Fig. 4–3A, where load voltage, V_L, is constant at V volts for all values of load current, I_L.

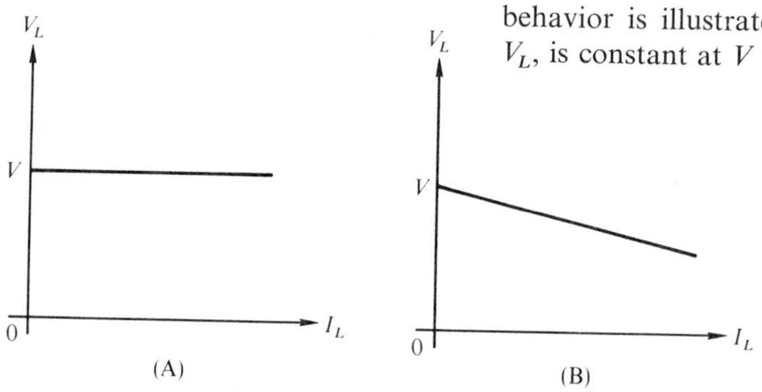

Fig. 4–3. *Load voltage, V_L, as a function of load current, I_L, for (A) an ideal voltage source and (B) a physical voltage source.*

For a *physical source*, however, the output voltage decreases with increasing load current, as shown in Fig. 4–3B. The reason for this behavior is the internal resistance of the source.

A physical source may be represented by a model of an ideal voltage source, V, in series with the internal source resistance, R_i (Fig. 4–4A). Connected across its output is a variable load resistance, R_L, as illustrated in Fig. 4–4B. By voltage division, load voltage, V', is

$$V' = \frac{VR_L}{R_i + R_L} \quad \textbf{(4–1)}$$

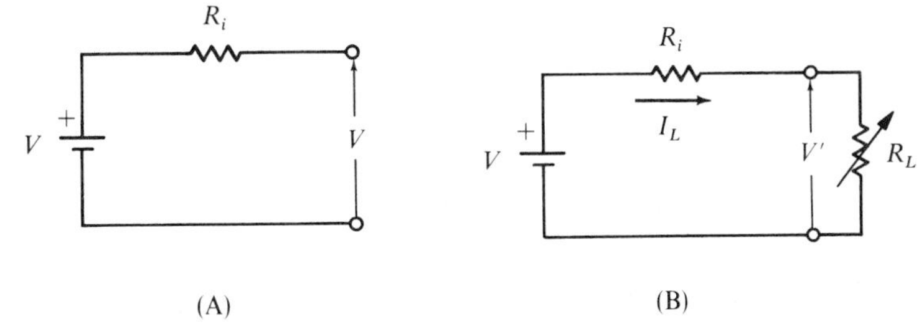

Fig. 4–4. *A physical voltage source may be represented by an ideal voltage source, V, in series with an ideal resistance, R_i. (A) Model. (B) Load resistance R_L connected across the source.*

From Eq. (4–1), we see that if R_L is infinitely large, $V' = V$. As R_L decreases (I_L, therefore, increases), load voltage V' drops. A power supply exhibiting these properties is termed an *unregulated supply*.

An example of a basic zener voltage regulator is given in Fig. 4–5A. It consists of a resistor, R, in series with a zener diode. Resistor R limits the zener current to its maximum value, I_{ZM}. For proper operation, the zener diode is connected so it is reverse biased. Its cathode is connected to point a, which is positive, and its anode to point b, which is negative. The input to the zener regulator is an unregulated voltage, V'. Because load resistor R_L is connected across the diode, the load voltage is equal to the zener voltage, V_Z.

For simplicity, assume that the zener voltage is absolutely constant over the current range of I_{ZK} to I_{ZM}. (The zener voltage actually varies with reverse current, as seen in Fig. 4–1.) Based on this simplification, the zener diode may be represented by a battery having a constant voltage, V_Z volts, illustrated in Fig. 4–5B. This simple model will be used in the ensuing analysis.

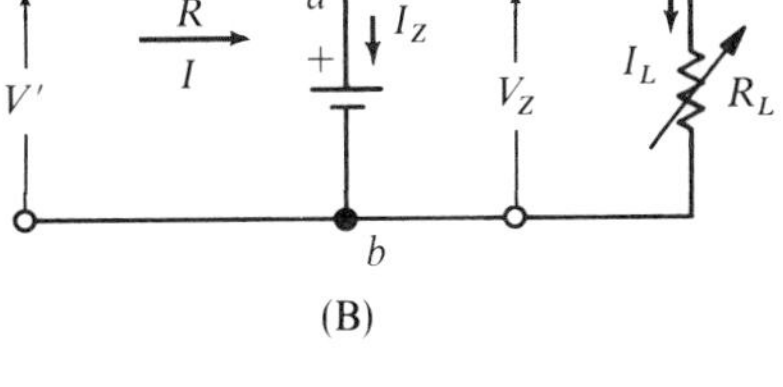

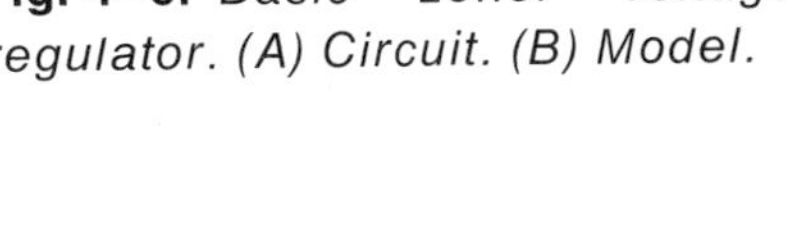

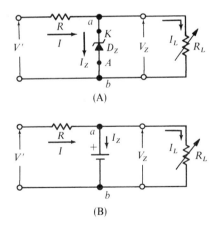

Fig. 4–5. *Basic zener voltage regulator. (A) Circuit. (B) Model.*

Current I flowing in resistance R is equal to the sum of the zener current (I_Z) and load current (I_L):

$$I = I_Z + I_L \quad \textbf{(4–2)}$$

In Fig. 4–5B, current I is also equal to the difference in the unregulated and zener voltages divided by R:

$$I = \frac{V' - V_Z}{R} \quad \textbf{(4–3)}$$

Assume R_L is infinite. In this case, the load current is zero, and current I is equal to the zener current. Maximum current, therefore, flows in the diode and must not exceed I_{ZM}. Letting $I = I_{ZM}$, Eq. (4–3) may be solved for R:

$$R = \frac{V' - V_Z}{I_{ZM}} \tag{4–4}$$

Minimum zener current, I_{ZK}, flows in the diode when load current I_L is maximum. Letting maximum load current equal I_{LM} and $I = I_{ZM}$ in Eq. (4–2), we obtain

$$I_{ZM} = I_{LM} + I_{ZK}$$

Solving for I_{LM}, we find

$$I_{LM} = I_{ZM} - I_{ZK} \tag{4–5}$$

EXAMPLE 4–1.

Figure 4–6 shows a simple zener voltage regulator where $V_Z = 20\,\text{V}$. For the diode, $I_{ZK} = 5\,\text{mA}$ and $I_{ZM} = 200\,\text{mA}$. Determine

(a) The value of R.

(b) The permissible variation in R_L over which the load voltage is still regulated at the zener voltage. $V' = 30\,\text{V}$.

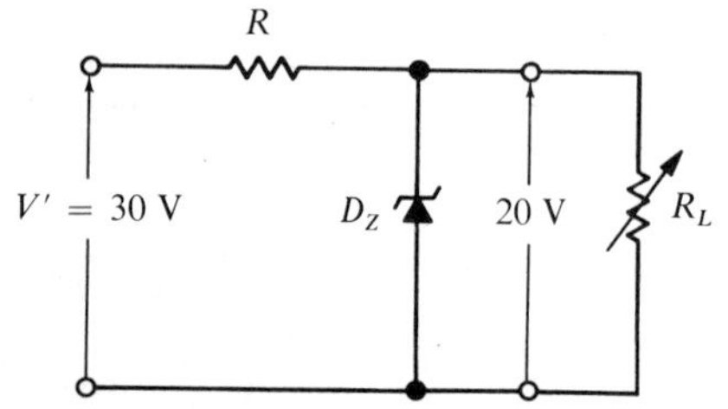

Fig. 4–6. *A simple zener regulator where the zener voltage equals 20 V. (See Example 4–1.)*

Solutions:

(a) Current $I_{ZM} = 200\,\text{mA}$. By Eq. (4–4),

$$R = \frac{30 - 20}{0.2} = \frac{10}{0.2} = 50\,\Omega$$

(b) By Eq. (4–5), $I_{LM} = 200 - 5 = 195\,\text{mA}$. The minimum value of load resistance, $R_{L(\text{min})}$, is equal to the zener voltage divided by the maximum load current. Hence,

$$R_{L(\text{min})} = \frac{20}{0.195} = 102.6\,\Omega$$

Load R_L may vary from infinity to $102.6\,\Omega$.

We see that the regulator keeps the load voltage essentially constant for varying load current. The zener regulator also maintains the load voltage for changes in the unregulated input voltage, V'. If, for example, V' increases, current I also increases. The increase in I is absorbed by the zener diode. For decreasing V', less zener current flows. In the design of a regulator, the allowable variation in V' depends on the values of I_{ZK}, I_{ZM}, and I_L.

Zener diodes used to maintain a fixed voltage for variations in load current or in input voltage are called *regulator diodes*. A zener diode is also used as a voltage reference element, in which the voltage is constant regardless of changes in temperature. If designed for this application, the diode is called a *reference diode.*

4.4 Double-Anode Regulator

A zener diode in which two anodes share a common cathode region is a *double-anode regulator.* Its electrical symbol is illustrated in Fig. 4–7. The double-anode regulator, for example, is used in protective circuits where negative, in addition to positive, overload voltages may occur. When the overload voltage equals the zener voltage, the regulator breaks down and clamps (maintains) the overload at the zener voltage.

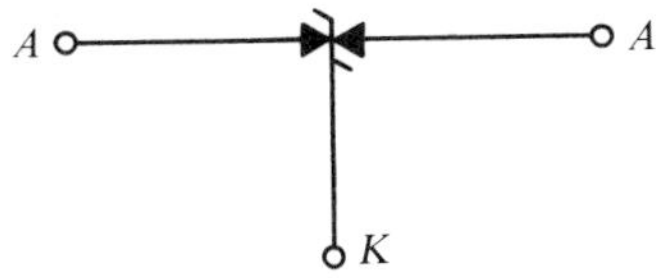

Fig. 4–7. *Electrical symbol for a double-anode regulator.*

4.5 Silicon-Controlled Rectifier

A cross-section of an elementary silicon-controlled rectifier (SCR), also called a *thyristor,* is shown in Fig. 4–8A. It may be regarded as a four-layer PNPN "sandwich." As in a junction diode, the anode and cathode terminals are connected to the outer P and N regions, respectively. Connected to the inner P region is the *gate* (G) terminal. The electrical symbol for an SCR is given in Fig. 4–8B.

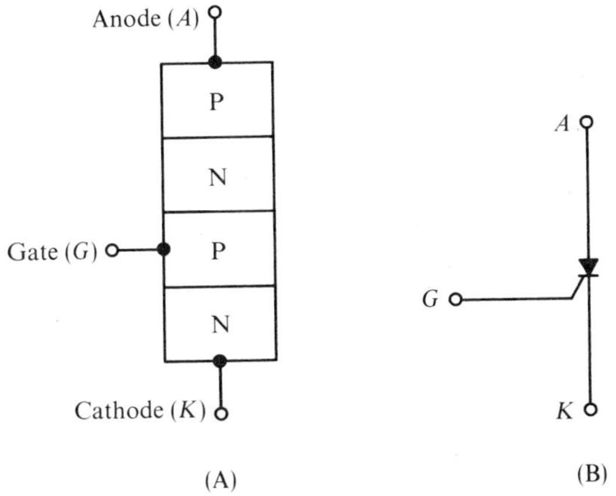

Fig. 4–8. *The silicon-controlled rectifier (SCR). (A) Cross-section. (B) Electrical symbol.*

In SCR operation, the anode is held positive with respect to the cathode. When the anode voltage is equal to, or exceeds, the *forward breakdown voltage,* $V_{BR(F)}$, the SCR fires. It is turned ON and acts like a conducting junction diode. It remains in the ON state until its anode current reaches a minimum value, called the *holding current,* I_H. If a pulse (trigger) of gate current, I_G, is applied to the gate terminal, the SCR fires at an anode voltage less than that for zero gate current.

The volt-ampere characteristics of a typical SCR are shown in Fig. 4–9. Anode current, I_A, is plotted as a function of anode voltage, V_A. For forward voltages less than $V_{BR(F)}$, the SCR is in its *forward blocking region*. The forward breakdown voltage is greater when no gate current flows ($I_{G_1} = 0$) than when gate current is applied to the gate ($I_{G_2} > 0$). The dashed line indicates a rapid transition from the forward blocking to the ON region. When an SCR is reverse biased (*reverse blocking region*), its characteristic is similar to a reverse-biased junction diode.

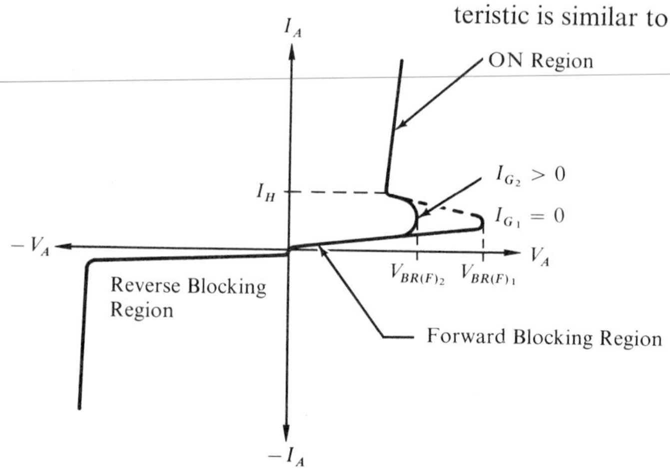

Fig. 4–9. *Volt-ampere characteristics for a typical SCR.*

4.6 SCR Operation

The PNPN sandwich of Fig. 4–8A may be visualized as a PNP transistor (Q_1) connected to an NPN transistor (Q_2) in the manner depicted in Fig. 4–10A. The N-type base of

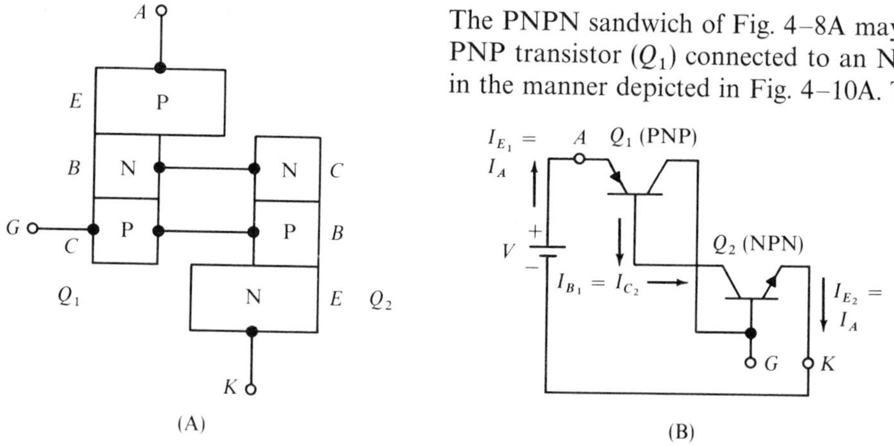

Fig. 4–10. *Visualizing an SCR as a PNP transistor (Q_1) connected to an NPN transistor (Q_2). (A) Pictorial. (B) Schematic.*

Q_1 is connected to the N-type collector of Q_2; the P-type collector of Q_1 is connected to the P-type base of Q_2. A schematic representation of Fig. 4–10A, with the anode biased positive with respect to the cathode, is provided in Fig. 4–10B.

Because the base of Q_1 is connected to the collector of Q_2, $I_{B_1} = I_{C_2}$. As was pointed out in Chapter 3, the collector current is related to the emitter current, using the notation of Fig. 4–10B, by

$$I_{C_2} = h_{FB_2} I_{E_2} + I_{CO_2} \qquad \textbf{(4–6)}$$

Also,

$$I_{B_1} = (1 - h_{FB_1}) I_{E_1} - I_{CO_1}$$

But $I_{B_1} = I_{C_2}$; hence,

$$I_{C_2} = (1 - h_{FB_1}) I_{E_1} - I_{CO_1} \qquad \textbf{(4–7)}$$

Recognizing that $I_{E_1} = I_{E_2} = I_A$, and equating Eq. (4–6) to Eq. (4–7),

$$h_{FB_2} I_A + I_{CO_2} = (1 - h_{FB_1}) I_A - I_{CO_1}$$

Solving for I_A,

$$I_A = \frac{I_{CO_1} + I_{CO_2}}{1 - (h_{FB_1} + h_{FB_2})} \qquad \textbf{(4–8)}$$

For an SCR to fire, the sum $h_{FB_1} + h_{FB_2}$ in the denominator of Eq. (4–8) must equal one. Current I_A then approaches infinity; physically, it is limited by the external resistance connected to the SCR. The value of h_{FB} increases by raising the collector voltage or by increasing the emitter current in a transistor.

The effect of increasing voltage is indicated by the curve, $I_{G_1} = 0$, in Fig. 4–9. At breakdown, the voltage is sufficient to make $h_{FB_1} + h_{FB_2} = 1$. If a gate current is applied, additional base current flows in Q_2. The emitter current is thereby increased, and the SCR fires at a lower voltage.

EXAMPLE 4–2.

The circuit of Fig. 4–11 employs an SCR to rectify ac and, at the same time, control the power delivered to load R_L.

(a) Explain the operation of the circuit.

(b) If current flows for one-half of a positive ac cycle, find the average current in R_L.

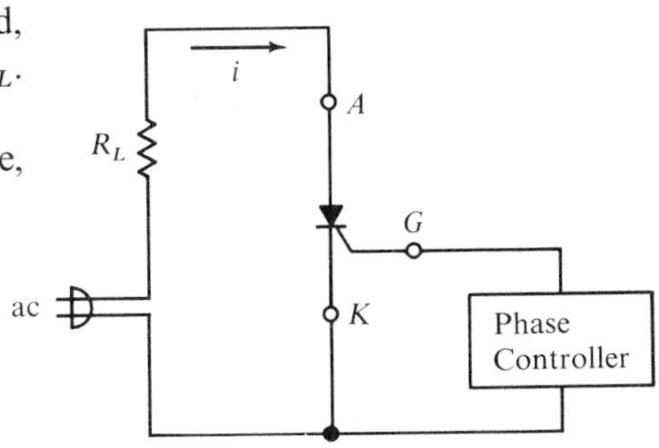

Fig. 4–11. *An SCR used to rectify ac and control power delivered to load R_L. (See Example 4–2.)*

Solutions:

(a) Because the anode and cathode of the SCR are connected to an ac source, the SCR conducts during the

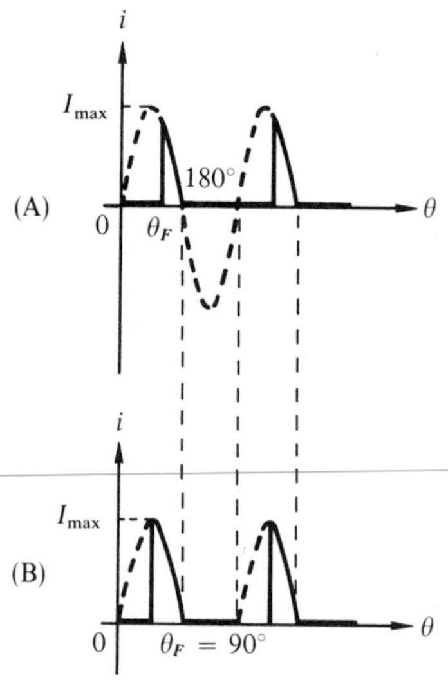

Fig. 4–12. *Current i flowing in the circuit of Fig. 4–11. (A) For an arbitrary firing angle, θ_F. (B) For $\theta_F = 90°$.*

positive half-cycle and is nonconducting during the negative half-cycle. Thus, it acts like a half-wave rectifier.

The purpose of the phase controller (to be described later) is to impress a narrow pulse (trigger) of current in the gate terminal. The controller is capable of providing a trigger at any angle between 0° and 180° during the positive half-cycle. This is illustrated in Fig. 4–12A, where current i is plotted as a function of θ (Greek letter theta).

At angle θ_F, referred to as the *firing angle*, the SCR conducts. At $\theta = 180° - 360°$, the SCR is reverse biased and nonconducting. By varying θ_F, it is possible to vary the average (dc) current and control the power delivered to the load resistor.

(b) Current flowing for one-half of the positive cycle corresponds to $\theta_F = 90°$, as illustrated in Fig. 4–12B. For a half-wave rectifier, $I_{dc} = 0.318 I_{max}$, where I_{max} is the maximum value of current. Hence, for $\theta_F = 90°$, $I_{dc} = 0.318 I_{max}/2 = 0.159 I_{max}$ A.

4.7 The TRIAC

The TRIAC (also called the *bidirectional triode thyristor*) is equivalent to two SCRs connected in inverse-parallel (Fig. 4–13A). The anode of SCR_1 is connected to the cathode of SCR_2, and the cathode of SCR_1 to the anode of SCR_2. These connections are called main terminal 2 (MT_2) and main terminal 1 (MT_1), respectively. Both gates are joined to form a common gate terminal, G. The electrical symbol for a TRIAC is given in Fig. 4–13B.

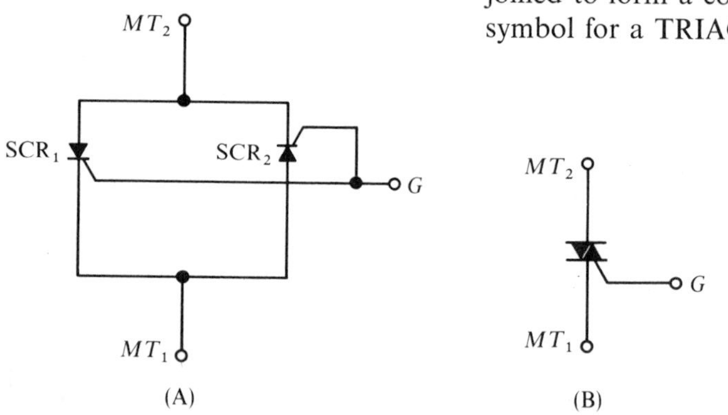

Fig. 4–13. *The TRIAC. (A) It may be viewed as two SCRs connected in inverse parallel. (B) Electrical symbol.*

Typical volt-ampere characteristics for a TRIAC are illustrated in Fig. 4–14. In quadrant I, MT_2 is positive with respect to MT_1; in quadrant III, MT_1 is positive with respect to MT_2. For each quadrant, the characteristics are like those for an SCR.

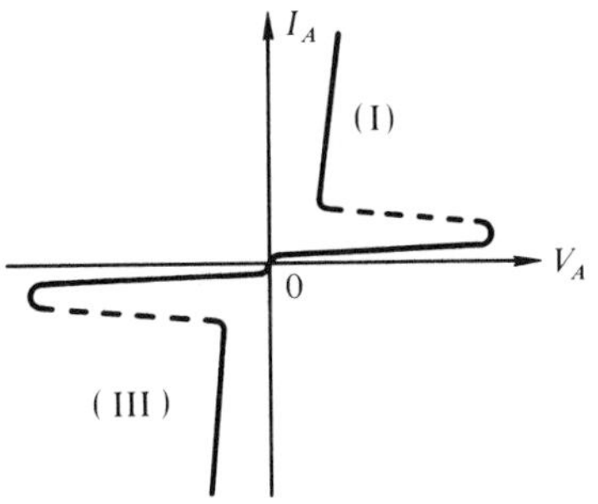

Fig. 4–14. *Volt-ampere characteristics for a typical SCR.*

EXAMPLE 4–3.

A common application for a TRIAC is its use as a light dimmer in homes. A basic circuit for such a dimmer is shown in Fig. 4–15. Connected in series with terminals MT_1 and MT_2 are a lamp and the ac supply. The gate and MT_1 terminals are connected to the phase controller. Explain the operation of the circuit.

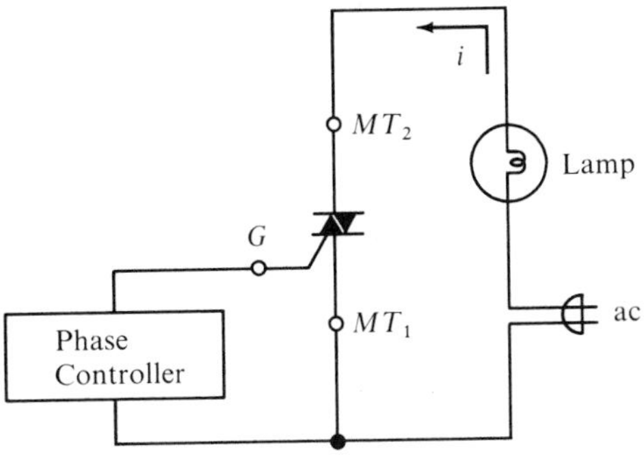

Fig. 4–15. *The TRIAC used in a light dimmer circuit. (See Example 4–3.)*

Solution:

Referring to Fig. 4–16, assume that the phase controller is set for a firing angle of $\theta_F = 120°$ during the positive half-cycle. Consequently, the TRIAC is nonconducting from 0° to 120°. At $\theta_F = 120°$, the current, following the shape of the sine wave, flows from 120° to 180°.

On the negative half-cycle, MT_1 is positive with respect to MT_2. The TRIAC is also nonconducting for 120° (300° − 180°) and fires at 300°. By adjusting the phase controller, the conduction angle for each half-cycle may be varied between 0° and 180°.

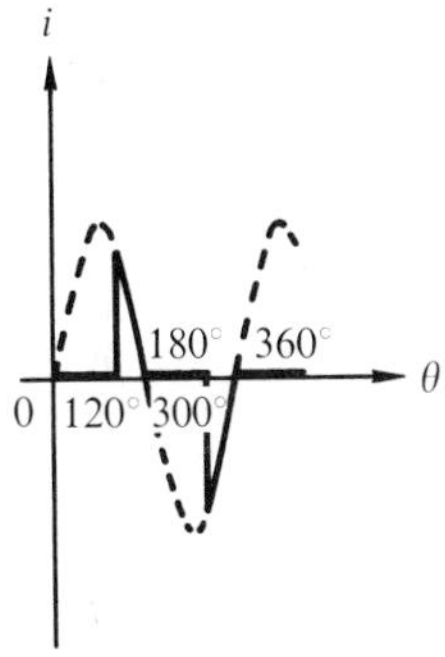

Fig. 4–16. *Current flow in the TRIAC lamp dimmer of Fig. 4–15.*

4.8 The Unijunction Transistor

A cross-section of a basic unijunction transistor (UJT) is illustrated in Fig. 4–17A. Two ohmic, or nonrectifying, contacts, B_1 and B_2, are made at the ends of an N-type silicon bar. (A nonrectifying contact is one at which no junction diode action occurs.) Contacts B_1 and B_2 are called base 1 and base 2, giving the device the name *double-base diode*. The electrical symbol for a UJT is given in Fig. 4–17B.

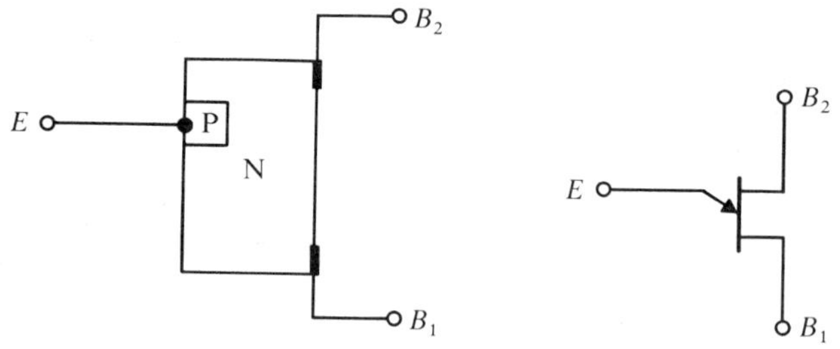

Fig. 4–17. *The unijunction transistor (UJT). (A) Cross-section. (B) Electrical symbol.*

The resistance of the N-type bar (*interbase resistance*, R_{BB}) is in the order of a few thousand to 10,000 ohms. Close to base 2, a P-type impurity is diffused into the N-type bar, and a PN junction is formed. Connected to the P region is the *emitter lead*, *E*. In operation, base 2 and the emitter are biased positively with respect to base 1.

To aid in understanding its operation, we study an electrical equivalent circuit for the UJT in Fig. 4–18. Interbase resistance R_{BB} between B_1 and B_2 is equal to the sum of two resistances: $R_{BB} = R_{B_1} + R_{B_2}$. Because R_{B_1} varies in value with the flow of emitter current I_E, it is represented by a variable resistance. The PN junction is shown as diode D with its anode connected to the emitter terminal. Its cathode is connected to point K, the intersection of R_{B_1} and R_{B_2}.

For $I_E = 0$, by voltage division, voltage V_K is

$$V_K = \frac{R_{B_1} V_{BB}}{R_{B_1} + R_{B_2}} = \eta V_{BB} \qquad \textbf{(4–9)}$$

where η (Greek letter eta) is defined as the *intrinsic standoff ratio* of a UJT. It is expressed by

$$\eta = \frac{R_{B_1}}{R_{BB}} \qquad \textbf{(4–10)}$$

Typical volt-ampere characteristics of a UJT are illustrated in Fig. 4–19. Plotted are emitter voltage, V_E, versus

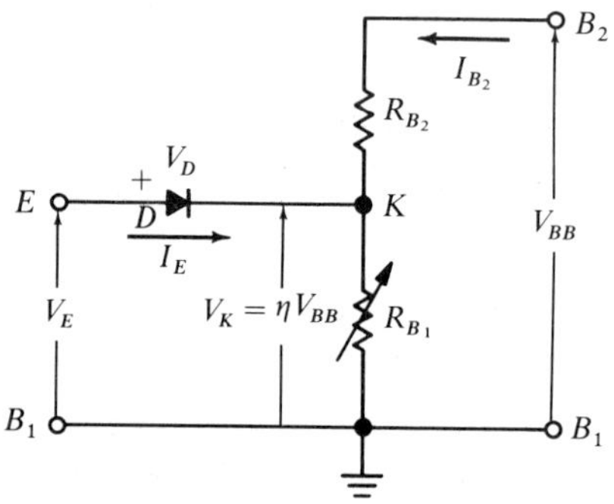

Fig. 4–18. *Electrical equivalent circuit for a UJT.*

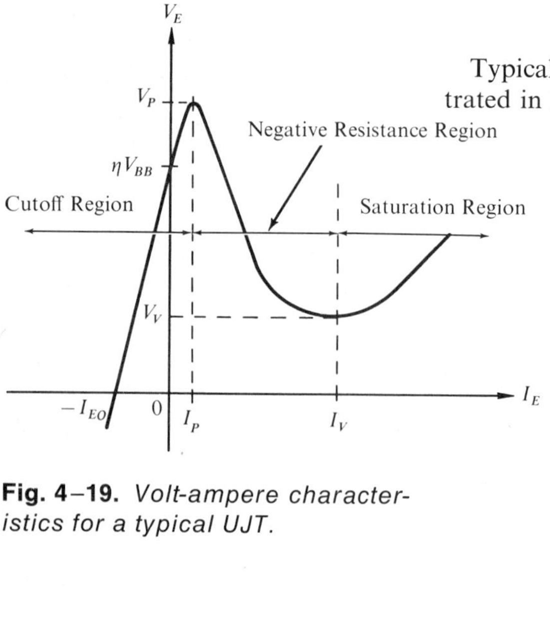

Fig. 4–19. *Volt-ampere characteristics for a typical UJT.*

emitter current, I_E. For V_E less than ηV_{BB}, diode D is reverse biased, and a minute emitter current flows. At $V_E = 0\,\text{V}$, the reverse current, $-I_{EO}$, is only a few microamperes, even at elevated temperatures.

As V_E is increased beyond ηV_{BB}, the diode becomes forward biased. Holes are injected in the region between point K and base 1. Because of the addition of holes, the value of R_{B_1} decreases. For example, at $I_E = 0$, R_{B_1} may be equal to $3000\,\Omega$. If $I_E = 50\,\text{mA}$, R_{B_1} may drop to $30\,\Omega$. As a result, the voltage across R_{B_1} begins to decrease as emitter current increases. Because of this behavior, where an increasing current results in a decreasing voltage, the device is said to exhibit *negative resistance.*

For emitter voltages less than the *peak voltage*, V_P (the corresponding emitter current is called the *peak current*, I_P), the UJT is in the *cutoff region*. Peak voltage, V_P, is the emitter voltage at which the UJT goes from the cutoff to the negative resistance region. The value of V_P, from Fig. 4–18, is equal to the sum of diode voltage V_D and ηV_{BB}:

$$V_P = V_D + \eta V_{BB} \tag{4–11}$$

Peak current, I_P, is the minimum emitter current required for turning ON a UJT.

As I_E increases beyond I_P, it reaches a magnitude that is much greater than base 2 current, I_{B_2}. At that point (the *valley point*), I_{B_2} may be neglected. The UJT begins to act like a conventional junction diode. At the valley point, the emitter voltage equals the *valley voltage*, V_V, and the emitter current equals the *valley current*, I_V. The region to the right of the valley point is the *saturation region.*

Programmable UJT

A variation of the UJT is the programmable unijunction transistor (PUT). The electrical symbol for a PUT is shown in Fig. 4–20. Resistors are connected in series with the gate and across the gate and cathode terminals of the device. The connected resistors determine the values of parameters, such as η and R_{BB}, needed for a specific application.

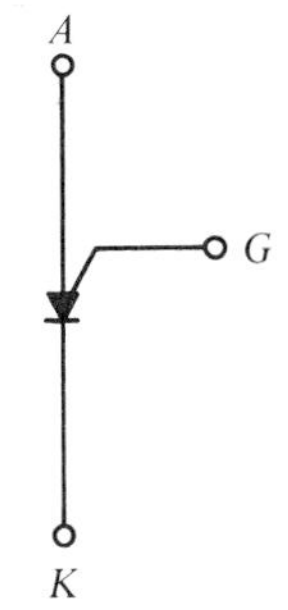

Fig. 4–20. *Electrical symbol for a programmable UJT (PUT).*

EXAMPLE 4–4.

The circuit employing a UJT in Fig. 4–21A is used for the generation of sawtooth and trigger waveforms. Analyze the circuit and draw the generated waveforms across capacitor C and resistor R_1.

Solution:

Before the switch is closed, assume that capacitor C is uncharged. The UJT is in the cutoff region. After the switch is closed, C charges exponentially through R toward the interbase voltage, V_{BB}. As soon as the voltage across C (v_C)

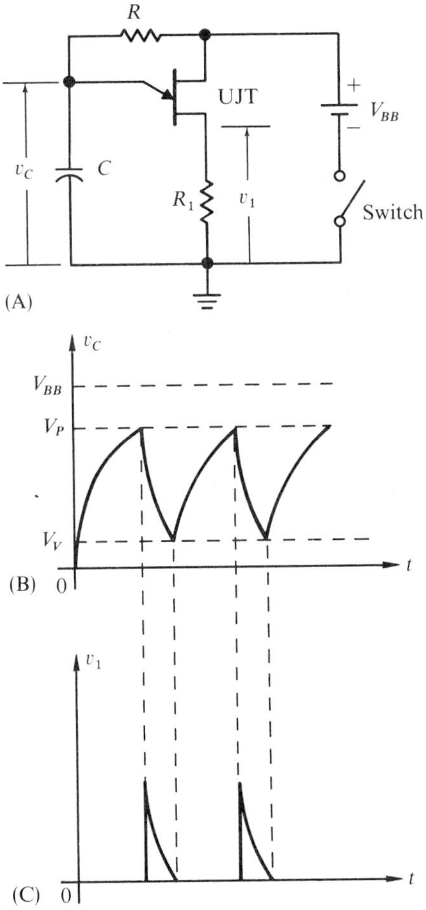

Fig. 4–21. *A UJT circuit for generating sawtooth and trigger waveforms. (A) Circuit. (B) Voltage across capacitor C. (C) Voltage across resistor R_1. (See Example 4–4.)*

reaches V_P, the emitter diode conducts, and the UJT is turned ON.

Capacitor C discharges through R_{B_1}, which has a low resistance value. When v_C reaches the valley voltage, the number of injected holes in the N-type silicon is very small, and the UJT turns OFF. Capacitor C begins to charge up again, and the preceding cycle is repeated, as shown in Fig. 4–21B. Because of its shape, the waveform across C is called a *sawtooth wave*. Its peak-to-peak value is equal to the difference in the peak and valley voltages: $V_P - V_V$ volts.

During the interval that C discharges, current flows in R_1. The resultant waveform (Fig. 4–21C) is a trigger voltage. By varying the values of C and R, the time between triggers can be changed. Thus, the circuit of Fig. 4–21A may be used as a phase controller for an SCR or a TRIAC.

4.9 The Schottky Diode

A cross-section of a Schottky diode (*hot-carrier* diode) and its electrical symbol are shown in Fig. 4–22. Cathode terminal K, because of the N^+ region diffused in the N substrate, makes an ohmic contact with the device. Since aluminum is a P-type material, a PN junction diode is formed at the anode terminal. Because of its structure, the Schottky diode is also called a *semiconductor-metal junction diode*. Its volt-ampere characteristics are similar to those of a junction diode.

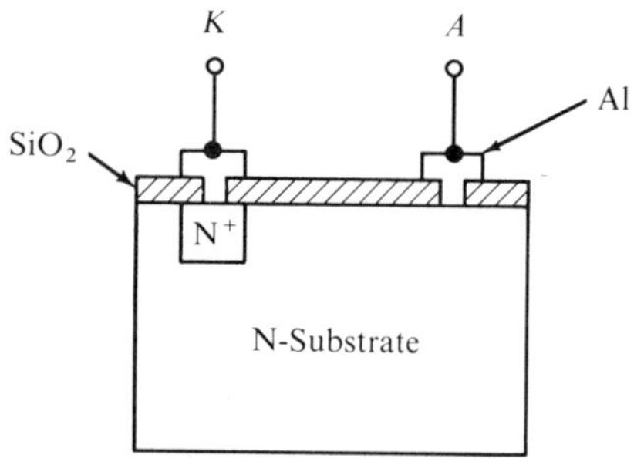

(A)

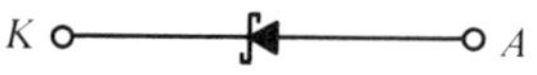

(B)

Fig. 4–22. *The Schottky diode. (A) Cross-section. (B) Electrical symbol.*

When the anode is forward biased with respect to the cathode, electrons flow in the N-type substrate, and the diode conducts. If the anode is negative with respect to the cathode, the PN junction at the anode terminal is reverse biased; the diode is nonconducting. Because conduction takes place primarily by electron flow, the Schottky diode is considered a majority carrier device and switches very rapidly. This property makes it ideal for switching circuits.

4.10 The Varactor Diode

In the discussion of diode operation in Chapter 2, it was pointed out that a depletion region exists in the vicinity of the PN junction. The depletion region is devoid of current carriers and, therefore, acts as a dielectric. Considering the P and N regions as plates of a capacitor, the PN junction may be viewed as a capacitor, shown in Fig. 4–23A. Such a device is called a *varactor*, or *variable-voltage capacitor diode*. Its electrical symbol is given in Fig. 4–23B.

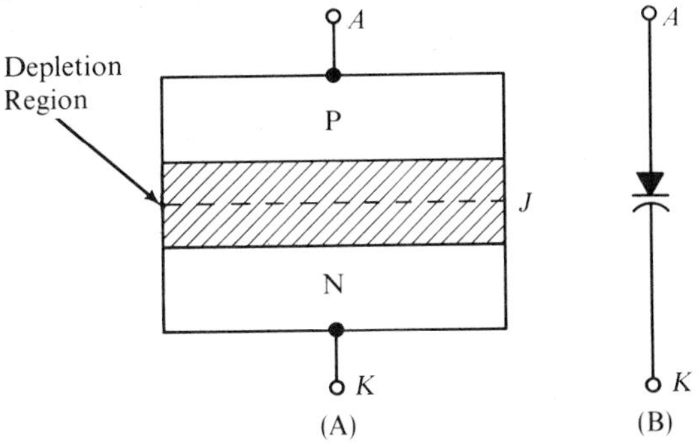

Fig. 4–23. *The Varactor diode. (A) Cross-section. (B) Electrical symbol.*

The capacitance, C, of any capacitor is expressed by

$$C = \frac{\epsilon A}{d} \quad \textbf{(4–12)}$$

where A is the area of the plates, d the thickness of the dielectric, and ϵ the dielectric constant. For a given junction diode, its geometry fixes the cross-section area, A, of the P and N regions. In addition, the dielectric constant depends on the material used, such as silicon, for the device. Consequently, the capacitance may be varied by changing the depletion thickness, d.

When a junction diode is reverse biased, the thickness of the depletion region increases. As the bias is made more negative, d becomes larger. Referring to Eq. (4–12), we see that as d increases, C decreases. In the varactor, the capacitance is varied by a dc voltage across the device.

The variation in capacitance C as a function of the reverse voltage V_R for a silicon diode may be approximated by the following expression:

$$C = \frac{C_0}{\left(1 + \frac{V_R}{0.6}\right)^{1/2}} \quad \textbf{(4–13)}$$

where C_0 is the capacitance at zero bias. An example of variation in C with V_R is illustrated in Fig. 4–24. Note that as V_R increases, C decreases. Maximum value of capacitance, C_0, occurs for $V_R = 0$.

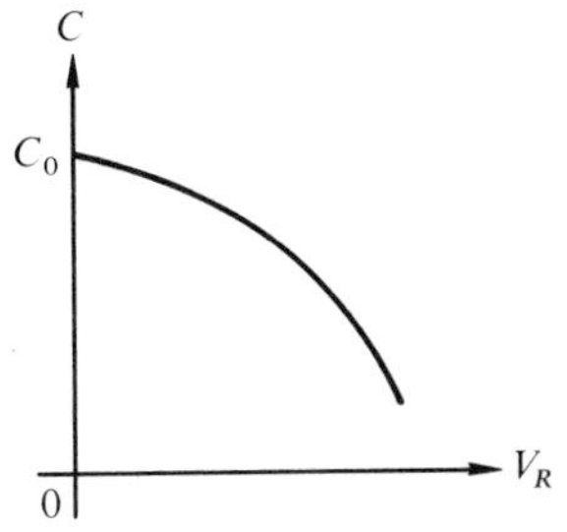

Fig. 4–24. *Variation in capacitance C of a varactor diode as a function of reverse voltage V_R.*

EXAMPLE 4–5.

A varactor diode has a capacitance of 100 pF at zero bias. Determine its capacitance at a reverse bias of 12 V.

Solution:

From the given values, $C_0 = 100\,\text{pF}$ and $V_R = 12\,\text{V}$. Substitution of the values in Eq. (4–13) yields

$$C = \frac{100}{\left(1 + \frac{12}{0{\cdot}6}\right)^{1/2}} = \frac{100}{4.6} = 21.8\,\text{pF}$$

4.11 The Light-Emitting Diode

In a forward-biased junction diode, electrons from the N region and holes from the P region cross the PN junction. Some of the electrons in the P region recombine with holes, and, similarly, some holes in the N region recombine with electrons. Because of recombination, radiant energy is released. This is the basis of operation for the light-emitting diode (LED), used so frequently for the display in the electronic hand-held calculator.

The electrical symbol and typical volt-ampere characteristics for a LED are shown in Fig. 4–25. Its forward characteristic curve is similar to that of a junction diode. Because material other than silicon is used in its fabrication, the threshold voltage is in the order of 1.5 V instead of 0.6 V.

To realize efficient operation and greater released energy, gallium (Ga), arsenic (As), and phosphorus (P) are used instead of silicon or germanium. The frequency (wavelength) of emitted light is a function of the energy gap of the material used in making the LED. A gallium-phosphide (GaP) LED emits green light, and a gallium-arsenide-phosphide (GaAsP) device emits red light.

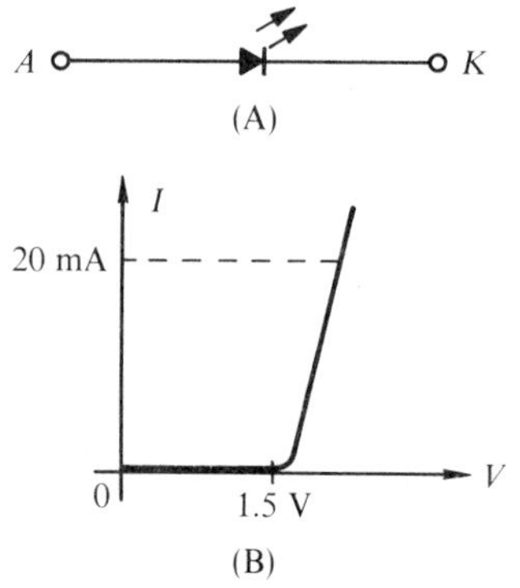

Fig. 4–25. *The light-emitting diode (LED). (A) Electrical symbol. (B) Typical volt-ampere characteristics.*

4.12 The Phototransistor

A phototransistor may be visualized as a PNP or an NPN transistor without a base terminal. Instead, radiant energy focused on the base region supplies base current to the transistor.

The electrical symbol and typical collector characteristics for an NPN phototransistor are illustrated in Fig. 4–26. Note that the collector characteristics are similar to those

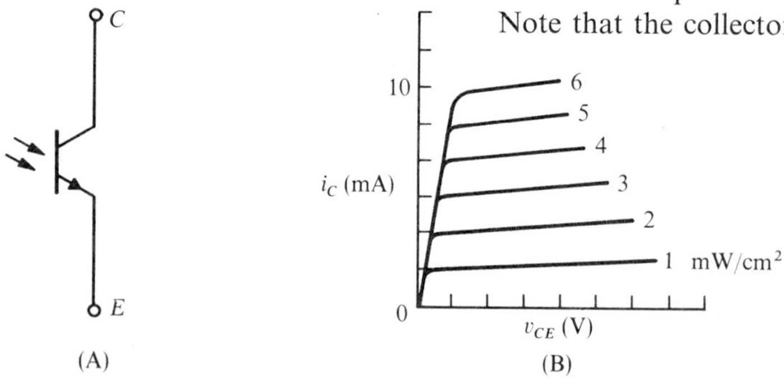

Fig. 4–26. *An NPN phototransistor. (A) Electrical symbol. (B) Typical collector characteristics.*

of a conventional NPN transistor. Instead of curves of base current, however, curves of illumination in mW/cm^2 are indicated.

SUMMARY

The operation of semiconductor devices described in this chapter is based on concepts developed in Chapters 2 and 3. For example, the zener diode is basically a reverse-biased silicon junction diode, and the SCR can be viewed as a connection of a PNP with an NPN transistor. The UJT, Schottky diode, varactor, LED, and phototransistor, in one way or another, involve the action of a PN junction.

Because a zener diode displays a nearly constant (zener) voltage for an appreciable range of reverse current, it is suited for the regulation of voltage. The properties of the SCR make it ideal for the efficient control of power in a load. Displaying negative resistance, the UJT can provide the trigger needed to control the angle of an SCR.

One important application for the Schottky diode is in digital switching circuits, considered later in the text. The varactor, in addition to its application as a variable capacitor, is also employed in frequency multiplying circuits. In these circuits, for example, a frequency may be doubled or tripled. Light-emitting diodes are widely used to display the results of calculations performed on an electronic calculator. Because of its unique properties, the phototransistor is used in circuits such as alarms, where light is the controlling signal.

Further Reading

Kaufman, M., and A. H. Seidman, eds. *Handbook for Electronics Engineering Technicians.* New York: McGraw-Hill Book Company, 1976, Chapter 8.

SCR Manual, 5th ed. Syracuse, N.Y.: General Electric, 1972.

Sowa, W. A., and J. M. Toole. *Special Semiconductor Devices.* New York: Holt, Rinehart and Winston, 1968, Chapters 1, 2, 3, 6, and 7.

Temes, Lloyd. *Electronic Circuits for Technicians.* New York: McGraw-Hill Book Company, 1970, Chapters 5 and 6.

Texas Instruments. *Understanding Solid-State Electronics.* Dallas, Tex.: Texas Instruments Learning Center, 1972, Chapter 9.

Tocci, Ronald J. *Fundamentals of Electronic Devices.* 2nd ed. Columbus, Ohio: Charles E. Merrill Publishing Company, 1975, Chapters 6, 8, 14, and 15.

REVIEW QUESTIONS

4.1 Define zener voltage.

4.2 Draw the electrical symbol for a zener diode.

4.3 Why is the zener diode a useful device?

4.4 What is meant by zener knee current?

4.5 Explain the differences between zener and avalanche breakdown.

4.6 Define an ideal voltage source.

4.7 What is meant by an unregulated power supply?

4.8 Discuss the differences between zener regulator and reference diodes.

4.9 How does the double-anode regulator differ from the zener diode? What is a useful application for the double-anode regulator?

4.10 Draw a cross-section and the electrical symbol for the SCR.

4.11 How do the volt-ampere characteristics of an SCR change with increasing gate current?

4.12 Draw typical volt-ampere characteristics and the electrical symbol for the TRIAC.

4.13 What is meant by an ohmic contact?

4.14 Draw a cross-section and electrical symbol for the UJT.

4.15 How does a UJT differ from a BJT and a FET?

4.16 Define intrinsic standoff ratio.

4.17 Draw the volt-ampere characteristics for a typical UJT.

4.18 Define negative resistance.

4.19 What are the characteristics of a PUT?

4.20 Draw a cross-section and electrical symbol for a Schottky diode.

4.21 Draw the electrical symbol for a varactor diode.

4.22 What is the principle of operation of the LED?

4.23 Draw the volt-ampere characteristics and electrical symbol for a LED.

4.24 What types of light-emitting diodes emit green light and red light?

4.25 Draw the volt-ampere characteristics and electrical symbol for a phototransistor.

PROBLEMS

P4–1 In Fig. 4–4B, assume that $V = 100\,\text{V}$ and $R_i = 100\,\Omega$. If R_L is varied from 100 to $1000\,\Omega$, draw curves of

(a) V' versus I_L.

(b) V' versus R_L.

P4–2 Repeat prob. P4–1 for $V = 150\,\text{V}$ and $R_i = 120\,\Omega$.

P4–3 In Fig. 4–4B, assume that $V = 100\,\text{V}$ and $R_L = 100\,\Omega$. If R_i is varied from 0 to $100\,\Omega$, draw curves of
(a) V' versus I_L.
(b) V' versus R_i.

P4–4 Repeat prob. P4–3 for $V = 150\,\text{V}$ and $R_L = 120\,\Omega$.

P4–5 Assume that $I_{ZK} = 10\,\text{mA}$ and $I_{ZM} = 100\,\text{mA}$ for the zener diode in the regulator of Fig. 4–6. Calculate
(a) The value of R.
(b) The variation in R_L over which the load voltage is regulated at 20 V.

P4–6 Repeat prob. P4–5 assuming that $I_{ZK} = 15\,\text{mA}$ and $I_{ZM} = 200\,\text{mA}$.

P4–7 In Example 4–1, assume that R_L is constant at $100\,\Omega$ and $R = 100\,\Omega$. Over what range can V' vary and regulation still be maintained?

P4–8 Repeat prob. P4–7 for R_L constant at $150\,\Omega$.

P4–9 In Example 4–1, assume that $V' = 30\,\text{V}$ is constant. If $R = 100\,\Omega$, over what range may R_L vary and regulation still be maintained?

P4–10 Repeat prob. P4–9 assuming $V' = 35\,\text{V}$ is constant.

P4–11 Beginning with Eq. (4–6), go through the necessary steps to derive Eq. (4–8).

P4–12 For the circuit of Fig. 4–11, $I_{\text{max}} = 10\,\text{A}$ and $R_L = 100\,\Omega$. If the firing angle is 90°, determine the dc power dissipated in R_L.

P4–13 Repeat prob. P4–12 for $I_{\text{max}} = 15\,\text{A}$ and $R_L = 120\,\Omega$.

P4–14 For the UJT circuit of Fig. 4–21 A, draw waveforms v_c and v_1 as capacitor C is varied from a low value to a high value. Assume that R is constant.

P4–15 Assuming that C is constant, repeat prob. P4–14 for variations in R from a low to a high value.

P4–16 Assume that a varactor diode has a capacitance of 50 pF at zero bias. What is its capacitance at a reverse bias of
(a) 3 V?
(b) 6 V?
(c) 10 V?

P4–17 Repeat prob. P4–16 for a varactor diode that has a capacitance of 75 pF at zero bias.

part ii

SMALL-SIGNAL OPERATION

The make-up and operation of transistor amplifiers are considered in this section. Since many amplifiers operate at small-signal levels, the transistor can be treated as a linear device, like a resistor, and its analysis easily performed algebraically.

Topics covered include general properties, development of small-signal models, biasing and stabilization of the operating point, low- and high-frequency operation, and feedback in amplifiers. These subjects are essential to the understanding of discrete and integrated circuits. The concluding chapters in the section cover integrated circuit technology and the operation and application of the operational amplifier.

5

Introduction to Amplifiers

In this chapter, we begin a study of amplifiers. Our objective is to gain an understanding and a perspective of basic amplifier types, classes of amplifier operation, and the difference between small-signal and large-signal operation. Once this picture is acquired, we can then study the operation and performance of amplifiers in detail.

5.1 What Is an Amplifier?

Figure 5–1 is a *block diagram* of an amplifier. A block diagram is a useful aid in describing the overall performance of a circuit, such as an amplifier, with respect to its terminals. In Fig. 5–1, there are four terminals, two input and two output terminals. Impressed across the input terminals is a signal to be amplified. The input signal may be a voltage, V_i, or a current, I_i.

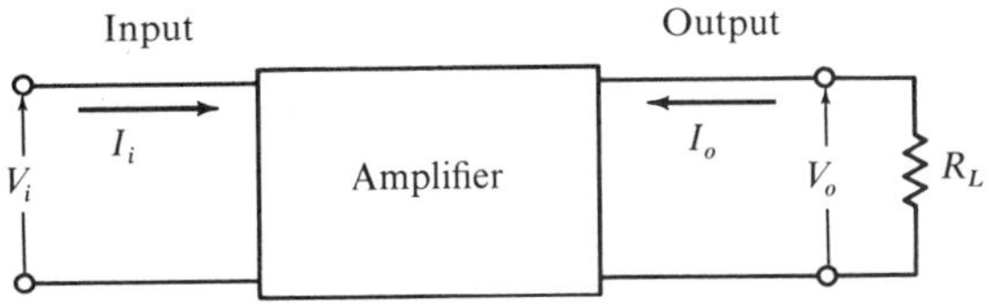

Fig. 5–1. *Block diagram of an amplifier. An amplifier is an example of a four-terminal circuit (network).*

Across the output terminals is a load resistor R_L. Resistor R_L may represent, for example, the coil resistance of a loudspeaker or the field winding resistance of a motor. The output signal may be specified as an output voltage V_o or an output current I_o.

There are three useful ways to define the gain of an amplifier. As defined in Chapter 3 and reviewed here, the *voltage gain*, A_v, is defined as the ratio of the output voltage V_o to the input voltage V_i:

$$A_v = \frac{V_o}{V_i} \quad \textbf{(5–1)}$$

(Voltage V_i, as well as V_s, is used to denote input voltage.) The *current gain*, A_i, is the ratio of output current I_o to input current I_i:

$$A_i = \frac{I_o}{I_i} \quad \textbf{(5–2)}$$

Finally, the *power gain*, A_p, is the ratio of output power $P_o = V_o I_o$ to input power $P_i = V_i I_i$:

$$A_p = \frac{P_o}{P_i} = \frac{V_o I_o}{V_i I_i} = \left(\frac{V_o}{V_i}\right)\left(\frac{I_o}{I_i}\right) \qquad \textbf{(5–3)}$$

By Eq. (5–1), $V_o/V_i = A_v$, and by Eq. (5–2), $I_o/I_i = A_i$. Therefore, the power gain also may be expressed as the product of the voltage and current gains:

$$A_p = A_v A_i \qquad \textbf{(5–4)}$$

In each of the gain ratios, the units, such as volts/volts, cancel. Hence, gain expressions have no units; that is, they are *numerics*.

EXAMPLE 5–1.

The following measured data were recorded for an amplifier: $V_i = 10$ mV, $V_o = 2$ V, $I_i = 0.1$ mA, and $I_o = 5$ mA. Calculate the voltage, current, and power gains of the amplifier.

Solution:

By Eq. (5–1), voltage gain $A_v = 2/0.01 = 200$. Using Eq. (5–2), current gain $A_i = 5/0.1 = 50$. Power gain, by Eq. (5–4), is $A_p = 200 \times 50 = 10{,}000$.

An amplifier designed to maximize voltage gain is called a *voltage amplifier*. If the amplifier is designed to maximize current gain, the circuit is a *current amplifier*. For applications in which the amplifier has to deliver appreciable power (generally 1 W or more), it is called a *power amplifier*.

5.2 The Need for Amplifiers

Applications of amplifiers are so numerous that only a few representative examples are considered here. Before we proceed, however, let us define a transducer. A *transducer* is a device that takes energy in one form and converts it into another form. For example, a microphone takes acoustical energy and converts it into electrical energy; a phonograph cartridge converts the mechanical vibrations of a needle riding on the grooves of a record to electrical energy; a receiver antenna converts the electromagnetic waves in space into electrical currents. More examples, many of which can be supplied by the reader, may be cited.

The electrical energy derived from transducers is generally of very small magnitude. In terms of voltage, it is typically in the order of microvolts and millivolts. Before it can be processed, therefore, these weak signals have to be amplified.

With suitable amplification, we can then hear sound from a stereo, view a picture on television, or guide a space capsule to the moon.

5.3 The Basic Amplifier

As pointed out in Chapter 3, the transistor exhibits power gain and is therefore an active device. Active devices generally have three terminals. Figure 5–2 is a generalized diagram of a basic amplifier. For the present, the active device is represented by a circle and the three terminals by the letters X, Y, and Z. Note that terminal Z is common to both the input and output. Thus, Fig. 5–2 is a four-terminal circuit like the one shown in Fig. 5–1.

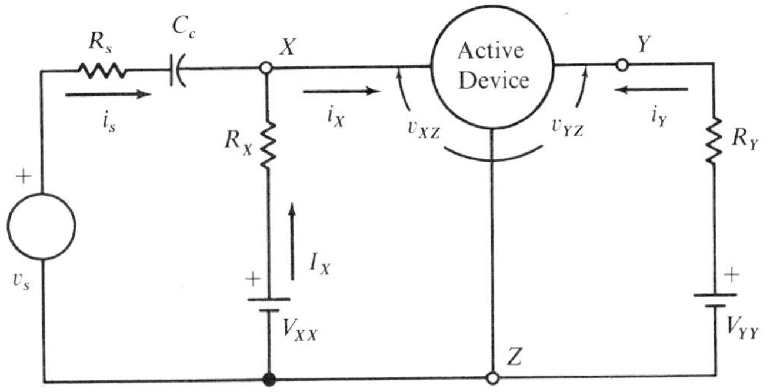

Fig. 5–2. *Generalized representation of a basic amplifier circuit.*

Resistors R_X and R_Y, in conjunction with dc sources V_{XX} V_{YY}, determine the dc operating point of the amplifier. Setting the dc operating point of an active device is known as *biasing*. Sources V_{XX} and V_{YY} are the *bias sources*. The operating point is also called the *Q point*. For proper operation, every active device must be biased. More will be said about this subject later.

In addition to its part in determining the Q point, resistor R_Y also acts as the load across which the amplified signal is developed. The input signal is shown as a voltage source v_s in series with source resistance R_s. The source resistance accounts for the internal resistance of the source. Capacitor C_c is a *coupling capacitor*. It serves to couple the ac, or varying, signal into the amplifier while blocking any dc that may be present in the source. The dc operating point of the amplifier is thereby not disturbed. Because it blocks dc, the coupling capacitor is sometimes called a *blocking capacitor*.

When the signal is dc or is slowly varying, a coupling capacitor is not used. Instead, the signal is *directly coupled* (referred to as *dc coupling*) into the amplifier. Because coupling capacitors tend to be relatively large in size, they are not found in monolithic integrated circuits.

The behavior of the active device in Fig. 5–2 may be described by a family of *output characteristic curves*, shown in Fig. 5–3. In Fig. 5–3, total output current i_Y, as a function of total output voltage v_{YZ}, is plotted for different values of dc bias current I_X. Instead of I_X, dc voltage V_{XZ} is another possibility. The choice is determined by the type of active device used. For a BJT, current is the variable; for a FET, voltage is the variable.

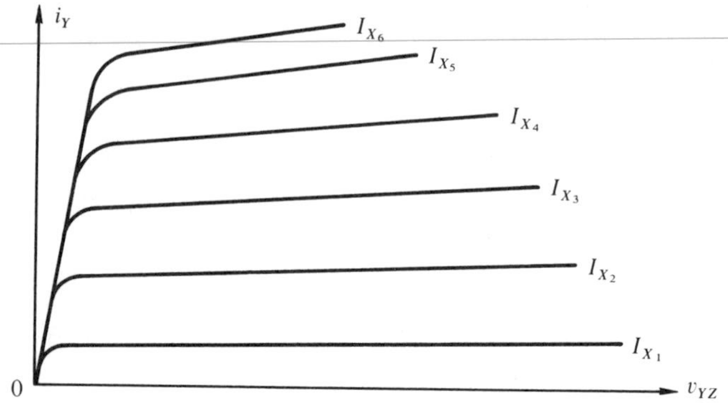

Fig. 5–3. *Typical output characteristics for an active device. The varying parameter is the dc bias current.*

If we apply Kirchhoff's voltage law (which states that the algebraic sum of the voltages in a closed circuit path is equal to zero) to the output side of Fig. 5–2, we obtain

$$V_{YY} = R_Y i_Y + v_{YZ}$$

or, solving for i_Y,

$$i_Y = -\frac{v_{YZ}}{R_Y} + \frac{V_{YY}}{R_Y} \qquad \textbf{(5–5)}$$

Expression (5–5) is an equation of a straight line of the form

$$y = mx + b$$

where m is the slope of the line and b is the intercept on the y-axis. Comparing Eq. (5–5) with the equation of a straight line, we see that $i_Y = y$, $v_{YZ} = x$, $-1/R_Y$ is the slope, and V_{YY}/R_Y is the intercept on the i_Y-axis. Because two points determine a straight line, it is very simple to plot Eq. (5–5) on the output characteristics. Two convenient points to select are $i_Y = 0$ and $v_{YZ} = 0$.

At $i_Y = 0$, Eq. (5–5) reduces to

$$v_{YZ} = V_{YY} \qquad \textbf{(5–6a)}$$

At $v_{YZ} = 0$, we have

$$i_Y = \frac{V_{YY}}{R_Y} \qquad \textbf{(5–6b)}$$

Using these results, we plot, or superimpose, Eq. (5–5) on

the output characteristics in Fig. 5–4. A straight line is drawn between point V_{YY} on the v_{YZ}-axis and point V_{YY}/R_Y on the i_Y-axis.

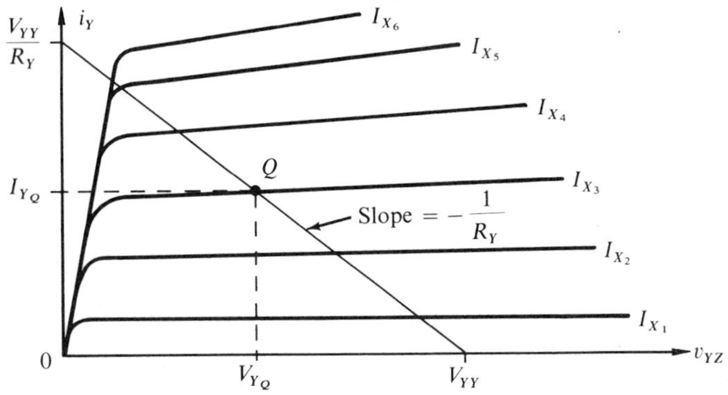

Fig. 5–4. *Superimposing a load line on output characteristics.*

Note that the load line intersects various I_X curves. If $I_X = I_{X_3}$ flows into terminal X (Fig. 5–2), the device is biased at the Q point corresponding to $v_{YZ} = V_{Y_Q}$ and $i_Y = I_{Y_Q}$. It is usually desirable to select the Q point close to the center of the load line for amplifier operation.

In the input circuit of Fig. 5–2, the value of I_X is

$$I_X = \frac{V_{XX} - v_{XZ}}{R_X} \qquad \textbf{(5–7)}$$

EXAMPLE 5–2.

Assume that in Fig. 5–2, $V_{YY} = 30\,\text{V}$, $R_Y = 3\,\text{k}\Omega$, $V_{XX} = 2.7\,\text{V}$, and $v_{XZ} = 0.7\,\text{V}$.

(a) Write the load-line equation and identify the slope and intercept.

(b) What two points should be selected for plotting the load line?

(c) If $I_X = 0.05\,\text{mA}$, determine R_X.

Solutions:

(a) Writing a voltage equation for the output circuit, we have

$$30 = 3000 i_Y + v_{YZ}$$

or, solving for i_Y,

$$i_Y = -\frac{v_{YZ}}{3000} + \frac{30}{3000}$$

$$= -\frac{v_{YZ}}{3000} + 0.01\ \text{A}$$

The slope is $-1/3000$; the intercept is 0.01 A (10 mA).

(b) At $i_Y = 0$, $v_{YZ} = 30\,\text{V}$; at $v_{YZ} = 0$, $i_Y = 10\,\text{mA}$.

(c) Solving Eq. (5–7) for R_X, we obtain

$$R_X = \frac{2.7 - 0.7}{0.05 \times 10^{-3}} = 40\,\text{k}\Omega$$

5.4 Notation

In the preceding discussion, we used, for example, i_X and I_X to denote current and v_{XZ} and V_{XZ} for voltage. The choice of notation is a matter of convention.

Figure 5–5 is a plot of a sinusoidal current waveform. The dc, or *average level*, is indicated by a capital I and a capital subscript X: I_X. (For a voltage waveform, the average value would be designated by V_X.) The *total current* is denoted by a lowercase i and a capital subscript X: i_X. The *instantaneous* value of current (with respect to the average value) is written in all lowercase letters: i_x.

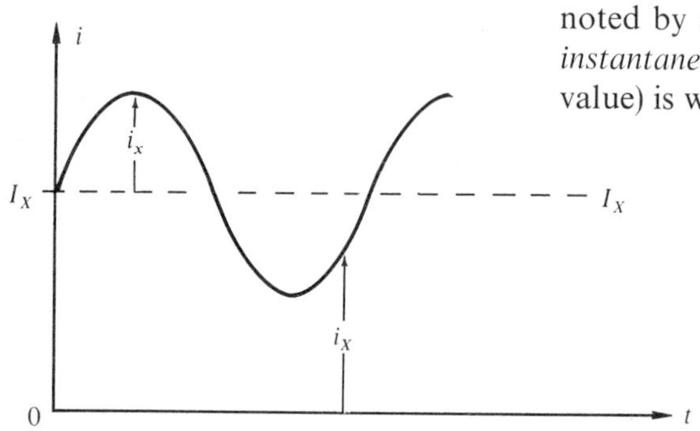

Fig. 5–5. *Illustration of standard notation.*

If we indicate the *rms* value of current (or voltage), a capital I and a lowercase x are used: I_x (or V_x). Dc bias sources and voltages are denoted by capital letters, including the subscript; for example, V_{XX}, V_{YZ}.

5.5 Large-Signal and Small-Signal Operation

Figure 5–6 is a graph of the waveforms resulting from a signal impressed across the input terminals of an amplifier. Superimposed on the output characteristics is the load line. The signal current i_x as a function of ωt radians (2π radians $= 360^\circ$) is shown with the ωt axis intersecting the Q point.

Assume that the peak amplitudes of i_x correspond to $I_{X_2} - I_{X_Q}$ and $I_{X_Q} - I_{X_1}$, respectively. Lines are extended from the peaks of i_x to the points of intersection of the load line with I_{X_2} and I_{X_1}. If lines are now projected from these points of intersection perpendicular to the i_Y- and v_{YZ}-axes, we obtain a graph of the output current and voltage waveforms.

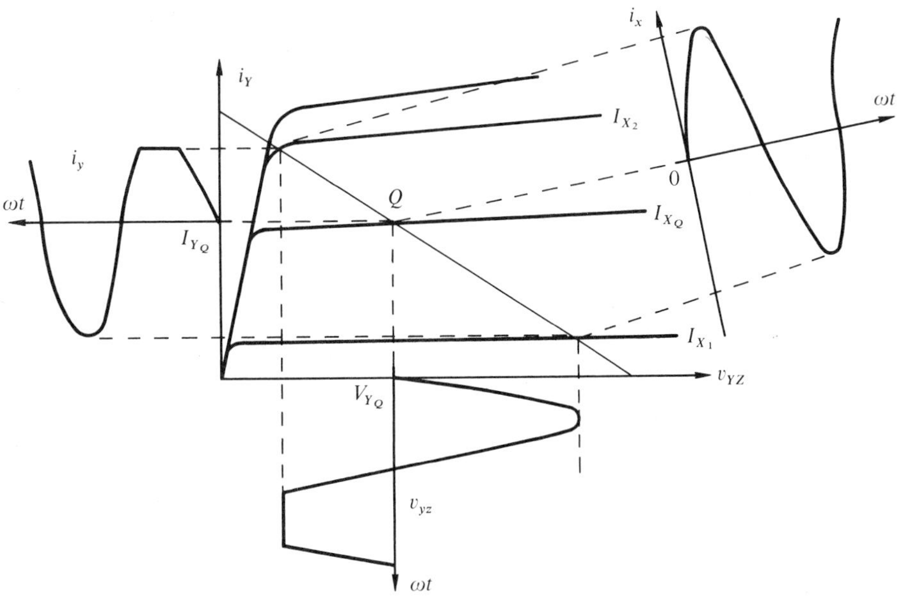

Fig. 5–6. *Graphical analysis of a large-signal amplifier. Note that the output current and voltage waveforms are distorted. This is an example of nonlinear distortion.*

Note that the output current and voltage waveforms are not sinusoidal like the input waveform. There appears to be some flattening in the output waveforms. The flattening is due to the output characteristics being *nonlinear* because of the crowding of the current curves for increasing bias current. When the output differs in shape from the input, *nonlinear distortion* is said to exist.

The preceding study is an example of *graphical analysis* of a large-signal amplifier. This method is invariably used when analyzing, for example, power amplifiers where large signal swings exist. For small signals, it is not practical to perform a graphical analysis. In this case, a *small-signal model* is developed, and the solution is obtained algebraically. This is the subject of the next chapter.

5.6 Classes of Operation

Depending on the location of the Q point, the output current of an amplifier can flow for as much as 360° of the input waveform. This is illustrated in Fig. 5–7. For reference, the input signal waveform is drawn in Fig. 5–7A.

In class A operation, output current flows for a full 360° (Fig. 5–7B). In class B, the output current flows for half a cycle, or 180° (Fig. 5–7C). The case in which the output current flows for more than 180° but less than 360° is a class AB operation (Fig. 5–7D). If the output current flows for less than half a cycle, as in Fig. 5–7E, we have a class C operation.

An examination of the waveforms of Fig. 5–7 reveals that for the basic amplifier of Fig. 5–2, only class A operation yields an output signal waveform with minimum distortion. The other types of operation (which will be considered later), however, have certain advantages over class A operation.

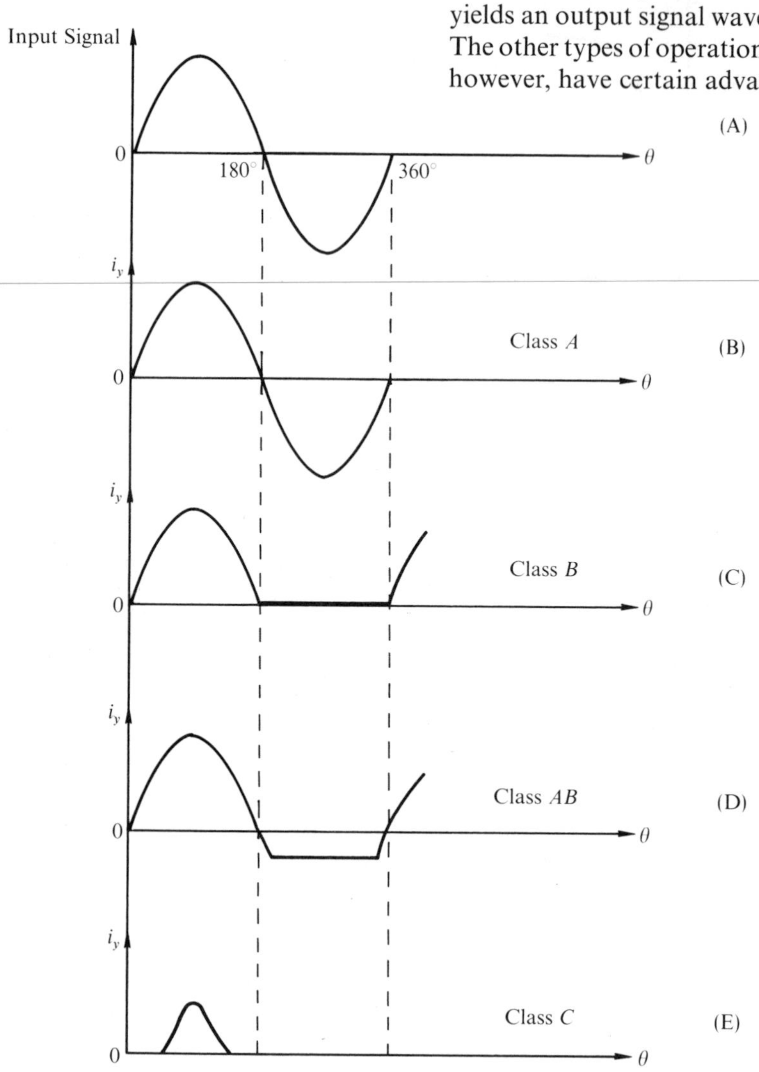

Fig. 5–7. *Classes of amplifier operation.*

5.7 The BJT Amplifier

A *bipolar junction transistor* (BJT) is an example of a three-terminal active device. Base B may correspond to terminal X, collector C to Y, and emitter E to Z in Fig. 5–2. The resulting configuration is illustrated in Fig. 5–8A for an NPN transistor and in Fig. 5–8B for a PNP transistor.

In each circuit, two bias sources are used, as in Fig. 5–2. For the PNP device, the bias sources are of opposite polarity

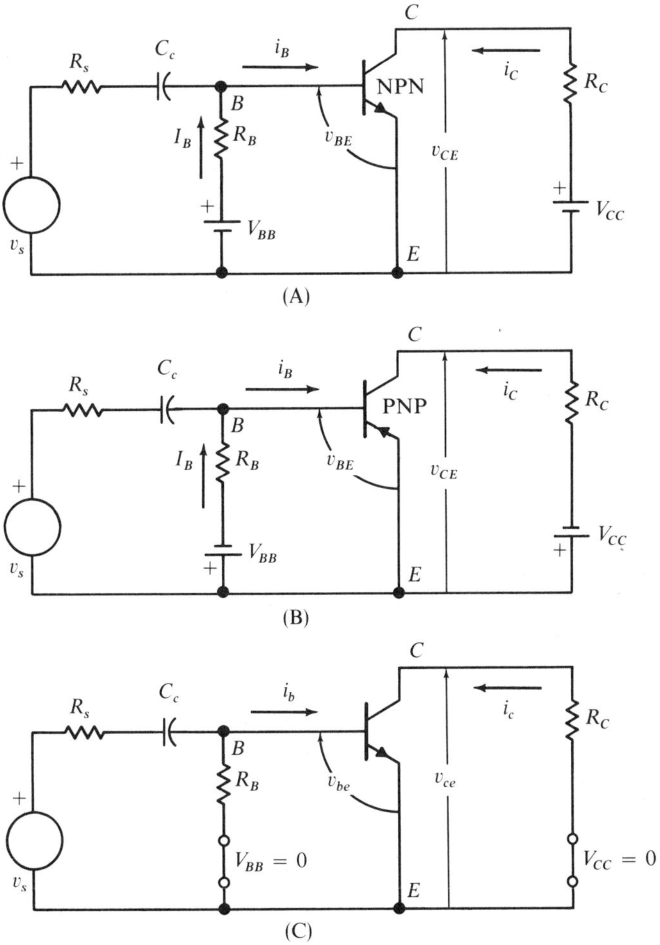

Fig. 5–8. *Basic junction transistor common-emitter amplifier. (A) Using an NPN transistor. (B) Using a PNP transistor. (C) Dc sources set to zero.*

with respect to the NPN transistor. Regardless of the transistor type, the emitter-base junction is forward biased, and the collector-base junction is reverse biased for amplifier operation.

Note that the designation R_C for the resistor in the output (collector circuit) is used instead of R_Y, and R_B is used instead of R_X for the bias resistor. Also, the bias and amplifier voltages and currents have new designations which are consistent and standard for the BJT.

To focus our attention on the amplifying properties of the circuit, as in Chapter 3, the dc bias sources in Fig. 5–8A or B are set to zero. (Remember, the dc sources are only required to provide the Q point for the device.) Setting a voltage source to zero implies that it is replaced by a short circuit, as shown in Fig. 5–8C. Because we are now concerned with instantaneous signals, symbols for voltages and currents are all lowercase.

In Fig. 5–8C, the emitter terminal is common to the input (base) circuit containing source v_s and to the output (collector) circuit containing resistor R_C. For this reason (as discussed in Chapter 3), the configuration is called the common-emitter (C-E) amplifier. Two other useful configurations, the common-base (C-B) and common-collector (C-C) (also called the emitter follower), are illustrated in Fig. 5–9.

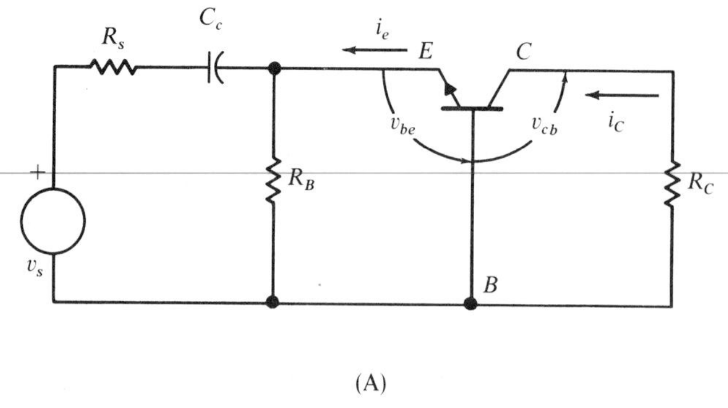

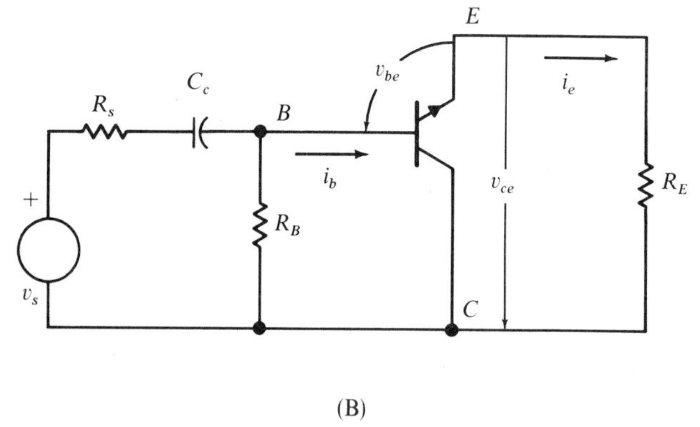

Fig. 5–9. *Two other useful BJT configurations using NPN transistors. (A) Common-base. (B) Common-collector (emitter follower). To emphasize the common terminal, dc bias sources are set to zero. A detailed discussion of biasing is provided in Chapter 7.*

Two other important quantities in addition to gain that characterize amplifiers are input and output impedances. As an example, consider Fig. 5–8C. The impedance "seen" across the emitter-base terminals is the *input impedance* of the amplifier. If the signal source is set to zero and R_C removed, the impedance "seen" across the collector-emitter terminals is the *output impedance*. Because in the chapter it is assumed that the input and output impedances are resistive, they are termed input resistance, R_i, and output resistance, R_o.

We are now ready to discuss the differences in the three basic transistor configurations. Each configuration is examined in terms of voltage gain, A_v, current gain, A_i, power gain, A_p, input resistance, R_i, and output resistance, R_o. To get an idea of magnitudes, we assume small-signal operation, source resistance $R_s = 0$, collector-load resistance $R_C = 1000\,\Omega$, and emitter resistance $R_E = 500\,\Omega$. The calculated values for A_v, A_i, etc., given in Table 5–1 will be verified in Chapter 6.

TABLE 5–1. Comparison of BJT amplifier performance.

Configuration	A_v	A_i	A_p	R_i	R_o
Common-base	50	$\simeq -1$	-50	$20\,\Omega$	$1\,\text{M}\Omega$
Common-emitter	-50	$\simeq 50$	-2500	$1\,\text{k}\Omega$	$20\,\text{k}\Omega$
Emitter-follower	$\simeq 1$	-51	-51	$26.6\,\text{k}\Omega$	$20\,\Omega$

Some observations of the data in Table 5–1 are in order.

1. The minus sign for voltage or current gain indicates that the output waveform is 180° out of phase with respect to the input waveform (see Fig. 5–10). This was also seen from the graph of Fig. 5–6. The minus sign before A_p arises because power gain, by Eq. (5–4), is the product of the voltage and current gains.
2. The *C-E* amplifier has maximum power gain.
3. The *C-C* amplifier (emitter follower) has the greatest input resistance; the *C-B* amplifier, the least. On the other hand, the output resistance is least for the emitter follower and greatest for the *C-B* amplifier.
4. The maximum voltage gain for the emitter follower is one; the maximum current gain for the *C-B* amplifier is also one.

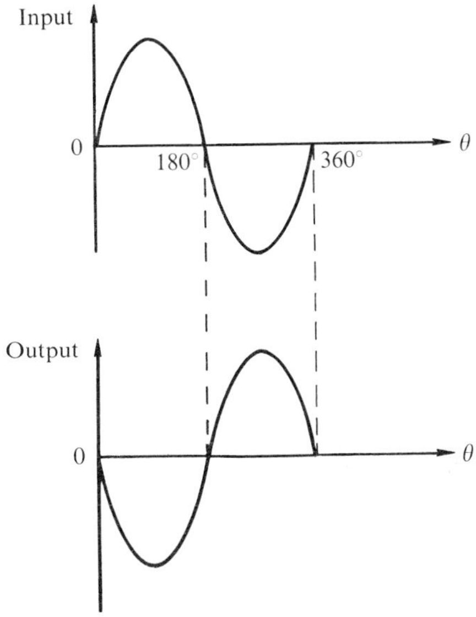

Fig. 5–10. *Input and output waveforms 180° out of phase.*

You may ask, What good is the emitter follower when its maximum voltage gain is one? The emitter follower is useful because it exhibits a relatively high input resistance and a very low output resistance. It is frequently used in electronic circuits as a buffer. A *buffer* provides for the efficient transfer of power from a high-impedance source to a low-impedance load. This is illustrated in Example 5–3.

EXAMPLE 5–3.

Assume a voltage source v_s having a source resistance of $2500\,\Omega$ is required to develop its voltage across a 500-Ω resistor, as shown in Fig. 5–11A.

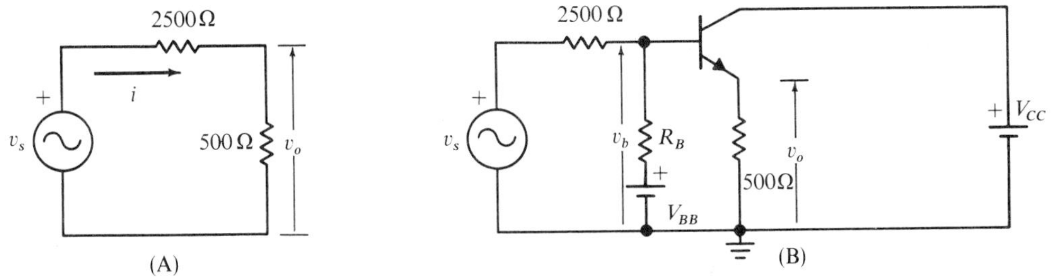

Fig. 5–11. *Application of an emitter follower as a buffer. (See Example 5–3.)*

(a) Determine the actual voltage developed across the resistor.

(b) In Fig. 5–11B, an emitter follower, having the characteristics listed in Table 5–1, is used. What is the voltage developed across the 500-Ω resistor which is connected between the emitter and ground? Assume that R_B is very large and may be neglected.

Solutions:

(a) In Fig. 5–11A, by voltage division,

$$v_o = \frac{500v_s}{2500 + 500} = \frac{v_s}{6}$$

This is not good; only one-sixth of v_s is developed across the 500-Ω resistor. The remaining voltage, $5v_s/6$, is wasted across the internal 2500-Ω source resistance.

(b) From Table 5–1, $R_i = 26{,}500\,\Omega$. This is much greater than the source resistance of 2500 Ω, and $v_b \simeq v_s$. But the voltage gain of an emitter follower is approximately one. Hence, the 500-Ω resistor "sees" a 20-Ω output resistance of the emitter follower in series with $v_b \simeq v_s$ (Fig. 5–12).

By voltage division,

$$v_o = \frac{500v_s}{500 + 20} = 0.97v_s$$

This is approximately equal to v_s, which was desired.

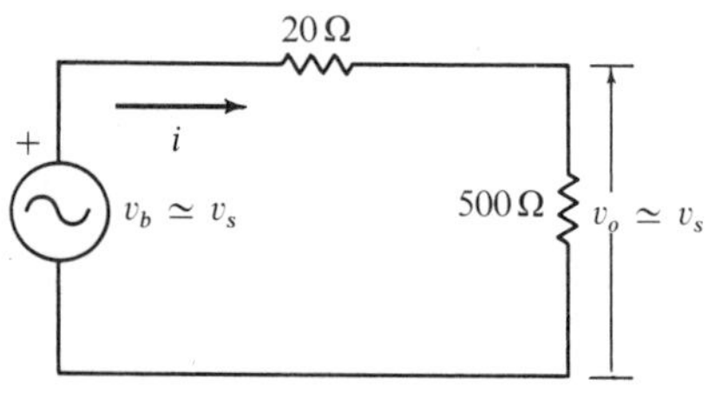

Fig. 5–12. *Simplification of Fig. 5–11B.*

5.8 The FET Amplifier

Another useful three-terminal device (Chapter 3) is the *field-effect transistor* (FET). An N-channel JFET connected in the basic configuration of Fig. 5–2 is illustrated in Fig. 5–13A, and a P-channel unit in Fig. 5–13B. As explained in Chapter 3, the gate-source is reverse biased, and the dc gate current is zero. (For the BJT, the input circuit is forward biased for amplifier operation.) This means that the dc input resistance of a FET amplifier is infinite. For this reason, a FET is referred to as a voltage-controlled device, and a BJT as a current-controlled device.

Because the FET is a voltage-controlled device, the output characteristics (for an N-channel device) appear as in Fig. 5–14A. The gate-source voltage, V_{GS}, is the varying parameter. For comparison, the output characteristics of a BJT are provided in Fig. 5–14B. For this device, base current is the varying parameter. As mentioned in Chapter 3, the output characteristics for a BJT are called collector characteristics; for a FET, they are drain characteristics.

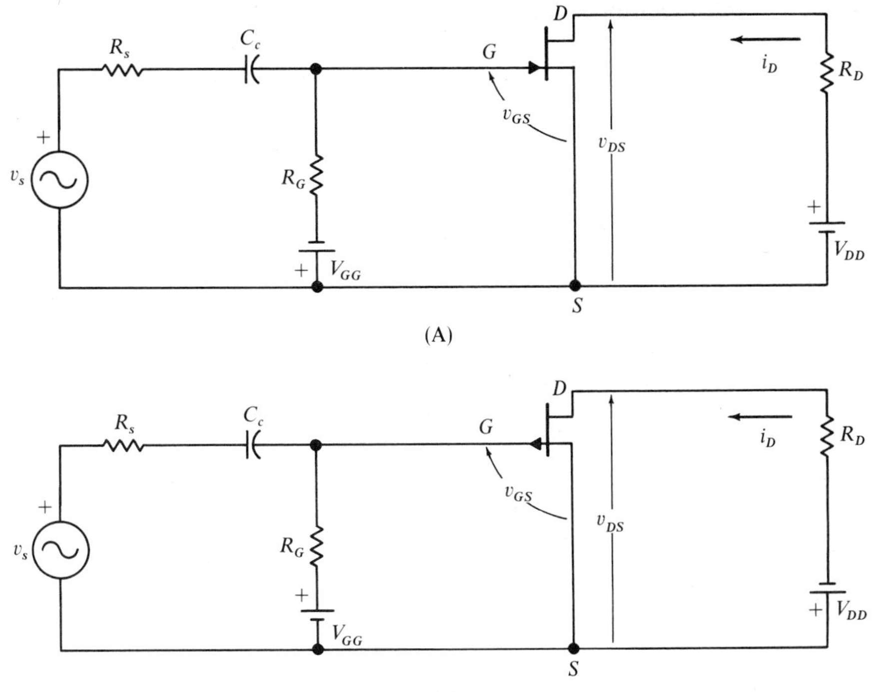

Fig. 5–13. *Basic FET common-source amplifier using (A) an N-channel FET and (B) a P-channel FET.*

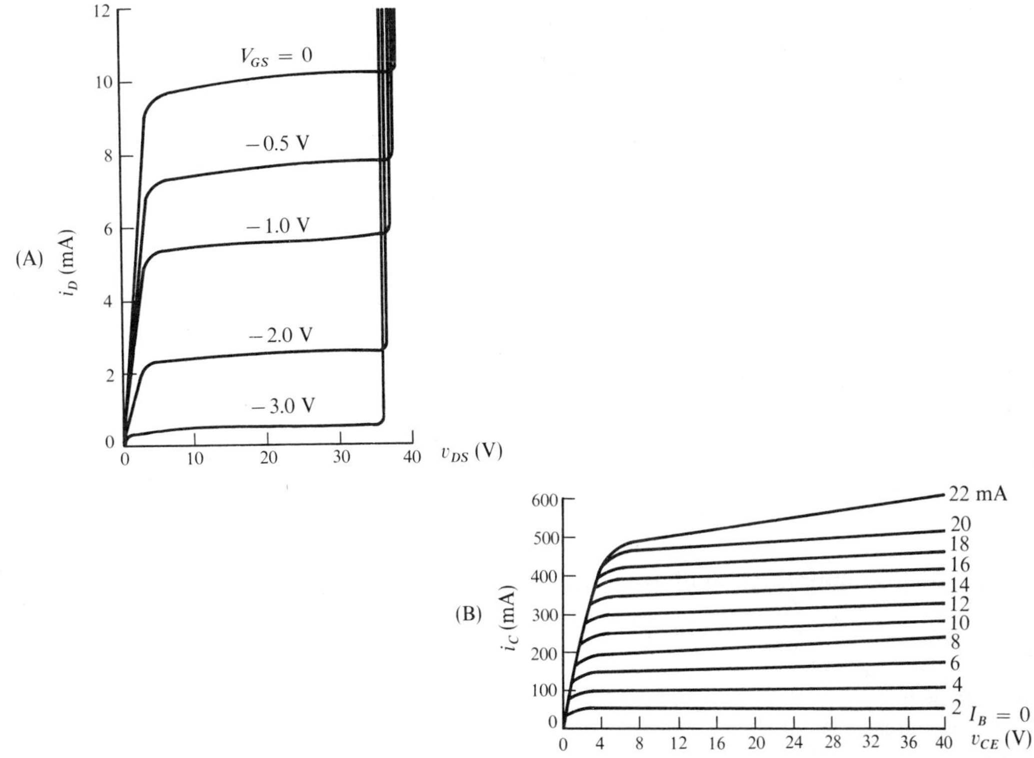

Fig. 5–14. *Comparison of (A) FET and (B) BJT output characteristics.*

The three useful configurations for the FET are reviewed in Fig. 5–15. These are the common-source (*C-S*), the common-gate (*C-G*), and common-drain (*C-D*), or source follower, amplifiers. Three other configurations are possible where the roles of the input and output terminals are switched, as is also possible for a BJT. Since these are rarely used, they will not be considered.

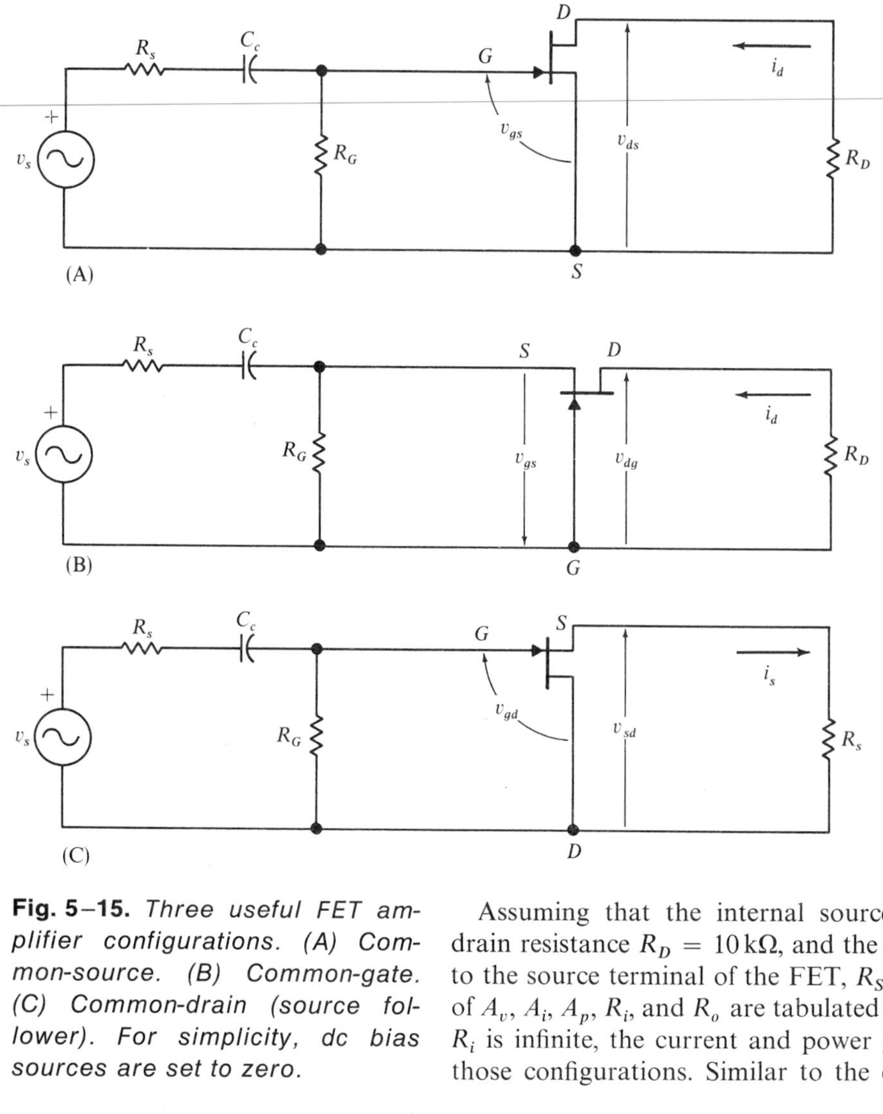

Fig. 5–15. *Three useful FET amplifier configurations. (A) Common-source. (B) Common-gate. (C) Common-drain (source follower). For simplicity, dc bias sources are set to zero.*

Assuming that the internal source resistance $R_s = 0$, drain resistance $R_D = 10\,\text{k}\Omega$, and the resistance connected to the source terminal of the FET, $R_S = 10\,\text{k}\Omega$, the values of A_v, A_i, A_p, R_i, and R_o are tabulated in Table 5–2. Where R_i is infinite, the current and power gains are infinite for those configurations. Similar to the emitter follower, the

TABLE 5–2. Comparison of FET amplifier performance.

Configuration	A_v	A_i	A_p	R_i	R_o
Common-gate	50	$\simeq -1$	-50	$200\,\Omega$	$100\,\text{k}\Omega$
Common-source	-50	∞	∞	∞	$100\,\text{k}\Omega$
Source-follower	$\simeq 1$	∞	∞	∞	$200\,\Omega$

source follower has a maximum voltage gain of one and a low output resistance. The tabulated values in Table 5–2 will be verified in Chapter 6.

EXAMPLE 5–4.

For the FET amplifier of Fig. 5–13A, assume that $V_{DD} = 40\,\text{V}$, $R_D = 5\,\text{k}\Omega$, and $V_{GG} = -1.5\,\text{V}$.

(a) Write the load-line equation for the circuit.

(b) If the transistor has the drain characteristics of Fig. 5–14A, determine graphically the Q point.

Solutions:

(a) From Fig. 5–13A, the equation of the load line is

$$V_{DD} = R_D i_D + v_{DS}$$

Solving for i_D, we obtain

$$i_D = -\frac{v_{DS}}{R_D} + \frac{V_{DD}}{R_D} \qquad \textbf{(5–8)}$$

where the slope is equal to $-1/R_D$ and the i_D intercept is equal to V_{DD}/R_D.

(b) Substitution of the given values in Eq. (5–8) yields

$$i_D = -\frac{v_{DS}}{5000} + \frac{40}{5000} = -\frac{v_{DS}}{5000} + 0.008\text{ A}$$

The slope is $-1/5000$, and the i_D intercept is 0.008 A (8 mA). The two points for plotting the load line are located at $i_D = 0$ ($v_{DS} = 40$ V) and $v_{DS} = 0$ ($i_D = 8$ mA). The load line is drawn between the two points, as in Fig. 5–16. Voltage $V_{GS} = -1.5$ V is interpolated between the -1-V and -2-V curves. The Q point is located at $I_{D_Q} = 4$ mA and $V_{D_Q} = 20$ V.

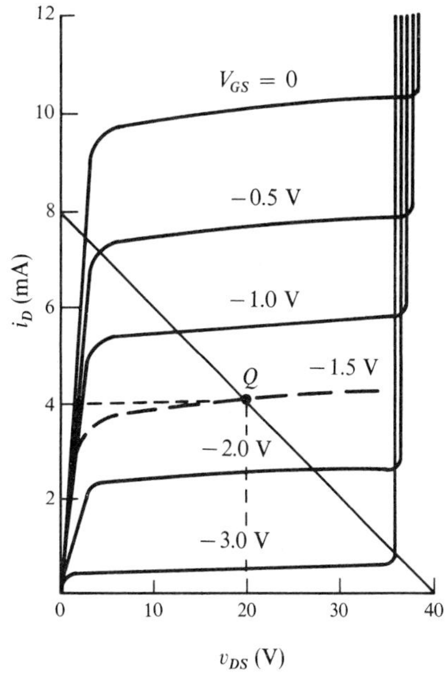

Fig. 5–16. *Determining the Q point graphically for a FET amplifier. (See Example 5–4.)*

5.9 The Decibel

An often-used measure for the gain of an amplifier is the *decibel* (dB). The decibel is defined as ten times the log, to the base ten, of the power gain (P_o/P_i) of a circuit such as an amplifier:

$$A_p(\text{dB}) = 10\log\left(\frac{P_o}{P_i}\right) \qquad \textbf{(5–9)}$$

But $P_o = V_o^2/R_L$, and $P_i = V_i^2/R_i$, where V_o and V_i are rms quantities, and R_L is the load resistance. Substituting these expressions in Eq. (5–9) yields

$$A_p(\text{dB}) = 10\log\left[\frac{(V_o^2/R_L)}{(V_i^2/R_i)}\right]$$

$$= 20\log\left(\frac{V_o}{V_i}\right) + 10\log\left(\frac{R_i}{R_L}\right) \qquad \textbf{(5–10)}$$

We now consider an alternate expression. If I_o is the rms load current, then the output power may be expressed by $P_o = I_o^2 R_L$. Letting I_i be the rms input current, $P_i = I_i^2 R_i$. Substituting these expressions in Eq. (5–9) and simplifying, we have

$$A_p(\text{dB}) = 20 \log\left(\frac{I_o}{I_i}\right) + 10 \log\left(\frac{R_L}{R_i}\right) \qquad \textbf{(5–11)}$$

Each of the three preceding equations yields identical results. If in Eq. (5–10) or Eq. (5–11) $R_L = R_i$, $10 \log(1) = 10 \times 0 = 0\,\text{dB}$. For this case, we have

$$A_v(\text{dB}) = 20 \log\left(\frac{V_o}{V_i}\right) \qquad \textbf{(5–12a)}$$

$$A_i(\text{dB}) = 20 \log\left(\frac{I_o}{I_i}\right) \qquad \textbf{(5–12b)}$$

In practice, when expressing voltage or current gain in decibels, we use Eq. (5–12a) and Eq. (5–12b) *even if R_L does not equal R_i*.

EXAMPLE 5–5.

Express the following gains in decibels:
(a) $A_p = 100$.
(b) $A_v = 60$.
(c) $A_i = 350$.

Solutions:

Using an electronic calculator or slide rule,
(a) Log(100) = 2; hence, $A_p(\text{dB}) = 10 \times 2 = 20\,\text{dB}$.
(b) Log(60) = 1.778; hence, $A_v(\text{dB}) = 20 \times 1.778 = 35.6\,\text{dB}$.
(c) Log(350) = 2.544; hence, $A_i(\text{dB}) = 20 \times 2.544 = 50.9\,\text{dB}$.

5.10 Cascading Amplifier Stages

The gain of a single amplifier stage often is inadequate in meeting overall gain requirements. A common method for increasing gain is to *cascade* single stages, as shown in the block diagram of Fig. 5–17. In cascading, the output of one stage is connected to the input of the following stage. Gains $A_1, A_2, \ldots, A_n$ represent voltage or current gain. The complete amplifier is called a *cascaded amplifier*.

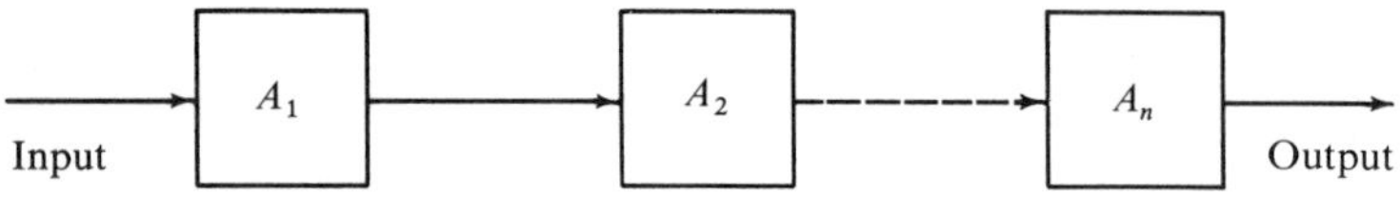

Fig. 5–17. *Block diagram of an n-stage cascaded amplifier.*

If it is assumed that each stage does not interact, that is, *load down* its succeeding stage, the overall gain, A, is the product of the gains of the individual stages:

$$A = A_1 A_2 \cdots A_n \tag{5-13}$$

EXAMPLE 5–6.

An integrated circuit (IC) operational amplifier can be thought of, in some cases, as being composed of three cascaded stages having voltage gains of A_{v1}, A_{v2}, and A_{v3}. If $A_{v1} = -10$, $A_{v2} = -100$, and $A_{v3} = -10$, express the overall voltage gain, A_v,

(a) Numerically.
(b) In decibels.

Solutions:

(a) By Eq. (5–13), $A_v = (-10)(-100)(-10) = -10{,}000$.
(b) In taking logs, magnitudes are used; hence,

$$\begin{aligned} A_v(\text{dB}) &= 20\log(10 \times 100 \times 10) \\ &= 20\log(10) + 20\log(100) + 20\log(10) \\ &= (20 \times 1) + (20 \times 2) + (20 \times 1) = 80\,\text{dB} \end{aligned}$$

In expressing the gain of a cascaded amplifier in decibels, the gain of each stage, in decibels, is added. Because it is more convenient to add than to multiply numbers, the decibel is used frequently for expressing the overall gain of an amplifier.

SUMMARY

We can characterize an amplifier as a voltage, current, or power amplifier. The input and output impedances are also important properties of an amplifier.

Active devices used for amplification, such as the BJT and the FET, have three terminals. Theoretically, there are six possible configurations for each device; only three, however, are useful. For the BJT, they are the common-emitter, common-base, and emitter-follower configurations. The common-source, common-gate, and source-follower are useful configurations for the FET.

The dc operating point, or Q point, must be established for the device. This may be accomplished graphically by superimposing the load line on the output characteristics and selecting the operating point. For a device operating as an amplifier, class A operation is generally chosen. Because a BJT draws an input bias current, it is called a current-controlled device. A FET does not draw bias current and is called a voltage-controlled device.

When a single stage is inadequate in providing the required gain, two or more stages are cascaded to increase the gain. If the individual gain of each stage is expressed in decibels, the overall gain of the amplifier equals the sum of the individual gains in decibels.

Further Reading

Faber, R. B. *Introduction to Electronic Amplifiers.* Columbus, Ohio: Charles E. Merrill Publishing Company, 1971, Chapter 2.

Ghaznavi, C., and A. H. Seidman. *Electronic Circuit Analysis.* New York: The Macmillan Company, 1972, Chapters 1 and 3.

Kaufman, M., and A. H. Seidman, eds. *Handbook for Electronics Engineering Technicians.* New York: McGraw-Hill Book Company, 1976, Chapter 12.

Matthews, John I. *Solid-State Electronics Concepts.* New York: McGraw-Hill Book Company, 1972, Chapters 8, 9, and 13.

Temes, Lloyd. *Electronic Circuits for Technicians.* New York: McGraw-Hill Book Company, 1970, Chapter 7.

Tocci, Ronald J. *Fundamentals of Electronic Devices.* 2nd ed. Columbus, Ohio: Charles E. Merrill Publishing Company, 1975, Chapters 3 and 10.

REVIEW QUESTIONS

5.1 Define
(a) Voltage gain.
(b) Current gain.
(c) Power gain.

5.2 What is the unit for voltage, current, and power gain?

5.3 Explain the differences between a voltage, current, and power amplifier.

5.4 Define transducer. Cite at least three examples of transducers.

5.5 What is meant by biasing an amplifier?

5.6 Define Q point of an amplifier.

5.7 What function does a coupling capacitor serve?

5.8 Define dc coupling.

5.9 Identify which of the symbols V_A, v_A, V_a, v_a denotes
(a) Average voltage.
(b) rms voltage.
(c) Instantaneous voltage.
(d) Total voltage.

5.10 Define nonlinear distortion.

5.11 What is the difference between graphical and small-signal analysis of an amplifier?

5.12 Define and illustrate class *A*, *B*, *AB*, and *C* operation.

5.13 Define input and output impedance. What is the significance of the terms *input* and *output resistance*?

5.14 What is denoted by a minus sign for voltage or current gain?

5.15 Define decibel.

5.16 What is meant by cascading amplifier stages? Why may cascading by necessary?

5.17 What is meant by one amplifier stage loading down another stage?

PROBLEMS

P5–1 In evaluating the performance of an amplifier in a lab, the following voltage and current readings were recorded: $V_i = 20\,\text{mV}$, $V_o = 4\,\text{V}$, $I_i = 0.1\,\text{mA}$, and $I_o = 6\,\text{mA}$. Calculate
(a) A_v.
(b) A_i.
(c) A_p.

P5–2 Referring to Fig. 5–2, assume that $V_{YY} = 20\,\text{V}$ and $R_Y = 1\,\text{k}\Omega$.
(a) Write the load-line equation.
(b) Identify the slope and intercept.
(c) What two points should be selected for plotting the load line?

P5–3 Repeat prob. P5–2 for $V_{YY} = 12\,\text{V}$ and $R_Y = 500\,\Omega$.

P5–4 In prob. P5–2, $V_{XX} = 3\,\text{V}$ and $v_{XZ} = 0.7\,\text{V}$. Determine R_X if $I_X = 0.04\,\text{mA}$.

P5–5 The output characteristics of the three-terminal device in Fig. 5–2 are shown in Fig. 5–18.
(a) Superimpose the load line determined in prob. P5–2.
(b) Superimpose the load line determined in prob. P5–3.
(c) If $I_X = 0.03\,\text{mA}$, determine the Q point for each case.

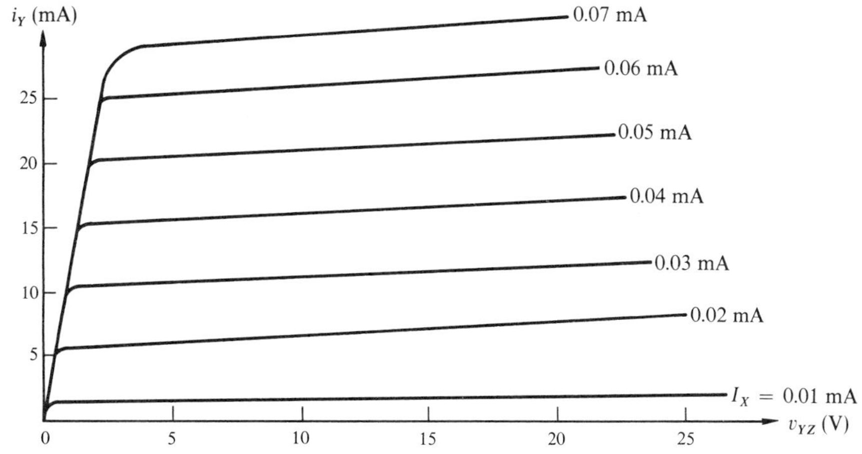

Fig. 5–18.

P5–6 Repeat Example 5–3 for a voltage source having a source resistance of 5000 Ω. Compare these results with those obtained in Example 5–3.

P5–7 Repeat Example 5–4 for $V_{DD} = 30$ V and $V_{GG} = -2$ V.

P5–8 Repeat Example 5–4 for $V_{DD} = 20$ V and $V_{GG} = -2.5$ V.

P5–9 In the FET amplifier of Fig. 15–13A, assume that $R_s = 50$ kΩ, $R_G = 100$ kΩ, $R_D = 20$ kΩ, $V_{DD} = 30$ V, and $V_{GG} = -2$ V.
(a) If $V_s = 100$ mV, what is the signal voltage developed across the gate and source of the device? Assume that C_c acts as a short circuit to the signal.
(b) What is the dc value of the gate-source voltage?
(c) If $v_{DS} = 15$ V, what is the value of i_D?
(d) Write the equation for the load line.

P5–10 Repeat prob. P5–9 for $V_{DD} = 40$ V and $V_{GG} = -2.4$ V.

P5–11 Derive Eq. (5–10) and Eq. (5–11).

P5–12 Express the following gains in decibels:
(a) $A_p = 1000$.
(b) $A_v = 500$.
(c) $A_i = 20$.

P5–13 Repeat prob. P5–12 for
(a) $A_p = 2560$.
(b) $A_v = 900$.
(c) $A_i = 35$.

P5–14 The voltage gains of individual noninteracting states of a cascaded amplifier are 2, −5, 10, and −3. Express the overall gain
(a) Numerically.
(b) In decibels.

P5–15 The voltage gains of individual noninteracting stages of a cascaded amplifier are 5 dB, 12 dB, and 15 dB.
(a) What is the overall gain in decibels?
(b) What is the numerical value of the overall gain?
(c) Express the gain of each state as a numeric.

6

Small-Signal Models

For small-signal operation of amplifiers, graphical analysis is not practical. What is required is the development of *small-signal*, or *incremental, models* for analyzing the performance of amplifiers. We shall develop these models in this chapter.

We first examine the frequency response of an amplifier. Then, we shall derive a model for the BJT based on its physical operation as explained in Chapter 3. (Small-signal models for the BJT and FET amplifiers are derived on the basis of elementary circuit theory in Appendix A1.) The chapter concludes with the derivation of equations that are useful in the calculation of gain, and input and output resistances. Wherever possible, approximations are made to simplify calculations.

6.1 Frequency Response of an Amplifier

The variation in output voltage, or gain, as a function of frequency is called the *frequency response* of a circuit. Consider the following experiment. The frequency response of an amplifier, represented by a block diagram in Fig. 6–1, is to be investigated. A variable ac frequency source, such as a *signal generator* whose signal amplitude is constant for all frequencies, is impressed across the input terminals of the amplifier. A voltmeter, whose reading is independent of frequency, such as an *ac solid-state voltmeter*, is connected across the output terminals.

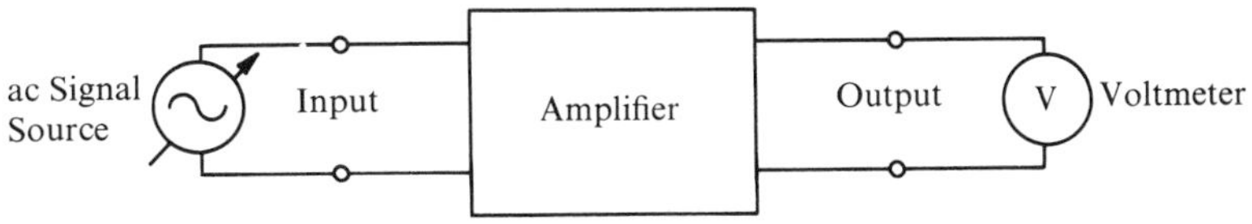

Fig. 6–1. *Obtaining the frequency response of an amplifier.*

As the frequency of the source is varied, the output voltage is recorded. The voltages at corresponding frequencies are then plotted, as shown in Fig. 6–2. The resultant curve is called a *frequency response curve.* Note that a log (four-cycle) scale is used for the frequency axis to compress the frequency range of 10 Hz to 100 kHz to a convenient scale. The output voltage may be expressed as a number or in decibels.

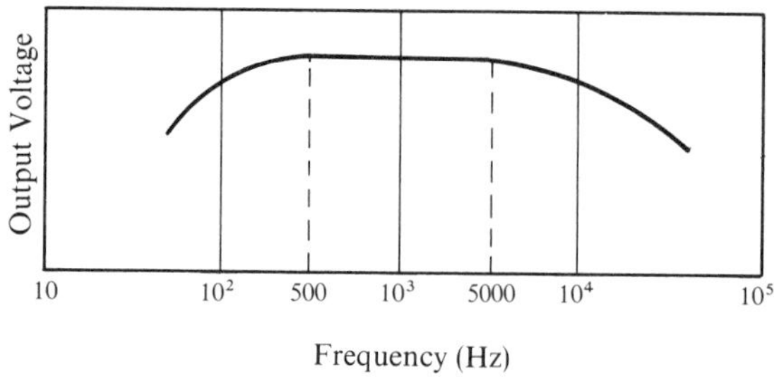

Fig. 6–2. *Example of a frequency response curve.*

From Fig. 6–2, we see that at low and high frequencies, the voltage gain decreases. Over a range of frequencies from approximately 500 Hz to 5 kHz, the gain is essentially constant, or *flat*. This flat range is called the *mid-band frequencies*.

The decrease, or attenuation, in gain at low and high frequencies is an example of *frequency distortion*. (Another type of distortion in amplifiers, nonlinear distortion, was considered in Chapter 5.) Let f_L and f_H equal the low- and high-end frequencies, respectively, where the output voltage (or voltage gain) is 0.707, its mid-band value. (The mid-band frequency generally chosen is 1000 Hz.) The *bandwidth*, BW, is defined by

$$\text{BW} = f_H - f_L \qquad \textbf{(6–1)}$$

In the literature and in practice, frequencies f_L and f_H are called the *half-power*, *break*, *−3-dB*, or *corner* frequencies. At the half-power frequency, the power developed in the load is one-half that at mid-band frequencies.

EXAMPLE 6–1.

Maximum gain of an amplifier may be normalized to one. The outputs at frequencies f_L and f_H are then equal to $0.707 \times 1 = 0.707$. Expressed in decibels, $20 \log(1) = 0\,\text{dB}$, and $20 \log(0.707) = -20 \log(1/0.707) = -3\,\text{dB}$. (When a log of a number less than one is taken, the number is inverted, and the value of its logarithm has a minus sign.)

Referring to the frequency response curve of Fig. 6–3, determine the bandwidth.

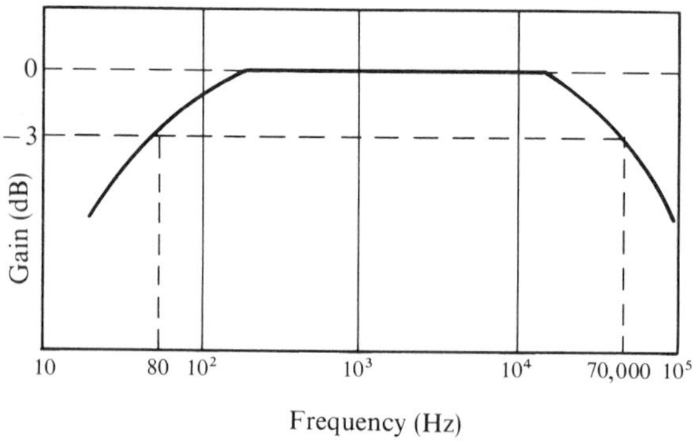

Fig. 6–3. *Finding amplifier bandwidths. (See Example 6–1.)*

Solution:

From Fig. 6–3, BW = 70,000 − 80 ≃ 70 kHz.

The decrease in output voltage at low frequencies may be attributed to series coupling capacitors present in the circuit. The reactance of a capacitor, X_C, is given by

$$X_C = \frac{1}{6.28fC} = \frac{0.159}{fC}\ \Omega \tag{6–2}$$

where f = frequency in hertz (Hz).
C = capacitance in farads (F).
$0.159 = 1/6.28$.

As the frequency is reduced, the capacitive reactance increases. Because a coupling capacitor is in series with the input to an amplifier, the increasing reactance reduces the signal base current in a BJT, or the signal gate-source voltage of a FET.

At high frequencies, the internal capacitances of transistors reduce the output voltage. The capacitances are essentially in shunt (parallel) with the input and, to a lesser extent, the output of the device. This behavior is explored in detail in Chapter 8.

The small-signal models developed in this chapter will be for mid-band frequency operation. At the mid frequencies, all capacitances may be ignored. This allows a simple analysis which has many practical applications. The results also can be used in the analysis of low- and high-frequency performance of amplifiers.

6.2 Physical Basis for the BJT Model

The operation of the junction transistor was explained in Chapter 3. We learned that the transistor exhibits a signal current gain and that the input resistance is generally low. These characteristics are reflected in the small-signal model of Fig. 6–4A, which is suitable for mid-frequency operation.

Resistance h_{ie} is the input resistance, and current source $h_{fe}i_b$ accounts for the current gain of the transistor. Source $h_{fe}i_b$ is called a *dependent*, or *controlled, source*. Its value *depends* on *base current*, i_b, flowing in another part of the circuit—the input side. For this reason, $h_{fe}i_b$ is sometimes called a current-dependent current source.

The output voltage actually has a small effect on the base current. This can be accounted for by the introduction of a voltage-dependent source, $h_{re}v_{ce}$, in series with h_{ie} (Fig. 6–4B). Also, there is some resistance across the output terminals. This is represented in Fig. 6–4B by resistance $1/h_{oe}$ connected between the collector and emitter terminals.

Figure 6–4B represents the *hybrid model* of a BJT in the common-emitter configuration. Parameters h_{ie}, h_{re}, h_{fe}, and h_{oe} are *hybrid parameters.*

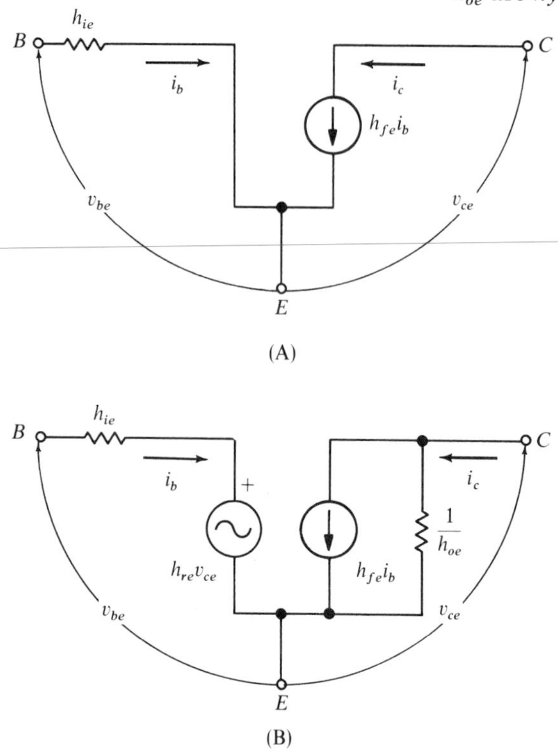

Fig. 6–4. *Small-signal models of a BJT in the common-emitter configuration based on physical operation. The models are valid for low- and mid-frequency operation. (A) Approximate model. (B) Exact model.*

In practice, the following approximations are usually made. Parameter h_{re} is assumed to be zero. Also, $1/h_{oe}$ is generally much greater than the load resistor connected across the collector and emitter. Consequently, $1/h_{oe}$ may be neglected. The simple model of Fig. 6–4A, therefore, is suitable for many applications.

EXAMPLE 6–2.

Determine the mid-band voltage gain of the amplifier of Fig. 6–5A. Assume that $R_B \gg h_{ie}$ and can be neglected, $h_{ie} = 1\,\text{k}\Omega$, $h_{fe} = 50$, and coupling capacitor C_c acts as a short circuit at mid frequencies.

Solution:

The model of the amplifier is given in Fig. 6–5B, where all dc sources have been set to zero. Base current $i_b = v_s/1\,\text{k}\Omega$. Output voltage $v_o = -50i_b \times 2\,\text{k}\Omega$.

Why the minus sign? The arrow for v_o points toward the collector terminal C. The direction of current $50i_b$ is away from C; hence the negative sign. If the current flowed toward C, no negative sign would be necessary. Physically, the negative sign indicates that the voltage is 180° out of phase with respect to the input voltage v_s, as explained in Chapter 5.

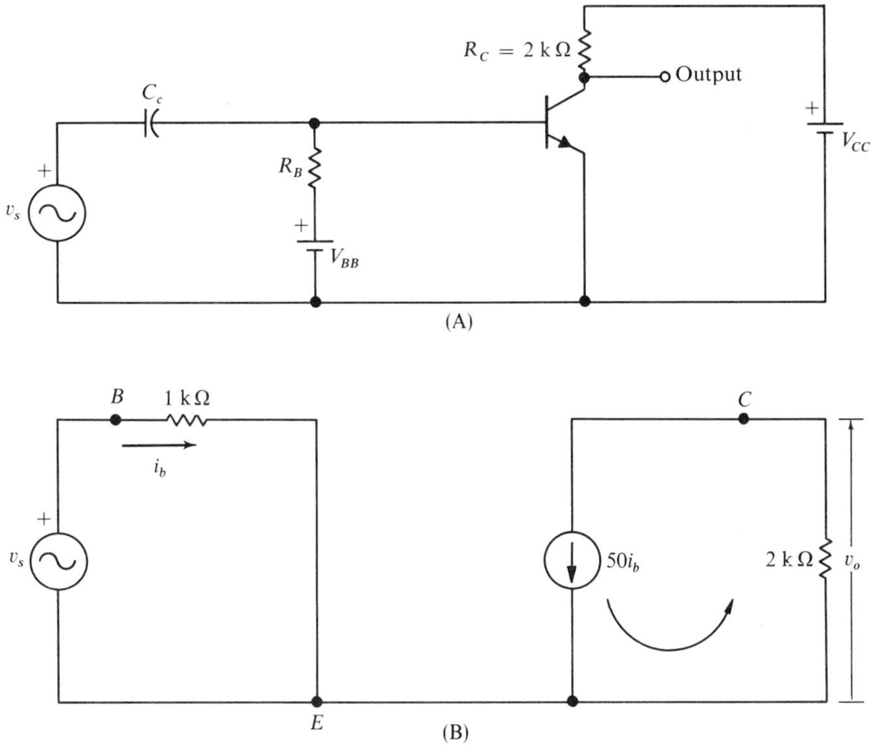

Substituting $i_b = v_s/1\text{ k}\Omega$ in the expression for v_o, we have

$$v_o = -50 \times \frac{v_s}{1\text{ k}\Omega} \times 2\text{k}\Omega = -100v_s$$

Solving for $A_v = v_o/v_s$, $A_v = -100$.

Fig. 6–5. *Determining the voltage gain of an amplifier. (A) Circuit. (B) Small-signal model. (See Example 6–2.)*

6.3 The Hybrid Model

At mid as well as low frequencies, where no external capacitors are present, the hybrid model is most useful for the BJT operating at small-signal levels. In this section, we shall develop a generalized set of equations that can be used for the calculation of voltage gain, current gain, etc., for the BJT in *any configuration.* Figure 6–4B is redrawn in Fig. 6–6. In the figure, h_{11} now corresponds to h_{ie}, h_{12} to h_{re}, h_{21} to h_{fe}, and h_{22} to h_{oe}.

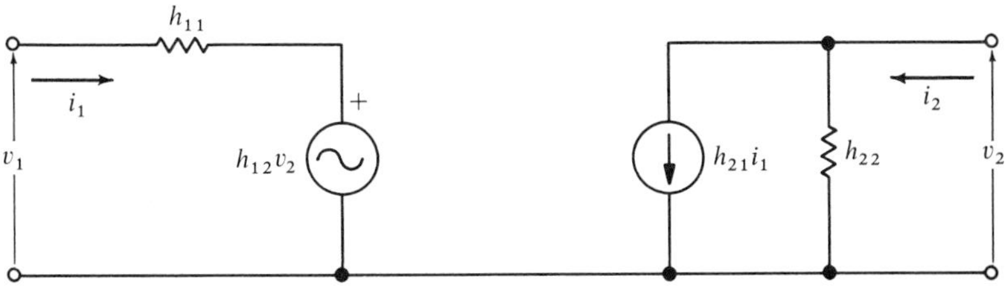

Fig. 6–6. *Generalized small-signal hybrid (h) model of a BJT.*

Applying Kirchhoff's voltage law to the input side, we obtain

$$v_1 = h_{11}i_1 + h_{12}v_2 \tag{6–3a}$$

Using Kirchhoff's current law at the output side yields

$$i_2 = h_{21}i_1 + h_{22}v_2 \tag{6–3b}$$

To determine what units should be assigned to the hybrid (h) parameters, let v_2 be set to zero in Eq. (6–3a). Solving for h_{11}, we have

$$h_{11} = \left.\frac{v_1}{i_1}\right|_{v_2=0} \tag{6–4a}$$

$$= \text{short-circuit input resistance} \qquad (\Omega)$$

Because h_{11} is a ratio of a voltage to a current, its unit is the ohm. The "$v_2 = 0$" at the lower right of the vertical bar reminds us that v_2 was set to zero. (How v_2 is set to zero in the lab is considered later in the chapter.) Since $v_2 = 0$, h_{11} is called the *short-circuit* input resistance.

If i_1 is set to zero in Eq. (6–3a), we obtain

$$h_{12} = \left.\frac{v_1}{v_2}\right|_{i_1=0} \tag{6–4b}$$

$$= \text{reverse voltage ratio} \qquad \text{(numeric)}$$

Setting v_2 and i_1 to zero in Eq. (6–3b) yields

$$h_{21} = \left.\frac{i_2}{i_1}\right|_{v_2=0} \tag{6–4c}$$

$$= \text{short-circuit forward current gain} \qquad \text{(numeric)}$$

and

$$h_{22} = \left.\frac{i_2}{v_2}\right|_{i_1=0} \tag{6–4d}$$

$$= \text{output admittance} \qquad (\mho)$$

Let the source resistance of v_s be R_s, and the load resistance be R_L. Figure 6–6 is modified as shown in Fig. 6–7.

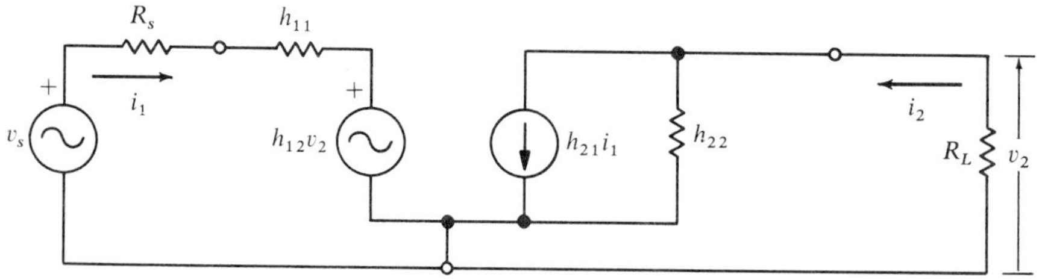

Fig. 6–7. *Basic hybrid model for a BJT amplifier.*

Writing an equation for the input side, we obtain

$$v_s = (R_s + h_{11})i_1 + h_{12}v_2 \tag{6–5}$$

At the output side,

$$i_2 = h_{21}i_1 + h_{22}v_2 \tag{6–6}$$

and

$$v_2 = -i_2R_L \tag{6–7}$$

If v_2 in Eq. (6–6) is replaced by Eq. (6–7),

$$i_2 = h_{21}i_1 - h_{22}R_Li_2$$

Solving for the current gain, $A_i = i_2/i_1$,

$$A_i = \frac{i_2}{i_1} = \frac{h_{21}}{1 + h_{22}R_L} \tag{6–8}$$

To obtain an expression for the voltage gain, $A_v = v_2/v_s$, $i_1 = i_2/A_i$ is substituted in Eq. (6–5):

$$v_s = (h_{11} + R_s)\frac{i_2}{A_i} + h_{12}v_2 \tag{6–9}$$

By Eq. (6–7), $i_2 = -v_2/R_L$. Substitution of this, and Eq. (6–8) for A_i in Eq. (6–9), yields the voltage gain, A_v:

$$A_v = \frac{h_{21}R_L}{h_{12}h_{21}R_L - (1 + h_{22}R_L)(h_{11} + R_s)} \tag{6–10}$$

Input resistance, R_i, is defined as $R_i = v_1/i_1$. Dividing both sides of Eq. (6–3a) by i_1,

$$R_i = \frac{v_1}{i_1} = h_{11} + \frac{h_{12}v_2}{i_1} \tag{6–11a}$$

Replacing $v_2 = -R_Li_2$ in Eq. (6–11a), we obtain

$$R_i = h_{11} - \frac{h_{12}R_Li_2}{i_1} \tag{6–11b}$$

But $i_2/i_1 = A_i$; hence, substitution of Eq. (6–8) in Eq. (6–11b) yields

$$R_i = h_{11} - \frac{h_{12}h_{21}R_L}{1 + h_{22}R_L} \tag{6–12}$$

To find the output resistance, R_o, the signal source v_s is set to zero and load resistor R_L is replaced by voltage source v_2 in Fig. 6–8. Current i_2 is

$$i_2 = h_{21}i_1 + h_{22}v_2 \tag{6–13}$$

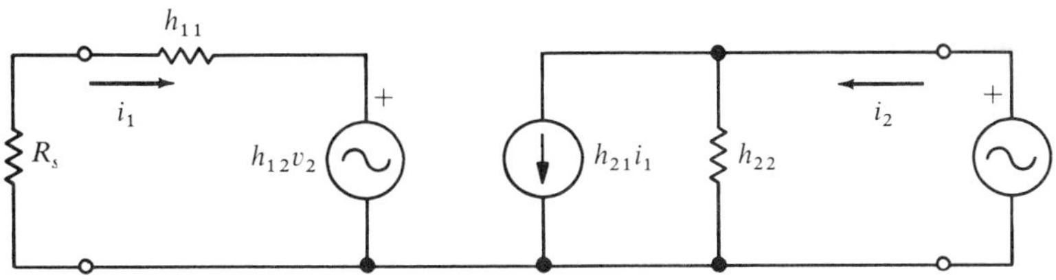

Fig. 6–8. *Determining output resistance, $R_o = v_2/i_2$, of an amplifier. Note that v_s was set to zero. The source resistance, R_s, however, is included in the circuit.*

At the input side,

$$i_1 = \frac{-h_{12}v_2}{h_{11} + R_s} \tag{6–14}$$

Substituting Eq. (6–14) in Eq. (6–13) and solving for $R_o = v_2/i_2$, we obtain

$$R_o = \frac{1}{h_{22} - \dfrac{h_{12}h_{21}}{h_{11} + R_s}} \tag{6–15}$$

For reference, the derived equations are included in Table 6–1.

TABLE 6–1. Summary of hybrid equations.

$$A_i = \frac{h_{21}}{1 + h_{22}R_L}$$

$$A_v = \frac{h_{21}R_L}{h_{12}h_{21}R_L - (1 + h_{22}R_L)(h_{11} + R_s)}$$

$$A_p = A_vA_i = A_iA_v$$

$$R_i = h_{11} - \frac{h_{12}h_{21}R_L}{1 + h_{22}R_L}$$

$$R_o = \frac{1}{h_{22} - \dfrac{h_{12}h_{21}}{h_{11} + R_s}}$$

As mentioned at the outset of this section, the equations summarized in Table 6–1 are applicable to *all junction transistor configurations*. What is different is the value of the h parameters. To differentiate the h parameters for the three transistor configurations (*C-E*, *C-B*, and *C-C*), consult Table 6–2. We see that $h_{11} = h_{ie}$ for the *C-E* amplifier, $h_{21} = h_{fb}$ for the *C-B* amplifier, etc. When analyzing the *C-E* amplifier, for example, $h_{11} = h_{ie}$, $h_{12} = h_{re}$, $h_{21} = h_{fe}$, and $h_{22} = h_{oe}$ are used in the equations of Table 6–1. The second letter in the subscript defines the configuration: *e* for *C-E*, *b* for *C-B*, and *c* for *C-C*.

TABLE 6–2. Definitions of *h* parameters.

Configuration	$h_{11}(\Omega)$	h_{12} (numeric)	h_{21} (numeric)	$h_{22}(\mho)$
C-E	h_{ie}	h_{re}	h_{fe}	h_{oe}
C-B	h_{ib}	h_{rb}	h_{fb}	h_{ob}
C-C	h_{ic}	h_{rc}	h_{fc}	h_{oc}

Variation in the *h* parameters

The values of the hybrid parameters vary with temperature, dc emitter current, and dc collector voltage. This is illustrated in the typical curves of Fig. 6–9. In each figure, the h parameters are normalized to one at a reference temperature, current, or voltage.

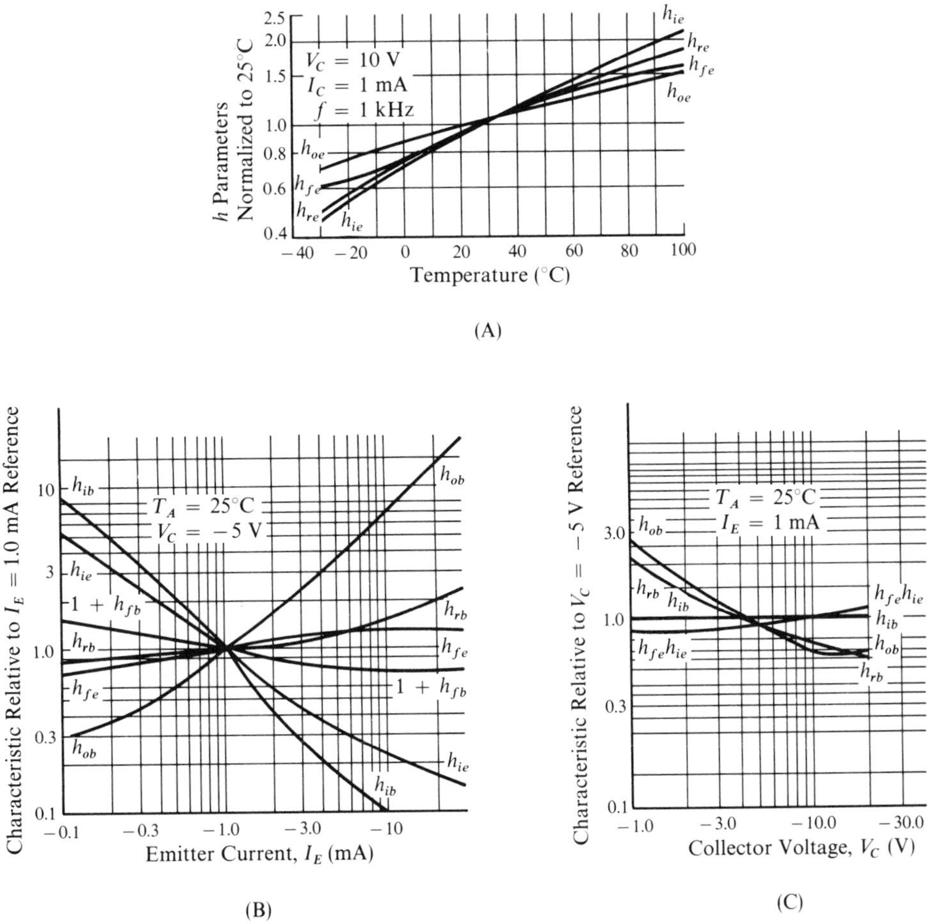

Variations in the C-E h parameters as a function of temperature are shown in Fig. 6–9A; the parameters increase with temperature.

Figure 6–9B illustrates how some C-E and C-B parameters change with emitter current. For example, as the emitter current increases, h_{ib} and h_{ie} decrease. On the other hand, h_{fe}, and especially h_{ob}, increase with emitter current.

The curves of Fig. 6–9C demonstrate how h parameters vary with collector voltage. Parameter h_{ib} is nearly constant; however, h_{fe} and h_{ie} tend to increase with increasing collector voltage. Parameters h_{ob} and h_{rb} decrease as the collector voltage is raised.

Fig. 6–9. *Typical curves for a BJT showing how h parameters vary with (A) temperature, (B) emitter current, and (C) collector voltage. (Courtesy General Electric Semiconductor Products Department, Syracuse, N.Y.)*

EXAMPLE 6–3.

For a BJT having $h_{ie} = 1\text{ k}\Omega$, $h_{fe} = 50$, $h_{re} = 0$, and $1/h_{oe} = 20\text{ k}\Omega$ ($h_{oe} = 50 \times 10^{-6}$ ℧), verify the values given in Table

5–1 for the C-E configuration. Assume that $R_s = 0$ and $R_L = R_C = 1\,\text{k}\Omega$.

Solution:

Because $R_L \ll 1/h_{oe}$, parameter h_{oe} may be neglected. In addition, $h_{re} = 0$ is given. The equations in Table 6–1, therefore, simplify to

$$A_i \simeq h_{21} = h_{fe} = 50$$

$$A_v \simeq -\frac{h_{21}R_L}{h_{11}} = -\frac{h_{fe}R_C}{h_{ie}} = -50 \times \frac{1}{1} = -50$$

$$R_i \simeq h_{11} = h_{ie} = 1\,\text{k}\Omega$$

$$R_o \simeq \frac{1}{h_{22}} = \frac{1}{h_{oe}} = 20\,\text{k}\Omega$$

$$A_p = A_i A_v = 50 \times (-50) = -2500$$

Example 6–3 illustrates the utility of h parameters. If $h_{re} = 0$ and $R_L \ll 1/h_{oe}$ (or $1 \gg h_{oe}R_L$)—approximations that are generally valid for small-signal operation of the C-E amplifier—then:

1. The current gain is approximately equal to the short-circuit current gain h_{fe}.
2. The input resistance is approximately equal to the short-circuit input resistance h_{ie}.
3. The output resistance is approximately equal to $1/h_{oe}$.
4. The voltage gain can be thought of as being equal to the short-circuit current gain h_{fe} multiplied by the ratio of the load resistance to the short-circuit input resistance plus the source resistance: $A_v \simeq -h_{fe}R_L/(h_{ie} + R_s)$.

To verify the values for the C-B and C-C amplifiers in Table 5–1, we have to express the h parameters for these configurations in terms of the h parameters for the C-E configuration. These relations are summarized in Table 6–3. Their application is illustrated in the following example.

TABLE 6–3. *h*-parameter conversions.

$h_{ib} \simeq \dfrac{h_{ie}}{1 + h_{fe}}$	$h_{ic} \simeq h_{ie}$
$h_{rb} \simeq \dfrac{\Delta_e - h_{re}}{1 + h_{fe}}$	$h_{rc} \simeq 1$
$h_{fb} \simeq -\dfrac{h_{fe}}{1 + h_{fe}}$	$h_{fc} \simeq -(1 + h_{fe})$
$h_{ob} \simeq \dfrac{h_{oe}}{1 + h_{fe}}$	$h_{oc} \simeq h_{oe}$
$\Delta_e = h_{ie}h_{oe} - h_{re}h_{fe}$	

EXAMPLE 6–4.

Verify the values in Table 5–1 for the
(a) *C-B* configuration.
(b) *C-C* configuration.
Use the h parameters provided in Example 6–3.

Solutions:

(a) From Table 6–3,

$$h_{ib} \simeq \frac{h_{ie}}{1 + h_{fe}} = \frac{1000}{51} \simeq 20\,\Omega$$

$$\Delta_e = h_{ie}h_{oe} - h_{re}h_{fe} = 10^3 \times 50 \times 10^{-6} = 0.05$$

$$h_{rb} \simeq \frac{\Delta_e - h_{re}}{1 + h_{fe}} = \frac{0.05}{51} \simeq 0$$

$$h_{fb} \simeq \frac{-h_{fe}}{1 + h_{fe}} = \frac{-50}{51} \simeq -1$$

$$h_{ob} \simeq \frac{h_{oe}}{1 + h_{fe}} = \frac{50 \times 10^{-6}}{51} \simeq 10^{-6}\,\mho$$

Referring to the equations in Table 6–1 and recognizing that $h_{rb} = 0$ and $R_L \ll 1/h_{ob}$, we obtain

$$A_i \simeq h_{fb} = -1$$

$$A_v \simeq -\frac{h_{fb}R_L}{h_{ib}} = -(-1)\frac{1000}{20} = 50$$

$$R_i \simeq h_{ib} = 20\,\Omega$$

$$R_o \simeq \frac{1}{h_{ob}} = 10^6\,\Omega$$

$$A_p = A_iA_v = (-1)50 = -50$$

(b) From Table 6–3,

$$h_{ic} \simeq h_{ie} = 1000\,\Omega$$

$$h_{rc} \simeq 1$$

$$h_{fc} \simeq -(1 + h_{fe}) = -51$$

$$h_{oc} \simeq h_{oe} = 50 \times 10^{-6}\,\mho$$

In the *C-C* configuration, $R_L = R_E = 500\,\Omega$. From Table 6–1,

$$A_i \simeq h_{ic} = -51$$

$$A_v \simeq -\frac{h_{fc}R_E}{h_{rc}h_{fc}R_E - h_{ic}}$$

$$= -\frac{-51 \times 500}{-1 \times 51 \times 500 - 1000} \simeq 1$$

$$R_i \simeq h_{ic} + h_{rc}h_{fc}R_E = 1000 + 1 \times 51 \times 500$$

$$= 26.5\,\text{k}\Omega$$

$$R_o \simeq \frac{h_{ic}}{h_{rc}h_{fc}} = \frac{1000}{1 \times 51} \simeq 20\,\Omega$$

$$A_p = -51$$

The results obtained in this example are identical with the values tabulated in Table 5–1 for the *C-B* and *C-C* configurations.

6.4 The FET Model

Because the FET is a voltage-controlled device, it is convenient to represent the FET at low and mid frequencies by the model of Fig. 6–10. (This is the *y model*, derived in Appendix A1). Parameters g_{11} and g_{22} are conductances; $g_{12}v_2$ and $g_{21}v_1$ are voltage-dependent current sources.

As in the analysis used for the BJT, expressions for A_v, A_i, R_i, and R_o are derived in Appendix A2. The resulting equations are summarized in Table 6–4, and their application is illustrated in Example 6–5.

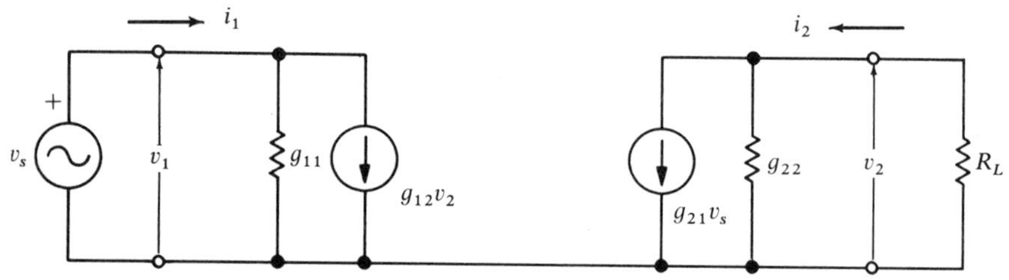

Fig. 6–10. *Basic small-signal model for a FET amplifier operating at mid and low frequencies.*

TABLE 6–4. Summary of equations for the FET amplifier.

$$A_v = \frac{-g_{21}}{\dfrac{1}{R_L} + g_{22}}$$

$$A_i = \frac{g_{21}}{g_{11} + R_L(g_{11}g_{22} - g_{12}g_{21})}$$

$$A_p = A_v A_i = A_i A_v$$

$$R_i = \frac{1}{g_{11} - \dfrac{g_{12}g_{21}}{1/R_L + g_{22}}}$$

$$R_o = \frac{1}{g_{22}}$$

EXAMPLE 6–5.

Typical parameters for a small-signal FET in the common-source configuration at mid frequencies are: $g_{11} = g_{12} = 0$, $g_{21} = g_{fs} = 5 \times 10^{-3}$ ℧ (where g_{fs} is the *forward transconductance*), and $g_{22} = g_d = 10 \times 10^{-6}$ ℧ (where g_d is the *output conductance*). Assuming $R_s = 0$ and $R_L = R_D = 10\,\text{k}\Omega$,

(a) Draw a model of the amplifier.
(b) Verify the values given in Table 5–2 for the *C-S* configuration.

Solutions:

(a) Because $g_{11} = g_{12} = 0$, the model of Fig. 6–10 reduces to the model of Fig. 6–11.

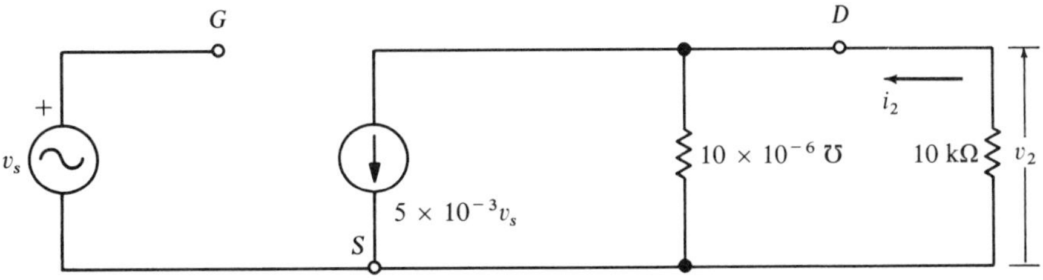

Fig. 6–11. *Practical current source model of a FET amplifier in the C-S configuration. (See Example 6–5.)*

(b) The value of $1/R_D = 1/10{,}000 = 100 \times 10^{-6}$ ℧. This is greater than $g_d = 10 \times 10^{-6}$ ℧. Therefore, $g_{22} = g_d$ may be neglected in the expression for voltage gain (Table 6–4). Hence,

$$A_v \simeq -g_{fs}R_D = -5 \times 10^{-3} \times 10 \times 10^3 = -50$$
$$A_i \simeq \infty$$
$$A_p \simeq \infty$$
$$R_i \simeq \infty$$
$$R_o = \frac{1}{g_{22}} = \frac{1}{g_d} = 100\,\text{k}\Omega$$

These values correspond to those tabulated for the *C-S* amplifier in Table 5–2.

6.5 Voltage Source Model

The current-dependent source in Fig. 6–11 may be converted to a voltage-dependent source, as illustrated in Fig. 6–12. For some applications, this model is more convenient

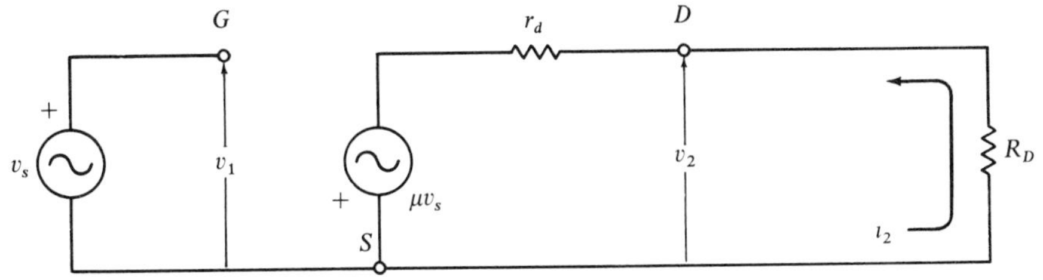

Fig. 6–12. *Voltage source model for a FET amplifier in the C-S configuration.*

to use than the current source model of Fig. 6–11. The Greek letter mu (μ) is defined as

$$\mu = \frac{g_{fs}}{g_d} = g_{fs} r_d \tag{6–16}$$

where $r_d = 1/g_d$ is the *drain resistance*. Drain resistance r_d is in series with the dependent voltage source μv_s.

The voltage source model of a FET gives the same results as the current source model used in Example 6–5. To verify this, we write equations for the output side of Fig. 6–12, obtaining

$$i_2 = \frac{\mu v_s}{r_d + R_D}$$

But

$$v_2 = -i_2 R_D = -\frac{\mu R_D v_s}{r_d + R_D}$$

Solving for the voltage gain,

$$A_v = -\frac{\mu R_D}{r_d + R_D} \tag{6–17}$$

For the values given in Example 6–5, $r_d = 1/g_d = 100\,\text{k}\Omega$; therefore, $\mu = 5 \times 10^{-3} \times 100 \times 10^3 = 500$. Because $r_d = 100\,\text{k}\Omega$ is much greater than $R_D = 10\,\text{k}\Omega$, R_D may be neglected in the denominator of Eq. (6–17). Substitution of values in Eq. (6–17) yields

$$A_v = -500 \times \frac{10^4}{10^5} = -50$$

This is the same result obtained in Example 6–5. The value of R_o may be verified by the student.

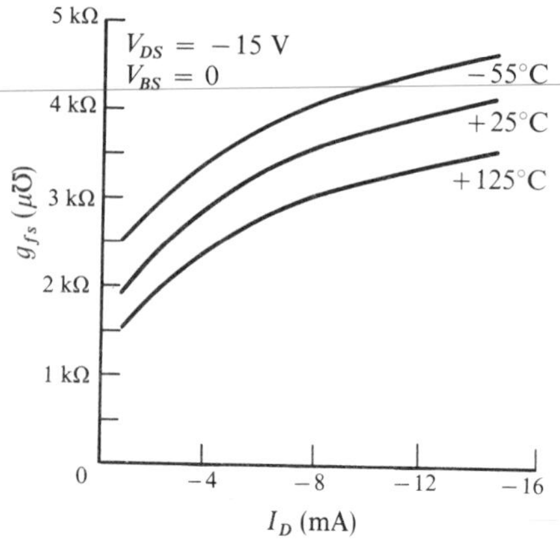

(A)

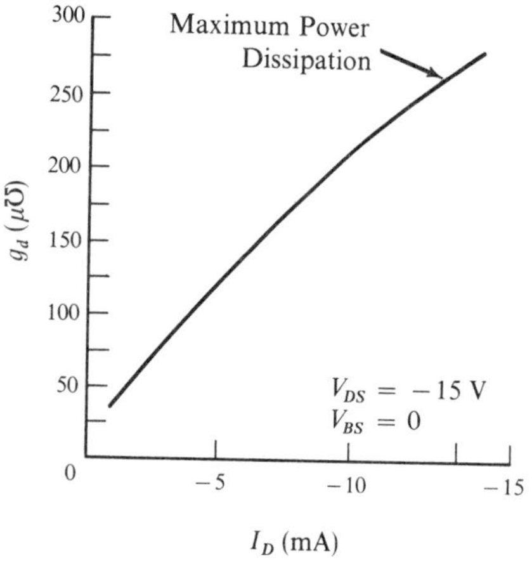

(B)

Fig. 6–13. *Typical variation in (A) g_{fs} and (B) g_d with drain current. Curves are for a P-channel enhancement-type MOSFET. Expression $V_{BS} = 0$ denotes that the substrate of the device is connected to the source terminal. (Courtesy Siliconix, Inc.)*

Variation in g_{fs} and g_d

Examples of how g_{fs} and g_d vary with drain current, I_D, are illustrated in Fig. 6–13. Shown are typical curves for a P-channel enhancement-type MOSFET. Note that both g_{fs} and g_d rise with increasing drain current. From Fig. 6–13A, we also see that g_{fs} is less at high than at low temperatures for a given drain current.

Generalized FET Equations

To minimize the number of expressions, our objective is to use the equations summarized in Table 6–4 for all three configurations of FET amplifiers: *C-S*, *C-G*, and *C-D*. This goal is also in keeping with our approach in the analysis of BJT amplifiers.

To accomplish this task, we need expressions for g parameters in the C-G and C-D configurations, in terms of g_{fs} and g_d. These relationships are summarized in Table 6–5. Their derivation is given in Appendix A.3.

TABLE 6–5. Parameters for the FET amplifier.

Configuration	g_{11} (℧)	g_{12} (℧)	g_{21} (℧)	g_{22} (℧)
C-S	0	0	g_{fs}	g_d
C-D	0	0	$-g_{fs}$	$g_{fs} + g_d$
C-G	$g_{fs} + g_d$	$-g_d$	$-(g_{fs} + g_d)$	g_d

EXAMPLE 6–6.

Verify the values given in Table 5–2 for the
(a) C-D (source-follower) amplifier.
(b) C-G amplifier.
Assume that $g_{fs} = 5 \times 10^{-3}$ ℧ and $g_d = 10 \times 10^{-6}$ ℧, as in Example 6–5. Let $R_s = 0$ and $R_L = R_D = R_S = 10\,\text{k}\Omega$.

Solutions:

(a) From Table 6–5, $g_{11} = g_{12} = 0$, $g_{21} = -g_{fs} = -5 \times 10^{-3}$ ℧, and $g_{22} = g_{fs} + g_d = 5 \times 10^{-3} + 10 \times 10^{-6} \simeq 5 \times 10^{-3}$ ℧. In Table 6–4,

$$A_v = -\frac{g_{fs}}{\dfrac{1}{R_S} + g_d} = \frac{5 \times 10^{-3}}{10^{-4} + 5 \times 10^{-3}} \simeq 1$$

$$A_i \simeq \infty$$
$$A_p \simeq \infty$$
$$R_i \simeq \infty$$

$$R_o = \frac{1}{g_{fs} + g_d} = \frac{1}{5 \times 10^{-3}} = 200\,\Omega$$

(b) From Table 6–5, $g_{11} \simeq 5 \times 10^{-3}$, $g_{12} = -10 \times 10^{-6}$, $g_{21} \simeq -5 \times 10^{-3}$, and $g_{22} = 10 \times 10^{-6}$. From Table 6–4,

$$A_v = -(-5 \times 10^{-3} \times 10 \times 10^3) = 50$$

$$A_i = -\frac{5 \times 10^{-3}}{5 \times 10^{-3} + 10^4(50 \times 10^{-9} - 50 \times 10^{-9})}$$
$$\simeq -1$$

$$A_p = -1 \times 50 = -50$$

$$R_i = \frac{1}{5 \times 10^{-3} - \dfrac{(-10^{-6})(-5 \times 10^{-3})}{10^{-4} + 10^{-5}}} \simeq 200\,\Omega$$

$$R_o = \frac{1}{10^{-5}} = 100\,\text{k}\Omega$$

The results obtained are identical with the values tabulated in Table 5–2 for the *C-D* and *C-G* amplifiers.

6.6 Setting Sources to Zero

In defining the h parameters, either a voltage or current source is set to zero. It must be emphasized that a *signal* voltage or current is set to zero—*never* a dc quantity. Otherwise, the dc operating point of the amplifier would be disturbed.

Figure 6–14 is a general representation of an amplifier with dc biasing sources, V_1 and V_2, isolated. In setting, for example, v_2 to zero, a sufficiently large value of capacitance is placed across the output of the amplifier. Because a capacitor acts like an *open circuit* to an unchanging, or *steady-state*, dc voltage, bias source V_2 is unaffected. If C_2 is selected to have a reactance of a few ohms at the source frequency, $v_2 = 0$ for all practical purposes.

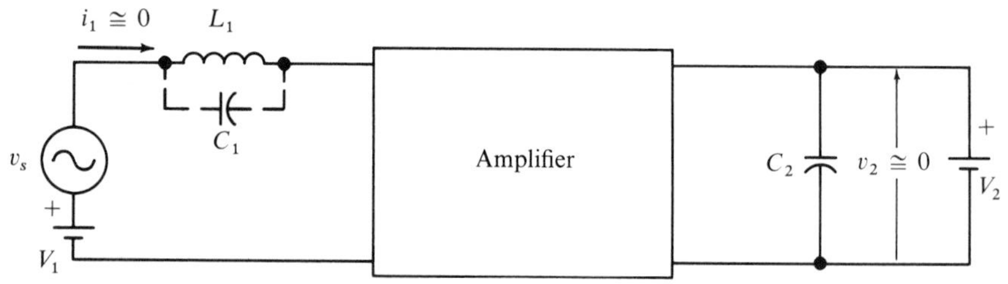

Fig. 6–14. *Setting a signal voltage v_2 or a signal current i_1 to zero. The dc operating point of the amplifier is not affected.*

When a current, such as i_1, is set to zero, a large-value inductor is placed in series with the signal source. Because an inductor acts like a *short circuit* to dc, bias source V_1 is not affected. To simulate a nearly perfect open circuit to i_1, a capacitor C_1 is sometimes placed in parallel with L_1. The result is a parallel-tuned circuit. If the values of C_1 and L_1 are chosen to resonate at the signal frequency, the impedance of the parallel circuit approaches infinity.

SUMMARY

For small-signal operation, voltage gain A_v, current gain A_i, input resistance R_i, and output resistance R_o of an amplifier can be determined algebraically. The mid-frequency range encompasses frequencies from approximately 500 Hz to 5 kHz, where the effects of internal and stray shunting and coupling capacitances may be neglected. If no external capacitors are present, the expressions derived for mid-band operation are also applicable to frequencies below 500 Hz.

For the BJT, the hybrid model is most useful. A set of equations which may be used for all three configurations, *C-E*, *C-B*, and *C-C*, is summarized in Table 6–1. In most instances, these equations can be simplified. For example, in the C-E configuration,

$$A_v \simeq -\frac{h_{fe}R_L}{h_{ie} + R_s}$$
$$A_i \simeq h_{fe}$$
$$R_i \simeq h_{ie}$$
$$R_o = \frac{1}{h_{oe}}$$

Expressions for hybrid parameters for the C-B and C-C configurations, in terms of the common-emitter h parameters, are obtained from Table 6–3.

A similar approach is taken for the FET amplifier, except that the y model is used. The expressions in Table 6–4 apply to all three configurations: C-S, C-G, and C-D. The appropriate parameters for the C-G and C-D configurations, in terms of g_{fs} and g_d, are summarized in Table 6–5.

Further Reading

Faber, R. B. *Introduction to Electronic Amplifiers.* Columbus, Ohio: Charles E. Merrill Publishing Company, 1971, Chapters 4 and 10.

Ghaznavi, C., and A. H. Seidman. *Electronic Circuit Analysis.* New York: Macmillan Company, 1972, Chapter 7.

Kaufman, M., and A. H. Seidman, eds. *Handbook for Electronics Engineering Technicians.* New York: McGraw-Hill Book Company, 1976, Chapters 6 and 12.

Matthews, John I. *Solid-State Electronics Concepts.* New York: McGraw-Hill Book Company, 1972, Chapters 9, 12, and 13.

Seidman, A. H., and S. L. Marshall. *Semiconductor Fundamentals: Devices and Circuits.* New York: John Wiley and Sons, Inc., 1963, Chapter 7.

Temes, Lloyd. *Electronic Circuits for Technicians.* New York: McGraw-Hill Book Company, 1970, Chapter 10.

Tocci, Ronald J. *Fundamentals of Electronic Devices.* 2nd ed. Columbus, Ohio: Charles E. Merrill Publishing Company, 1975, Chapters 11, 12, 13, and 16.

REVIEW QUESTIONS

6.1 Define frequency response.

6.2 Why is semilog paper used for plotting a frequency response curve?

6.3 Define mid-band frequencies.

6.4 What is meant by frequency distortion?

6.5 Define bandwidth.

6.6 What is the significance of the half-power frequency? What other terms are used to designate the half-power frequency?

6.7 Why is the small-signal model of an amplifier at mid frequencies useful?

6.8 Define
(a) Current-dependent current source.
(b) Voltage-dependent voltage source.

6.9 What is the difference between linear and nonlinear operation of a circuit element?

6.10 Define the units for the hybrid (h) parameters. Why are h parameters called hybrid parameters?

6.11 Define the units for the admittance (y) parameters. Why are y parameters called short-circuit parameters? (Refer to Appendix A.1.)

6.12 Define the units for the impedance (z) parameters. Why are z parameters referred to as open-circuit parameters? (Refer to Appendix A.1.)

6.13 Referring to the curves of Fig. 6–9, ascertain how h_{ie} and h_{fe} vary with
(a) Temperature.
(b) Emitter current.
(c) Collector voltage.

6.14 Referring to the curves of Fig. 6–13,
(a) How does g_{fs} vary with temperature and drain current?
(b) What is the variation in g_d with drain current?

6.15 What is an important property of the indefinite-y matrix? (Refer to Appendix A.3.)

6.16 In determining h_{11}, for example, the output voltage is set to zero. Is the dc or signal voltage set to zero? Why?

PROBLEMS

P6–1 Data obtained from measurements on an amplifier are the following:

f (Hz)	V_o (V)
40	7
1000	10
15,000	7

What is the bandwidth of the amplifier?

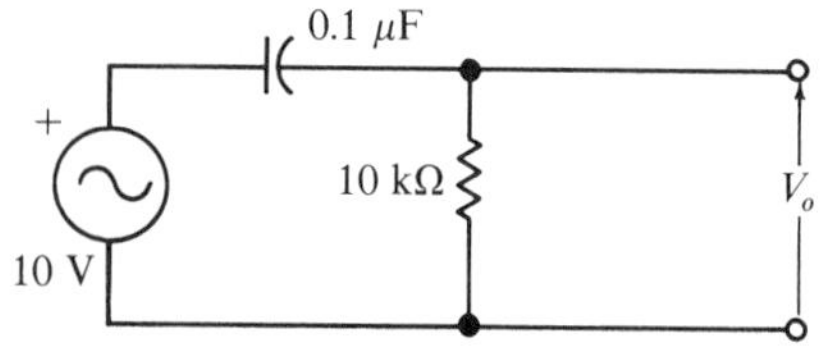

Fig. 6–15.

P6–2 Referring to Fig. 6–15, determine V_o if the frequency is
(a) 0 Hz.
(b) 100 Hz.

(c) 1 kHz.
(d) 10 kHz.
(e) Why is the circuit of Fig. 6–15 called a *high-pass* network?

P6–3 Referring to Fig. 6–16, determine V_o if the frequency is
(a) 0 Hz.
(b) 1 kHz.
(c) 5 kHz.
(d) 10 kHz.
(e) Why is the circuit of Fig. 6–16 termed a *low-pass* network?

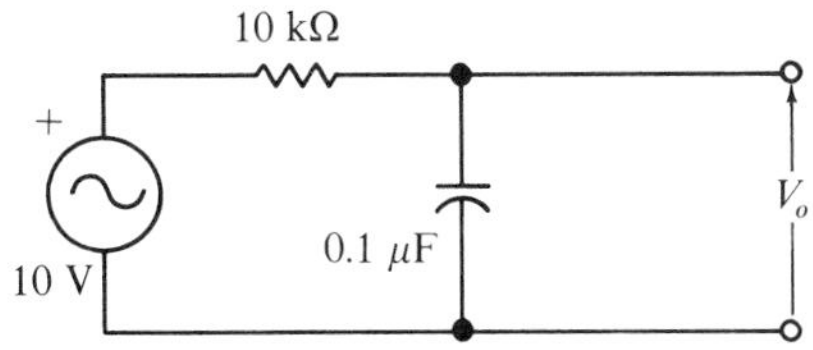

Fig. 6–16.

P6–4 For the amplifier of Fig. 6–17, assume that $h_{ie} = 2\,\text{k}\Omega$, $h_{fe} = 100$, $h_{re} = h_{oe} = 0$, $R_C = 5\,\text{k}\Omega$, $R_B \gg h_{ie}$, and C_c acts as a short circuit to signals.
(a) Draw a small-signal model of the amplifier.
(b) If the source resistance $R_s = 0$, calculate the voltage gain of the amplifier.

P6–5 Repeat prob. P6–4 for
(a) $R_s = 2\,\text{k}\Omega$.
(b) $R_s = 10\,\text{k}\Omega$.

What effect does the source resistance have on the voltage gain of an amplifier?

P6–6 In Fig. 6–17, $h_{ie} = 1\,\text{k}\Omega$, $R_s = 5\,\text{k}\Omega$, $R_C = 10\,\text{k}\Omega$, and the voltage gain $A_v = -25$. Determine the value of h_{fe}.

P6–7 Repeat prob. P6–6 for a voltage gain of $A_v = -35$.

P6–8 By setting i_1 and then v_2 to zero in Eqs. (6–3a) and (6–3b), derive the h parameters.

P6–9 Given the following, determine the h parameters:

$$v_1 = 1000 i_1 + 10^{-4} v_2$$
$$i_2 = 40 i_1 + 10^{-5} v_2$$

P6–10 Determine the h parameters for the network of Fig. 6–18.

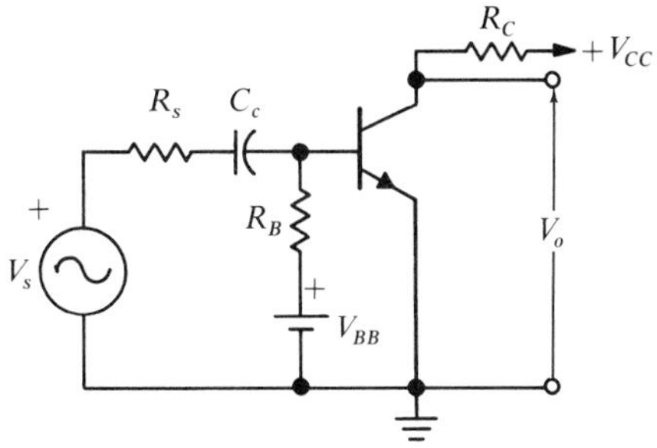

Fig. 6–17.

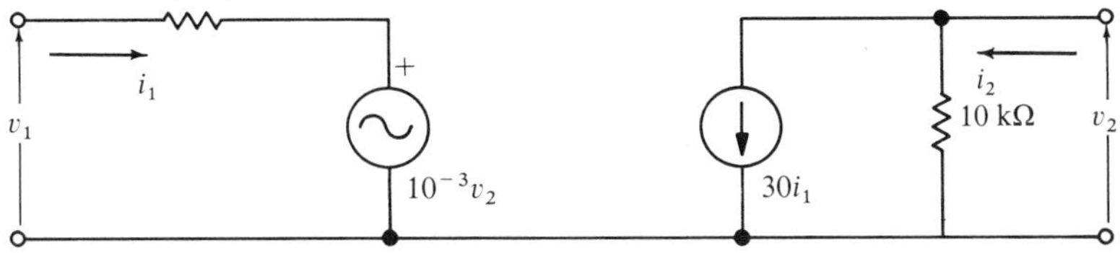

Fig. 6–18.

P6–11 A BJT in the *C-E* configuration has the following parameters: $h_{ie} = 2\,\text{k}\Omega$, $h_{fe} = 100$, $h_{re} = 0$, and $h_{oe} = 10^{-5}\,\mho$. Assume that $R_s = 0$ and $R_L = 5\,\text{k}\Omega$. Calculate the values of
(a) A_v.
(b) A_i.
(c) A_p.
(d) R_i.
(e) R_o.

P6–12 Repeat prob. P6–11 for the transistor in the *C-B* configuration.

P6–13 Repeat prob. P6–11 for the transistor used as an emitter follower. (In this case, $R_L = R_E = 5\,\text{k}\Omega$.)

P6–14 Repeat prob. P6–11 for $R_s = 5\,\text{k}\Omega$.

P6–15 The parameters for a BJT are $h_{ie} = 1\,\text{k}\Omega$, $h_{fe} = 50$, $1/h_{oe} = 50\,\text{k}\Omega$, and $h_{re} = 0$. Assuming $R_L = R_s = 1\,\text{k}\Omega$, approximate the values of

(a) A_i.
(b) R_i.
(c) A_v.
(d) R_o.

P6–16 Figure 6–19 illustrates a common-source FET amplifier.

(a) Draw a small-signal current source model of the amplifier. Assume that $g_{11} = g_{12} = 0$.
(b) If $R_s = 0$, $R_G = 100\,\text{k}\Omega$, $R_L = 10\,\text{k}\Omega$, $g_{fs} = 10^{-2}\,\mho$, and $g_d = 10^{-6}\,\mho$, what is the voltage gain, A_v?
(c) What is the voltage gain for part (b) if $R_s = 50\,\text{k}\Omega$?

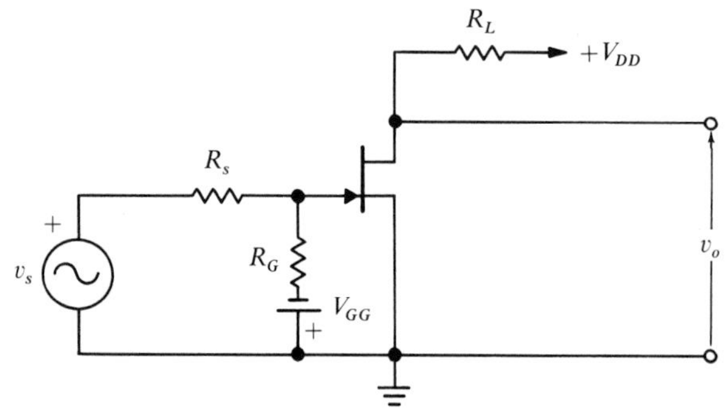

Fig. 6–19.

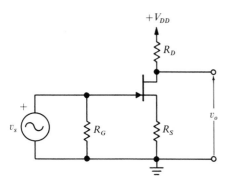

P6–17 Repeat prob. P6–16 using the voltage source model for the FET.

P6–18 Figure 6–20 illustrates a C-S amplifier with a resistor, R_S, connected between the source and ground. The purpose of R_S is to provide biasing without the need of a second dc source, V_{GG}. Using the voltage source model for the FET, derive an equation for voltage gain.

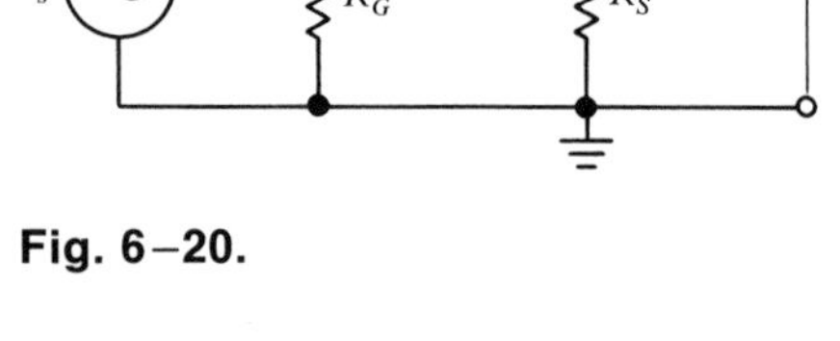

Fig. 6–20.

P6–19 A FET has the following parameters: $g_{11} = g_{12} = 0$, $g_{fs} = 10^{-3}\,\mho$, and $g_d = 10^{-6}\,\mho$. If $R_L = 20\,\text{k}\Omega$, what is the voltage gain of the amplifier in

(a) The C-G configuration?
(b) The C-D configuration?

P6–20 Repeat prob. P6–19 for $R_L = 36\,\text{k}\Omega$.

P6–21 You are required to measure the C-E hybrid parameters of a BJT. How would you do it? Draw a schematic diagram showing what must be done for each of the four h parameters.

7

Single-Source Biasing and Stabilization

In Chapter 5, two dc bias sources were used to establish the dc operating (Q) point of an amplifier. One was required for the base-emitter junction and the other for the collector-base junction of a transistor. Similarly, one bias source was used to bias the gate and another the drain circuits of a FET. In this chapter, we shall explore methods for biasing BJT and FET amplifiers from a *single* dc source. An obvious advantage is that only one, instead of two, dc sources is required.

Once the Q point of a transistor has been established, does it stay put? Does the Q point, for example, shift because of temperature changes? When a transistor is replaced by another bearing the same type number, can we still be sure of the Q point? In seeking answers to these questions, we shall learn how to stabilize the operating point of a transistor.

7.1 Single-Source Biasing for the BJT

A single-source biasing circuit for a C-E amplifier is shown in Fig. 7–1. Note that, as required for amplifier operation, the emitter-base junction is forward biased, and the collector-base junction reverse biased. Biasing resistor R_1 is connected between the collector supply voltage, V_{CC}, and the transistor base. Base current, I_B, is, therefore,

$$I_B = \frac{V_{CC} - V_{BE}}{R_1} \tag{7–1}$$

Collector current, I_C, flowing in the transistor is

$$I_C = h_{FE} I_B \tag{7–2}$$

where h_{FE} is the dc current gain of the transistor. Collector-emitter voltage, V_{CE}, is

$$V_{CE} = V_{CC} - I_C R_C \tag{7–3}$$

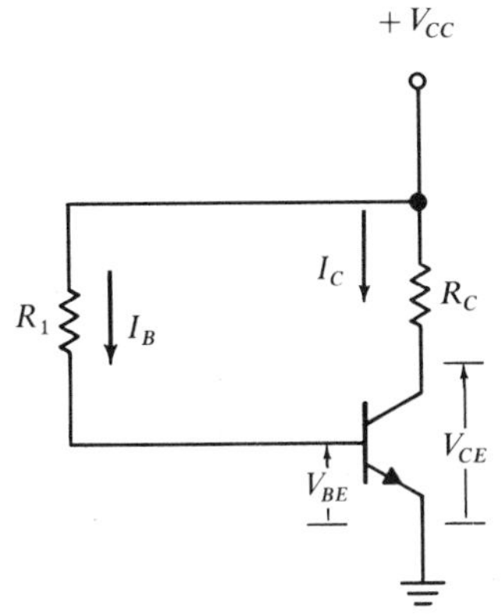

Fig. 7–1. *Biasing a common-emitter amplifier from a single source, V_{CC}. (See Example 7–1.)*

EXAMPLE 7–1.

Assume that in Fig. 7–1, $V_{CC} = 30$ V. The desired Q point is $V_{CE} = 15$ V and $I_C = 3$ mA to ensure maximum output voltage swing with minimum distortion. The dc current gain of the transistor, h_{FE}, is 60 and $V_{BE} = 0.7\,\text{V}$. Determine the values of R_C and R_1.

Solution:

By Eq. (7–3), the value of the collector resistor is

$$R_C = \frac{V_{CC} - V_{CE}}{I_C} = \frac{30 - 15}{3 \times 10^{-3}} = 5\,\text{k}\Omega$$

By Eq. (7–2),

$$I_B = \frac{I_C}{h_{FE}} = \frac{3}{60} \times 10^{-3} = 0.05\,\text{mA}$$

Solving Eq. (7–1) for R_1, we get

$$R_1 = \frac{V_{CC} - V_{BE}}{I_B} = \frac{30 - 0.7}{0.05 \times 10^{-3}} = 586\,\text{k}\Omega$$

7.2 Stabilizing the *Q* Point

In Chapter 3, it was pointed out that a transistor is sensitive to variations in temperature. Consider, at present, the BJT; the reverse saturation current I_{CO} approximately doubles for every 10°C rise in temperature, and the base-emitter voltage V_{BE} decreases by approximately 2 mV for a 1°C rise in temperature. In addition, the dc current gain increases with temperature, as illustrated in Fig. 7–2A. Also, h_{FE} varies with dc collector current, as shown in Fig. 7–2B.

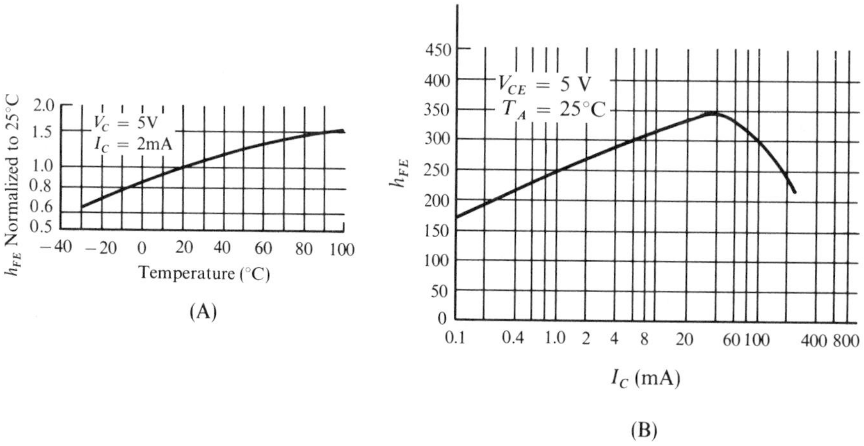

Fig. 7–2. *Examples of variation in h_{FE} with (A) temperature and (B) collector current.*

Even if the transistor is operating in a fixed-temperature environment, we still have problems. The dc current gain for transistors bearing the same type number used in discrete and hybrid circuits may vary by as much as three to one. This is due to variations in doping and other processing steps in their manufacture.

EXAMPLE 7–2.

Assume that the values of $R_C = 5\,\text{k}\Omega$ and $R_1 = 586\,\text{k}\Omega$ found in Example 7–1 are used in the amplifier of Fig. 7–1. The transistor initially had an h_{FE} of 60. It is now replaced with another unit bearing the same type number but having an h_{FE} of 100. What are the new coordinates of the Q point?

Solution:

The base current $I_B = 0.05\,\text{mA}$. (Why?) In Example 7–1, the values of $V_{CC} = 30\,\text{V}$, $V_{BE} = 0.7\,\text{V}$, and $R_1 = 586\,\text{k}\Omega$ are the same for this example. Collector current, I_C, now equals

$$I_C = 100 \times 0.05(10^{-3}) = 5\,\text{mA}$$

By Eq. (7–3),

$$V_{CE} = 30 - 5(10^3) \times 5(10^{-3}) = 5\,\text{V}$$

The new Q point is located at $V_{CE} = 5\,\text{V}$ and $I_C = 5\,\text{mA}$.

Figure 7–3 illustrates the shift in the Q point encountered in the preceding example. Point Q_1 is for a transistor having an h_{FE} of 60; Q_2 is the new operating point for the same type transistor, but with an h_{FE} of 100. Point Q_2 is undesirable because for any appreciable input signal current, the output signal becomes badly distorted.

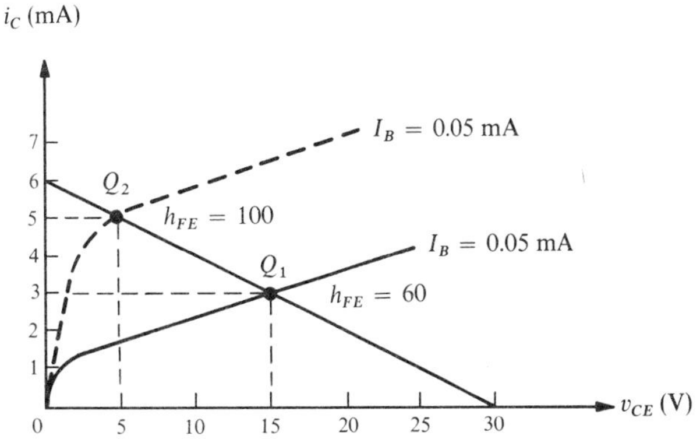

Fig. 7–3. *Shifting of the Q point because a transistor with an h_{FE} of 60 is replaced by the same type device having an h_{FE} of 100. (See Example 7–2.)*

To ensure that the Q point does not shift appreciably because of changes in h_{FE} or temperature, we must devise a special circuit. In this circuit, if the Q point tends to move upward along the load line, the base current is automatically reduced, and the Q point is "pulled back" close to its initial location. Also, if the Q point moves downward along the load line, the base current is compelled to increase, forcing the Q point to return close to its original position. This "automatic regulation" of the operating point is an example of negative feedback, which will be considered in depth in Chapter 9.

The regulating action may be achieved by the circuit of Fig. 7–4, which employs *current feedback stabilization.* Compared with the circuit of Fig. 7–1, in the circuit of Fig. 7–4, an emitter resistor, R_E, is connected between the emitter and ground. Also, resistor R_2 is connected between the base and ground. Resistors R_1 and R_2 are *biasing resistors.*

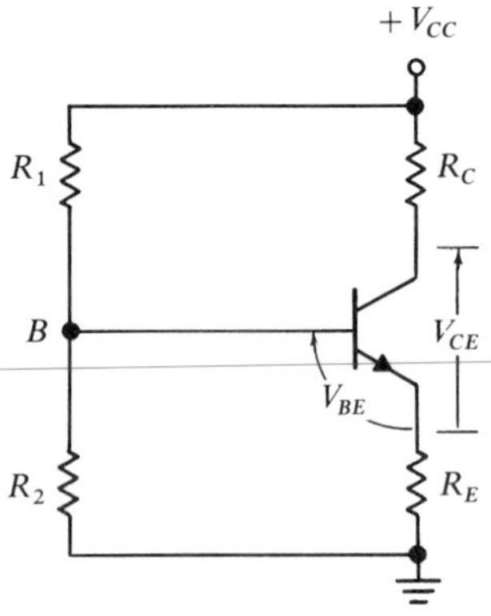

Fig. 7–4. *Current feedback stabilization of a transistor amplifier.*

To better understand the operation of the circuit, we replace the biasing network comprised of R_1, R_2, and V_{CC} by its Thevenin equivalent circuit. The biasing network is isolated in Fig. 7–5A. The open-circuit Thevenin voltage, V_B, is

$$V_B = \frac{R_2 V_{CC}}{R_1 + R_2} \tag{7–4}$$

and the equivalent resistance, R_B, is

$$R_B = R_1 \| R_2 = \frac{R_1 R_2}{R_1 + R_2} \tag{7–5}$$

The circuit of Fig. 7–4A is redrawn in Fig. 7–5B, where R_1, R_2, and V_{CC} have been replaced by their Thevenin equivalent circuit.

Assume that collector current, I_C, tends to increase because, for example, of a rising temperature. Emitter current, I_E, is approximately equal to I_C. The rising collector current increases the voltage V_E across emitter resistor R_E with the indicated polarity shown in Fig. 7–5B. The net voltage, $V_B - V_E$, across the base-emitter junction is thereby reduced, and less base current flows. If, on the other hand, I_C decreases, $V_B - V_E$ increases, and more base current flows. This is exactly the regulating mechanism we are seeking to stabilize the Q point.

Writing a voltage equation for the input side (base loop) of Fig. 7–5B, we obtain

$$V_B = R_B I_B + V_{BE} + (I_B + I_C)R_E \tag{7–6}$$

Substituting $I_B = I_C/h_{FE}$ in Eq. (7–6) and solving for I_C, we have

$$I_C = \frac{(V_B - V_{BE})h_{FE}}{R_B + R_E(1 + h_{FE})} \tag{7–7}$$

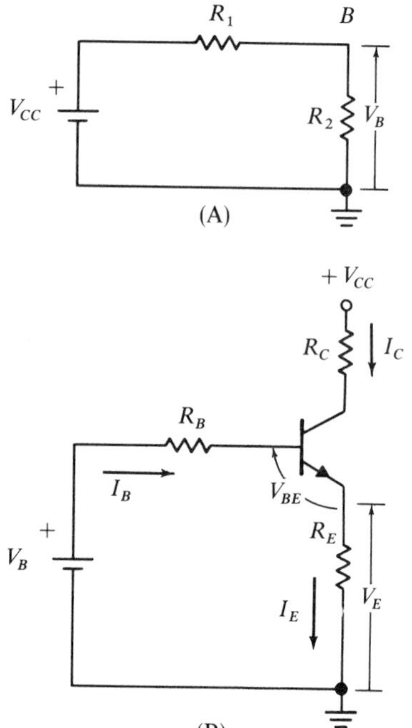

Fig. 7–5. *Simplifying the circuit of Fig. 7–4. (A) Obtaining the Thevenin equivalent of base circuit. (B) Simplified circuit to be analyzed.*

If $R_E(1 + h_{FE}) \gg R_B$, Eq. (7–7) reduces to

$$I_C \simeq \frac{(V_B - V_{BE})h_{FE}}{R_E(1 + h_{FE})}$$

Quantity $(1 + h_{FE}) \simeq h_{FE}$; hence, the h_{FE} terms cancel, and

$$I_C \simeq \frac{V_B - V_{BE}}{R_E} \qquad \textbf{(7–8)}$$

From Eq. (7–8), we see that collector current, I_C, is *independent* of h_{FE}.

Because $I_E \simeq I_C$, if we write an equation for the load line, we get

$$V_{CC} = v_{CE} + (R_C + R_E)i_C \qquad \textbf{(7–9)}$$

or

$$i_C = -\frac{v_{CE}}{R_C + R_E} + \frac{V_{CC}}{R_C + R_E} \qquad \textbf{(7–10)}$$

Thus, the current intercept is $V_{CC}/(R_C + R_E)$, and the slope is now $-1/(R_C + R_E)$, as illustrated in Fig. 7–6.

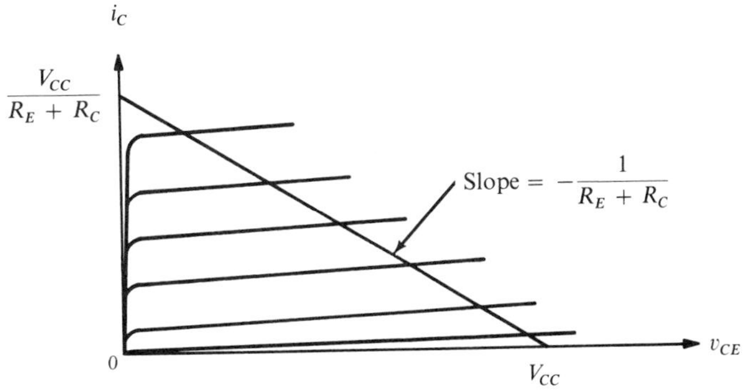

Fig. 7–6. *Superimposing the load line given by Eq. (7–10) on collector characteristics.*

EXAMPLE 7–3.

Referring to Fig. 7–5B, let $R_B = 5\,\text{k}\Omega$, $V_B = 3.95\,\text{V}$, $V_{BE} = 0.7\,\text{V}$, $V_{CC} = 30\,\text{V}$, and $R_E = 1\,\text{k}\Omega$. At $h_{FE} = 60$, the Q point is at $I_C = 3\,\text{mA}$ and $V_{CE} = 15\,\text{V}$. Determine

(a) The value of R_C.

(b) The Q point for a transistor having an $h_{FE} = 100$.

Solutions:

(a) To obtain a Q point of 15 V and 3 mA, by Eq. (7–9),

$$30 = 15 + (1 + R_C)3 \times 10^{-3}$$

Solving, $R_C = 4\,\text{k}\Omega$.

(b) By Eq. (7–7), we have

$$I_C = \frac{(3.95 - 0.7)(100)}{[5 + 1(101)] \times 10^3} = 3.06\text{ mA}$$

and

$$V_{CE} = 30 - [(1 + 4) \times 10^3(3.06 \times 10^{-3})] = 14.7\text{ V}$$

The Q point is essentially fixed. For example, the variation in the quiescent voltage is $[(15 - 14.7)/15] \times 100\% = 2\%$.

7.3 Effect of R_E on Voltage Gain

To learn the effect of emitter resistor R_E on the voltage gain of an amplifier, we draw the small-signal model of Fig. 7–5B in Fig. 7–7. For simplicity, h_{re} and h_{oe} are neglected. Replacing v_s, R_s, and R_B by a Thevenin equivalent circuit, we arrive at the circuit of Fig. 7–8, which shall be analyzed. Resistor $R'_s = R_B \| R_s$ and $a = R_B/(R_s + R_B)$.

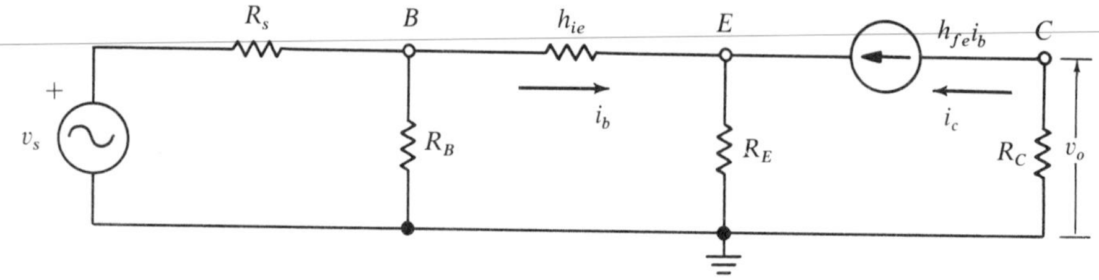

Fig. 7–7. *Small-signal model of Fig. 7–5B.*

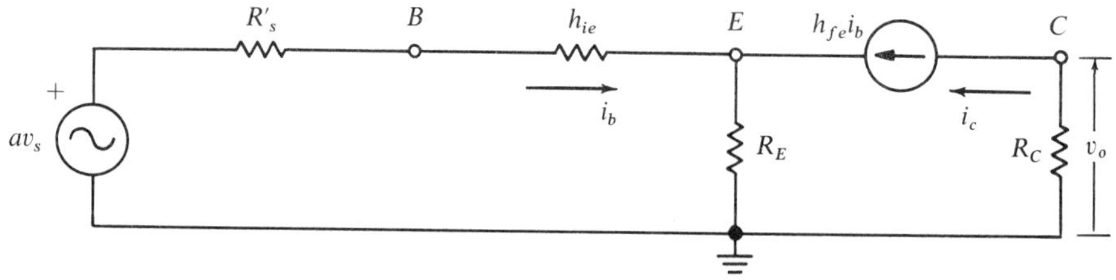

Fig. 7–8. *Simplified version of Fig. 7–7. (See Example 7–4.)*

At the input side, we have

$$av_s = (R'_s + h_{ie} + R_E)i_b + h_{fe}i_bR_E \qquad \textbf{(7–11)}$$

Solving for i_b gives us

$$i_b = \frac{av_s}{R'_s + h_{ie} + R_E(1 + h_{fe})} \qquad \textbf{(7–12)}$$

Since $i_c = h_{fe}i_b$ and $v_o = -R_Ci_c$, the voltage gain for the circuit of Fig. 7–7 is

$$A_v = \frac{-aR_Ch_{fe}}{R'_s + h_{ie} + R_E(1 + h_{fe})} \qquad \textbf{(7–13a)}$$

If the emitter resistor is *not* used, the voltage gain is given by

$$A_v = \frac{-aR_Ch_{fe}}{R'_s + h_{ie}} \qquad \textbf{(7–13b)}$$

from the results of Chapter 6. A comparison of Eq. (7–13a) and Eq. (7–13b) indicates that the voltage gain is much less with an emitter resistor.

EXAMPLE 7–4.

In the model of Fig. 7–7, let $R_C = 4\,\text{k}\Omega$, $R_E = 1\,\text{k}\Omega$, $R_B = R_s = 5\,\text{k}\Omega$, $h_{fe} = 60$, and $h_{ie} = 1\,\text{k}\Omega$. Determine the voltage gain if

(a) R_E is present.
(b) The emitter is returned to ground.

Solutions:

(a) $R'_s = R_B \| R_s = 5\,\text{k}\Omega \| 5\,\text{k}\Omega = 2.5\,\text{k}\Omega$

$$a = \frac{5\,\text{k}\Omega}{5\,\text{k}\Omega + 5\,\text{k}\Omega} = 0.5$$

By Eq. (7–13a),

$$A_v = -0.5 \times 4\,\text{k}\Omega \times \frac{60}{2.5\,\text{k}\Omega + 1\,\text{k}\Omega + 1\,\text{k}\Omega \times 61}$$

$$= -1.86$$

(b) By Eq. (7–13b),

$$A_v = -0.5 \times 4\,\text{k}\Omega \times \frac{60}{2.5\,\text{k}\Omega + 1\,\text{k}\Omega} = -34.3$$

7.4 Bypassing the Emitter Resistor

In the previous example, it was demonstrated that the presence of an emitter resistor results in an amplifier with a low voltage gain. To obtain reasonable voltage gain, in addition to a stabilized Q point, we bypass the emitter resistor by capacitor C_E, as shown in Fig. 7–9A. Capacitor C_E is called a *bypass capacitor*.

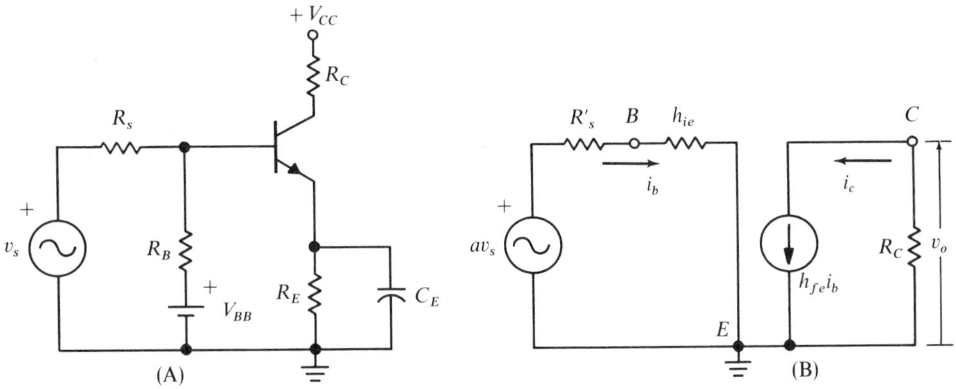

Fig. 7–9. Bypassing the emitter resistor with capacitor C_E to obtain good signal gain. (A) Circuit. (B) Small-signal model. (See Example 7–5.)

The value of C_E is chosen such that at the lowest frequency to be amplified, its reactance is one-tenth the value of $R_E \| (R'_s + h_{ie})$. For this condition, we may assume that the emitter is returned to ground as far as the signals are concerned. Stated mathematically, if $R'_s + h_{ie} \gg R_E$,

$$X_C \leq 0.1 R_E \qquad \textbf{(7–14)}$$

or

$$C_E \geq \frac{1.59}{fR_E} \tag{7-15}$$

EXAMPLE 7–5.

Assume that the lowest frequency to be amplified is 100 Hz. In Fig. 7–9A, $R'_s + h_{ie} = 3.5\,\text{k}\Omega$, $a = 0.5$, $R_C = 4\,\text{k}\Omega$, and $R_E = 500\,\Omega$.

(a) Choose a suitable value for bypass capacitor C_E.
(b) Draw a small-signal model of the amplifier.
(c) Determine its voltage gain.

Solutions:

(a) Because $R'_s + h_{ie} = 3.5\,\text{k}\Omega$ is seven times as great as $R_E = 500\,\Omega$, by Eq. (7–14) and Eq. (7–15),

$$X_C = 0.1 \times 500 = 50\,\Omega$$

$$C_E = \frac{1.59}{100 \times 500} = 31.8 \times 10^{-6}\,\text{F} = 31.8\,\mu\text{F}$$

(b) The model is drawn in Fig. 7–9B.
(c) By Eq. (7–13b),

$$A_v = -0.5 \times 4 \times \frac{60}{3.5} = -34.3$$

This is the same value obtained in Example 7–4(b) where the emitter was returned to ground.

The use of bypass capacitors is convenient for discrete and hybrid circuits. For monolithic integrated circuits, because of the large value of the typical bypass capacitor, other methods are used. They are described in Chapter 11.

7.5 Calculating the Biasing Network

From a signal point of view, the effect of $R_B = R_1 \| R_2$ is to divert some of the signal current from the base of the transistor to ground. Assuming the emitter resistor is suitably bypassed, a useful engineering approximation is that R_B should be at least five times the value of the input resistance. At mid frequencies, the input resistance is approximately equal to h_{ie}. Stating this relationship as an equation, we have

$$R_B \geq 5h_{ie} \tag{7-16}$$

For purposes of calculation, let $R_B = 5h_{ie}$ and R_B expressed by $R_1R_2/(R_1 + R_2)$:

$$\frac{R_1R_2}{R_1 + R_2} = 5h_{ie} \tag{7-17}$$

Also, it was shown that

$$V_B = \frac{R_2V_{CC}}{R_1 + R_2} \tag{7-4}$$

Solving Eq. (7–17) for $R_1 + R_2$ and substituting the result in Eq. (7–4), R_1 is obtained:

$$R_1 = \frac{5h_{ie}V_{CC}}{V_B} \tag{7–18}$$

The value of R_2 may be determined by substituting Eq. (7–18) in either Eq. (7–4) or Eq. (7–17).

7.6 Voltage Feedback Stabilization

Another method for stabilizing a BJT amplifier, called *voltage feedback stabilization*, is illustrated in Fig. 7–10A. *Feedback resistor* R_F is connected between collector and base. In general, feedback current I_F will be greater than the base current. Resistor R_2 acts to "drain off" the excess current, thereby ensuring that the desired Q point is realized.

Feedback current I_F is equal to the sum of the base current I_B and the current I_R (excess current) flowing in resistor R_2:

$$I_F = I_B + I_R$$

or

$$I_B = I_F - I_R \tag{7–19}$$

From Fig. 7–10A, we see that the feedback current is equal to the difference in the collector and base voltages divided by R_F:

$$I_F = \frac{V_{CE} - V_{BE}}{R_F} \tag{7–20}$$

Also,

$$I_R = \frac{V_{BE}}{R_2} \tag{7–21}$$

and

$$V_{CE} = V_{CC} - I_C R_C \tag{7–22}$$

where, since I_C is generally much greater than I_F, current I_F has been neglected.

To understand its regulating action, assume that because of temperature variation or a change in h_{FE}, the collector-emitter voltage V_{CE} tends to drop. If this occurs, by Eq. (7–20), I_F also drops. Since I_R is constant [by Eq. (7–21)], I_B falls as I_F decreases [by Eq. (7–19)]. As a result, I_C also decreases, and V_{CE} tends to rise. If V_{CE} tends to rise, I_F and I_B increase, and V_{CE} is forced to drop. Thus, the Q point is prevented from wandering to any great degree from its initial location.

Just as an unbypassed emitter resistor in current feedback stabilization results in a lower voltage gain, the feedback resistor also reduces the voltage gain of an amplifier. This reduction may be minimized by connecting a capacitor C_D, called a *decoupling capacitor*, as shown in Fig. 7–10B, where C_D is connected between the junction of R_{F_1} and R_{F_2} and ground.

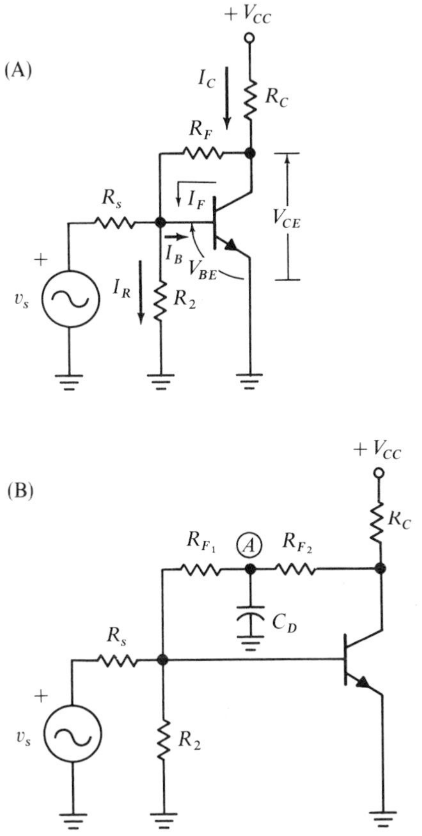

Fig. 7–10. *Voltage feedback stabilization. (A) Basic circuit. (B) Feedback resistor, $R_F = R_{F_1} + R_{F_2}$, decoupled by capacitor C_D.*

The sum of R_{F_1} and R_{F_2} is chosen to equal R_F. It is not required that $R_{F_1} = R_{F_2}$; their sum must equal R_F. If the decoupling capacitor is selected so its reactance, X_{CD}, is equal to one-tenth R_{F_1} or R_{F_2} (whichever is smaller) at the lowest frequency to be amplified, then point A is effectively returned to ground (Fig. 7–11). The dc stabilization of the Q point is not affected by the decoupling capacitor.

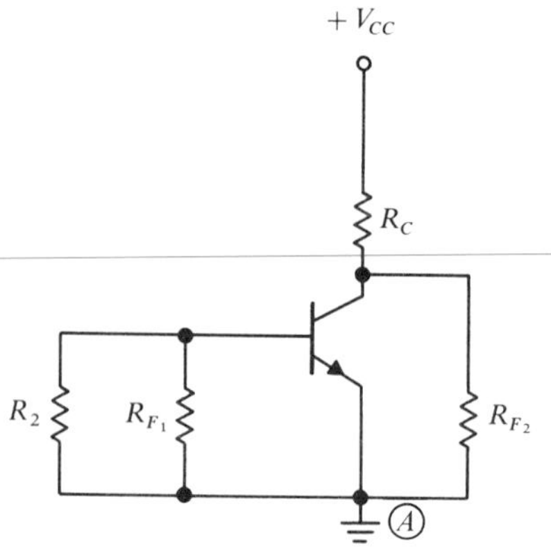

Fig. 7–11. *Effect of decoupling R_{F_1} and R_{F_2}. Point A in Fig. 7–10(B) is returned to ground, thereby placing R_{F_1} in parallel with R_2 and R_{F_2} across the collector and ground.*

EXAMPLE 7–6.

In Fig. 7–10B, $R_C = 10\ \text{k}\Omega$, $R_2 = R_{F_1} = R_{F_2} = 20\ \text{k}\Omega$, $R_s = 10\ \text{k}\Omega$, $h_{ie} = 1\ \text{k}\Omega$, $h_{fe} = 100$, and $h_{re} = h_{oe} = 0$. The lowest frequency to be amplified is 100 Hz.

(a) Determine a suitable value of C_D.
(b) Draw the small-signal model.
(c) Determine the voltage gain.

Solutions:

(a) The reactance of C_D is

$$X_{CD} = \frac{0.159}{fC_D}$$

or

$$C_D = \frac{0.159}{fX_{CD}}$$

Let $X_{CD} = 0.1 \times 20\,\text{k}\Omega = 2\,\text{k}\Omega$; therefore,

$$C_D = \frac{0.159}{2000 \times 100} \simeq 0.8\ \mu\text{F}$$

(b) See Fig. 7–12A. The parallel combination of the two 20-kΩ resistors is equivalent to a single 10-kΩ resistor. Across the output, 1 kΩ in parallel with 20 kΩ is

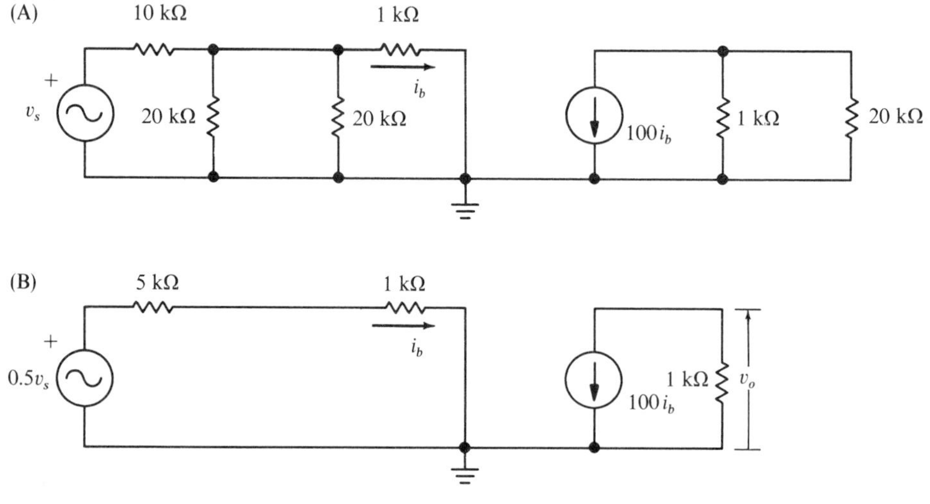

Fig. 7–12. *Example 7–6. (A) Small-signal model of amplifier. (B) Simplified small-signal model.*

approximately equal to 1 kΩ. The Thevenin voltage and resistance with respect to the base are

$$v'_s = \frac{10\,\text{k}\Omega\ v_s}{10\,\text{k}\Omega + 10\,\text{k}\Omega} = 0.5v_s$$

$$R' = 10\,\text{k}\Omega \| 10\,\text{k}\Omega = 5\,\text{k}\Omega$$

Figure 7–12A is redrawn in Fig. 7–12B.

(c) From Fig. 7–12B,

$$i_b = \frac{0.5v_s}{6\,\text{k}\Omega}$$

$$v_o = -100 \times \left(\frac{0.5v_s}{6\,\text{k}\Omega}\right) \times 1\,\text{k}\Omega = -8.33v_s$$

Hence,

$$A_v = \frac{v_o}{v_s} = -8.33$$

7.7 Biasing the *C-B* Amplifier

When a BJT is biased, the base-emitter junction is forward biased and the collector-base junction reverse biased. Let us attempt to bias the *C-B* amplifier of Fig. 7–13A from a single bias source, V_{CC}, as was done for the *C-E* amplifier. Resistor R_1 is connected between the positive terminal of V_{CC} and the emitter of the transistor. An examination of voltage polarities, however, shows that the emitter is positive with respect to the base. Because the transistor is NPN, the base-emitter junction is *reverse*, instead of *forward*, biased. A similar conclusion is reached if a PNP transistor were used instead of an NPN type.

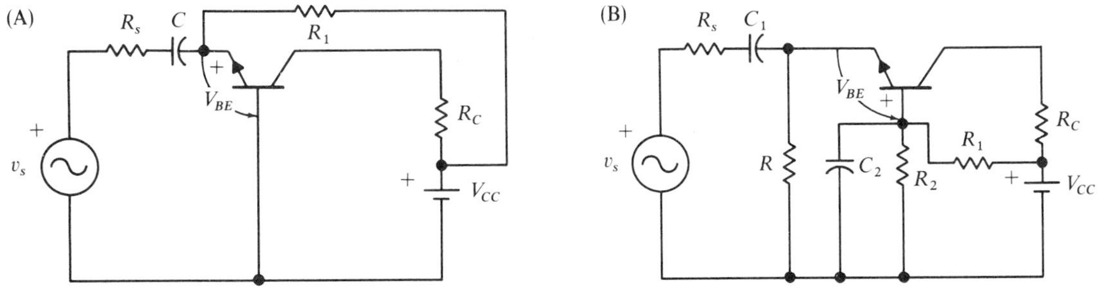

Fig. 7–13. *Biasing the common-base amplifier from a single source, V_{CC}. (A) This connection reverse biases the base-emitter junction. (B) Correct circuit to use.*

A method that permits a *C-B* amplifier to be biased from a single source is illustrated in Fig. 7–13B. Biasing resistors, R_1 and R_2, provide the correct polarities for the base-emitter and collector-base junctions, as for the *C-E* amplifier. Capacitor C_2 is a bypass capacitor. From the point of view of the signal, if C_2 is properly chosen, as in bypassing an emitter resistor, the *base is common* to the input and output signals. Resistor R is needed to complete the dc path between the emitter and base of the transistor. To minimize the loss of signal current, R should be at least five times the value of h_{ib}.

7.8 Biasing the Emitter Follower

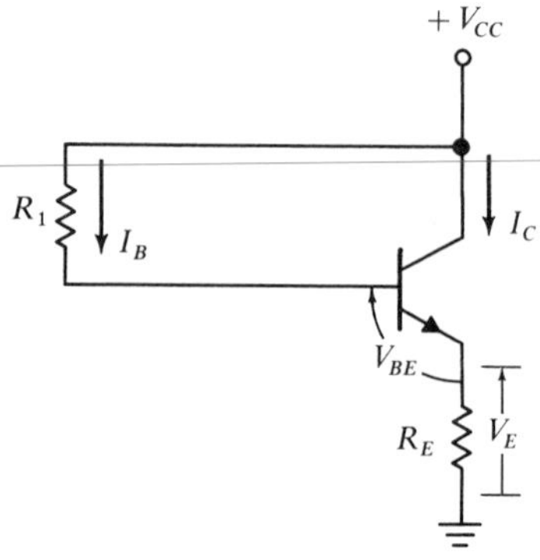

Fig. 7–14. *Biasing the emitter follower from a single bias source.*

Biasing the emitter follower (C-C amplifier) from a single bias source is shown in Fig. 7–14. Base current I_B flows in R_1. Because $I_E \simeq I_C$, by writing an equation for the input circuit, we obtain

$$V_{CC} = R_1 I_B + V_{BE} + R_E I_C$$

Solving for R_1, we have

$$R_1 = \frac{V_{CC} - V_{BE} - R_E I_C}{I_B} \tag{7–23}$$

The equation for the load line is

$$i_C = -\frac{v_{CE}}{R_E} + \frac{V_{CC}}{R_E} \tag{7–24}$$

A practical procedure for establishing the operating point of an emitter follower is to first superimpose the load line on the collector characteristics. Then, the desired Q point is selected. Based on the choice, the value of the bias resistor is calculated from Eq. (7–23). The procedure is illustrated in the next example.

EXAMPLE 7–7.

The collector characteristics of an NPN transistor are shown in Fig. 7–15A. The emitter follower circuit is given in Fig. 7–15B. $V_{BE} = 0.7$ V.

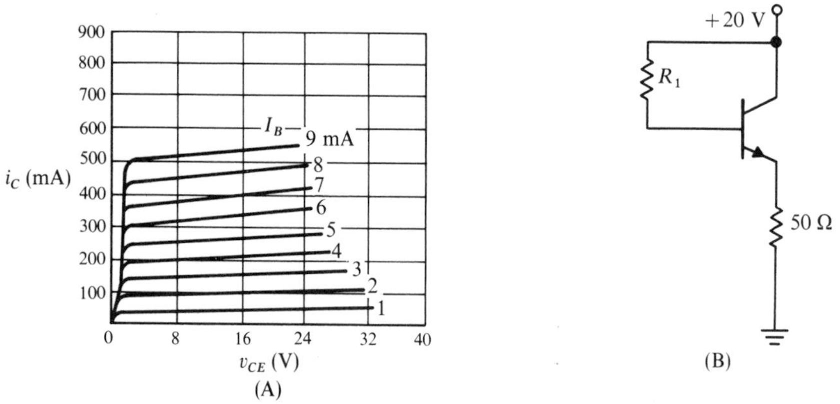

Fig. 7–15. *Example 7–7. (A) Collector characteristics. (B) Emitter-follower circuit.*

(a) Choose a suitable Q point.
(b) Determine the value of the bias resistor, R_1.

Solutions:

(a) By Eq. (7–24),

$$i_C = -\frac{v_{CE}}{50} + \frac{20}{50}$$
$$= -\frac{v_{CE}}{50} + 400\,\text{mA}$$

By superimposing the load line on the collector characteristics (Fig. 7–16), a Q point of $I_C = 200\,\text{mA}$ and $V_{CE} = 10\,\text{V}$ is selected. (Why?) The required base current is 5 mA. The dc emitter voltage is $50 \times 0.2 = 10\,\text{V}$.

(b) By Eq. (7–23),

$$R_1 = \frac{20 - 0.7 - 10}{0.005} = 1860\,\Omega$$

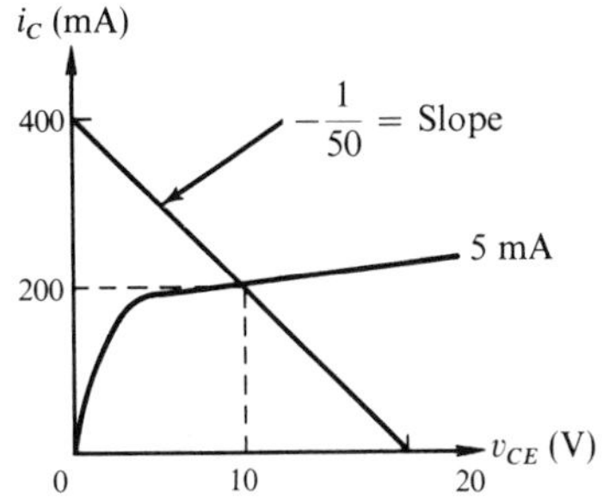

Fig. 7–16. *Superimposing load line on collector characteristics. (See Example 7–7.)*

7.9 Self-Biasing the FET

Before we consider the biasing and stabilization of FET amplifiers, a review of the different types of field-effect transistors is in order. Recall that the FET is a voltage-controlled device; that is, no dc gate current ever flows in the gate-source circuit. For the junction- and depletion-type FET, the gate-source circuit is generally reverse biased. For the enhancement-type FET, the gate-source circuit is forward biased. The drain is always positive with respect to the source for an N-channel FET and negative for a P-channel FET. The biasing of a FET is summarized in Table 7–1.

TABLE 7–1. Biasing (with respect to source) of field-effect transistors.

	N-channel	P-channel
JFET or depletion-type MOSFET		
Drain	positive	negative
Gate	negative	positive
Enhancement-type MOSFET		
Drain	positive	negative
Gate	positive	negative

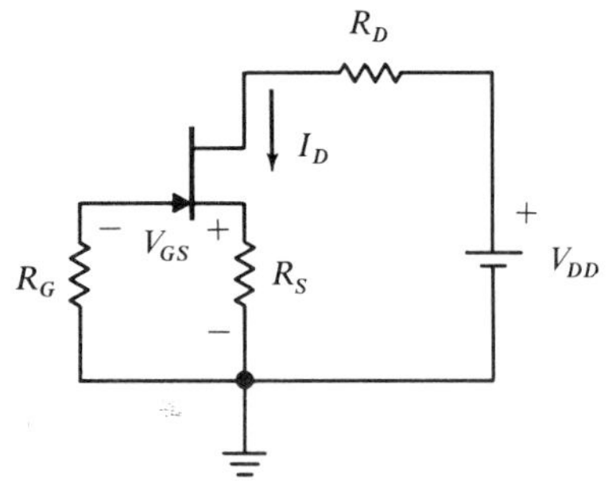

Fig. 7–17. *Self-biasing a FET amplifier.*

The circuit of Fig. 7–17 provides *self-biasing* for the JFET and the depletion-type MOSFET. A source resistor, R_S, is connected between the source terminal of the device and ground. The voltage across R_S is equal to the product of I_D and R_S. From Fig. 7–17, we see that the polarity of the voltage is such that the source terminal is positive with respect to ground. Resistor R_G provides a dc return path between gate and ground. Hence, the gate-source voltage, V_{GS}, is equal to the *negative* of I_DR_S, which is the correct bias polarity for an N-channel device:

$$V_{GS} = -I_DR_S \tag{7–25}$$

Solving for R_S, we obtain

$$R_S = -\frac{V_{GS}}{I_D} \tag{7–26}$$

In addition to self-biasing, the source resistor also provides stabilization of the Q point, similar to that for a BJT. If, for example, the given FET is replaced by the same type number unit having a greater gain, more drain current will flow. Consequently, the negative bias voltage increases. This forces the drain current to fall. A self-regulating mechanism, therefore, exists which keeps the Q point relatively fixed.

EXAMPLE 7–8.

From the drain characteristics of an N-channel JFET (Fig. 7–18), the Q point is at 15 V and 2 mA; $V_{GS} = -1$ V. Determine the values of R_S and R_D in the circuit of Fig. 7–17.

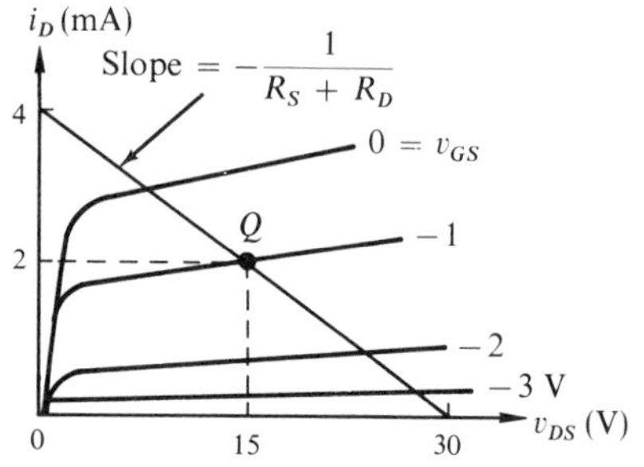

Fig. 7–18. *Determining R_S and R_D for a given Q point in a FET amplifier. (See Example 7–8.)*

Solution:

By Eq. (7–26),

$$R_S = -\left(\frac{-1}{0.002}\right) = 500\,\Omega$$

The expression for the dc load line is

$$V_{DD} = (R_S + R_D)i_D + v_{DS}$$

Solving for i_D, we have

$$i_D = -\frac{v_{DS}}{R_S + R_D} + \frac{V_{DD}}{R_S + R_D} \tag{7–27}$$

From Fig. 7–18, the i_D-intercept is 4 mA; hence,

$$R_S + R_D = \frac{30}{0.004} = 7500\,\Omega$$

Therefore, $R_D = 7500 - R_S = 7500 - 500 = 7000\,\Omega$.

In biasing an N-channel enhancement-type MOSFET, the gate is made positive with respect to the source. (For a P-channel device, the gate is made negative with respect to the source.) In either case, the gate-source circuit is forward biased. It must be remembered, however, that no dc gate current flows. This is due to the gate structure of the MOSFET described in Chapter 3.

A circuit for biasing an N-channel MOSFET operating in the enhancement mode is shown in Fig. 7–19. The bias voltage is provided by the voltage divider consisting of resistors R_1 and R_2. The value of the bias voltage V_{GS}, by voltage division, is

$$V_{GS} = \frac{V_{DD}R_2}{R_1 + R_2} \qquad \textbf{(7–28)}$$

In practice, $R_1 \| R_2$ is usually chosen to be equal to at least 100 kΩ.

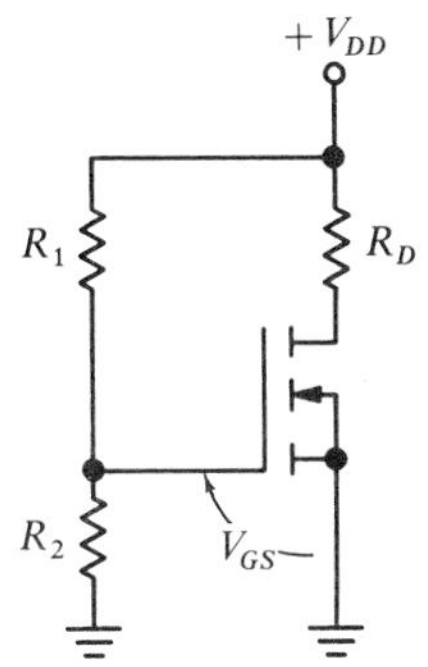

Fig. 7–19. *Biasing a MOSFET operating in the enhancement mode. (See Example 7–9.)*

EXAMPLE 7–9.

Referring to Fig. 7–19, determine the values of R_1 and R_2. Voltage $V_{DD} = 20$ V, $V_{GS} = 1$ V, and $R_1 \| R_2 = 100$ kΩ.

Solution:

The parallel combination of R_1 and R_2 is

$$\frac{R_1 R_2}{R_1 + R_2} = 100 \text{ k}\Omega$$

By Eq. (7–28),

$$1 = \frac{20R_2}{R_1 + R_2}$$

Substitution of $R_1 + R_2 = R_1R_2/100$ in the preceding equation yields

$$1 = \frac{20R_2}{R_1R_2/100}$$

Solving, $R_1 = 2000$ kΩ. Hence,

$$1 = \frac{20R_2}{2000 + R_2}$$

Solving, $R_2 = 105$ kΩ.

7.10 Bypassing the Source Resistor

As for a BJT with an unbypassed emitter resistor, a FET with an unbypassed source resistor reduces the amplifier gain. This is illustrated in the next example.

EXAMPLE 7–10.

For the amplifier of Fig. 7–20A, assume that $g_{fs} = 1\,\text{m℧}$ ($10^{-3}\,℧$) and $r_d = 100\,\text{k}\Omega$. Determine the voltage gain with the source resistor

(a) Unbypassed.

(b) Bypassed.

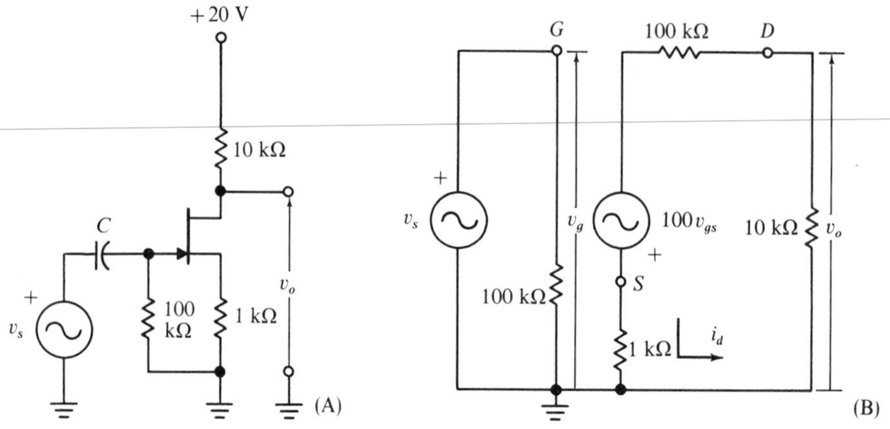

Fig. 7–20. *Effect of an unbypassed source resistor. (A) A FET amplifier with unbypassed source resistor. (B) Small-signal model. (See Example 7–10.)*

Solutions:

(a) A small-signal voltage source model with the source resistor unbypassed is shown in Fig. 7–20B. The value of $\mu = g_{fs}r_d = 10^{-3} \times 10^5 = 100$. The gate-source voltage for the signal, v_{gs}, is

$$v_{gs} = v_g - 1(i_d) = v_s - i_d$$

The signal drain current, i_d, is

$$i_d = \frac{100v_{gs}}{100 + 10 + 1}$$
$$= \frac{100v_s - 100i_d}{111}$$

Solving for i_d,

$$i_d = \frac{100v_s}{211}$$

Output voltage, v_o, is

$$v_o = -10i_d = -\frac{1000v_s}{211}$$

Hence,

$$A_v = \frac{v_o}{v_s} = -4.75$$

(b) With the source resistor bypassed,

$$A_v = -\frac{\mu R_D}{r_d + R_D}$$
$$= -100 \times \frac{10}{110} = -9.1$$

7.11 Stabilizing a FET Amplifier

Although less than the BJT, the FET is also sensitive to temperature changes and to variations in unit characteristics of the same type number. A useful approach in stabilizing the Q point is the aid of transfer curves. A transfer curve relates an output quantity, such as drain current, to an input quantity, such as gate-source voltage. A set of transfer curves for the maximum and minimum values of I_{DSS} and pinch-off voltage, V_P, is illustrated in Fig. 7–21.

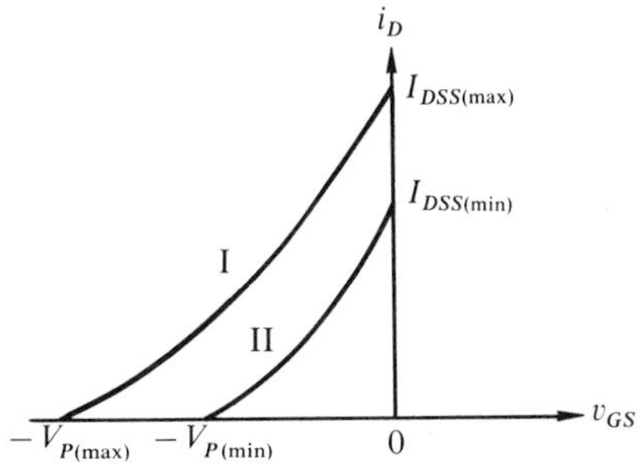

Fig. 7–21. *Set of transfer characteristics for a FET.*

Assuming a JFET or depletion-type MOSFET, let the Q point be located such that its current value never exceeds I_{D_1} or is less than I_{D_2}. Referring to Fig. 7–22, we see that lines are projected from I_{D_1} to curve I (point A) and from I_{D_2} to curve II (point B), respectively. A line, called the *bias line*, is drawn through the two points and intersects the v_{GS}-axis. The equation of the bias line is

$$v_{GS} = -i_D R_S + V_{GG} \tag{7–29}$$

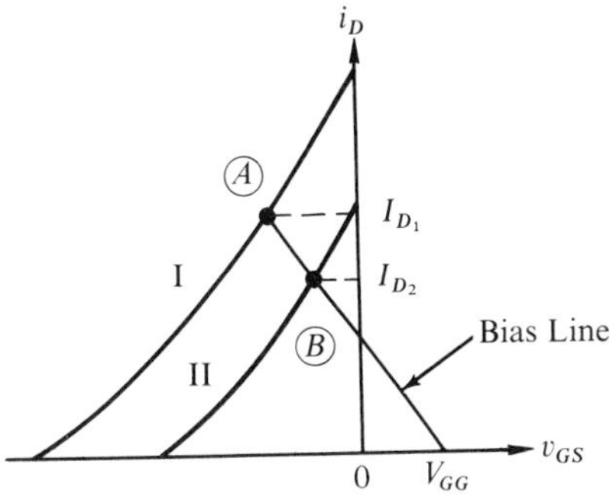

Fig. 7–22. *Construction of the bias line.*

The circuit of Fig. 7–23 satisfies Eq. (7–29). Voltage V_{GG}, by voltage division, is

$$V_{GG} = \frac{R_2 V_{DD}}{R_1 + R_2} \tag{7–30}$$

An examination of Fig. 7–23 reveals that $v_{GS} = -i_D R_S + V_{GG}$, as specified by Eq. (7–29). If $V_{GG} = 0$, the biasing network of resistors R_1 and R_2 is not required.

EXAMPLE 7–11.

The transfer characteristics for the FET in the amplifier of Fig. 7–23 are given in Fig. 7–24. The Q point is to be located between $I_D = 2$ mA and 1 mA. Determine the values of V_{GG}, V_{GS}, and R_S.

Solution:

Lines are projected from 2 mA to curve I (point A) and from 1 mA to curve II (point B). The bias line is drawn through points A and B. The line intersects the v_{GS}-axis at $V_{GG} = 2$ V. The quiescent current selected is 1.5 mA and $V_{GS} = -2$ V. By Eq. (7–29),

$$-2 = -1.5R_S + 2$$

Solving, $R_S = 2.66\ \text{k}\Omega$.

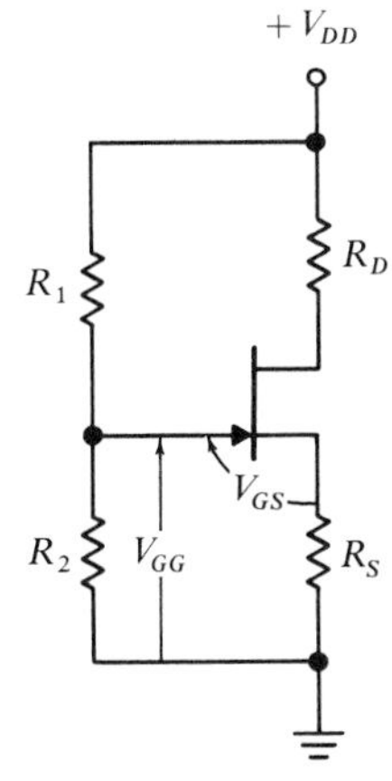

Fig. 7–23. *Biasing circuit which satisfies the equation of the bias line.*

A convenient method for stabilizing the enhancement-type MOSFET is shown in Fig. 7–25A. Resistor R_F, connected between drain and gate, maintains the Q point essentially fixed, similar to voltage feedback stabilization used

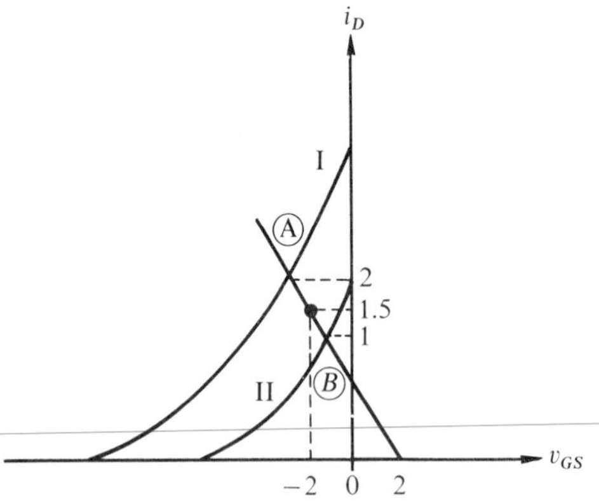

Fig. 7–24. *Biasing a FET amplifier by using the transfer characteristics. (See Example 7–11.)*

for the BJT. Neglecting current flow in R_F, the drain-source voltage, V_{DS}, is

$$V_{DS} = V_{DD} - R_D I_D \tag{7–31}$$

The gate-source voltage, V_{GS}, is

$$V_{GS} = \frac{V_{DS}R_2}{R_F + R_2} \tag{7–32}$$

To minimize the loss in voltage gain, feedback resistor R_F may be decoupled, as illustrated in Fig. 7–25B. The comments made in regard to the equivalent BJT circuit in the selection of C_D also apply here.

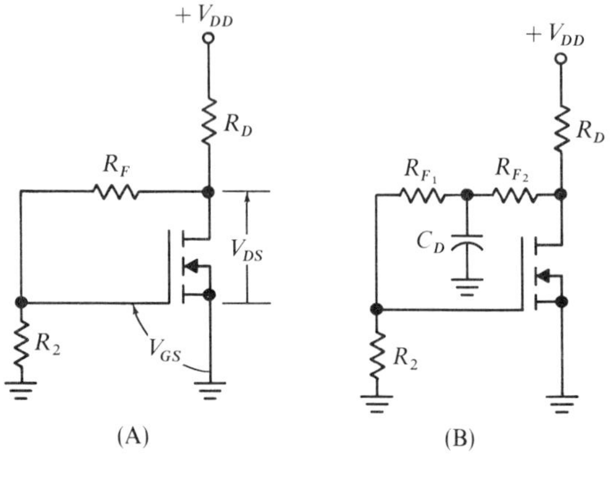

Fig. 7–25. *Stabilizing an enhancement-mode MOSFET. (A) Circuit using feedback resistor R_F. (B) Resistor R_F decoupled.*

7.12 Diode Stabilization

In a silicon transistor, the base-emitter voltage, V_{BE}, is extremely sensitive to variations in temperature. As mentioned earlier in the chapter, V_{BE} decreases by 2 mV for each 1°C rise in temperature. A circuit that compensates for the variation in V_{BE} is illustrated in Fig. 7–26A.

Connected to the emitter is the cathode, and to ground, the anode of diode D. Source V_D forward biases the device, and resistor R_D limits the diode current. Assuming the diode is ideal, it may be represented by a battery of V_D volts, as shown in Fig. 7–26B. The dc base-emitter voltage of the transistor is also represented by a battery of V_{BE} volts.

If the diode and the base-emitter junction are matched, they cancel each other. In this case, the dc collector current becomes insensitive to changes in V_{BE}. To ensure good matching, the base-emitter junction of a transistor that is identical to Q is used in place of a junction diode.

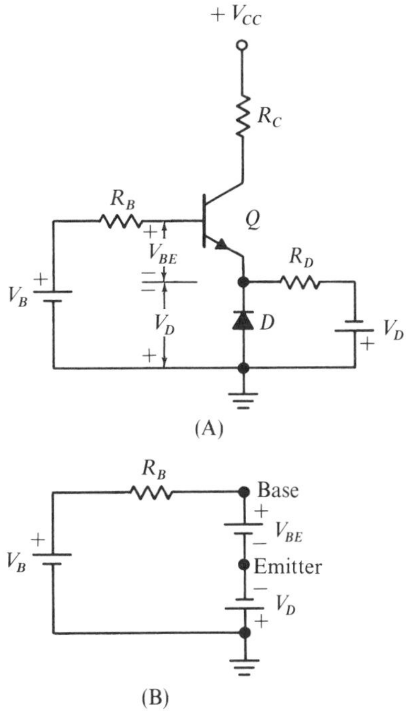

Fig. 7–26. *Compensating for the variations in V_{BE}. (A) Circuit. (B) Model.*

SUMMARY

By using suitable circuitry, the *C-E*, *C-B*, and emitter-follower amplifiers may be biased from a single dc source. Once the Q point has been established, it must stay put, regardless of changes in temperature, h_{FE}, V_{BE}, and so on.

Two methods used to obtain a stabilized Q point are current and voltage feedback stabilization. In each case, the ac signal gain is reduced. Suitable bypass or decoupling capacitors may be used to compensate for the loss in gain. Another method used for stabilizing the Q point is diode stabilization. This technique is effective in cancelling out the variations in V_{BE}, which is critical in a silicon transistor.

For the junction- and depletion-type field-effect transistors, self-biasing is employed. This is achieved by connecting a source resistor between the source terminal and ground. In an enhancement-type MOSFET, the gate-source junction is forward biased. Forward biasing may be accomplished by connecting a feedback resistor between the drain and gate terminals of the device.

Further Reading

Faber, R. B. *Introduction to Electronic Amplifiers.* Columbus, Ohio: Charles E. Merrill Publishing Company, 1971, Chapters 3 and 10.

Ghaznavi, C., and A. H. Seidman. *Electronic Circuit Analysis.* New York: Macmillan Company, 1972, Chapter 5.

Matthews, John I. *Solid-State Electronics Concepts.* New York: McGraw-Hill Book Company, 1972, Chapters 10, 11, and 13.

Temes, Lloyd. *Electronic Circuits for Technicians.* New York: McGraw-Hill Book Company, 1970, Chapter 8.

Tocci, Ronald J. *Fundamentals of Electronic Devices.* 2nd ed. Columbus, Ohio: Charles E. Merrill Publishing Company, 1975, Chapters 11, 12, 13, and 16.

REVIEW QUESTIONS

7.1 What is an advantage in biasing a transistor amplifier from a single dc source?

7.2 Referring to Fig. 7–2, describe how h_{FE} varies with
(a) Temperature.
(b) Collector current.

7.3 Explain how the regulating mechanism in current feedback stabilization helps keep the Q point nearly constant.

7.4 What is the purpose of a bypass capacitor across an emitter resistor?

7.5 Explain how the regulating mechanism in voltage feedback stabilization helps keep the Q point nearly constant.

7.6 What is the purpose of a decoupling capacitor?

7.7 How can a C-B amplifier be biased from a single dc source?

7.8 How is self-biasing achieved for a junction- or depletion-type FET? Can self-biasing be realized for a BJT? Why?

7.9 Explain how a source resistor provides dc stabilization of the Q point in a FET amplifier.

7.10 Draw a typical transfer curve for a FET. Label axes.

7.11 How can an enhancement-type MOSFET amplifier be stabilized?

7.12 Draw a circuit showing how to compensate for variations in V_{BE}. Explain the operation of the circuit.

PROBLEMS

P7–1 In Fig. 7–1, $V_{CC} = 20\,\text{V}$, $I_C = 2\,\text{mA}$, $h_{FE} = 50$, and $V_{BE} = 0.7\,\text{V}$. If $R_C = 5\,\text{k}\Omega$,
(a) Determine V_{CE}.
(b) What is the value of R_1?

P7–2 In Fig. 7–1, $V_{CC} = 15\,\text{V}$, $R_1 = 100\,\text{k}\Omega$, $V_{CE} = 8\,\text{V}$, and $V_{BE} = 0.7\,\text{V}$.
(a) What is the value of I_B?
(b) If $h_{FE} = 40$, calculate the value of R_C.

P7–3 Assume that the Q point for the transistor in Fig. 7–1 is $V_{CE} = 12\,\text{V}$ and $I_C = 1\,\text{mA}$. If $V_{CC} = 24\,\text{V}$, $V_{BE} = 0.7\,\text{V}$, and $h_{FE} = 20$, determine
(a) R_1.
(b) R_C.

P7–4 Calculate V_{CE} if in prob. P7–1, h_{FE}
(a) Increases to 60.
(b) Decreases to 40.

P7–5 Determine the Q point in prob. P7–3 if h_{FE} is
(a) 30.
(b) 40.

P7–6 Determine the Thevenin equivalent circuit of the network in Fig. 7–27 with respect to terminals B-E.

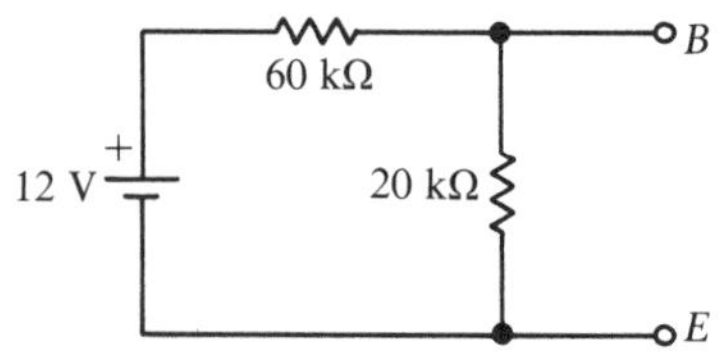

Fig. 7–27.

P7–7 Referring to Fig. 7–28, if $h_{FE} = 40$, calculate
(a) Base current I_B.
(b) The Q point (V_{CE}, I_C).

P7–8 In prob. P7–7, determine the Q point if
(a) $h_{FE} = 25$.
(b) $h_{FE} = 60$.
For each case, calculate the percent change (variation) in the quiescent voltage with respect to that in prob. P7–7.

P7–9 Referring to Fig. 7–28, assume that $h_{fe} = 100$ and $h_{ie} = 2\,\text{k}\Omega$; h_{re} and h_{oe} are negligible.
(a) Determine the voltage gain for the circuit.
(b) What is the voltage gain if the emitter is returned to ground?

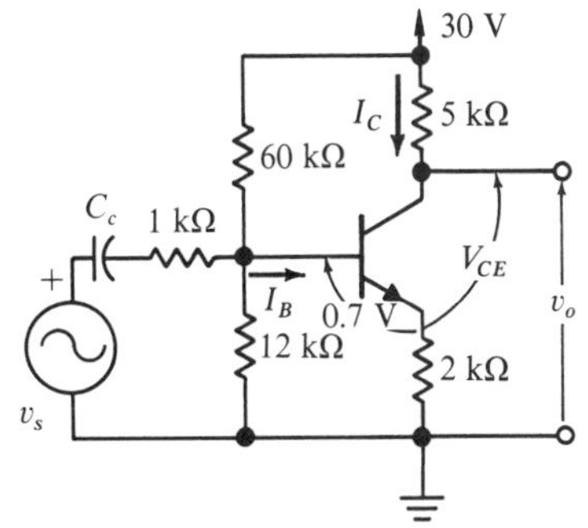

Fig. 7–28.

P7–10 If $R_E(1 + h_{fe}) \gg R'_s + h_{ie}$ and $(1 + h_{fe}) \simeq h_{fe}$, show that Eq. (7–13a) reduces to $A_v \simeq -aR_C/R_E$.

P7–11 Repeat prob. P7–9(a) using the approximation for voltage gain, $A_v \simeq -aR_C/R_E$. Compare results.

P7–12 If the 2-kΩ emitter resistor in prob. P7–9 is bypassed, what value should the bypass capacitor have? Assume $f = 100$ Hz.

P7–13 A transistor whose emitter resistance is suitably bypassed has a value of $h_{ie} = 1\,\text{k}\Omega$. If $V_{CC} = 15$ V and $V_B = 3$ V, determine the values of R_1 and R_2 for the biasing network.

P7–14 For the circuit of Fig. 7–10B, $R_C = 10\,\text{k}\Omega$, $R_{F_1} = R_{F_2} = 25\,\text{k}\Omega$, $R_2 = 25\,\text{k}\Omega$, $R_s = 5\,\text{k}\Omega$, $h_{ie} = 1\,\text{k}\Omega$, $h_{fe} = 60$, and $h_{re} = h_{oe} = 0$. The lowest frequency to be amplified is 60 Hz.
(a) Determine a suitable value of C_D for decoupling.
(b) Draw a small-signal model for the circuit.
(c) Calculate the voltage gain.

P7–15 Repeat prob. P7–14 if $R_{F_1} = 10\,\text{k}\Omega$ and $R_{F_2} = 40\,\text{k}\Omega$.

P7–16 For the emitter follower of Fig. 7–29A, assume that $V_{CC} = 24$ V, $V_{BE} = 0.7$ V, $R_E = 60\,\Omega$, and $I_B = 5$ mA. The collector characteristics are given in Fig. 7–29B.
(a) Superimpose the load line on the collector characteristics, and determine the Q point.
(b) What is the dc voltage across R_E?
(c) Determine the value of R_1.

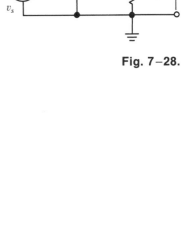

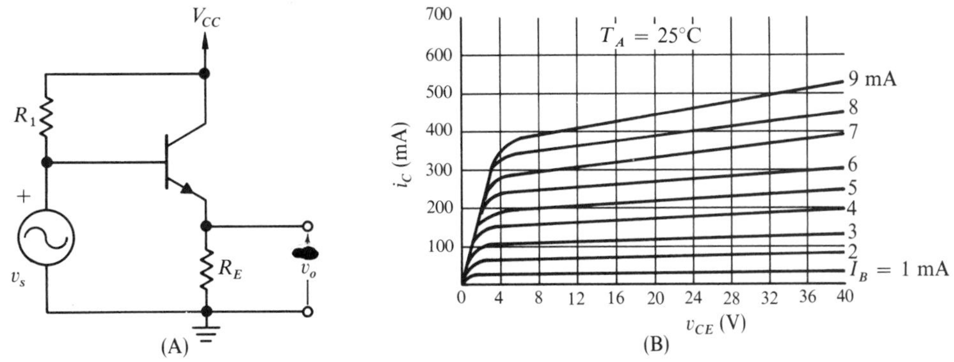

Fig. 7–29.

P7–17 Repeat prob. P7–16 for $V_{CC} = 36\,\text{V}$, $R_E = 90\,\Omega$, and $I_B = 3.5\,\text{mA}$.

P7–18 Drain characteristics for the JFET in Fig. 7–30A are provided in Fig. 7–30B. If $V_{DD} = 20\,\text{V}$ and the Q point is at $V_{DS} = 10\,\text{V}$ and $I_D = 50\,\text{mA}$, determine the values of R_S and R_D.

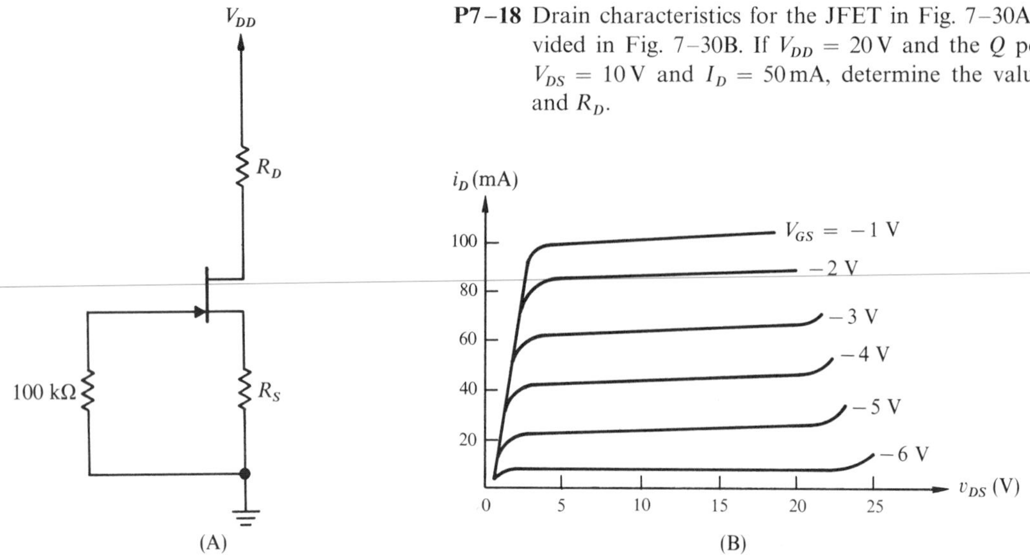

Fig. 7–30.

P7–19 Repeat prob. P7–18 for a Q point of $V_{DS} = 10\,\text{V}$ and $I_D = 30\,\text{mA}$.

P7–20 Referring to Fig. 7–19, assume that $V_{DD} = 30\,\text{V}$ and $V_{GS} = 2\,\text{V}$. Calculate the values of R_1 and R_2. Assume that $R_1 \| R_2 = 100\,\text{k}\Omega$.

P7–21 Repeat prob. P7–20 for $V_{DD} = 15\,\text{V}$ and $V_{GS} = 1\,\text{V}$.

P7–22 For the FET amplifier of Fig. 7–31,

(a) Draw a small-signal model.

(b) Calculate the voltage gain if the source resistance is unbypassed.

(c) Calculate the voltage gain if the source resistance is suitably bypassed.

Assume $g_{fs} = 2\,\text{m}\mho$ and $r_d = 50\,\text{k}\Omega$.

P7–23 Assume that the transfer characteristics for the FET amplifier of Fig. 7–23 are those given in Fig. 7–32. Determine the values of

(a) V_{GG}.

(b) V_{GS}.

(c) R_S.

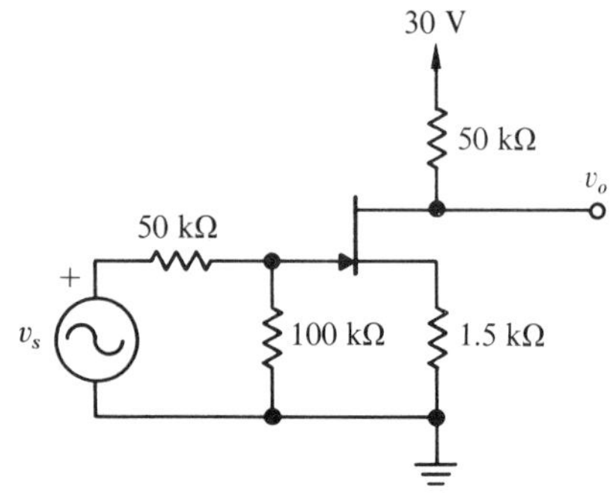

Fig. 7–31.

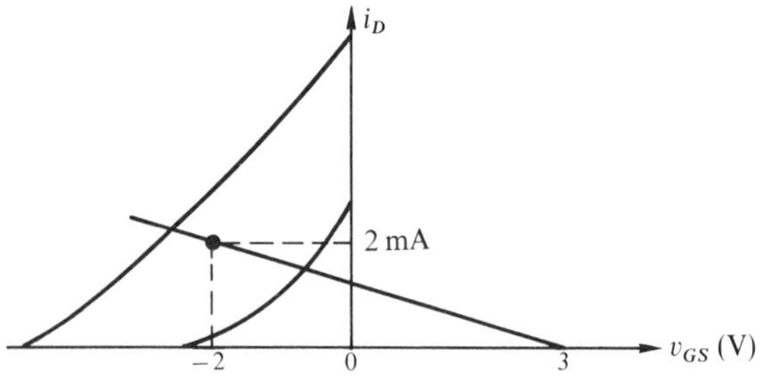

Fig. 7–32.

P7–24 Repeat prob. P7–23 for the transfer characteristics of Fig. 7–33.

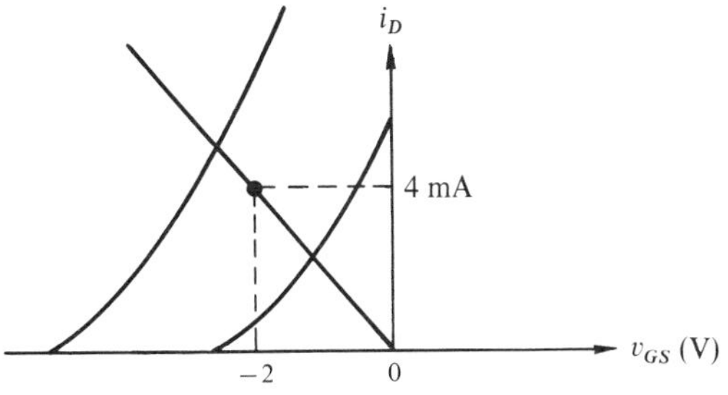

Fig. 7–33.

P7–25 Referring to Fig. 7–34, $I_D = 1$ mA and $V_{GS} = 1$ V. Calculate the values of

(a) R_D.

(b) R_F.

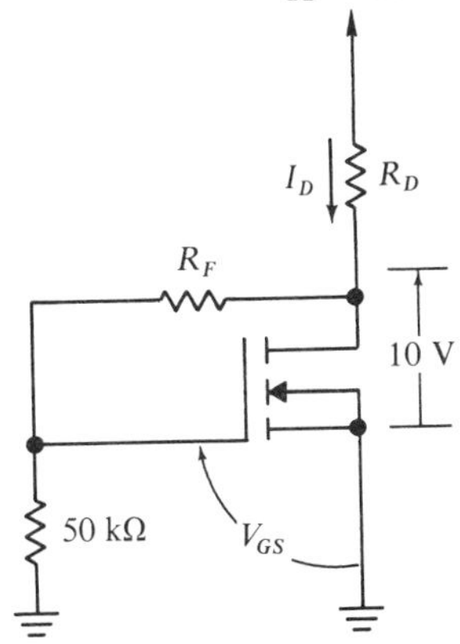

Fig. 7–34.

8

The Frequency Response of Amplifiers

In Chapter 6, the small-signal models developed for amplifiers were for moderately low- and mid-frequency operation. This allowed us to draw models containing only resistors and dependent sources. The analysis of these circuits was found to be relatively simple. For many applications, such an elementary analysis is all that is required.

At high frequencies and very low frequencies, however, one needs to consider the effect of capacitance in the circuit. At high frequencies, say greater than 5 kHz, the internal transistor, stray, wiring, and parasitic capacitances in a monolithic IC deserve close attention. At very low frequencies, the coupling capacitors, for example, have to be considered.

Suitable high- and low-frequency models for the BJT and FET will be developed in this chapter. Simplifications are introduced, permitting the prediction of frequency response with minimum calculation. The response of cascaded amplifiers is also considered.

8.1 Low-pass *RC* Network

To get a feel for how a capacitor affects the high-frequency response of an amplifier, consider the *low-pass* (also called an *integrator*) *RC* network of Fig. 8–1. It consists of a series connection of a resistor and capacitor. Output voltage, V_o,* is taken across capacitor C_s. A sinusoidal source of V_s volts and frequency ω (Greek letter omega) radians/second is impressed across the network.

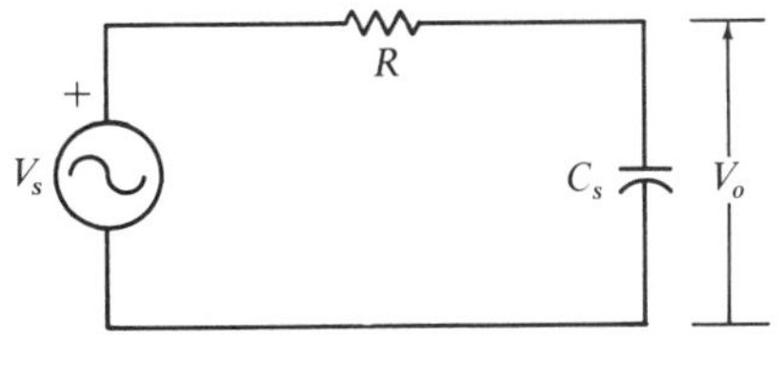

Fig. 8–1. *Basic low-pass RC network.*

At zero frequency (dc), output V_o is equal to input voltage V_s. This is true because a capacitor at dc acts like an open circuit. As the frequency of the source increases, the capacitive reactance of C_s decreases. (Remember, the reactance of a capacitor varies inversely with frequency.) This means that the output voltage decreases and, at very high frequencies, it approaches zero. The reactance is so low that the capacitor acts like a short circuit.

* In keeping with general usage, in this and succeeding chapters, unless otherwise noted, rms quantities for ac signals are assumed. An rms current or voltage is indicated by a capital *I* or *V* and a lowercase subscript.

Let us describe the behavior of the low-pass RC network in more explicit terms. By voltage division, the output voltage is

$$V_o = \frac{\dfrac{V_s}{j\omega C_s}}{R + \dfrac{1}{j\omega C_s}} = \frac{V_s}{1 + j\omega RC_s}$$

Solving for V_o/V_s, we have

$$\frac{V_o}{V_s} = \frac{1}{1 + j\omega RC_s} \tag{8–1}$$

Now, let $RC_s = 1/\omega_H$ or, as it is usually stated,

$$\omega_H = \frac{1}{RC_s} \tag{8–2}$$

Substitution of Eq. (8–2) in Eq. (8–1) yields

$$\frac{V_o}{V_s} = \frac{1}{1 + \dfrac{j\omega}{\omega_H}} \tag{8–3}$$

In polar form, Eq. (8–3) appears as

$$\left|\frac{V_o}{V_s}\right| = \frac{1}{\sqrt{1 + \left(\dfrac{\omega}{\omega_H}\right)^2}} \tag{8–4a}$$

and

$$\theta = -\tan^{-1}\left(\frac{\omega}{\omega_H}\right) \tag{8–4b}$$

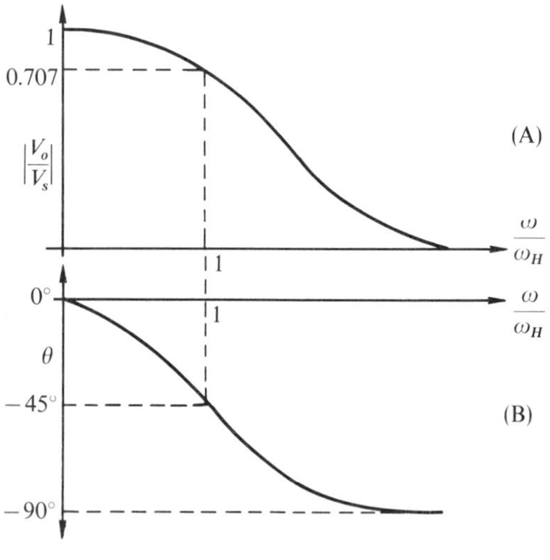

Fig. 8–2. *(A) Gain and (B) phase angle as a function of frequency for a low-pass network.*

Equations (8–4a) and (8–4b) are plotted in Fig. 8–2. Note that at $\omega = \omega_H$ $(\omega/\omega_H = 1)$, the magnitude of $V_o/V_s = 0.707$, and the phase angle $= -45°$. Frequency ω_H defines the *upper* -3-dB frequency for the low-pass network. Expressed in hertz, Eq. (8–2) is divided by 2π:

$$f_H = \frac{1}{2\pi R C_s}$$
$$= \frac{0.159}{R C_s} \qquad \textbf{(8–5)}$$

For a large value of f_H (which is generally desirable), from Eq. (8–5), we see that R and C_s must have small values. In the development of high-frequency models for the BJT and FET, we shall see that the -3-dB frequency is determined essentially by a low-pass network like that of Fig. 8–1.

EXAMPLE 8–1.

If for the low-pass network of Fig. 8–1, $R = 10\,\text{k}\Omega$, determine the value of C_s for an upperbreak frequency of 10 kHz.

Solution:

Solving Eq. (8–5) for C_s, we have

$$C_s = \frac{0.159}{fR}$$
$$= \frac{0.159}{10^4 \times 10^4} = 1590\,\text{pF}$$

8.2 Hybrid-Pi Model

The common-emitter configuration is most popular because of its superior power gain. For this reason, we shall develop a high-frequency model for the *C-E* amplifier. The resulting model, called the *hybrid-pi*, or *Giacoletto*, model, is valid for frequencies at which the transistor provides reasonable gain. Typically, these frequencies are in the order of 100 MHz.

To derive the model, we begin by examining Fig. 8–3A. The model drawn is the same as was derived in Chapter 6, except that h_{re} is neglected and h_{ie} is expressed as the sum of two resistances:

$$h_{ie} = r_{bb'} + r_{b'e} \qquad \textbf{(8–6)}$$

Resistance $r_{bb'}$, the *base-spreading resistance*, represents the ohmic resistance of the base region. *Base-emitter resistance* $r_{b'e}$ is the junction resistance and varies inversely with emitter current. (Typical ranges of values for these and

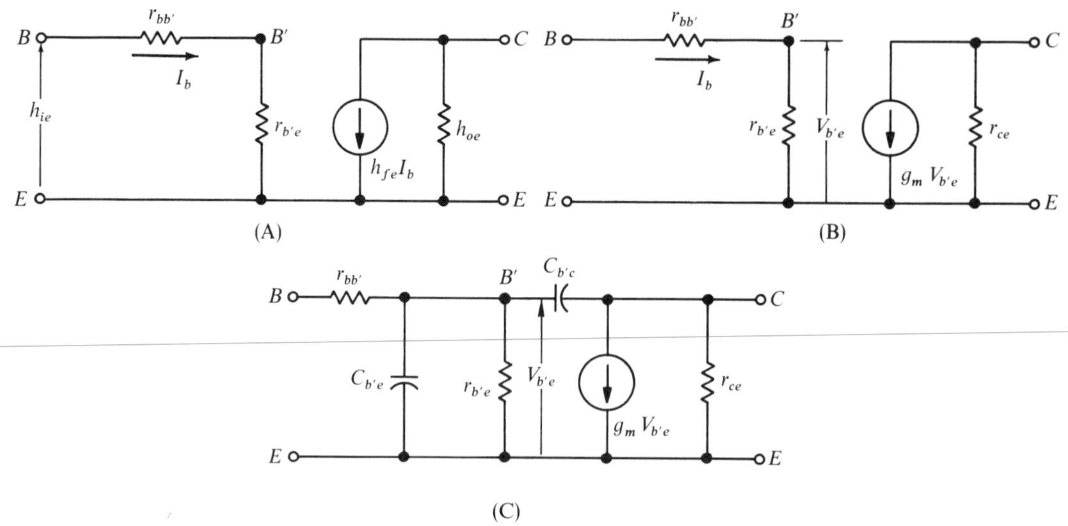

Fig. 8–3. *Developing the hybrid-pi model for the BJT operating at high frequencies. (A) Basic hybrid model with h_{ie} replaced by $r_{bb'} + r_{b'e}$. (B) Current-dependent source replaced by voltage-dependent source. (C) Hybrid-pi model completed by adding internal capacitances $C_{b'e}$ and $C_{b'c}$.*

other hybrid-pi parameters are summarized in Table 8–1.) Point B' is *internal* to the transistor and is not, therefore, available for external connection.

TABLE 8–1. Typical values of hybrid-pi parameters.*

g_m	$= 20\,\text{m℧}–100\,\text{m}\Omega$
$r_{bb'}$	$= 50\,\Omega–100\,\Omega$
$r_{b'e}$	$= 1\,\text{k}\Omega$ or greater
r_{ce}	$= 50\,\text{k}\Omega–100\,\text{k}\Omega$
$C_{b'c}$	$= 2\,\text{pF}–5\,\text{pF}$
$C_{b'e}$	$= 50\,\text{pF}–200\,\text{pF}$

* The precise value depends on the dc operating point and type of transistor.

In Fig. 8–3B, the current-dependent source $h_{fe}I_b$ has been replaced by a voltage-dependent source, $g_m V_{b'e}$. Voltage $V_{b'e}$ is the internal voltage between terminals B' and E, and g_m is the transconductance. For high-frequency calculations, it is convenient to work with a voltage-dependent source. We note that $V_{b'e} = I_b r_{b'e}$, or $I_b = V_{b'e}/r_{b'e}$. Hence,

$$h_{fe}I_b = \frac{h_{fe}V_{b'e}}{r_{b'e}}$$

Therefore,

$$g_m = \frac{h_{fe}}{r_{b'e}} \tag{8–7}$$

Resistance r_{ce} is shown instead of conductance h_{oe}. Their relationship is

$$r_{ce} = \frac{1}{h_{oe}} \tag{8–8}$$

Transconductance also may be defined as the *ratio of a small increment in collector current,* ΔI_C, *to a small increment in the base-emitter voltage,* $\Delta V_{B'E}$, *with the collector-emitter voltage held constant*:

$$g_m = \frac{\Delta I_C}{\Delta V_{B'E}} \tag{8–9}$$

From Chapter 2, the current flowing in a forward-biased PN junction may be expressed by

$$I_E \simeq I_s \varepsilon^{qV/kT} \tag{8–10}$$

where I_E is the emitter current and I_s the reverse saturation current. If Eq. (8–10) is solved for $V_{B'E}$, we obtain

$$V_{B'E} = \frac{kT}{q}(\ln I_E) \tag{8–11}$$

Solving Eq. (8-11) for the ratio $\Delta I_E/\Delta V_{B'E}$, we get

$$\frac{\Delta I_E}{\Delta V_{B'E}} = \frac{qI_E}{kT} \tag{8–12}$$

For a transistor, $I_E \simeq I_C$; hence, comparing Eq. (8–12) with Eq. (8–9), we find

$$g_m = \frac{qI_C}{kT} \tag{8–13}$$

Because $I_C = h_{FE}I_B$, Eq. (8–13) may also be expressed by

$$g_m = \frac{qh_{FE}I_B}{kT} \tag{8–14}$$

Equations (8–13) and (8–14) are useful in many applitions, as will be seen later in the text. At room temperature, $T = 300\,\text{K}$, and, therefore, $q/kT \simeq 1/25$. Consequently, Eq. (8–13) and Eq. (8–14) may be stated as

$$g_m \simeq \frac{I_C}{25} \tag{8–15a}$$

$$g_m \simeq \frac{h_{FE}I_B}{25} \tag{8–15b}$$

EXAMPLE 8–2.

At room temperature, the value of g_m is 2 m℧. If $I_B = 0.5$ mA, determine the value of h_{FE}.

Solution:

Solving Eq. (8–15b) for h_{FE} gives us

$$h_{FE} = \frac{25 g_m}{I_B} = \frac{25 \times 2 \times 10^{-3}}{0.5 \times 10^{-3}} = 100$$

In Fig. 8–3C, the hybrid-pi model is completed with the addition of internal capacitances $C_{b'e}$ across B' and E and capacitance $C_{b'c}$ across B' and C. Capacitance $C_{b'e}$, the *diffusion capacitance*, accounts for electric charge stored in the base region of a transistor. Capacitance $C_{b'c}$, the *depletion capacitance*, represents capacitance owing to a reverse-biased, collector-base junction. At low and mid frequencies, these capacitances may be neglected. Results obtained in this case are equivalent to those for the hybrid model of Chapter 6, as illustrated in the next example.

EXAMPLE 8–3.

For the amplifier of Fig. 8–4A,

(a) Draw the hybrid-pi model at mid frequencies.

(b) Derive an expression for voltage gain at mid frequencies.

Assume that $R_1 \| R_2 \gg r_{bb'} + r_{b'e}$ and $r_{ce} \gg R_C$.

Solutions:

(a) The model is drawn in Fig. 8–4B. At mid frequencies, C_c acts like a short circuit; $C_{b'e}$ and $C_{b'c}$ act like open circuits.

(b) From Fig. 8–4B, we derive the following:

$$V_{b'e} = \frac{r_{b'e} V_s}{r_{b'e} + r_{bb'}}$$

$$I_c = g_m V_{b'e} = \frac{g_m r_{b'e} V_s}{r_{b'e} + r_{bb'}}$$

$$V_o = -I_c R_C = -\frac{g_m r_{b'e} R_C V_s}{r_{b'e} + r_{bb'}}$$

Labeling the voltage gain at mid frequencies by A_o,

$$A_o = \frac{V_o}{V_s} = -\frac{g_m r_{b'e} R_C}{r_{b'e} + r_{bb'}} \tag{8–16}$$

Noting that $g_m r_{b'e} = h_{fe}$ and $r_{b'e} + r_{bb'} = h_{ie}$, we have

$$A_o = -\frac{h_{fe} R_C}{h_{ie}}$$

which is identical to the equation obtained using the hybrid model.

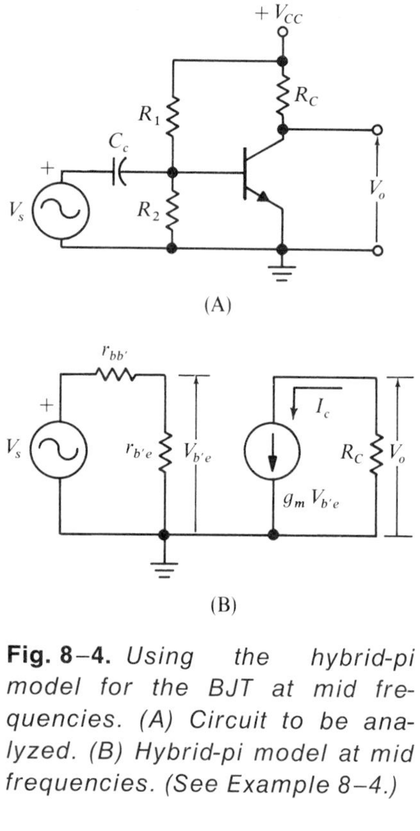

Fig. 8–4. *Using the hybrid-pi model for the BJT at mid frequencies. (A) Circuit to be analyzed. (B) Hybrid-pi model at mid frequencies. (See Example 8–4.)*

Equation (8–16) can be simplified if we recognize that $r_{bb'} \ll r_{b'e}$ (see Table 8–1). Hence,

$$A_o \simeq -g_m R_C \qquad \text{(8–17)}$$

8.3 The Miller Effect

Before using the hybrid-pi model for high-frequency calculations, we must simplify its structure. To understand the basis of the simplification, we first consider the circuit shown in Fig. 8–5A. Because of the *Miller effect*, impedance Z, which is connected across the input and output terminals, may be replaced by modified impedances across the input and output of the amplifier (Fig. 8–5B). The modified circuit is easier to analyze than the original network of Fig. 8–5A.

It is shown in Appendix B1 that the modified impedance $Z/(1 - A_v)$ is placed across the input terminals and the modified impedance $Z/(1 - 1/A_v)$ across the output terminals. The Miller effect is now used to simplify the hybrid-pi model of Fig. 8–3C. The reader, however, must be reminded that the impedance of a capacitor C, called capacitive reactance X_C, is

$$X_C = \frac{0.159}{fC}$$

If X_C is divided by $1 - A_v$, we obtain

$$\frac{X_C}{1 - A_v} = \frac{0.159}{fC(1 - A_v)}$$

Capacitor C has been multiplied by $(1 - A_v)$. Similarly, if X_C is divided by $(1 - 1/A_v)$, this is equivalent to multiplying C by $(1 - 1/A_v)$.

The preceding facts applied to the hybrid-pi model yield the modified hybrid-pi model of Fig. 8–6. Note that $C_{b'c}$ is reflected across the input as $C_{b'c}(1 - A_v)$ and across the output as $C_{b'c}(1 - 1/A_v)$. Voltage gain A_v is defined as the gain between collector C and internal point B'. By Eq. (8–17), $A_v \simeq A_o = -g_m R_C$. If we let $r_{ce} \| R_C = R'_L$,

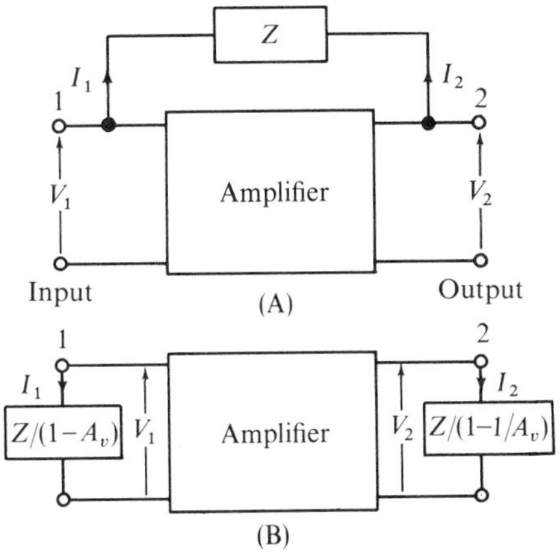

Fig. 8–5. *The Miller effect. Replacing feedback impedance Z in (A) by two modified impedances across the input and output terminals of the amplifier in (B).*

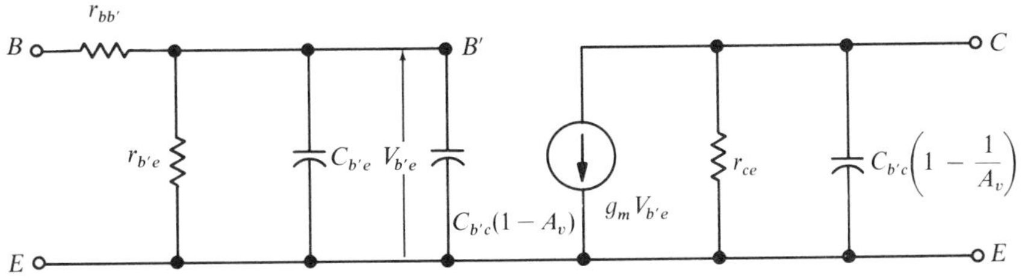

Fig. 8–6. *Modified hybrid-pi model for a BJT based on the Miller effect.*

Eq. (8–17) reduces to

$$A_v = -g_m R'_L \tag{8–18}$$

Adding $C_{b'e}$ and $C_{b'c}(1 - A_v)$, which are in parallel, we have

$$C_i = C_{b'e} + C_{b'c}(1 - A_v)$$

Substituting Eq. (8–18) for A_v gives us

$$C_i = C_{b'e} + C_{b'c}(1 + g_m R'_L) \tag{8–19}$$

The effect of $C_{b'c}(1 - 1/A_v)$ across the output is generally negligible compared with the effect of C_i on the frequency response of an amplifier. For this reason, it will be omitted from Fig. 8–6. The resulting *simplified* hybrid-pi model, therefore, appears as shown in Fig. 8–7. This model will be used in the remainder of the chapter for the BJT.

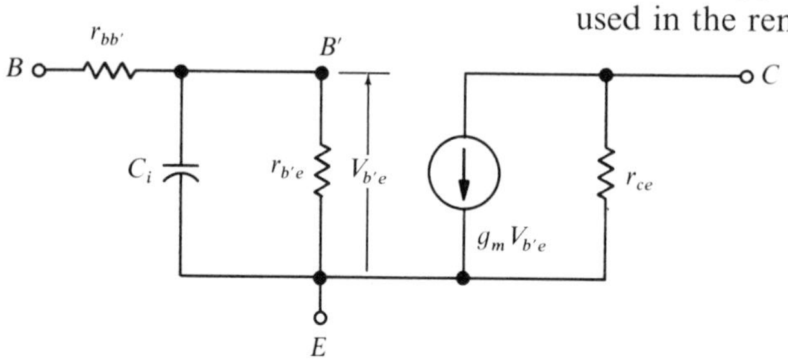

Fig. 8–7. A simplified hybrid-pi model of a BJT.

EXAMPLE 8–4.

For the *C-E* amplifier of Fig. 8–8A, assume that capacitors C_E and C_c act as short circuits at mid and high frequencies. For the transistor, $g_m = 0.2\,℧$, $r_{bb'} = 100\,\Omega$, $r_{b'e} = 1\,\text{k}\Omega$, $C_{b'e} = 200\,\text{pF}$, $C_{b'c} = 4\,\text{pF}$, and $r_{ce} = 30\,\text{k}\Omega$.

(a) Draw a simplified hybrid-pi model for the circuit.

(b) Calculate the mid-frequency gain.

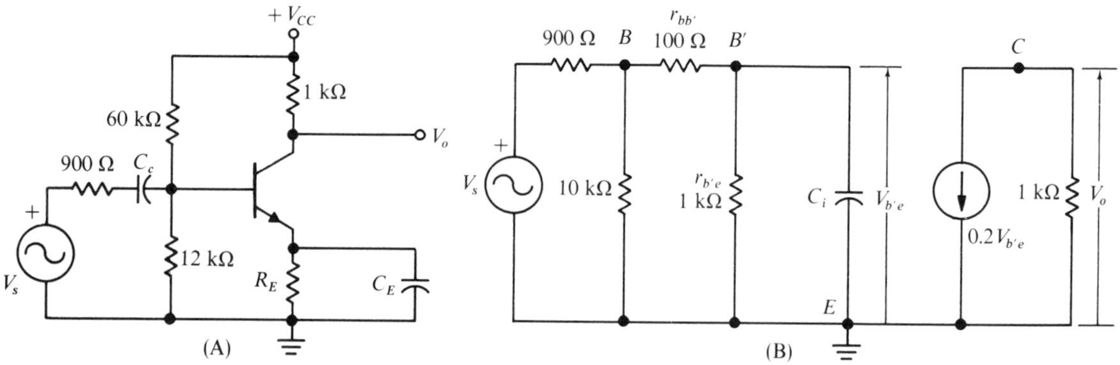

Fig. 8–8. Example 8–4. (A) Circuit to be analyzed. (B) Simplified hybrid-pi model of the circuit.

Solutions:

(a) The simplified hybrid-pi model is drawn in Fig. 8–8B. The parallel combination of the 60-kΩ and 12-kΩ biasing resistors is shown by an equivalent 10-kΩ resistor connected between terminals *B* and *E*. Also, $R'_L = 30\,\text{k}\Omega \| 1\,\text{k}\Omega \simeq 1\,\text{k}\Omega$. By Eq. (8–19),

$$C_i = 200 + 4(1 + 0.2 \times 1000) \simeq 1000\,\text{pF}$$

If a Thevenin equivalent is first taken with respect to terminal B and ground (Fig. 8–9A), we get

$$V'_s = \frac{10{,}000V_s}{10{,}900} \simeq V_s$$

and

$$R'_s = 900 \| 10{,}000 \simeq 900\,\Omega$$

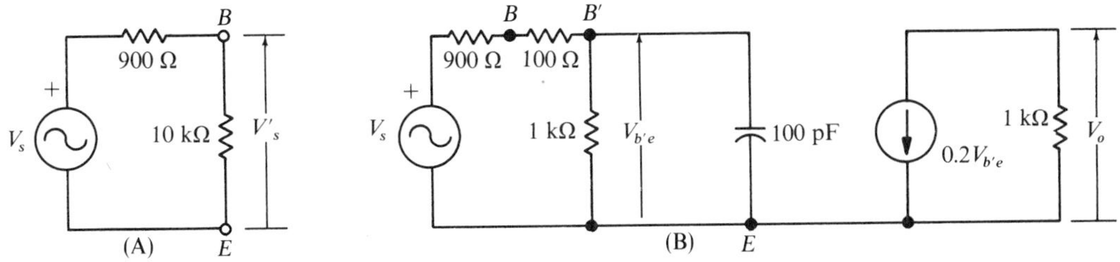

Fig. 8–9. *Example 8–4 continued. (A) Thevenin equivalent circuit taken at the base of the transistor. (B) Model containing the Thevenin circuit.*

This is reflected in Fig. 8–9B. If a second Thevenin circuit is taken with respect to terminal B' and ground, we obtain

$$V''_s = \frac{1000V_s}{900 + 100 + 1000} = 0.5V_s$$

and

$$R''_s = (900 + 100) \| 1000 = 500\,\Omega$$

The final circuit is shown in Fig. 8–10.

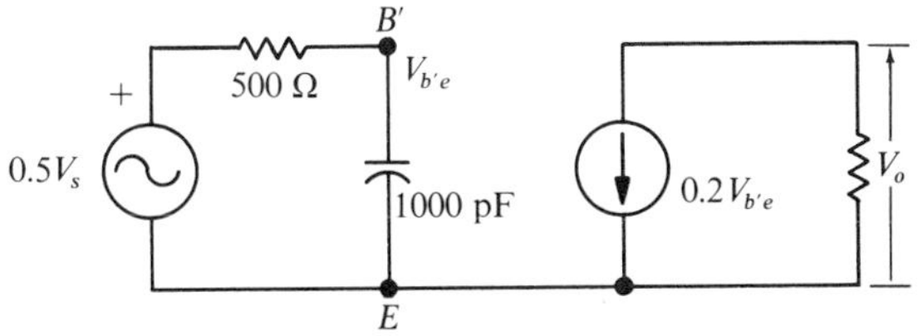

Fig. 8–10. *Final model obtained in Example 8–4.*

(b) At mid frequencies, the 1000-pF capacitor acts like an open circuit. Hence, $V_{b'e} = 0.5V_s$, and

$$V_o = -0.2 \times 0.5V_s \times 1000$$

$$A_o = \frac{V_o}{V_s} = -100$$

EXAMPLE 8–5.

Using the values of Example 8–4 and the model of Fig. 8–10,

(a) Calculate the upper −3-dB frequency.
(b) Write an expression for voltage gain as a function of frequency.

Solutions:

(a) Note that the input circuit of Fig. 8–10 is equivalent to the low-pass network of Fig. 8–1. In this example, $R = 500\,\Omega$ and $C_s = C_i = 1000\text{ pF} = 10^{-9}$ F. By Eq. (8–5),

$$f_H = \frac{0.159}{500 \times 10^{-9}} = 318\text{ kHz}$$

(b) Voltage gain as a function of frequency, expressed by $A_v(jf)$, is

$$A_v(jf) = \frac{A_o}{1 + \dfrac{jf}{f_H}} = \frac{-100}{1 + \dfrac{jf}{318{,}000}}$$

If we retrace our calculations in the two previous examples, we can derive a general expression for R and f_H. First, the Thevenin resistance with respect to the base and ground was found to be

$$R'_s = R_s \| R_B$$

Adding R'_s to $r_{bb'}$ and calculating their sum in parallel with $r_{b'e}$, R is

$$R = (R'_s + r_{bb'}) \| r_{b'e} = \frac{(R'_s + r_{bb'})r_{b'e}}{R'_s + r_{bb'} + r_{b'e}} \qquad \textbf{(8–20)}$$

The upper -3-dB frequency may be expressed as

$$f_H = \frac{0.159}{RC_s} = \frac{0.159(R'_s + r_{bb'} + r_{b'e})}{(R'_s + r_{bb'})r_{b'e}C_i} \qquad \textbf{(8–21)}$$

8.4 Figure of Merit

A figure of merit for a device gives its user an idea of how good the device is for his application. Two figures of merit that are used to characterize the BJT at high frequencies are the *beta cutoff frequency*, f_β, and the *current gain-bandwidth product*, f_T. We shall first consider f_β.

The frequency at which the short-circuit current gain is $0.707h_{fe}$ is the beta cutoff frequency, f_β. In Appendix B.2, it is expressed by

$$f_\beta = \frac{0.159}{(C_{b'e} + C_{b'c})r_{b'e}} \qquad \textbf{(8–22)}$$

For large values of f_β (which are desirable), capacitances $C_{b'e}$ and $C_{b'c}$, and resistance $r_{b'e}$, should be small.

The current gain-bandwidth product, f_T, is defined as *the frequency at which the magnitude of the short-circuit current gain is unity*. In Appendix B.2, it is shown to be equal to

$$f_T = h_{fe}f_\beta \qquad \textbf{(8–23)}$$

An approximate expression for f_T is

$$f_T = \frac{0.159g_m}{C_{b'e} + C_{b'c}} \qquad \textbf{(8–24)}$$

Because f_T is the product of the short-circuit current gain h_{fe} at mid frequencies, and the short-circuit beta cutoff frequency, f_β, it is called the current gain-bandwidth product of a transistor. Typical variation in f_T with collector current is illustrated in Fig. 8–11. For a large range of values, f_T increases with collector current.

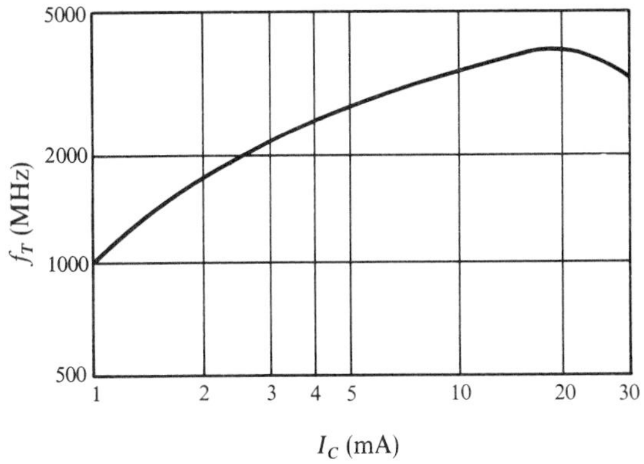

Fig. 8–11. *Typical variation in current gain-bandwidth product, f_T, with collector current, I_C.*

EXAMPLE 8–6.

Using the values given in Example 8–4, determine f_β and f_T for the transistor.

Solution:

By Eq. (8–22),

$$f_\beta = \frac{0.159}{204 \times 10^{-12} \times 10^3} = 780\,\text{kHz}$$

By Eq. (8–24),

$$f_T = \frac{0.159 \times 0.2}{204 \times 10^{-12}} = 1.56\text{ MHz}$$

8.5 The FET at High Frequencies

A high-frequency model for the field-effect transistor (JFET or MOSFET) in the common-source configuration is given in Fig. 8–12A. Capacitances C_{gs} and C_{gd} are internal capacitances because of the biasing of the gate-source and

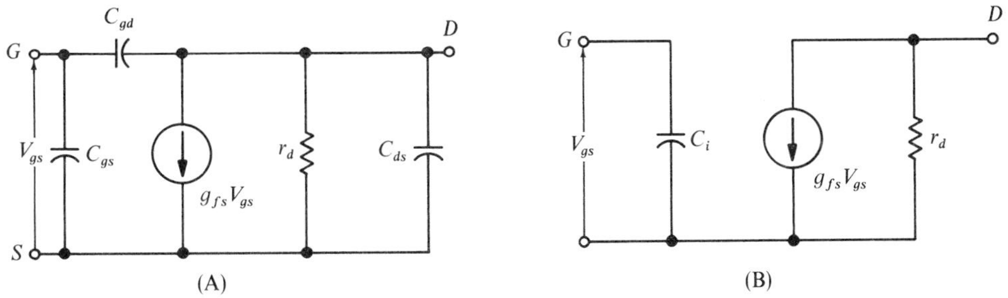

Fig. 8–12. *The FET at high frequencies. (A) Small-signal model. (B) Simplified model based on the Miller effect.*

gate-drain junctions, respectively. Capacitance C_{ds}, across the drain-source terminals, is associated with the channel of a FET.

Typical values of C_{gd} and C_{gs} range from 1 to 10 pF; C_{ds} is generally less than 1 pF. (Table 8–2 provides a summary of FET parameter values.) Because the input resistance of a FET can be taken to be infinite, no resistance is shown across C_{gs}.

TABLE 8–2. Typical values of FET parameters.*

$g_{fs} = 0.1\ \text{m℧}–20\ \text{m℧}$
$r_d = 1\ \text{k}\Omega–1\ \text{M}\Omega$
$C_{gs} = 1\ \text{pF}–10\ \text{pF}$
$C_{gd} = 1\ \text{pF}–10\ \text{pF}$
$C_{ds} = 0.1\ \text{pF}–1\ \text{pF}$

* The precise value depends on the dc operating point and type of FET.

Using the Miller effect, we arrive at the simplified high-frequency model of Fig. 8–12B. Based on an analysis similar to that used for the BJT, capacitance C_i is

$$C_i = C_{gs} + C_{gd}(1 + g_{fs}R'_D) \qquad \textbf{(8–25)}$$

where $R'_D = r_d \| R_D$. Because it is assumed that the break frequency is determined essentially by C_i, capacitance C_{ds} has been neglected in Fig. 8–12B.

Defining the gain at mid frequencies as $A_o = -g_{fs}R'_D$, the gain of the amplifier as a function of frequency may be expressed by

$$A_v(jf) = \frac{A_o}{1 + \dfrac{jf}{f_H}} \qquad \textbf{(8–26)}$$

and

$$f_H = \frac{0.159}{RC_i} \qquad \textbf{(8–27)}$$

where R is the equivalent resistance between the signal source and gate terminal.

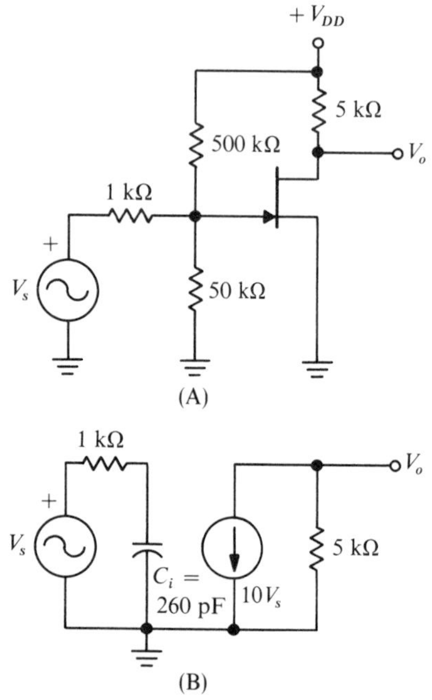

Fig. 8–13. Example 8–7. (A) Circuit to be analyzed. (B) High-frequency model of the circuit.

EXAMPLE 8–7.

For the FET amplifier of Fig. 8–13A, assume that $g_{fs} = 10\ \text{m℧}$, $r_d \gg R_D = 5\ \text{k}\Omega$, $C_{gs} = C_{gd} = 5\ \text{pF}$, and C_{ds} is negligible.

(a) Draw a simplified high-frequency model of the circuit.
(b) Determine the values of A_o and f_H.
(c) Express A_v as a function of frequency.

Solutions:

(a) A simplified high-frequency model based on the Miller effect is drawn in Fig. 8–13B. Because $50\,\text{k}\Omega \,||\, 500\,\text{k}\Omega \gg 1\,\text{k}\Omega$, the biasing network is omitted from the model.

(b) $A_o = -g_{fs}R'_D = -10 \times 10^{-3} \times 5000 = -50$. By Eq. (8–25),

$$C_i = 5 + 5(1 + 50) = 260\,\text{pF}$$

Using Eq. (8–27),

$$f_H = \frac{0.159}{10^3 \times 260 \times 10^{-12}} \simeq 611\,\text{kHz}$$

(c) By Eq. (8–26),

$$A_v(jf) = \frac{-50}{1 + \dfrac{jf}{611 \times 10^3}}$$

8.6 Integrated Transistors at High Frequencies

In our study of integrated circuits in Chapter 10, we shall learn that we get more than we bargain for in an integrated transistor. In addition to the transistor, we often obtain undesired elements, called *parasitics*, such as capacitance and resistance.

A simplified high-frequency model of an IC transistor is shown in Fig. 8–14. The parasitic bulk resistance, R_p, of the substrate (a silicon chip in which the monolithic integrated circuit is formed) and the parasitic capacitance, C_p, between the collector and substrate have been added to the output of the hybrid-pi model. The model is referred to as a *lumped model*, because parasitic elements R_p and C_p are represented by single elements. Actually, parasitics are *distributed*, like the resistance and capacitance in a television transmission line. Because of its complexity, the high-frequency response of a distributed model is generally calculated on a digital computer.

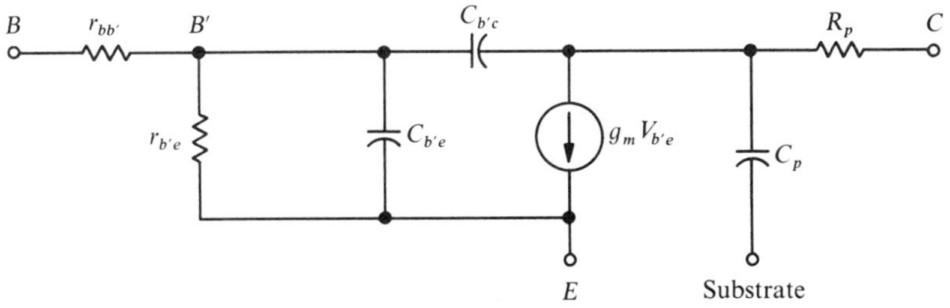

Fig. 8–14. *Simplified high-frequency model of an integrated circuit (IC) diffused transistor.*

From a signal point of view, parasitic resistance R_p is in series with the load resistance which is connected between the collector and ground. Because of voltage division, the output is reduced. Parasitic capacitance C_p generally lowers the high-frequency response of an amplifier.

8.7 Low-Frequency Response of Amplifiers

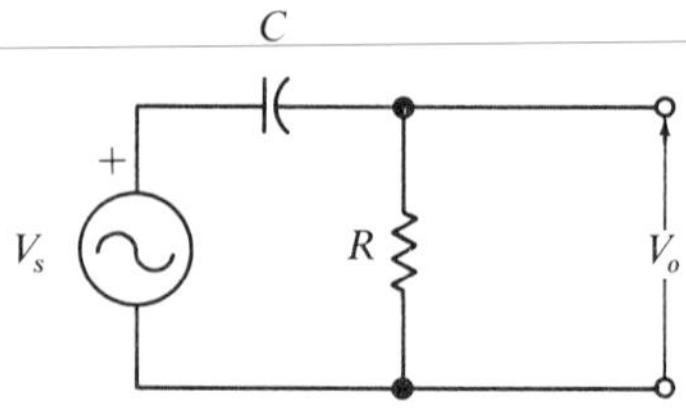

Fig. 8–15. *Basic high-pass RC network.*

To understand the effects of a coupling capacitor in the low-frequency performance of an amplifier, we consider first the *high-pass RC* network of Fig. 8–15. It has the same circuit configuration as the low-pass network of Fig. 8–1, except that the output voltage is taken across the resistor. The high-pass RC network is also called a *differentiator*.

At very high frequencies, the capacitor acts like a short circuit, and $V_o = V_s$. At very low frequencies and dc, the capacitor behaves like an open circuit, and $V_o = 0$. Between these two ranges of frequencies, the output voltage is less than the source voltage.

As in the analysis for the low-pass network (see Appendix B3), the gain for a high-pass network may be expressed by

$$\left|\frac{V_o}{V_s}\right| = \frac{1}{\sqrt{1 + \left(\frac{\omega_L}{\omega}\right)^2}} \quad \textbf{(8–28a)}$$

and

$$\theta = \tan^{-1}\left(\frac{\omega_L}{\omega}\right) \quad \textbf{(8–28b)}$$

Equation (8–28) is plotted in Fig. 8–16. Note that at $\omega_L/\omega = 1$, $|V_o/V_s| = -3\,\text{dB}$ and $\theta = 45°$. Consequently, ω_L is the *lower* -3-dB frequency. Expressed in hertz,

$$f_L = \frac{0.159}{RC} \quad \textbf{(8–29)}$$

From Eq. (8–29), we see that for a low -3-dB frequency, the values of R and C should be large.

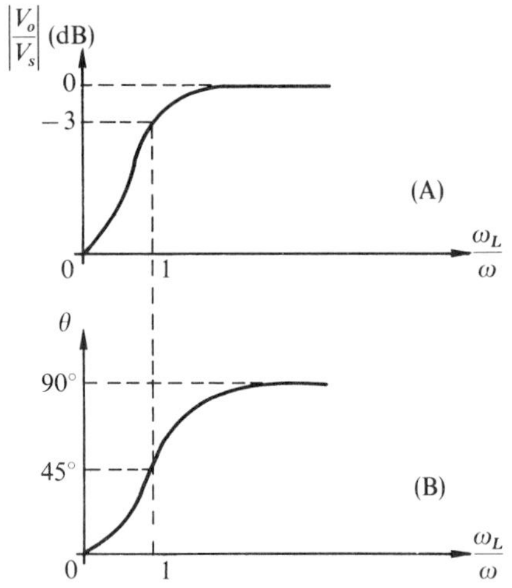

Fig. 8–16. *(A) Gain and (B) phase angle as a function of frequency for a high-pass network.*

Capacitor-Coupled Amplifier

Consider the transistor amplifier of Fig. 8–17A. Coupling capacitor C_c is in series with source resistor R_s and the transistor base. Assuming that $R_1 \| R_2$ is much greater than the input resistance ($R_i \simeq h_{ie}$), we draw the model for the input circuit in Fig. 8–17B. Note the similarity of this circuit with that of the high-pass network of Fig. 8–15. We should therefore anticipate that voltage V_{be} will fall with decreasing frequencies.

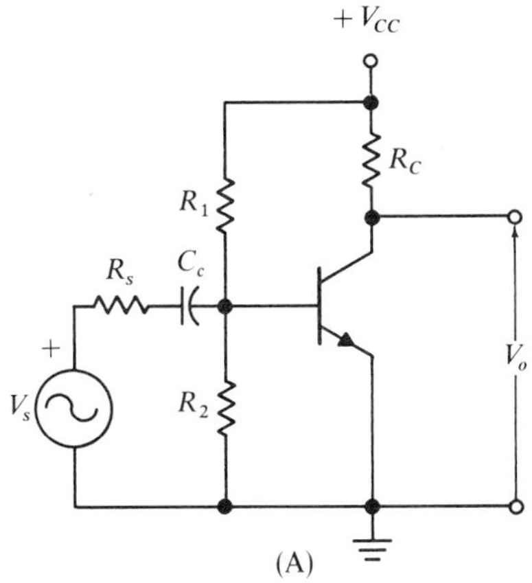

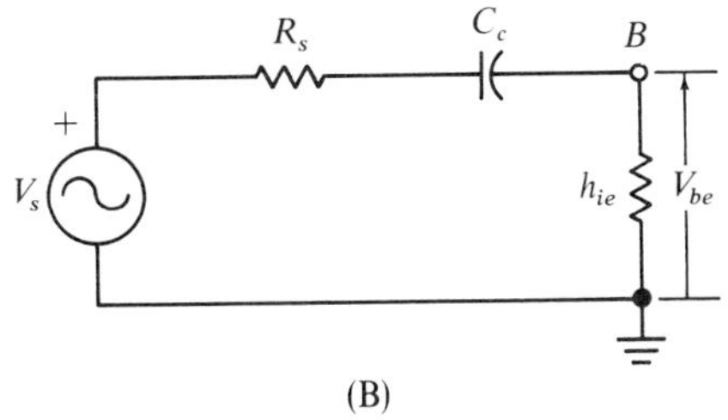

Fig. 8–17. *Capacitor-coupled amplifier. (A) Circuit. (B) Model of the input (base-emitter) circuit.*

Using voltage division,

$$V_{be} = \frac{h_{ie}V_s}{h_{ie} + R_s - \dfrac{1}{j\omega C_c}}$$

Dividing numerator and denominator by $h_{ie} + R_s$,

$$V_{be} = \left(\frac{h_{ie}}{h_{ie} + R_s}\right)\left(\frac{V_s}{1 - \dfrac{j}{\omega C_c(R_s + h_{ie})}}\right)$$

Letting

$$\omega'_L = \frac{1}{(R_s + h_{ie})C_c} \qquad \textbf{(8–30)}$$

and solving for V_{be}/V_s, we obtain

$$\frac{V_{be}}{V_s} = \frac{h_{ie}}{h_{ie} + R_s}\left(\frac{1}{1 - \dfrac{j\omega'_L}{\omega}}\right) \qquad \textbf{(8–31)}$$

The term in parentheses has the same form as the expression for the high-pass network of Fig. 8–15. Because of source resistor R_s, the coefficient $h_{ie}/(h_{ie} + R_s) < 1$.

In terms of frequency, the lower -3-dB frequency is

$$f'_L = \frac{0.159}{(R_s + h_{ie})C_c} \qquad \textbf{(8–32)}$$

EXAMPLE 8–8.

Assume that in Fig. 8–17A, $R_s = 0$, $h_{ie} = 1\,\text{k}\Omega$, and $R_1 \| R_2 \gg h_{ie}$. Determine the value of C_c for a lower -3-dB frequency of 10 Hz.

Solution:

By Eq. (8–32) with $R_s = 0$,

$$C_c = \frac{0.159}{h_{ie} f'_L} = \frac{0.159}{1000 \times 10} = 15.9\,\mu\text{F}$$

Bypass and Decoupling Capacitors

Capacitors used for bypassing and decoupling resistors also affect the low-frequency response of an amplifier. It is possible to design an amplifier such that the lower −3-dB frequency is determined by the bypass or decoupling capacitor, instead of by the coupling capacitor. Values of these capacitors will be of the same order of magnitude as for the coupling capacitor.

In the monolithic IC, it is impossible to obtain large-value capacitors. At best, 200 pF appears to be the practical limit. Because the monolithic IC is of such significance, a different philosophy is adopted when capacitors are eliminated entirely or minimized in circuits.

8.8 Cascading Transistor Stages

To obtain more gain than is available from a single transistor stage, two or more stages are cascaded, as mentioned in Chapter 5. An example of a three-stage cascaded FET amplifier using *RC coupling* is shown in Fig. 8–18. The output of a stage is capacitor-coupled to the following stage, and a resistor, R_G, is connected across the gate terminal and ground. Each source resistor in this example is bypassed. (In monolithic IC amplifiers, the stages are *direct-coupled*; that is, no coupling capacitors are used.)

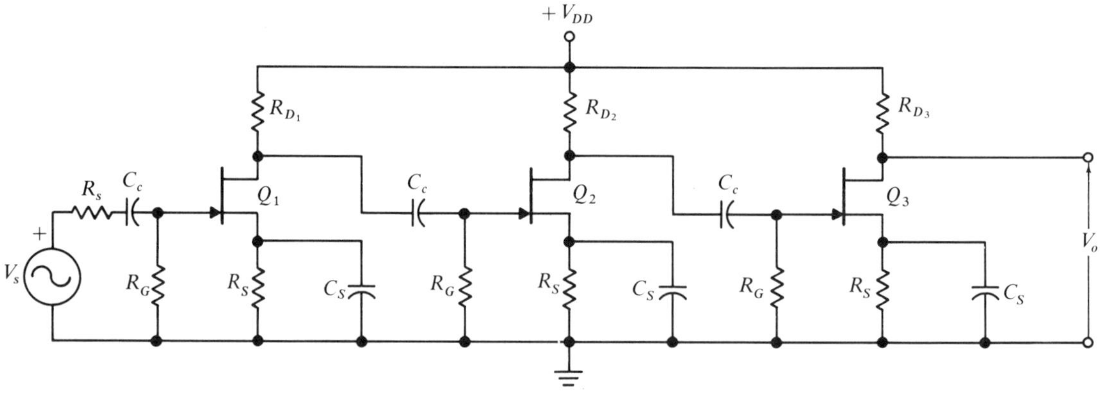

Fig. 8–18. *Example of a three-stage FET amplifier using RC (R_gC_c) coupling. (See Example 8–9.)*

As you recall, the FET is a voltage-controlled device, and its input resistance is so large as to be considered infinite. Because of this, an amplifier stage does not affect (*load down*) the preceding stage which feeds it. In other words, there is no interaction between stages. *Under these conditions only*, where no loading exists, the overall voltage gain, A_v, is the product of the individual gains, A_{v1}, A_{v2}, and so on:

$$A_v = A_{v1}A_{v2} \cdots A_{vn} \qquad \textbf{(8–33)}$$

EXAMPLE 8–9.

For the three-stage FET amplifier of Fig. 8–18, $g_{fs} = 5\,\text{m℧}$ and $r_d = 100\,\text{k}\Omega$ for each transistor. If $R_{D_1} = R_{D_2} = 5\,\text{k}\Omega$, $R_{D_3} = 1\,\text{k}\Omega$, $R_G = 1\,\text{M}\Omega$, and R_s is negligible, determine the overall voltage gain at mid frequencies.

Solution:

Because r_d and R_G are much greater than R_{D_1}, R_{D_2}, or R_{D_3}, $A_v \simeq -g_m R_D$, at mid frequencies. Hence,

$$A_{v1} = A_{v2} = -5 \times 10^{-3} \times 5000 = -25$$
$$A_{v3} = -5 \times 10^{-3} \times 1000 = -5$$

By Eq. (8–33),

$$A_v = (-25)(-25)(-5) = -1325$$

In finding the overall voltage gain of a cascaded amplifier composed of current-controlled devices, such as the BJT, the assumption of no stage loading cannot be made. Consequently, Eq. (8–33) may only be used if loading is considered. We now must work from the output stage toward the input stage, including the loading effect of each cascaded stage. This procedure is illustrated in the next example.

EXAMPLE 8–10.

A two-stage BJT cascaded amplifier is illustrated in Fig. 8–19. Assume that for each transistor, $h_{ie} = 1\,\text{k}\Omega$ and $h_{fe} = 100$; h_{re}, h_{oe}, and the biasing network may be neglected. At mid frequencies,

(a) Draw the small-signal model.
(b) Calculate the overall voltage gain.

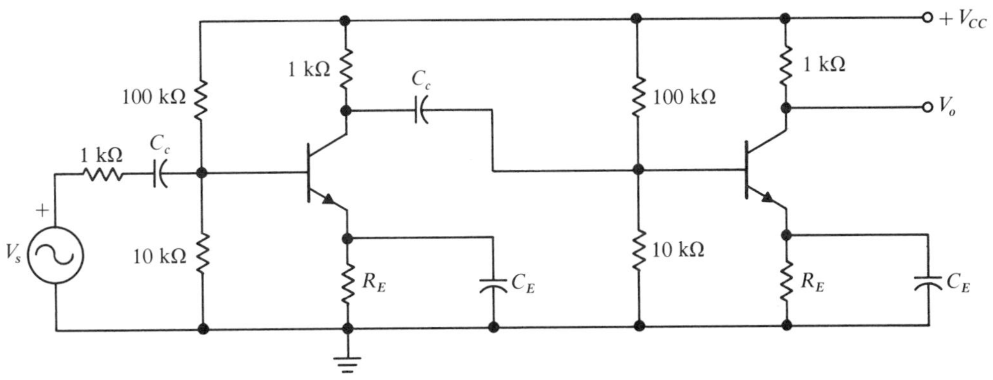

Fig. 8–19. *Two-stage RC-coupled amplifier using BJTs. (See Example 8–10.)*

Solutions:

(a) The small-signal model is shown in Fig. 8–20. Because at mid frequencies the coupling and bypass capacitors act as short circuits, they are shown as direct connections in the figure.

(b) Output voltage V_o is

$$V_o = -100 I_{b_2}(1\ \text{k}\Omega) = -100 I_{b_2}$$

Because of current division,

$$I_{b_2} = -\frac{100 I_{b_1}(1\ \text{k}\Omega)}{(1+1)\text{k}\Omega} = -50 I_{b_1}$$

But

$$I_{b_1} = \frac{V_s}{(1+1)\text{k}\Omega} = \frac{V_s}{2}$$

Hence,

$$V_o = -100\left(\frac{-50 V_s}{2}\right) = 2500 V_s$$

$$A_v = \frac{V_o}{V_s} = 2500$$

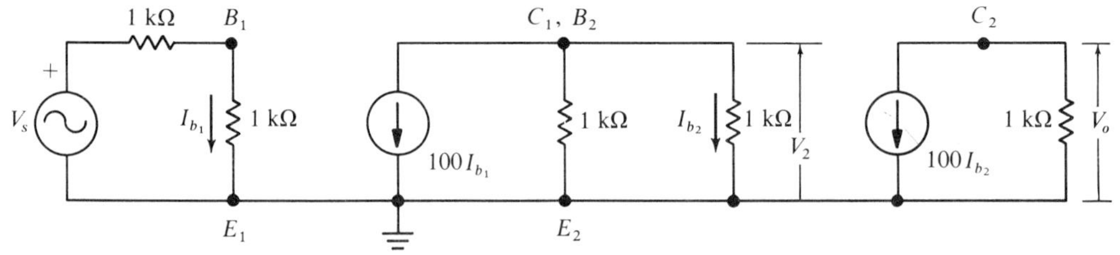

Fig. 8–20. *Small-signal model at mid frequencies for the amplifier of Fig. 8–19.*

Frequency Response of Cascaded Stages

We shall first consider the case where there is no loading between stages, as in the cascaded FET amplifier. Assume n identical stages, each stage having a bandwidth equal to $f_H - f_L$. The frequency reponse of the first stage is limited by the frequency response of the second stage. Likewise, the frequency response of the second stage is limited by the response of the third stage, and so on. The overall bandwidth is, therefore, *less* than the bandwidth of an individual stage.

If f_{H_n} is the upper -3-dB frequency of an n-cascaded stage amplifier with no loading effect, and f_H is the upper -3-dB frequency for an individual stage, then

$$f_{H_n} = f_H\sqrt{2^{1/n} - 1} \tag{8–34}$$

If f_{L_n} is the lower -3-dB frequency of an n-cascaded stage amplifier with no loading effect, and f_L is the lower -3-dB frequency for an individual stage, then

$$f_{L_n} = \frac{f_L}{\sqrt{2^{1/n} - 1}} \tag{8–35}$$

EXAMPLE 8–11.

For each stage of the three-stage amplifier of Fig. 8–18, $f_H = 20\,\text{kHz}$ and $f_L = 100\,\text{Hz}$. The bandwidth for a single stage is therefore equal to $20{,}000 - 100 \simeq 20\,\text{kHz}$. Determine the overall bandwidth of the cascaded amplifier.

Solution:

In this example, $n = 3$; therefore, $2^{1/3}$ is the cube root of 2 and equals 1.26. By Eq. (8–34),

$$f_{H_n} = 20\sqrt{1.26 - 1} = 10.2\,\text{kHz}$$

By Eq. (8–35),

$$f_{L_n} = \frac{100}{\sqrt{1.26 - 1}} = 0.196\,\text{kHz} \simeq 0.2\,\text{kHz}$$

The overall bandwidth, BW, is

$$\text{BW} = 10.2 - 0.2 = 10\,\text{kHz}$$

The bandwidth of the three-stage amplifier is about one-half that of an individual stage.

In calculating the overall bandwidth of a cascaded BJT amplifier, Eq. (8–34) and Eq. (8–35) *cannot be used.* We must calculate the overall frequency response of the complete amplifier. The resultant expression contains a number of frequency terms.

If, for a high-frequency analysis, the smallest break frequency is about one-fifth that of the next higher break frequency, the smaller frequency is the *dominant frequency.* The dominant frequency defines the upper −3-dB frequency of the cascaded amplifier.

A similar approach is taken in the analysis of the low-frequency response of a cascaded amplifier. If the highest of the low-frequency terms is about five times that of the next lower frequency, this is the dominant term and defines the lower −3-dB frequency.

SUMMARY

In obtaining the high-frequency response of a BJT amplifier, the BJT is represented by a hybrid-pi model. Using the Miller effect, the model may be modified by reflecting the internal capacitance, $C_{b'c}$, across the input and output of the transistor. The input circuit of the simplified hybrid-pi model has the same characteristics as a low-pass RC network. At low and mid frequencies, results obtained using the hybrid-pi model are identical with those obtained by the hybrid model. The high-frequency model of a FET is very similar to the simplified hybrid-pi model.

Two figures of merit for characterizing the BJT are the beta cutoff frequency, f_β, and the current gain-bandwidth product, f_T. The short-circuit current gain is equal to 0.707, its mid-frequency value, at f_β, and is equal to 1 at f_T.

Low-frequency response of an amplifier is influenced by coupling, bypass, and decoupling capacitors. Considering the coupling capacitor, the low-frequency model is equivalent to a high-pass network.

The overall voltage gain of a cascaded FET amplifier is equal to the product of the voltage gain for each stage. Because of loading effects, this is not generally true for a cascaded BJT amplifier. The overall frequency response of an amplifier shrinks as more BJT or FET stages are cascaded.

Further Reading

Faber, R. B. *Introduction to Electronic Amplifiers.* Columbus, Ohio: Charles E. Merrill Publishing Company, 1971, Chapters 5 and 6.

Ghaznavi, C., and A. H. Seidman. *Electronic Circuit Analysis.* New York: Macmillan Company, 1972, Chapters 8 and 9.

Matthews, John I. *Solid-State Electronics Concepts.* New York: McGraw-Hill Book Company, 1972, Chapter 14.

Temes, Lloyd. *Electronic Circuits for Technicians.* New York: McGraw-Hill Book Company, 1970, Chapters 11, 12, and 14.

REVIEW QUESTIONS

8.1 What capacitances influence
(a) The high-frequency response of an amplifier?
(b) The low-frequency response of an amplifier?

8.2 How does a capacitor act to a dc voltage?

8.3 How does a capacitor behave at high frequencies?

8.4 What is meant by the base-spreading resistance of a BJT?

8.5 What do diffusion and depletion capacitances in a BJT represent?

8.6 At mid frequencies, what is the approximate voltage gain of a *C-E* amplifier if g_m and R_C are known?

8.7 Describe the Miller effect.

8.8 How does the modified hybrid-pi model, based on the Miller effect, differ from the model of Fig. 8–3C?

8.9 Define
(a) f_β.
(b) f_T.

8.10 How does f_T vary with collector current?

8.11 What is meant by a parasitic? Give examples of parasitic elements.

8.12 What is the difference between a lumped and distributed model?

8.13 How does the RC high-pass network of Fig. 8–15 differ from the RC low-pass network of Fig. 8–1?

8.14 What is meant by RC coupling? How does RC coupling differ from dc coupling?

8.15 Define dominant frequency. Give examples.

PROBLEMS

P8–1 In the low-pass network of Fig. 8–1, $f_H = 50\,\text{kHz}$. What is the value of R if $C_s = 500\,\text{pF}$?

P8–2 In Fig. 8–1, $R = 1\,\text{k}\Omega$ and $\omega = 10^6$ radians/s.
(a) Determine and plot the magnitude $|V_o/V_s|$ for $C_s = 10\,\text{pF}$, 100 pF, 1000 pF, 0.01 μF, and 1 μF.
(b) What conclusions can you draw from the results?

P8–3 (a) Calculate the values of h_{FE} if $g_m = 4\,\text{m℧}$ and $I_B = 0.25$, 0.5, 1, 2, and 3 mA.
(b) Plot h_{FE} as a function of I_B.
(c) How does h_{FE} vary with I_B?

P8–4 Referring to Fig. 8–21, assume that capacitors C_E and C_c act as short circuits at high and mid frequencies. For the transistor, $g_m = 0.05\,℧$, $r_{bb'} = 50\,\Omega$, $r_{b'e} = 2\,\text{k}\Omega$, $C_{b'e} = 100\,\text{pF}$, $C_{b'c} = 5\,\text{pF}$, and $r_{ce} = 100\,\text{k}\Omega$. If $R_C = 1\,\text{k}\Omega$,
(a) Draw a simplified model of the circuit based on the Miller effect.
(b) Calculate the mid-frequency gain.
(c) What is the upper -3-dB frequency?
(d) Write an expression for voltage gain as a function of frequency.

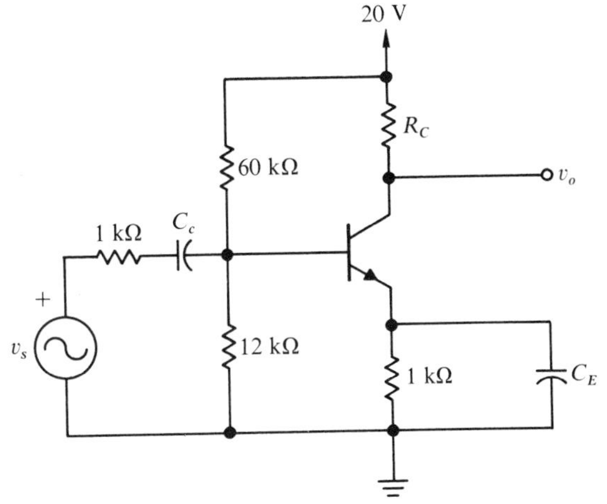

Fig. 8–21.

P8–5 Repeat prob. P8–4 for $R_C = 8\,\text{k}\Omega$.

P8–6 Assuming that $C_{b'e} + C_{b'c} = 150\,\text{pF}$ and $f_\beta = 18\,\text{MHz}$, calculate the value of $r_{b'e}$.

P8–7 If $f_T = 2\,\text{MHz}$ and $f_\beta = 50\,\text{kHz}$, what is the value of h_{fe}?

P8–8 Measurements obtained in the lab are $f_T = 1000\,\text{MHz}$ and $C_{b'e} = 150\,\text{pF}$. What is the value of $C_{b'c}$?

P8–9 For the FET amplifier of Fig. 8–22, $g_{fs} = 20\,\text{m℧}$, $r_d = 100\,\text{k}\Omega$, $C_{gs} = C_{gd} = 8\,\text{pF}$, and $C_{ds} = 0.1\,\text{pF}$. If $R_D = 10\,\text{k}\Omega$,
(a) Draw a simplified high-frequency model of the circuit.
(b) Determine the values of A_o and f_H.
(c) Express A_v as a function of frequency.

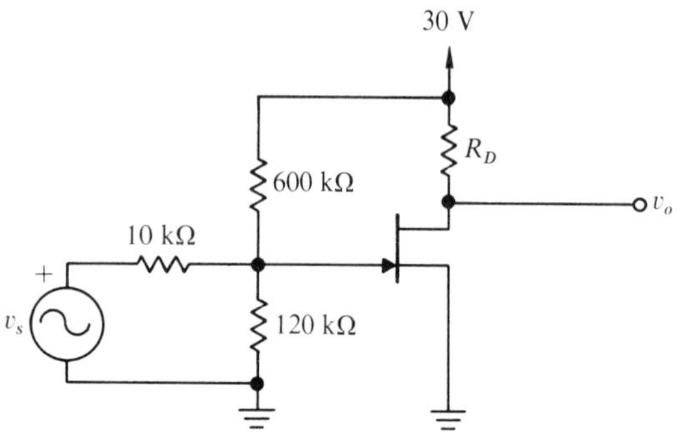

Fig. 8–22.

P8–10 Repeat prob. P8–9 for $R_D = 50\,\text{k}\Omega$.

P8–11 In the high-pass network of Fig. 8–15, $f_L = 50\,\text{Hz}$. If $R = 10\,\text{k}\Omega$, what is the value of C?

P8–12 In Fig. 8–15, $C = 1\,\mu\text{F}$ and $\omega = 1000$ radians/s. Determine and plot the magnitude $|V_o/V_s|$ for $R = 10, 100, 1000,$ and $10{,}000\,\Omega$. What conclusions do you draw from your results?

P8–13 Repeat prob. P8–12 if $R = 10\,\text{k}\Omega$ and C assumes the values of 0.01, 0.1, 1, and $10\,\mu\text{F}$.

P8–14 In Fig. 8–17A, $R_s = 5\,\text{k}\Omega$, $R_1 \| R_2 = 10\,\text{k}\Omega$, and $h_{ie} = 2\,\text{k}\Omega$. What value of C_c is required for a lower -3-dB frequency of 60 Hz?

P8–15 Referring to Fig. 8–17A, if $R_s = 0$, $R_1 \| R_2 = 50\,\text{k}\Omega$, $h_{ie} = 1\,\text{k}\Omega$, and $C_c = 5\,\mu\text{F}$, what is the lower -3-dB frequency?

P8–16 Assume that the coupling and bypass capacitors in Fig. 8–18 act as short circuits. If, for each stage, $g_{fs} = 10\,\text{m℧}$ and $r_d = 100\,\text{k}\Omega$, determine the overall voltage gain if $R_s = 0$, $R_{D_1} = 10\,\text{k}\Omega$, $R_{D_2} = R_{D_3} = 5\,\text{k}\Omega$, and $R_G = 100\,\text{k}\Omega$.

P8–17 Repeat prob. P8–16 for $R_s = 10\,\text{k}\Omega$ and $R_{D_1} = R_{D_2} = R_{D_3} = 1\,\text{k}\Omega$.

P8–18 Referring to Fig. 8–19, assume that for each transistor, $h_{ie} = 2\,\text{k}\Omega$, $h_{fe} = 60$, and $h_{re} = h_{oe} = 0$.
(a) Draw the small-signal model of the circuit.
(b) Calculate the overall voltage gain.

P8–19 In a two-stage cascaded amplifier (no loading exists between stages), each stage has an $f_H = 100\,\text{kHz}$ and $f_L = 50\,\text{Hz}$. What is the bandwidth of the cascaded amplifier? How does this compare with a single stage?

P8–20 Repeat prob. P8–19 for four identical cascaded stages.

9

Feedback

In Chapter 7, we saw how feedback is employed to stabilize the dc operating point of an amplifier. A regulating mechanism, in both current and voltage feedback stabilization, adjusts the base current to maintain the Q point regardless of temperature or parameter changes. In this chapter, we enlarge the concept of feedback to include its effect on the signal performance of amplifiers.

9.1 An Overview of Feedback

In feedback, a portion or all of the output signal is *fed back* to the input to influence the operation of a system. As a simple illustration, consider the heating system in a home. Assume that the thermostat is set for 68°F (20°C). The setting of the thermostat is the *input* to the system. If the actual room temperature, identified as the *output* of the system, drops below 68°F, the furnace turns on. Heat is generated, and when the temperature reaches 68°F, the furnace turns off. The system is completely automatic, requiring no human intervention to maintain the room at a desired temperature.

Let us consider an amplifier. The objective is to keep its gain, frequency response, and other operating characteristics constant. The behavior of the amplifier should not change because of variations in temperature, tolerance, or aging of components. With feedback, the operation of the amplifier is influenced by the output signal. As in the heating system example where temperature is held constant, feedback maintains the operating characteristics of an amplifier essentially constant.

Another useful application of feedback is the simulation of special functions. With suitable feedback applied to a very high-gain amplifier, one can build summers, integrators, differentiators, and inductorless filters. These topics are covered in Chapter 12.

9.2 Types of Feedback

The essential elements of a feedback amplifier are illustrated in the block diagram of Fig. 9–1. In describing the function of each block, it is advantageous for us to work

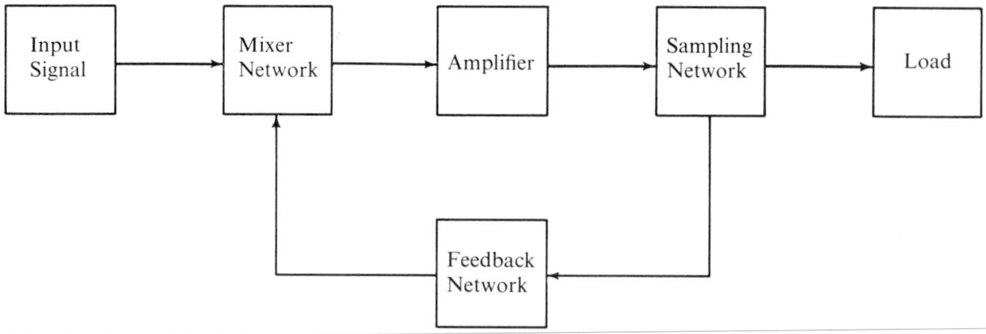

Fig. 9–1. *Essential elements of a feedback amplifier.*

from the load toward the signal source. The load may represent the input of a cascaded amplifier stage or a transducer, such as a loudspeaker.

Between the output of the amplifier and the load is a sampling network. Its function is to return a portion, or all, of the output signal of the amplifier to the input of the feedback network. The amplifier may contain one or more cascaded stages employing BJTs, FETs, or both types of transistors.

The feedback network generally contains passive elements, such as resistors and capacitors. It is assumed that the signal from the sampling network is returned only through the feedback network, and not through the amplifier. Also, the signal is transmitted to the load through the amplifier, not through the feedback network. Any loading of the sampling or feedback network on the amplifier is assumed to be negligible. These assumptions are realistic for most practical amplifier circuits.

Negative and Positive Feedback

The input signal can either be a voltage or a current signal. The input and feedback signals are processed in the mixer network. If the feedback signal subtracts from the input signal, *negative feedback* is said to exist. If the feedback and input signals reinforce one another (both signals add), *positive feedback* exists. Because negative feedback is widely used in amplifiers, our concern will be primarily with it.

9.3 Characteristics of Feedback Amplifiers

To show the important characteristics of feedback amplifiers, the general block diagram of Fig. 9–1 is simplified in Fig. 9–2. Note that the output voltage is sampled, and the sampling network may be thought of as being two leads connected across the amplifier output terminals. Mixing at the input side is accomplished by connecting the output of the feedback network, V_f, in series with the input signal, V_s. The gain of the amplifier is denoted by $A_v = V_o/V_i$ and the

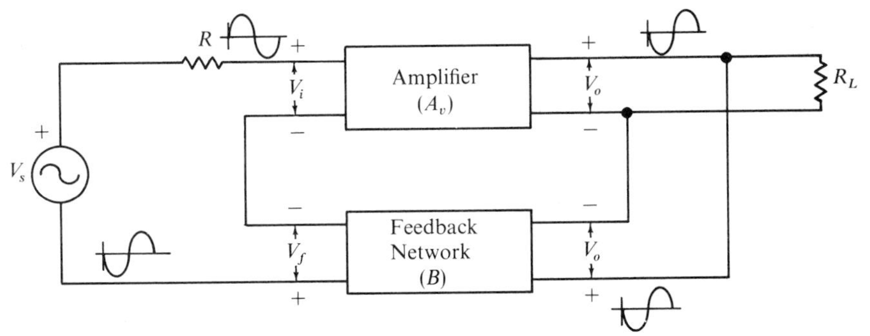

Fig. 9–2. *Block diagram of a voltage feedback, series input amplifier.*

gain of the feedback network by $B = V_f/V_o$. (Regardless of the type of network, it is common practice to use gain as the ratio of output to input. For a passive network, the voltage gain is less than one.) The input signal to the feedback network is the output signal of the amplifier.

In the circuit of Fig. 9–2, the feedback voltage is proportional to the output voltage. Hence, Fig. 9–2 is an example of *voltage feedback*. Also, feedback voltage V_f is in *series* with input voltage V_s. For these reasons, the configuration of Fig. 9–2 is called a *voltage feedback, series input* amplifier. The results derived for this feedback circuit will, in general, apply to other configurations to be considered later.

From Fig. 9–2, we see that input V_i to the amplifier is equal to the algebraic sum of the source and feedback signals:

$$V_i = V_s + V_f \tag{9–1}$$

Feedback voltage V_f is

$$V_f = BV_o \tag{9–2}$$

Substituting Eq. (9–2) in Eq. (9–1), we have

$$V_i = V_s + BV_o \tag{9–3}$$

Voltage gain of the amplifier, A_v, is

$$A_v = \frac{V_o}{V_i} \tag{9–4}$$

Substituting Eq. (9–3) in Eq. (9–4) and solving for the voltage gain with feedback, $A_{vf} = V_o/V_s$, yields the following important equation:

$$A_{vf} = \frac{A_v}{1 - BA_v} \tag{9–5}$$

Expression (9–5) is basic to an understanding of feedback amplifiers and merits careful examination.

1. If no feedback is present, $B = 0$ and $A_{vf} = A_v$.
2. If the product BA_v is negative, the denominator is greater than one. Hence, the magnitude of gain with feedback, A_{vf}, is less than the gain without feedback,

A_v. For BA_v to be negative, either B or A_v has to be negative. The feedback network is generally composed of a single resistor or a pair of resistors. Therefore, B must be positive, and A_v negative. As explained in Chapter 5, for negative voltage gain, the output voltage is 180° out of phase with respect to the input voltage.

In Fig. 9–2, if V_i has the indicated polarity, then V_o has the opposite polarity. Feedback voltage, V_f, *subtracts* from V_s, and negative feedback exists. In general, when the magnitude of A_{vf} is less than the magnitude of A_v,

$$|A_{vf}| < |A_v|$$

we have negative feedback.

3. If the product of BA_v is positive and less than one, the gain with feedback is greater than without feedback:

$$|A_{vf}| > |A_v|$$

This condition is another definition of positive feedback.

4. If $BA_v = 1$, A_{vf} approaches infinity. This is a requirement for a sinusoidal oscillator, a circuit that generates sine waves.

The gain with feedback, A_{vf}, is called the *closed-loop gain* of the amplifier. The gain without feedback, A_v, is called the *open-loop gain. Loop gain* refers to the product BA_v.

Gain Stability

If $BA_v \gg 1$, the 1 in the denominator of Eq. (9–5) may be neglected; then Eq. (9–5) reduces to

$$A_{vf} \simeq -\frac{1}{B} \tag{9–6}$$

Equation (9–6) points out a significant characteristic of feedback amplifiers. The gain of a feedback amplifier may be made independent of the amplifier gain and will depend primarily on the feedback network. Because B is generally composed of resistors, if necessary these components can be used as precision elements with low temperature coefficients. Thus, *the gain of a feedback amplifier can be extremely stable.*

The overall gain of a negative feedback amplifier is less than the gain of an amplifier without feedback. Additional cascaded stages are therefore necessary to make up the lost gain. Addition of these stages is illustrated in the following examples.

EXAMPLE 9–1.

The open-loop gain of an amplifier is -100. Feedback is introduced (Fig. 9–2) to achieve a closed-loop gain also of

-100. Because of feedback, the open-loop gain must be increased. To accomplish this, three cascaded stages each having a voltage gain of -10 are used (Fig. 9–3). Determine the value of B.

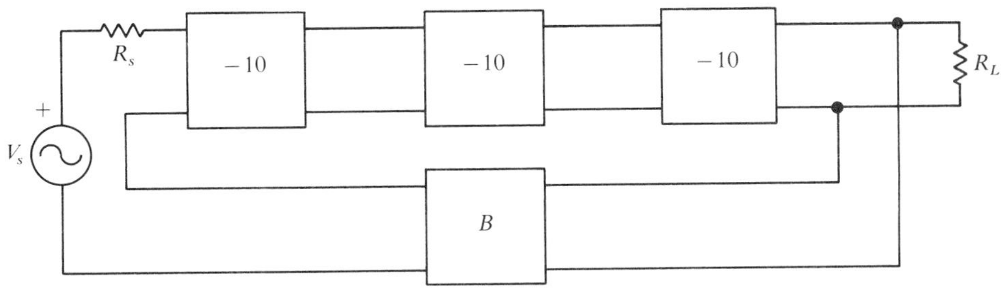

Fig. 9–3. *Cascading three amplifier stages to realize a required voltage gain with feedback. (See Example 9–1.)*

Solution:

The open-loop gain is $A_v = (-10)^3 = -1000$. By Eq. (9–5),

$$-100 = -\frac{1000}{1 + 1000B}$$

Hence,

$$1 + 1000B = 10 \quad \text{and} \quad B = 9 \times 10^{-3}$$

Note that $BA_v = 0.009 \times 1000 = 9$, which is much greater than one. Using Eq. (9–6),

$$A_{vf} \simeq -\frac{1}{B} = \frac{-1}{0.009} = -111.1$$

EXAMPLE 9–2.

Assume that, because of the transistors used in the amplifier of Fig. 9–3, the gain of each stage increases by 10 percent. Determine the overall voltage gain without and with feedback. Use $B = 0.009$.

Solution:

Without feedback, only two stages are required to provide an overall voltage gain of -100. One stage has a nominal gain of 10 and the other stage a gain of -10. Ten percent of $10 = 1$; therefore, the gain of each stage increased to $10 + 1 = 11$. The gain without feedback is

$$A_v = (11)(-11) = -121$$

With feedback, all three stages are used; hence, $A_v = (-11)^3 = -1331$. By Eq. (9–5),

$$A_{vf} = \frac{-1331}{1 - 0.009(-1331)} = -102.55$$

With feedback, a 2.55 percent change in overall voltage gain occurred, compared with a 21 percent change without feedback.

Extending Amplifier Bandwidth

We have seen that negative feedback reduces the effects of parameter and temperature variations in keeping the gain of an amplifier essentially constant. Another dividend gained from negative feedback is an increase in amplifier bandwidth.

In Chapter 8, the gain of an amplifier as a function of frequency was expressed by

$$A_v(jf) = \frac{A_o}{1 + \dfrac{jf}{f_H}} \qquad \textbf{(8–26)}$$

where A_o is the voltage gain at low and mid frequencies. Substituting Eq. (8–26) in Eq. (9–5) and solving for the closed-loop gain as a function of frequency, we obtain

$$A_{vf}(jf) = \frac{\dfrac{A_o}{1 - BA_o}}{1 + \dfrac{jf}{f_H(1 - BA_o)}} \qquad \textbf{(9–7)}$$

Letting the numerator be $A_{fo} = A_o/(1 - BA_o)$ and the upper -3-dB frequency be f_{Hf}, where

$$f_{Hf} = f_H(1 - BA_o) \qquad \textbf{(9–8)}$$

Eq. (9–7) may be expressed by

$$A_{vf}(jf) = \frac{A_{fo}}{1 + \dfrac{jf}{f_{Hf}}} \qquad \textbf{(9–9)}$$

For negative feedback, $(1 - BA_o) > 1$. The upper -3-dB frequency with feedback is greater than without feedback, and the high-frequency response of the feedback amplifier has been extended. A similar analysis at low frequencies results in a lower -3-dB frequency with feedback, f_{Lf}, given by

$$f_{Lf} = \frac{f_L}{1 - BA_o} \qquad \textbf{(9–10)}$$

where f_L is the lower -3-dB frequency without feedback. Because $(1 - BA_o) > 1$, $f_{Lf} < f_L$.

EXAMPLE 9–3.

An amplifier without feedback has $f_L = 100$ Hz and $f_H = 10$ kHz. Feedback is used such that $1 - BA_o = 10$. Determine the bandwidth of the amplifier

(a) Without feedback.

(b) With feedback.

(c) Draw a normalized plot of gain versus frequency for each case.

Solutions:

(a) $BW = f_H - f_L = 10{,}000 - 100 = 9900$ Hz.

(b) By Eq. (9–8), $f_{Hf} = 10\,\text{kHz} \times 10 = 100\,\text{kHz}$, and by Eq. (9–10), $f_{Lf} = 100/10 = 10$ Hz. Therefore,

$$BW_f = 100{,}000 - 10 \simeq 100{,}000 \text{ Hz}$$

(c) See Fig. 9–4.

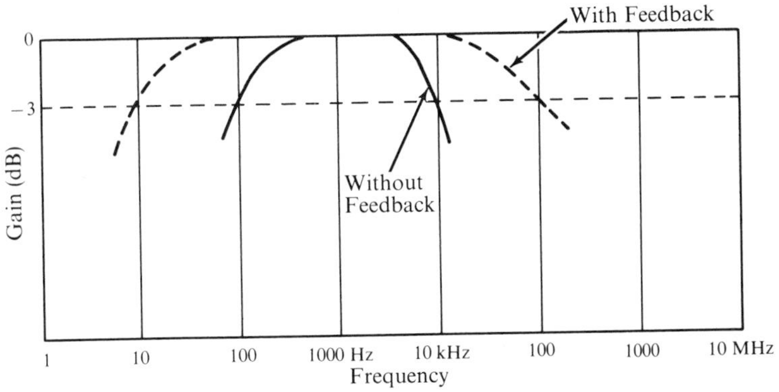

Fig. 9–4. *Normalized plots of frequency response of amplifiers with and without feedback. (See Example 9–3.)*

Nonlinear Distortion

Because of the nonlinear characteristics of a BJT or FET, nonlinear distortion occurs for large-signal operation. For large signals, a transistor operates over a wide range of collector (or drain) current. Distortion arises because the gain of a transistor is a function of collector (or drain) current. Negative feedback tends to keep the gain of an amplifier essentially constant. It is reasonable to expect, therefore, that negative feedback also reduces distortion. However, any distortion present in the signal itself is not reduced by feedback.

Let D be the output distortion produced by the device without feedback, and D_f the output distortion with feedback. The distortion returned by the feedback network to the input is BD_f. This is multiplied by the gain of the amplifier, A_v. Hence, at the output, we have

$$D_f = D + BA_vD_f$$

Solving for D_f,

$$D_f = \frac{D}{1 - BA_v} \qquad \textbf{(9–11)}$$

If, for example, $D = 10$ percent and $(1 - BA_v) = 10$, distortion with feedback is reduced by a factor of 10: $D_f = 10$ percent$/10 = 1$ percent.

Because gain is sacrificed when negative feedback is used, the open-loop gain must be greater than the closed-loop gain. This means that additional amplifier stages are required (see Example 9–1). We may think that the addition of cascaded stages will increase distortion. This is not generally true because most distortion occurs in the output stage where large signals are present. Cascading low-level stages does not measurably add distortion to the overall amplifier.

9.4 Other Basic Feedback Amplifiers

To this point, we have identified only one basic feedback amplifier, the voltage feedback, series input feedback amplifier of Fig. 9–2. Three other basic types of feedback amplifiers are illustrated in block diagram form in Fig. 9–5.

In Fig. 9–5A, the feedback signal is proportional to load current I_L. For this reason, it is called *current feedback*, and it tends to stabilize load current. (In voltage feedback, the output voltage is stabilized.) Because the feedback signal is in series with input signal V_s, the configuration is called a *current feedback, series input* amplifier.

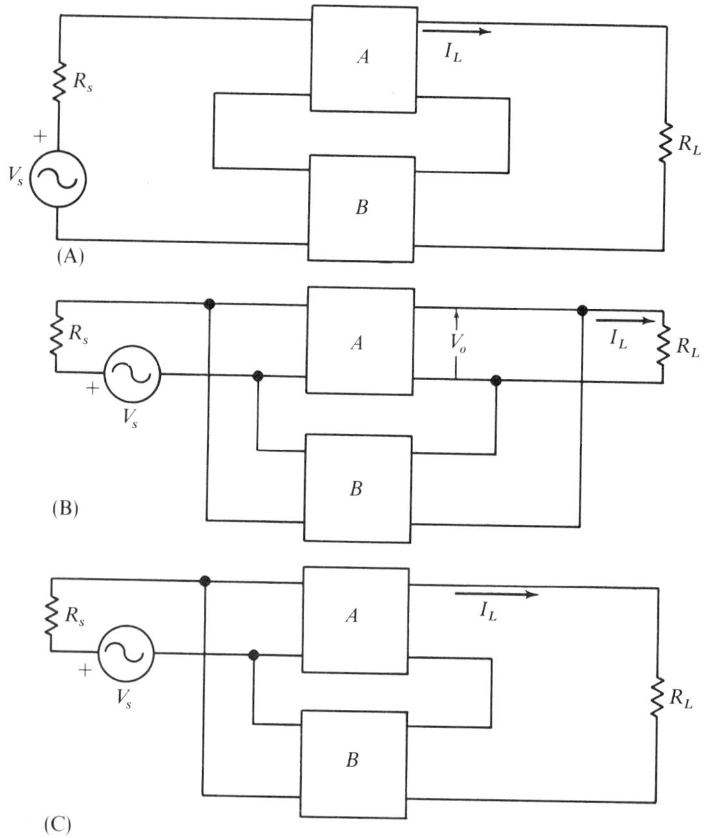

Fig. 9–5. *Other examples of feedback amplifiers. (A) Current feedback, series input. (B) Voltage feedback, shunt input. (C) Current feedback, shunt input.*

In Figs. 9–5B and 9–5C, the feedback is returned in parallel, or *shunt*, with the input. The configuration of Fig. 9–5B is, therefore, a *voltage feedback, shunt input* amplifier, and that of Fig. 9–5C a *current feedback, shunt input* amplifier. The characteristics of the different types of feedback amplifiers are explored in the remainder of the chapter.

9.5 Effects of Feedback on Input and Output Impedance (Resistance)

In negative feedback, if the feedback signal is returned in series with the input signal, *the input resistance is increased.* (At mid frequencies, a state assumed here, input and output impedances are resistive; therefore, we can speak of input and output resistance instead of impedance.) Resistance is increased because the feedback signal opposes the input signal and less signal current flows. Consequently, the input resistance with feedback appears greater than the input resistance without feedback.

Consider the input circuit of a feedback amplifier with series feedback (Fig. 9–6). For simplicity, the source resistance is neglected. It is noted that $V_i = V_s + V_f$, or

$$V_s = V_i - V_f$$

The input resistance with feedback, R_{if}, is

$$R_{if} = \frac{V_s}{I_s} = \frac{V_i - V_f}{I_s} \qquad (9\text{–}12)$$

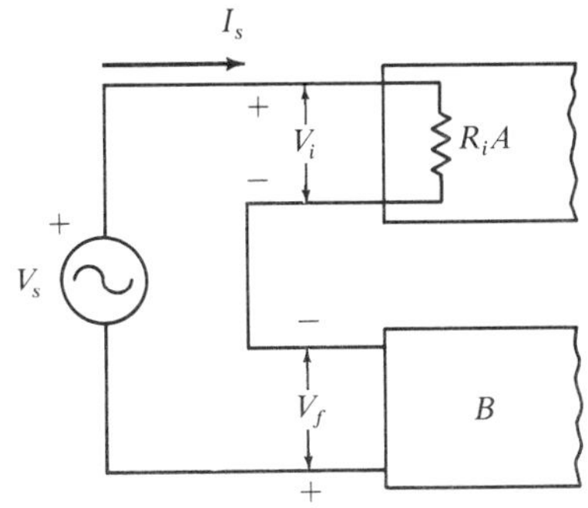

Fig. 9–6. *Input circuit of feedback amplifier with series feedback.*

But $V_f = BV_o$ and $I_s = V_i/R_i$, where R_i is the input resistance of the amplifier without feedback. Substitution of these quantities in Eq. (9–12) yields

$$R_{if} = \frac{V_i - BV_o}{V_i/R_i} = R_i - R_iB\left(\frac{V_o}{V_i}\right)$$

Also,

$$\frac{V_o}{V_i} = A_v$$

Hence,

$$R_{if} = R_i(1 - BA_v) \qquad (9\text{–}13)$$

Since $(1 - BA_v) > 1$, then $R_{if} > R_i$. This result holds for both the voltage and current feedback networks of Figs. 9–2 and 9–5A, respectively.

Now consider the input circuit of a feedback amplifier with shunt feedback (Fig. 9–7). Input current I_i is equal to the sum of feedback current I_f and signal current I_s. Without feedback, $I_i = I_s$. With feedback, however, I_i is increased by I_f, and the input resistance is lowered.

From Fig. 9–7, $V_s = V_i$ and $I_s = I_i - I_f$. Hence,

$$R_{if} = \frac{V_s}{I_s} = \frac{V_i}{I_i - I_f} \qquad (9\text{–}14)$$

Dividing the numerator and denominator of Eq. (9–14) by I_i, we obtain

$$R_{if} = \frac{V_i/I_i}{1 - I_f/I_i} \qquad (9\text{–}15)$$

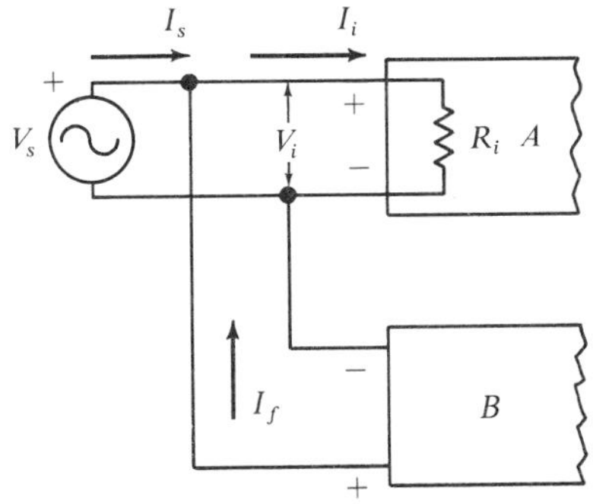

Fig. 9–7. *Input circuit of feedback amplifier with shunt feedback.*

But $V_i/I_i = R_i$ and $I_f/I_i = BI_o/I_i$, where I_o is the load current. Because $I_o/I_i = A_i$, then $BI_o/I_i = BA_i$. Making these substitutions in Eq. (9–15), we get

$$R_{if} = \frac{R_i}{1 - BA_i} \tag{9-16}$$

Since $(1 - BA_i) > 1$, $R_{if} < R_i$ for shunt feedback.

We now consider the effects of negative feedback on the output resistance of an amplifier. Assume that voltage feedback is employed and the load resistance connected to the amplifier is increased. This results in an increase in output voltage, V_o, which is multiplied by B and returned to the input. At the input, BV_o is subtracted from V_s, and the output voltage therefore tends to decrease. In other words, voltage feedback attempts to keep constant the output voltage, or gain, of an amplifier. This is a characteristic of a voltage source having a low source resistance. Hence, we may conclude that the output resistance of an amplifier with voltage feedback is less than the output resistance of an amplifier without feedback.

A method for calculating the output resistance with feedback, R_{of}, is indicated in Fig. 9–8. The amplifier is represented by a simple equivalent network consisting of a dependent source, A_vV_i, in series with output resistance, R_o, without feedback. The signal source is set to zero; source resistance, R_s, however, is included in the circuit. Generally, the load resistance is removed from the amplifier.

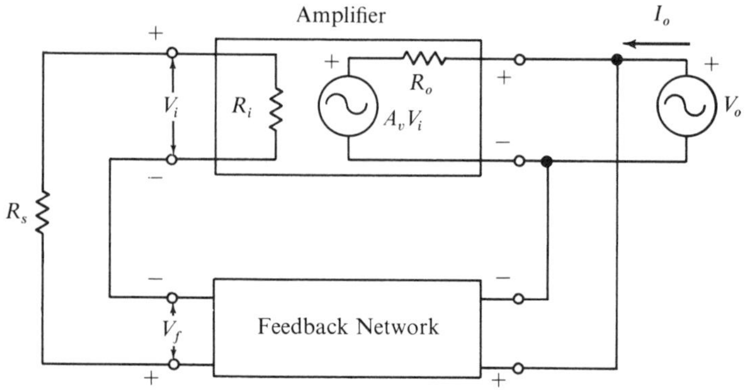

Fig. 9–8. *Determining the output resistance of a shunt feedback amplifier.*

Signal source V_o is connected across the output terminals. Current I_o flows, and the output resistance with feedback, $R_{of} = V_o/I_o$. Because $V_s = 0$, input voltage $V_i = V_f = BV_o$. From the figure,

$$V_o = I_oR_o + A_vBV_o$$

Solving for V_o/I_o,

$$R_{of} = \frac{R_o}{1 - BA_v} \tag{9-17}$$

Since $(1 - BA_v) > 1$, $R_{of} < R_o$.

In current feedback, the load current tends to remain constant. This behavior is typical of an ideal current source which maintains its current regardless of the value of resistance connected across it. Hence, current feedback tends to increase the output resistance of an amplifier.

The circuit of Fig. 9–9 is convenient to use in the calculation of output resistance of a current feedback amplifier. Source V_s is set to zero, and $I_i = -BI_o$ because they oppose each other. An external current source I_o is applied to the output terminals of the amplifier. Summing the currents at node A, we have

$$I_o = A_i B I_o + \frac{V_o}{R_o}$$

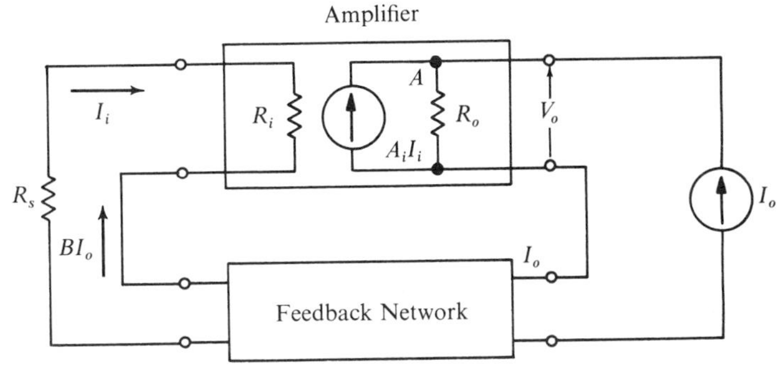

Fig. 9–9. Determining the output resistance of a series feedback amplifier.

Solving for $R_{of} = V_o/I_o$ gives us

$$R_{of} = R_o(1 - BA_i) \qquad \textbf{(9–18)}$$

Since $(1 - BA_i) > 1$, $R_{of} > R_o$. The results derived in this section are summarized in Table 9–1.

TABLE 9–1. Output and input resistances of a negative feedback amplifier.

Type of feedback	R_{of}/R_o	R_{if}/R_i
Voltage feedback, series input	< 1	> 1
Voltage feedback, shunt input	< 1	< 1
Current feedback, series input	> 1	> 1
Current feedback, shunt input	> 1	< 1

9.6 Examples of Practical Feedback Amplifiers

We are ready to apply our knowledge of feedback to practical circuits. This will be done for the four basic types of feedback summarized in Table 9–1 and illustrated in Figs. 9–2 and 9–5.

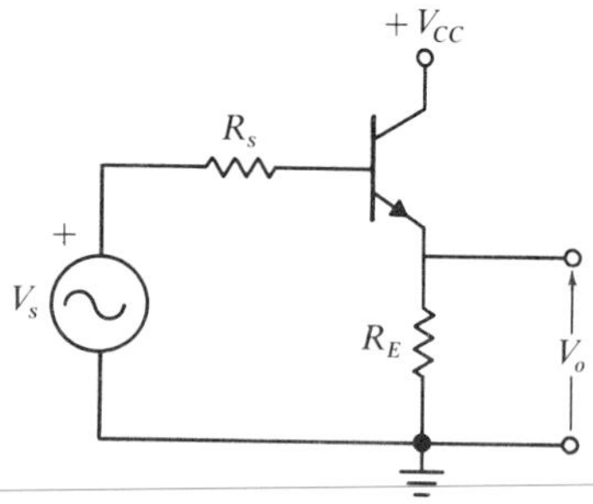

Fig. 9–10. *An emitter follower is an example of a voltage feedback, series input amplifier.*

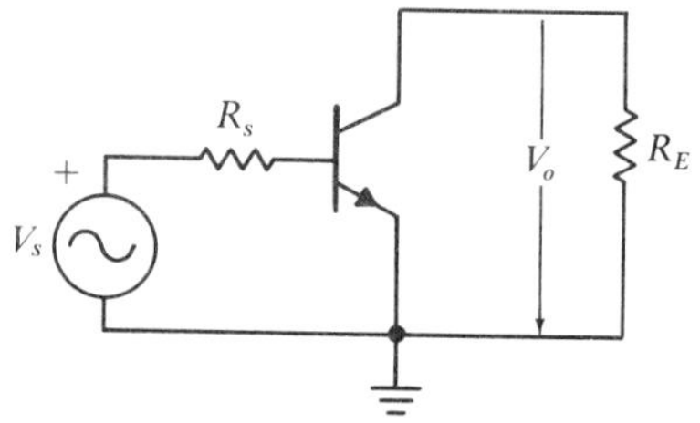

Fig. 9–11. *Model for calculating the open-loop gain of an emitter follower.*

Voltage Feedback, Series Input

An example of a voltage feedback, series input amplifier is the emitter follower of Fig. 9–10. From the figure, we see that the total output voltage, V_o, is sampled and returned in series with the input voltage, V_s. The output voltage in an emitter follower is in phase with the input voltage. Because V_o is approximately equal to V_s and they are in phase with each other, $B = -1$. (In the basic derivation of the feedback expression, Eq. (9–5), the output was assumed to be 180° out of phase with the input. For that case, B is taken as a positive quantity.)

In an analysis of feedback amplifiers, it is advantageous to isolate the amplifier without feedback from the feedback network. To determine the open-loop gain, A_v, the total resistance in the collector-emitter circuit must be included in the amplifier. For the emitter follower, emitter resistance, R_E, is placed in the output circuit, as shown in Fig. 9–11. From Chapter 6, the open-loop gain, where the output is taken across the emitter with respect to the collector, is

$$A_v = \frac{h_{fe}R_E}{h_{ie} + R_s} \tag{9–19}$$

where h_{re} and h_{oe} have been neglected.

The quantity $(1 - BA_v)$ is, therefore,

$$\begin{aligned} 1 - BA_v &= 1 + \frac{h_{fe}R_E}{h_{ie} + R_s} \\ &= \frac{h_{ie} + R_s + h_{fe}R_E}{h_{ie} + R_s} \end{aligned} \tag{9–20}$$

With the aid of Eq. (9–20), we can calculate A_{vf}, R_{if}, and R_{of}.

EXAMPLE 9–4.

For the emitter follower of Fig. 9–10, $h_{ie} = 2\,\text{k}\Omega$, $h_{fe} = 100$, $h_{re} = h_{oe} = 0$, $R_E = 1\,\text{k}\Omega$, and $R_s = 0$. Determine

(a) A_{vf}.
(b) R_{if}.
(c) R_{of}.

Solutions:

(a) With $R_s = 0$, by Eq. (9–19),

$$A_v = \frac{h_{fe}R_E}{h_{ie}} = \frac{100 \times 10^3}{2 \times 10^3} = 50$$

The value of B is -1. Therefore, $1 - BA_v = 51$, and by Eq. (9–5),

$$A_{vf} = \frac{A_v}{1 - BA_v} = \frac{50}{51} = 0.98$$

(b) Without feedback, $R_i = h_{ie} = 2\,\text{k}\Omega$; by Eq. (9–13),

$$R_{if} = R_i(1 - BA_v) = 2\,\text{k}\Omega \times 51 = 102\,\text{k}\Omega$$

(c) By Eq. (9–17),

$$R_{of} = \frac{R_o}{1 - BA_v}$$

Substitution of Eq. (9–20) with $R_s = 0$ and $R_o = R_E$ in Eq. (9–17) yields

$$R'_{of} = \frac{h_{ie}R_E}{h_{ie} + h_{fe}R_E} \qquad \textbf{(9–21)}$$

Dividing the numerator and denominator of Eq. (9–21) by R_E and letting R_E approach infinity gives us

$$R_{of} = \frac{h_{ie}}{h_{fe}} \qquad \textbf{(9–22)}$$

Hence, the output resistance, *not including* R_E, is $h_{ie}/h_{fe} = 2000/100 = 20\,\Omega$.

Voltage Feedback, Shunt Input

An example of the voltage feedback, shunt input amplifier is illustrated in Fig. 9–12. Assume that C_S is sufficiently large to act as a short circuit and $R_G \gg R_s$. The feedback ratio, B, is determined by setting V_s to zero:

$$V_f = \frac{R_s V_o}{R_s + R_F}$$

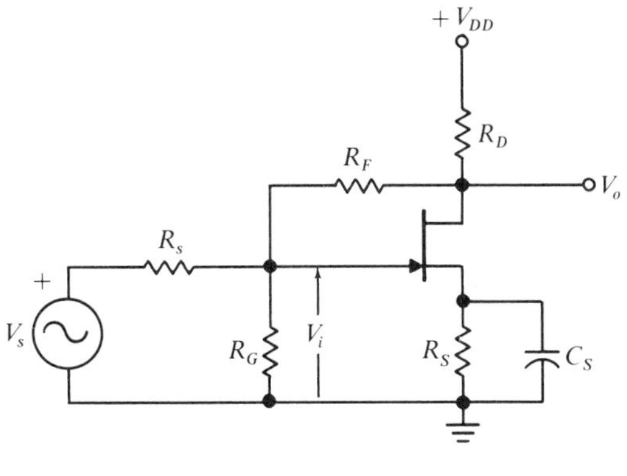

Fig. 9–12. Example of a voltage feedback, shunt input FET amplifier.

Solving for B,

$$B = \frac{V_f}{V_o} = \frac{R_s}{R_s + R_F} \qquad \textbf{(9–23)}$$

To find the open-loop gain, we modify Fig. 9–12 by removing feedback resistor, R_F. This is done by first setting V_o to zero. For this condition, one end of R_F is returned to ground, and the other end is connected to the gate terminal of the FET, placing R_F in parallel with R_G. Then, setting V_i

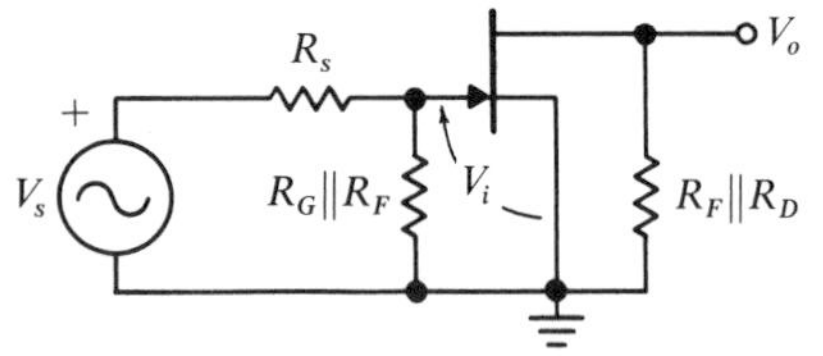

Fig. 9–13. *Model of Fig. 9–12 used for the calculation of open-loop gain.*

to zero, R_F is in parallel with R_D: $R_F \| R_D$. The resultant circuit is illustrated in Fig. 9–13.

Assuming that $R_D \ll R_F$, then $R_F \| R_D \simeq R_D$. Also, if $R_s \ll R_F \| R_G$, $V_i \simeq V_s$. From Chapter 6, then,

$$A_v = -\frac{\mu R_D}{r_d + R_D} \tag{9–24}$$

Therefore,

$$1 - BA_v = 1 + \left(\frac{\mu R_D}{r_d + R_D}\right)\left(\frac{R_s}{R_s + R_F}\right) \tag{9–25}$$

If $BA_v \gg 1$,

$$A_{vf} \simeq -\frac{1}{B} = -\frac{R_s + R_F}{R_s}$$
$$\simeq -\frac{R_F}{R_s} \tag{9–26}$$

assuming $R_F \gg R_s$. Equation (9–26) is a significant result. It states that under some conditions, the voltage gain with feedback is equal to the ratio of the feedback and signal source resistances.

Although the input resistance with feedback may be determined by Eq. (9–16), for this circuit it is much more convenient to apply the Miller effect described in Chapter 8. Feedback resistor R_F is modified as $R_F/(1 - A_v)$ and reflected across R_G. Resistance R_G is taken as the input resistance without feedback. The input resistance with feedback is

$$R_{if} = R_G \| R_F/(1 - A_v) \tag{9–27}$$

Output resistance R_{of} may be determined by Eq. (9–17).

EXAMPLE 9–5.

For the voltage feedback, shunt input FET amplifier of Fig. 9–12, $g_{fs} = 5 \times 10^{-3}\,\mho$, $r_d = 20\,\text{k}\Omega$, $R_D = 5\,\text{k}\Omega$, $R_F = 50\,\text{k}\Omega$, $R_G = 100\,\text{k}\Omega$, and $R_s = 5\,\text{k}\Omega$. Find

(a) A_{vf}.
(b) R_{if}.
(c) R_{of}.

Assume that C_S acts as a short.

Solutions:

(a) The value of $\mu = g_{fs} r_d = 5 \times 10^{-3} \times 20 \times 10^3 = 100$. By Eq. (9–24),

$$A_v = -\frac{100 \times 5\,\text{k}\Omega}{20\,\text{k}\Omega + 5\,\text{k}\Omega} = -20$$

By Eq. (9–23),

$$B = \frac{5\,\text{k}\Omega}{5\,\text{k}\Omega + 50\,\text{k}\Omega} = 0.09$$

and

$$BA_v = 0.09(-20) = -1.8$$

Because the magnitude of $BA_v = 1.8$ is not much greater than one, Eq. (9–26) cannot be used. By Eq. (9–5),

$$A_{vf} = \frac{-20}{1 + 1.8} = \frac{-20}{2.8} = -7.14$$

(b) The value of the modified feedback resistance is $50\,\text{k}\Omega/(1 + 20) \simeq 2.4\,\text{k}\Omega$. By Eq. (9–27),

$$R_{if} = 100\,\text{k}\Omega \,\|\, 2.4\,\text{k}\Omega \simeq 2.4\,\text{k}\Omega$$

(c) Without feedback, $R_o = r_d = 20\,\text{k}\Omega$. With feedback, by Eq. (9–17),

$$R_{of} = \frac{20}{2.8} = 7.14\,\text{k}\Omega$$

Another example of a voltage feedback, shunt input amplifier is the BJT feedback amplifier of Fig. 9–14. Because a BJT is a current-controlled device, it is best to analyze the feedback in terms of current. For this configuration, the feedback ratio is defined by $B = I_f/V_o$. From Fig. 9–14, $I_f = (V_o - V_i)/R_F$. Since, in general, $V_i \ll V_o$, feedback current $I_f = V_o/R_F$. Hence,

$$B = \frac{I_f}{V_o} = \frac{1}{R_F} \qquad \textbf{(9–28)}$$

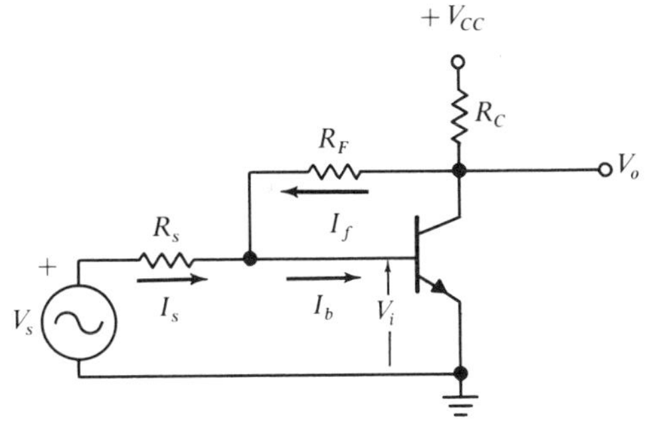

Fig. 9–14. *Another example of a voltage feedback, shunt input amplifier employing a BJT for the active device.*

The circuit without feedback, determined in a manner similar to that for the FET amplifier of Fig. 9–12, is illustrated in Fig. 9–15. Because the effect of feedback is being determined in terms of current, the circuit is modified.

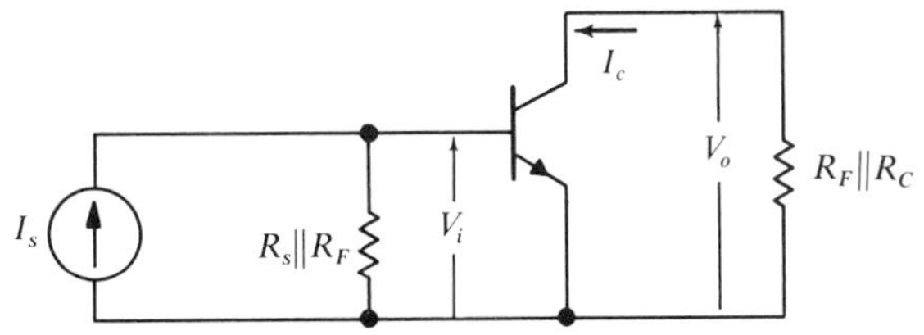

Fig. 9–15. *Model of Fig. 9–14 used for determining the open-loop voltage gain.*

Voltage source, V_s, in series with source resistance, R_s, is replaced by an equivalent current source, I_s, in parallel with R_s. Current $I_s = V_s/R_s$.

It is easy to solve for the ratio V_o/I_s in Fig. 9–15. The ratio $V_o/I_s = R_M$ [unit is the ohm (Ω)] is called the *trans-resistance* of the amplifier. Assuming that $R_F \gg R_s$ and R_C, then $V_o = -I_c R_C = -h_{fe} I_b R_C$. Base current I_b, by current division, is equal to $R_s I_s/(h_{ie} + R_s)$; hence,

$$V_o = -\frac{h_{fe} I_s R_s R_C}{h_{ie} + R_s}$$

and

$$R_M = \frac{V_o}{I_s} = -\frac{h_{fe} R_s R_C}{h_{ie} + R_s} \qquad \textbf{(9–29)}$$

Because $V_s = I_s R_s$, by Eq. (9–29), the voltage gain of Fig. 9–15 is

$$A_v = \frac{R_M}{R_s} \qquad \textbf{(9–30)}$$

The voltage gain with feedback, A_{vf}, is

$$A_{vf} = \frac{R_M/R_s}{1 - BR_M} \qquad \textbf{(9–31)}$$

where $1 - BR_M$ is analogous to $1 - BA_v$.

If the input resistance without feedback is R_i, the input resistance with feedback is

$$R_{if} = \frac{R_i}{1 - BR_M} \qquad \textbf{(9–32)}$$

Including R_C, the output resistance with feedback is

$$R_{of} = \frac{R_C}{1 - BR_M} \qquad \textbf{(9–33)}$$

EXAMPLE 9–6.

For the feedback amplifier of Fig. 9–14, $R_C = 2\,\text{k}\Omega$, $R_F = 50\,\text{k}\Omega$, $R_s = h_{ie} = 1\,\text{k}\Omega$, $h_{fe} = 50$, and $h_{re} = h_{oe} = 0$. Calculate

(a) R_M and B.
(b) A_{vf}.
(c) R_{if} and R_{of}.

Solutions:

(a) Note that R_F is much greater than either R_C or R_s. By Eq. (9–29),

$$R_M = -50 \times 10^3 \times \frac{2000}{2000} = -50\,\text{k}\Omega$$

By Eq. (9–28),

$$B = \frac{1}{50{,}000} = 0.02 \times 10^{-3}\,\mho$$

(b) Term $(1 - BR_M)$ is

$$1 - BR_M = 1 - (-50)(0.02) = 2$$

Therefore, by Eq. (9–31),

$$A_{vf} = -\frac{50/1}{2} = -25$$

(c) At the input to the transistor, without feedback, $R_i = h_{ie} = 1\ \text{k}\Omega$. By Eq. (9–32),

$$R_{if} = \frac{1000}{2} = 500\ \Omega$$

By Eq. (9–33),

$$R_{of} = \frac{2\ \text{k}\Omega}{2} = 1\ \text{k}\Omega$$

Current Feedback, Series Input

The common-emitter configuration with an unbypassed emitter resistor of Fig. 9–16 is an example of a current feedback, series input amplifier. Voltage V_f across R_E is directly proportional to load current $I_c \simeq I_e$. For this circuit, it is convenient to take the feedback factor as the ratio of the voltage across the emitter resistor to the load current:

$$B = \frac{V_f}{I_c} = \frac{I_c R_E}{I_c} = R_E \qquad \textbf{(9–34)}$$

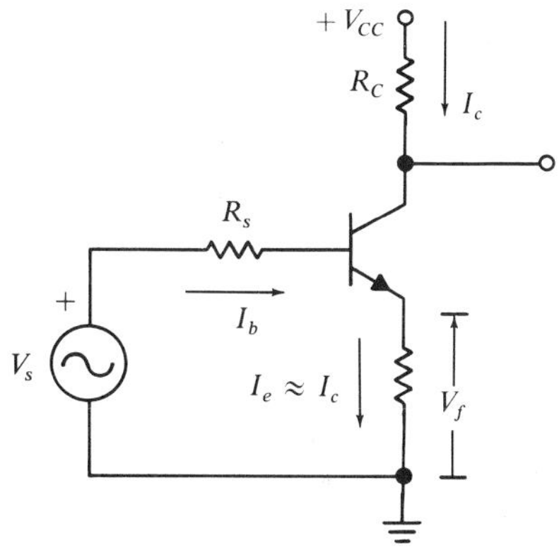

Fig. 9–16. *Example of a current feedback, series input amplifier.*

The amplifier with the feedback disconnected is drawn in Fig. 9–17. To maintain the same emitter resistance, it is necessary to include R_E in the input and output circuits. In an analysis of the circuit, it is easy to calculate the ratio of load current to source voltage: $G_M = I_c/V_s$, where G_M is the *transconductance* of the amplifier. Load current $I_c = -h_{fe}I_b$ and source voltage $V_s = I_b(R_s + R_E + h_{ie})$. Therefore,

$$G_M = -\frac{h_{fe}}{R_s + R_E + h_{ie}} \qquad \textbf{(9–35)}$$

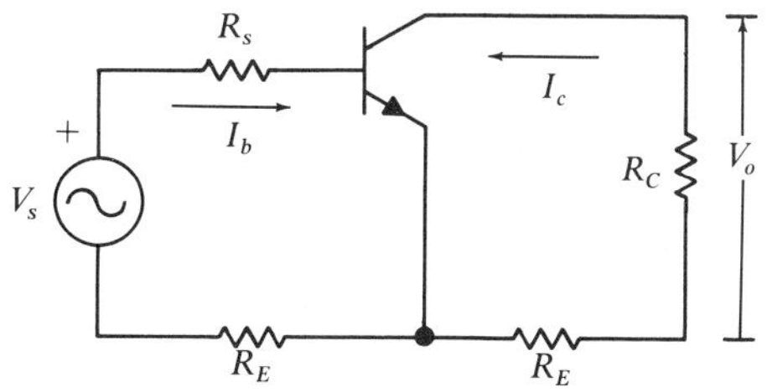

Fig. 9–17. *Model of Fig. 9–16 for determining the open-loop voltage gain.*

From Fig. 9–17, the voltage gain without feedback is $V_o/V_s = -I_c R_C/V_s = G_M R_C$. The gain of the feedback amplifier is

$$A_{vf} = \frac{G_M R_C}{1 - BG_M} \qquad \textbf{(9–36)}$$

The input resistance with feedback is

$$R_{if} = R_i(1 - BG_M) \tag{9-37}$$

If h_{oe} is not neglected, the output resistance is

$$R_{of} = \left(\frac{1}{h_{oe}}\right)(1 - BG_M) \tag{9-38}$$

Current Feedback, Shunt Input

In Fig. 9–18, feedback current, I_f, is derived from the emitter of Q_2. Because the voltage across R_E is proportional to the load current, it is current feedback. The feedback signal is in shunt with the input of the amplifier. Hence, Fig. 9–18 is an example of a current feedback, shunt input amplifier.

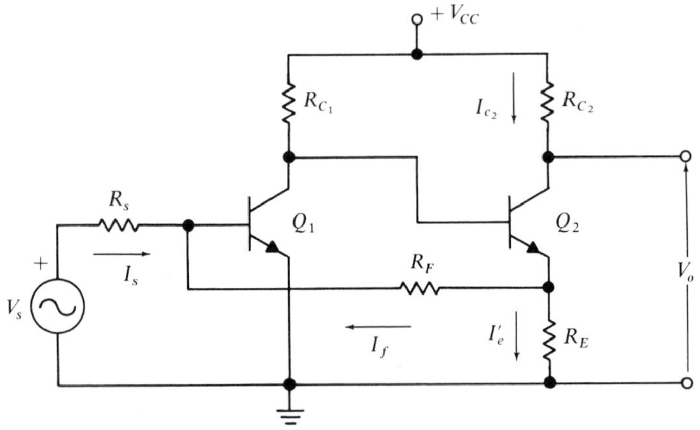

Fig. 9–18. *Example of a current feedback, shunt input amplifier.*

The reader may wonder why the feedback signal is derived from the emitter of Q_2. Transistor Q_1 provides a 180° phase shift at its output with respect to its input. Therefore, the signal at the base (or emitter) of Q_2 is 180° out of phase with respect to V_s. If the feedback signal were derived from the collector of Q_2 instead, a 360° phase shift would exist, and positive, instead of negative, feedback would be realized.

The *feedback factor* for the circuit is defined as the *ratio of feedback current, I_f, to current in the emitter resistance, I'_e*. By current division,

$$B = \frac{R_E}{R_F + R_E} \tag{9-39}$$

Assuming that the product of current gain without feedback and B is much greater than unity, the current gain with feedback, $A_{if} = I_{c_2}/I_s$, is

$$A_{if} = \frac{1}{B} = \frac{R_F + R_E}{R_E} \tag{9-40}$$

If $R_F \gg R_E$, Eq. (9–40) reduces to

$$A_{if} \simeq \frac{R_F}{R_E} \tag{9-41}$$

The derivation of an expression for voltage gain with feedback is left as a problem at the end of the chapter.

9.7 Stability of Feedback Amplifiers

In our discussion and examples of feedback amplifiers, midfrequency operation was assumed. This was done to keep the discussion on an elementary level to stress the concept and types of feedback. At low frequencies, coupling and bypass (and, if present, decoupling) capacitors influence the performance of the amplifier. At high frequencies, the transistor and stray capacitances affect the performance. For these ranges of frequencies, the gain and feedback ratios are, in general, not real numbers any more, but complex numbers.

To emphasize this fact, Eq. (9–5) is rewritten in boldface letters, reminding us that the quantities are complex numbers that vary with frequency:

$$\mathbf{A}_{vf} = \frac{\mathbf{A}_v}{1 - \mathbf{BA}_v} \tag{9–42}$$

Let us concentrate on the loop gain, $-\mathbf{BA}_v$ of Eq. (9–42). If $-\mathbf{BA}_v = -1 + j0$, $\mathbf{A}_{vf}$ goes to infinity. Practically, this means that instead of an amplifier, we have an oscillator that generates sine waves. This is another way of saying that *the amplifier is unstable.*

Let us plot the loop gain $-\mathbf{BA}_v$ as a function of frequency. The result is called a *Nyquist diagram,* examples of which are given in Fig. 9–19. There is an important criterion for determining the stability of a feedback amplifier. Called the *Nyquist criterion,* it states that *oscillations may exist if the locus of* $-\mathbf{BA}_v$ *encloses the* $-1 + j0$ *point.*

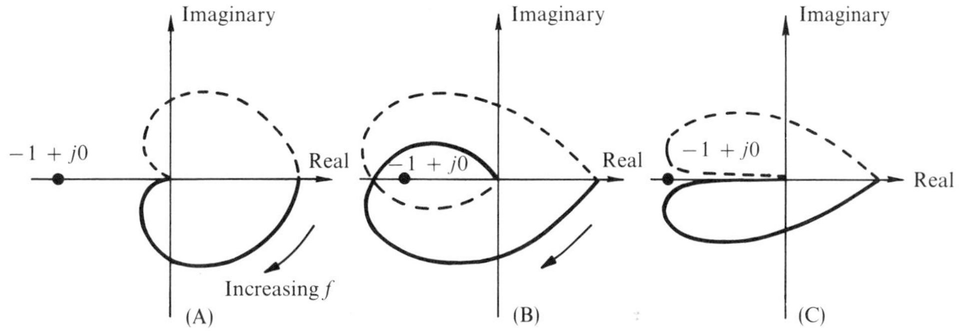

Fig. 9–19. *Examples of Nyquist diagrams. (A) Stable. (B) Unstable. (C) Potentially unstable.*

In Fig. 9–19, curve *A* indicates a stable feedback amplifier because the locus of $-\mathbf{BA}_v$ does not enclose the $-1 + j0$ point. (The dashed portion of the curve is a mirror image of the solid portion. Consequently, only the lower half, or solid, curve is necessary to plot $-\mathbf{BA}_v$.)

Curve *B* is that of an unstable amplifier because $-\mathbf{BA}_v$ encloses the $-1 + j0$ point. Curve *C* represents an essentially stable amplifier. Because the locus of $-\mathbf{BA}_v$ is very close to the $-1 + j0$ point, however, the amplifier is said to be *potentially unstable*. Further discussion of feedback stability is provided in Chapter 12.

SUMMARY

Negative feedback exists if a portion, or all, of the output signal in an amplifier is subtracted from its input. In addition to stabilizing gain, negative feedback expands bandwidth and lowers distortion in an amplifier. It also reduces noise (unwanted signals) if the noise is introduced after the first stage in a cascaded amplifier.

There are four basic types of feedback: voltage feedback, series input; voltage feedback, shunt input; current feedback, series input; and current feedback, shunt input. In voltage feedback, the returned signal is proportional to the output voltage. In current feedback, the returned signal is proportional to the output current.

Voltage feedback reduces, and current feedback increases, the output impedance of a feedback amplifier. If the feedback signal is returned in series with the input of the amplifier, the input resistance is increased. If, however, it is returned in shunt with the input, the input resistance is reduced.

At low and high frequencies, a feedback amplifier may become unstable and oscillate. The Nyquist criterion helps to predict the stability of a feedback amplifier. Networks are available which convert an unstable to a stable amplifier. These networks are examined in Chapter 12.

Further Reading

Faber, R. B. *Introduction to Electronic Amplifiers*. Columbus, Ohio: Charles E. Merrill Publishing Company, 1971, Chapter 8.

Ghaznavi, C., and A. H. Seidman. *Electronic Circuit Analysis*. New York: Macmillan Company, 1972, Chapter 11.

Jennings, R. R. "Negative Feedback in Voltage Amplifiers." *Electro-Technology*, December 1962, pp. 80–83.

Jennings, R. R. "Negative Feedback in Current Amplifiers." *Electro-Technology*, July 1963, pp. 100–103.

Millman, J., and C. C. Halkias. *Integrated Electronics: Analog and Digital Circuits and Systems*. New York: McGraw-Hill Book Company, 1972, Chapter 13.

Temes, Lloyd. *Electronic Circuits for Technicians*. New York: McGraw-Hill Book Company, 1970, Chapter 21.

REVIEW QUESTIONS

9.1 Define the input and output of a thermostatically controlled heating system.

9.2 What does feedback accomplish for an amplifier?

9.3 Explain the purpose of each element in Fig. 9–1.

9.4 What is the difference between negative and positive feedback?

9.5 Explain what is meant by a voltage feedback, series input amplifier.

9.6 Is the voltage gain of a negative feedback amplifier more or less than without feedback? Why?

9.7 Define (a) closed-loop, (b) open-loop, and (c) loop gain of a feedback amplifier.

9.8 What effect does negative feedback have on the bandwidth of an amplifier?

9.9 Why does the cascading of additional low-level amplifier stages hardly affect the distortion of the overall amplifier?

9.10 Explain what is meant by the following types of amplifiers:
(a) Current feedback, series input.
(b) Voltage feedback, shunt input.
(c) Current feedback, shunt input.

9.11 If the negative feedback signal is returned in series with the input signal, is the input resistance of the amplifier decreased or increased? Why?

9.12 Is the output resistance of an amplifier with voltage feedback less or more than without feedback? Explain your answer.

9.13 Is the output resistance of an amplifier with current feedback less or more than without feedback? Why?

9.14 Define transresistance of a feedback amplifier.

9.15 What is meant by the transconductance of a feedback amplifier?

9.16 Explain why the amplifier of Fig. 9–18 is an example of a current feedback, shunt input amplifier.

9.17 If a feedback amplifier begins to oscillate, what is the value of $-\mathbf{BA}_v$?

9.18 What is a Nyquist diagram?

9.19 Define the Nyquist criterion.

PROBLEMS

P9–1 Feedback is introduced in an amplifier to realize a closed-loop gain of -60. To accomplish this, three identical cascaded stages, each having a voltage gain of -10, are used. What is the value of B?

P9–2 Repeat prob. P9–1 for each stage having a voltage gain of -8.

P9–3 In prob. P9–1, assume that the gain of an amplifier stage increases by 10 percent. For this condition, determine the voltage gain
(a) With feedback.
(b) Without feedback.
(c) Is there any difference in your results? Why?

P9–4 For an amplifier without feedback, $f_L = 70\,\text{Hz}$ and $f_H = 8\,\text{kHz}$.
(a) If, with feedback, $f_{Hf} = 96\,\text{kHz}$, what is the value of the loop gain, BA_o?
(b) For the value of BA_o found in (a), calculate f_{Lf}.

P9–5 Using semilog paper, draw normalized plots of gain (dB) versus frequency for
(a) $f_H = 20\,\text{kHz}$, $f_L = 500\,\text{Hz}$.
(b) $f_{Hf} = 100\,\text{kHz}$, $f_{Lf} = 100\,\text{Hz}$.

P9–6 The measured distortion of a large-signal amplifier without feedback is 12 percent. If $BA_o = -9$, calculate the percentage distortion with negative feedback.

P9–7 In a feedback amplifier, the feedback signal is returned in series with the input signal. If $R_{if} = 6\,\text{k}\Omega$ and $R_i = 1\,\text{k}\Omega$, calculate the value of the loop gain, BA_v.

P9–8 With shunt feedback, $R_{if} = 200\,\Omega$. If $R_i = 1500\,\Omega$, calculate the value of the loop gain, BA_i.

P9–9 For a given amplifier without feedback, $R_o = 20\,\text{k}\Omega$. Calculate the loop gain for the following:
(a) If voltage feedback is used, $R_{of} = 4\,\text{k}\Omega$.
(b) For current feedback, $R_{of} = 100\,\text{k}\Omega$.

P9–10 For the emitter follower of Fig. 9–10, assume that $h_{ie} = 1\,\text{k}\Omega$, $h_{fe} = 80$, $h_{re} = h_{oe} = 0$, and $R_s = 0$. If $R_E = 500\,\Omega$, calculate
(a) A_{vf}.
(b) R_{if}.
(c) R_{of}.

P9–11 Repeat prob. P9–10 for $R_E = 2\,\text{k}\Omega$.

P9–12 For the voltage feedback, shunt input FET amplifier of Fig. 9–12, assume that $g_{fs} = 8\,\text{m℧}$, $r_d = 100\,\text{k}\Omega$, $R_D = 10\,\text{k}\Omega$, and $R_F = R_G = 100\,\text{k}\Omega$. If $R_s = 5\,\text{k}\Omega$, calculate
(a) A_{vf}.
(b) R_{if}.
(c) R_{of}.
Assume that C_S acts as a short.

P9–13 Repeat prob. P9–12 for $R_s = 0.1\,\text{k}\Omega$.

P9–14 Referring to Fig. 9–14, assume that $h_{ie} = 2\,\text{k}\Omega$, $h_{fe} = 100$, $h_{re} = h_{oe} = 0$, $R_C = 5\,\text{k}\Omega$, and $R_F = 40\,\text{k}\Omega$. If $R_s = 1\,\text{k}\Omega$, calculate
(a) R_M.
(b) B.
(c) A_{vf}.
(d) R_{if}.
(e) R_{of} (including R_C).

P9–15 Repeat prob. P9–14 $R_s = 0.1\,\text{k}\Omega$.

P9–16 For the current feedback, series input amplifier of Fig. 9–16, assume that $h_{ie} = 1\,\text{k}\Omega$, $h_{fe} = 60$, $h_{re} = 0$, and $1/h_{oe} = 100\,\text{k}\Omega$, $R_C = 2\,\text{k}\Omega$, $R_s = 1\,\text{k}\Omega$, and $R_E = 500\,\Omega$. Calculate
(a) B.
(b) G_M.
(c) A_{vf}.
(d) R_{if}.
(e) R_{of}.

P9–17 Repeat prob. P9–16 for $R_E = 0.1\,\text{k}\Omega$.

P9–18 Derive an expression for voltage gain for the current feedback, shunt input amplifier of Fig. 9–18.

P9–19 Draw Nyquist diagrams for
(a) A stable amplifier.
(b) A potentially unstable amplifier.
(c) An unstable amplifier.

10

Integrated Circuit Technology

Since the invention of the transistor in 1948, nothing comparable to the integrated circuit has had an impact of such magnitude on technology and society. Indeed, it is difficult to appreciate fully all of its consequences. From the viewpoint of technology, the integrated circuit (IC), in packages as small as transistors, is equivalent to discrete circuits containing a dozen or more transistors and at least an equal number of resistors. The cost of integrated circuits is much less and their reliability is much greater than for their discrete counterparts.

The impact of the integrated circuit on society has many facets. The hand-held calculator has evolved into a sophisticated instrument that outperforms the slide rule. Electronic watches are available. Its circuitry, containing more than 1300 transistors, occupies a volume of only 0.01 in.^{3} on a silicon chip. The increasing use of integrated circuits in automobiles and in household appliances is bound to have profound effects on our lifestyles.

In this chapter, we shall study how the circuits analyzed in the preceding chapters are integrated. Our main concern will be with fabrication—how integrated circuits are manufactured.

10.1 Types of ICs

Referring to the family tree of Fig. 10–1, we may categorize integrated circuits as being either *monolithic* or *hybrid*. *Monolithic* is derived from a Greek word meaning "single stone." This is indeed an apt description. In the monolithic IC, *all* transistors and passive elements are formed in a single chip of silicon.

Because the circuit elements in a monolithic IC share the same chip, it is necessary that they be electrically isolated from each other. Three methods of isolation are indicated in Fig. 10–1. They are PN-junction, dielectric, and beam-lead isolation. The most common and economical is PN-junction isolation.

In the hybrid IC, resistors, capacitors, and interconnections are deposited on an insulating substrate. Transistors, as well as integrated circuits and passive components, are then attached to the circuit. When the resistors, capacitors, and interconnection pattern are deposited by evaporation

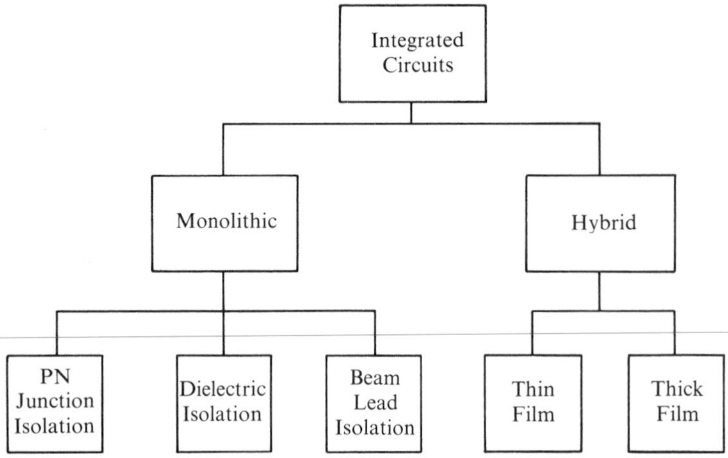

Fig. 10–1. *Family tree of integrated circuits.*

of a suitable material on a substrate, the result is called a *thin-film* hybrid. If the resistors, capacitors, and interconnections are deposited on the substrate by silk screening, a *thick-film* hybrid is obtained.

The monolithic process is best suited for mass production of integrated circuits. In addition to the high cost of initial artwork for laying out the circuit to be integrated, if the IC does not function to specification, additional artwork and processing are required. These changes could be very costly. For this reason, the monolithic IC is economical only when produced in large quantities.

Because the initial costs are less and it is relatively simple to change the circuit design to meet specifications, hybrid technology is appropriate for small production runs. Hybrid circuits are also mass-produced if circuit requirements cannot be met by the monolithic IC. Examples of these include circuits that operate at microwave frequencies, circuits requiring inductance, and power amplifiers. Parasitic (unwanted) elements existing in monolithic structures impair their operation at microwave frequencies, and inductors are not practical. Because of its structure, power dissipation is limited in a monolithic IC.

10.2 Processing Silicon

For clarity in discussing monolithic fabrication, we shall refer to a single chip. In production, hundreds, or even thousands, of circuits are produced simultaneously. A *silicon wafer* of 1.5 to 4 in. in diameter is used, as shown in Fig. 10–2. Each one of the squares, called a *chip*, contains a complete circuit. At the completion of fabrication, the wafer is scribed and broken along the vertical and horizontal lines to yield single chips. The chips are then tested and packaged.

Because each process step is shared by hundreds or thousands of chips on a wafer, the cost per chip is very low. The *flat* at the bottom of the wafer is used as a reference in the various fabrication steps to be described.

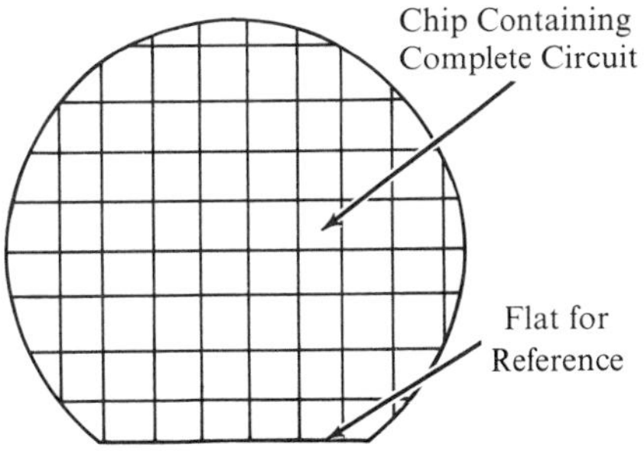

Fig. 10–2. *Silicon wafers, typically 7.62 cm in diameter, are used in the manufacture of monolithic ICs.*

Silicon

The temperatures used in monolithic processing lie typically between 1100°C and 1200°C. The melting temperature of germanium is less than 1000°C; for silicon, it is approximately 1400°C. For this, and because silicon devices operate at temperatures as high as 150°C, silicon is used in making monolithic ICs.

Silicon is obtained from sand. Chemically, sand is basically silicon dioxide, SiO_2. The silicon dioxide is reduced by carbon, resulting in silicon and carbon dioxide. The silicon obtained in this manner is about 98 percent pure. This purity level is much too low for integrated circuits, as well as for discrete semiconductor devices. What is required is silicon with less than one impurity atom for every 10^9 silicon atoms.

Zone Refining

Zone refining is a technique for achieving the required purity level in silicon. In Fig. 10–3, a silicon bar in a graphite boat is pulled to the right at a constant rate. The silicon is heated by *rf* energy, and a narrow zone of molten silicon is created in the vicinity of the *rf* coils. The impurities are concentrated in the molten silicon.

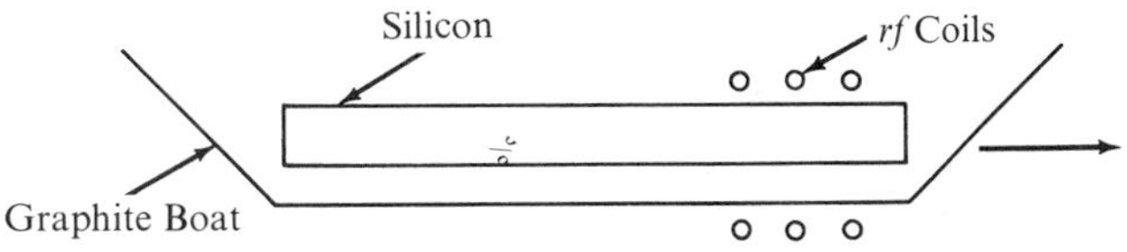

Fig. 10–3. *Zone refining is used for obtaining high-purity silicon.*

As the boat is pulled to the right, the molten zone of impurities travels to the left. Upon completion of travel, the left end, which contains the bulk of impurities, is sawed off and discarded. The process is repeated until a level of at least one impurity atom per 10^9 silicon atoms is obtained.

Single-Crystal Silicon

In addition to being ultrapure, the silicon must also exhibit a *single-crystal* structure. In single-crystal silicon, the atoms in the crystal lattice are arranged in a regular and well-defined pattern. Silicon obtained after zone refining, however, is *polycrystalline* where the atoms in the lattice are disordered.

Czochralski Pulling

Czochralski pulling is a method for obtaining single-crystal silicon. In Fig. 10–4, a small seed of single-crystal silicon is brought into contact with the polycrystalline melt. As the

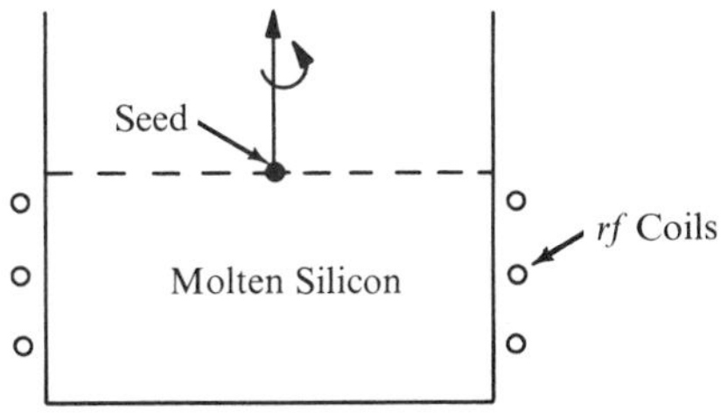

Fig. 10–4. *Growing single-crystal silicon with Czochralski pulling.*

seed is withdrawn at a constant rate, it is also rotated. Because the seed is at a lower temperature than the melt, the molten silicon solidifies as it touches the seed and assumes the single-crystal orientation of the seed. A P- or an N-type dopant may be added to the melt before the crystal is pulled to yield P- or N-type silicon.

The pulled silicon is typically from 1 in. to 4 in. in diameter and a foot or more in length. The bar is sawed into slices 10–12 mils (1 mil $= 10^{-3}$ in.) thick. The slices are then lapped and polished to a mirrorlike finish, required for IC processing. After polishing, the slice is called a wafer and is about 6 mils thick.

10.3 Manufacturing an Integrated Circuit

The basic processes used in the manufacture of a monolithic IC include the following:

1. *Artwork.* The circuit is laid out to be integrated, and the masks are cut.
2. *Oxidation.* The wafer is placed in an oxidation furnace which is maintained at approximately 1200°C. Generally, steam is forced through the furnace and a layer of SiO_2 is formed on top of the wafer. The oxide layer serves two important functions:
   (a) It becomes the surface for the application of a substance which is sensitive to light, called *photoresist.*
   (b) It helps reduce contamination, which is always a problem in processing integrated circuits and transistors. This property of SiO_2 is called *passivation.*

   Photoresist is an organic substance in which is suspended material that is sensitive to ultraviolet (UV) light. Upon exposure to ultraviolet light, the photoresist becomes *polymerized.* When polymerized, the resist undergoes a change in its molecular structure. The change in structure makes the polymerized SiO_2 resistant to etchants and impurity atoms.
3. *Diffusion.* Diffusion is a process where P- or N-type impurities for doping the silicon are introduced in a diffusion furnace at about 1200°C $\pm$ 0.5°C. The impurity may be in gaseous or vapor form. A typical P-type impurity is boron, B; for N-type doping, phosphorus, P, is commonly used. The penetration depth of the impurity in silicon depends on the dopant used, time, concentration, and temperature of the diffusion. The process is well understood and controllable.

Before these processes are discussed in detail, we shall describe the basic manufacturing steps in making a monolithic IC. The simple emitter follower of Fig. 10–5 will be the circuit to be integrated. Resistor R_E is connected between the emitter and terminal 4. The emitter is connected to terminal 3, the collector to terminal 2, and the base to terminal 1.

In the ensuing description, Fig. 10–6 refers to the processing steps, and Fig. 10–7 the masks.

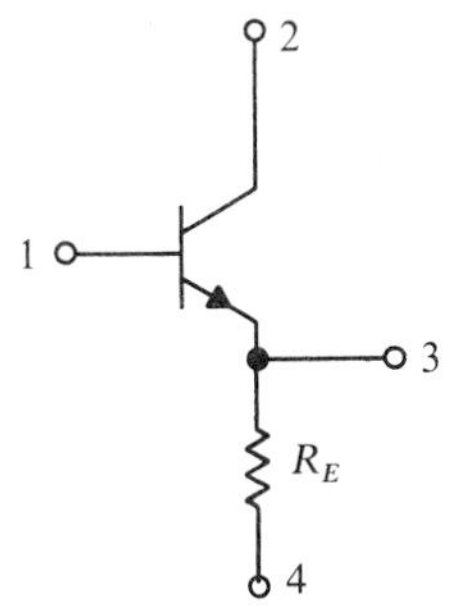

Fig. 10–5. *Emitter follower to be integrated.*

A. *P-type silicon substrate.* This is the starting material. Typical resistivity is 10 Ω-cm, and thickness is 6 mils.

B. *Epitaxial growth.* An epitaxial layer of N-type silicon is formed over the P-type silicon in an epitaxial reactor. The epitaxial layer formed is an *extension* of the P-type substrate, having the same single-crystal structure.

C. *Oxidation.* The wafer is placed in an oxidation furnace, and a layer of SiO_2 is formed.

D. *Application of photoresist.* Photoresist is applied to the SiO_2 layer.

Mask No. 1. The layout of the integrated circuit is shown in Fig. 10–7A. Mask No. 1 (Fig. 10–7B) contains the isolation pattern. Electrical isolation between the diffused elements is obtained by the formation of PN junctions which are reverse biased. The crosshatched areas in Fig. 10–7B are opaque.

E. *Exposing Mask No. 1.* The mask is placed on top of the substrate and exposed to ultraviolet light. Upon development, the unexposed resist is dissolved. The exposed areas, which have become polymerized, remain intact.

F. *Etching.* Hydrofluoric acid, HF, is used to etch away the unexposed SiO_2. This results in the opening of "windows" for the diffusion of impurities to form *isolation pockets*, or *islands.*

G. *Forming isolation regions.* Sufficient P-type impurity is diffused through the open windows. The P regions formed make contact with the P-type substrate, resulting in isolation pockets. Because there is some *lateral* diffusion, in addition to vertical diffusion, the edge of the junction has spread under the SiO_2. This is desirable because contamination is thereby minimized. Upon completion of a diffusion, the photoresist is removed, or *stripped*, from the substrate.

H. *Oxidation.* A new layer of SiO_2 is grown in the oxidation furnace, closing the windows. Photoresist is applied, readying the substrate for its exposure to the second mask.

Mask No. 2. Mask No. 2 (Fig. 10-7C) contains windows for the diffusion of P-type dopant for the transistor base and emitter resistor.

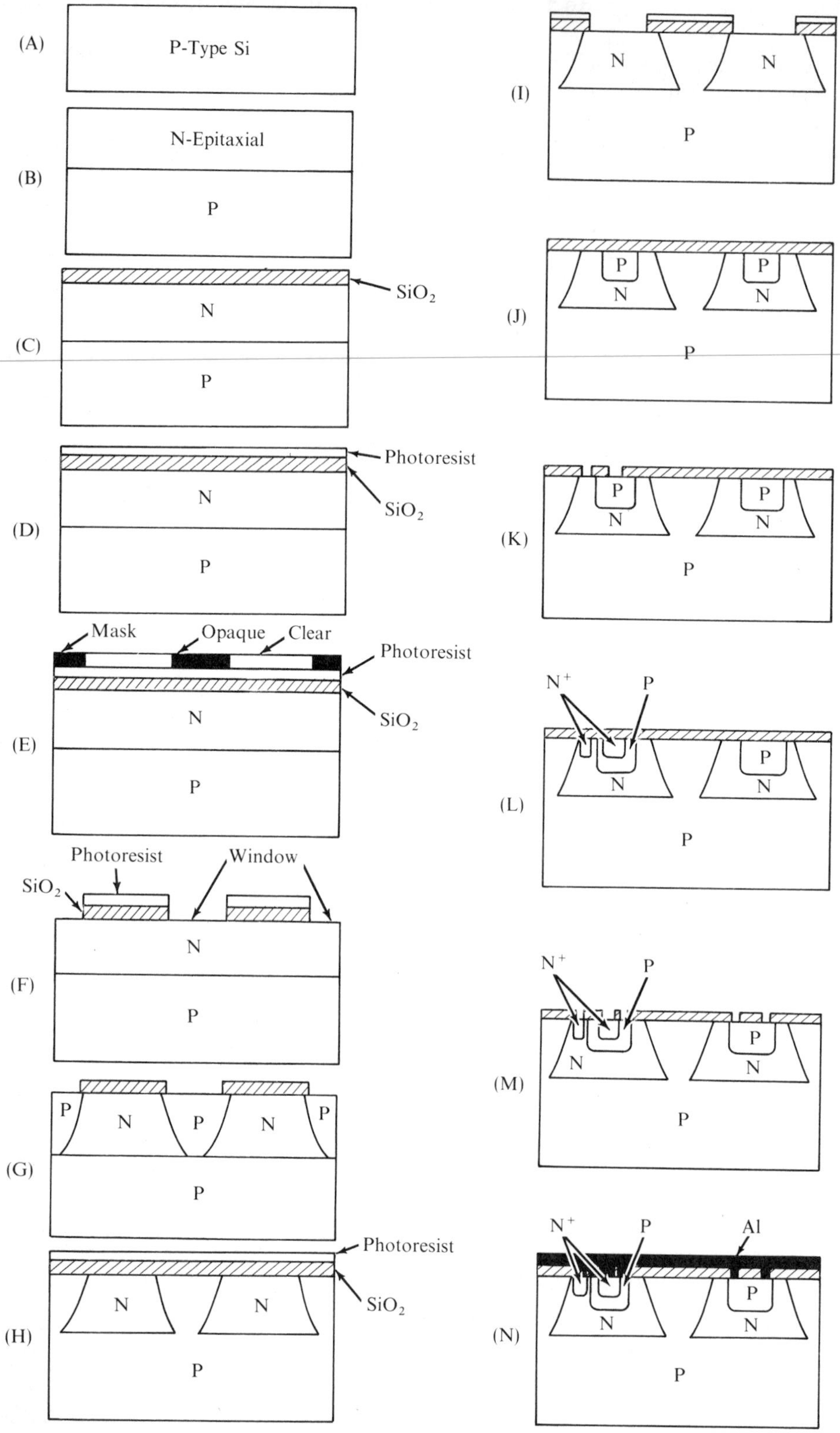

Fig. 10–6. *Integrated circuit processing of emitter follower in Fig. 10–5. (See text for details.)*

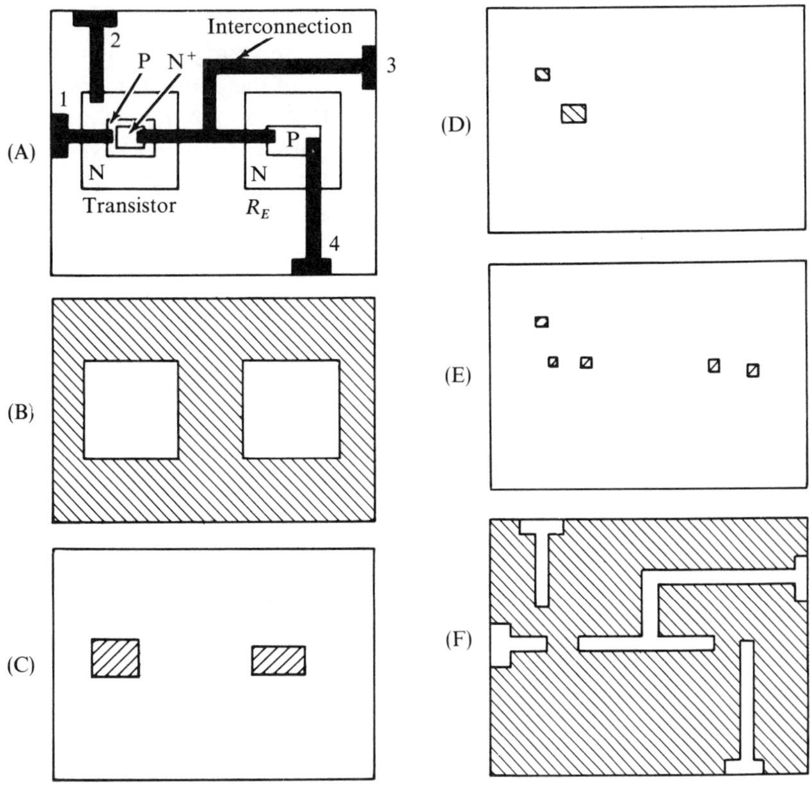

Fig. 10–7. *Generation of masks for emitter follower of Fig. 10–5. (A) Overall layout. (B) Mask No. 1, isolation. (C) Mask No. 2, P-type diffusion. (D) Mask No. 3, N⁺ diffusion. (E) Mask No. 4, contacts. (F) Mask No. 5, interconnection pattern.*

I. *Exposing Mask No. 2.* The mask is exposed to ultraviolet light, and the unexposed oxide is etched away to open windows for a P-type diffusion.

J. *Forming base and emitter resistor.* A P-type dopant is diffused through the open windows to form the base of the transistor and the emitter resistor. The wafer is covered with a new oxide layer.

Mask No. 3. This mask (Fig. 10–7D) contains the pattern for the emitter and other required N-type regions. To ensure a nonrectifying, or ohmic, contact between the N-type material and the interconnecting metal (to be described later), the region is *heavily doped* with the N-type dopant. This is designated by N^+. The emitter is also formed with N^+ doping. For the circuit of Fig. 10–5, in addition to the emitter, an N^+ region is required for connection to the N-type island which also serves as the collector of the transistor.

K. *Exposing Mask No. 3.* Photoresist is applied and exposed to Mask No. 3. Unexposed oxide is etched away, opening two windows for N^+ diffusion.

L. *Forming emitter and contact.* An N^+ impurity is diffused through the open windows for the emitter and collector contact. Another oxide layer is formed over the substrate.

Mask No. 4. This mask (Fig. 10–7E) contains the necessary windows for contacts for the connection of the transistor, emitter resistor, and terminals 1–4.

M. *Exposing Mask No. 4.* The substrate is covered with photoresist and exposed to Mask No. 4. Unexposed oxide is etched away, opening windows for contacts.

N. *Metallization.* The entire top of the substrate is deposited with a metallic film of conducting material, typically aluminum (Al), for the interconnection of circuit elements.

Mask No. 5. The last mask (Fig. 10–7F) contains the interconnection pattern for the integrated circuit.

After exposure to Mask No. 5, the excess metal not needed is removed by etching. Upon the completion of the last step, the individual chips on the wafer are tested. Those that pass the test are packaged and tested again.

Five masks were required in the manufacture of the emitter follower. This is typical, regardless of the complexity of the circuit being integrated.

10.4 Electrical Isolation

Electrical isolation of the elements in the IC emitter follower is achieved by reverse-biased PN junctions. The junctions are formed between the N islands and the P-type substrate. To show this clearly, Fig. 10–6N, including biasing sources, is redrawn in Fig. 10–8.

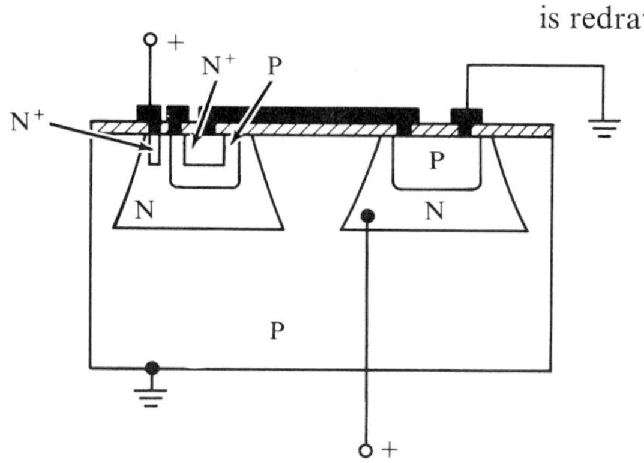

Fig. 10–8. *Electrical isolation of diffused elements obtained by reverse-biased PN junctions.*

The P substrate is returned to the most negative potential available in the circuit, such as ground. The collector (and also the N island for the resistor, although for simplicity it is not included in Fig. 10–6) is connected to the most positive potential, such as the collector supply voltage. Thus, both N islands are reverse biased with respect to the substrate, and electrical isolation is thereby obtained.

Useful guidelines for determining the number of N-type islands required include the following:

1. Transistor collectors at different potentials must be isolated.

2. Resistors connected to different portions of the circuit can share the same N island, provided the island is connected to the most positive potential used for the circuit.

EXAMPLE 10–1.

The amplifier of Fig. 10–9 is to be integrated.

(a) Draw a layout of the circuit.

(b) From the layout, develop a set of masks needed for monolithic processing.

Solutions:

(a) Because transistors Q_1 and Q_2 are at different collector potentials, each transistor requires its own N island. Resistors R_C and R_E may share a third island. One possible layout is shown in Fig. 10–10A. Other layouts that are acceptable also could be drawn.

(b) A set of five masks required for the processing of the IC amplifier is illustrated in Fig. 10–10B–F.

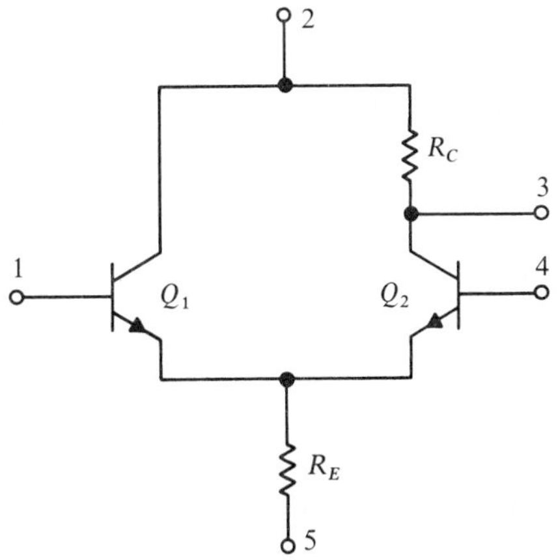

Fig. 10–9. *Amplifier to be integrated in Example 10–1.*

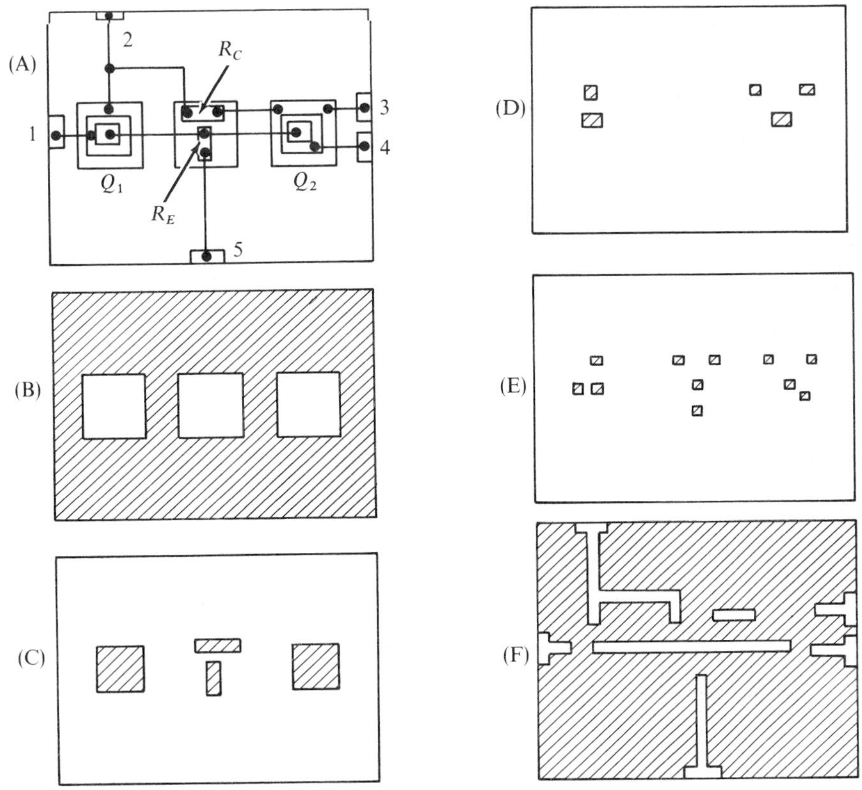

Fig. 10–10. *Results for Example 10–1. (A) General layout of circuit. (B) Isolation mask. (C) P-type diffusion mask. (D) N^+ diffusion mask. (E) Contact mask. (F) Interconnection mask.*

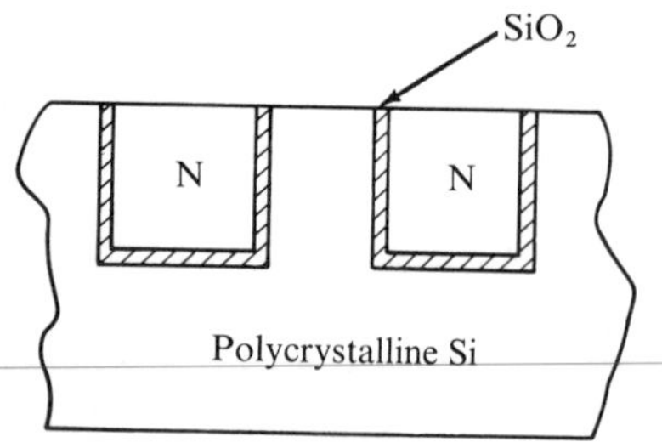

Fig. 10–11. *Example of dielectric isolation.*

Dielectric Isolation

In dielectric isolation, a dielectric material, such as silicon dioxide, surrounds and isolates components from each other and from the substrate. An example of dielectric isolation is shown in Fig. 10–11. Note that the substrate used is polycrystalline silicon. Parasitics are greatly minimized with dielectric isolation. Because of additional processing steps, however, this method is more costly than PN junction isolation.

Beam-Lead Isolation

Beam-lead isolation yields integrated circuits free from parasitics. The circuit elements are formed as in the PN junction isolated IC described in Section 10.3. An extra heavy metallization (1 mil thick) is deposited on the oxide layer, and the superfluous silicon removed. The result is a semirigid interconnected circuit with the elements physically separated.

10.5 Crossover Point

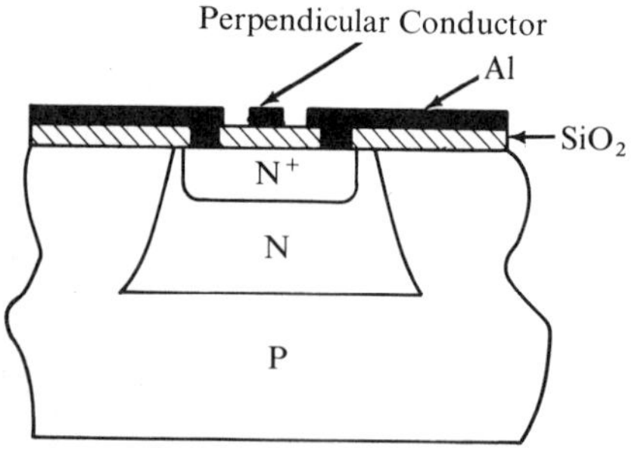

Fig. 10–12. *Crossover point.*

In complex circuits, a situation might arise where two conducting paths cross each other. To circumvent this, a *crossover point*, shown in Fig. 10–12, may be used. An N^+ region is diffused in an N isolation pocket. The metallized conductor (typically aluminum, Al) makes contact to both ends of the diffused region. The conductor running perpendicular to the N^+ region is insulated from it by the SiO_2 layer. Because a diffused resistor is insulated by the SiO_2 layer, no crossover point is required when a metallized conductor crosses over a resistor.

10.6 Artwork

The first step in the fabrication of integrated circuits is the cutting of masks. Because of the final minute dimensions of the different diffused elements, accuracy is vital. For this reason, the mask is cut on a large scale and reduced in the order of 200 : 1–1000 : 1. A machine for cutting the mask, called a *coordinatograph*, is illustrated in Fig. 10–13.

The mask material consists of a mylar base over which is placed a red peelable material. Mylar is dimensionally stable with respect to temperature and humidity. Because of the minute dimensions of diffused elements, dimensional stability of the mask is important. The peelable covering is easily cut and cleanly separated from the mylar base. (Commercially, the trade name for a commonly used mask material is *Rubylith*. Henceforth, the mask will be called Rubylith.)

In the final photoreduction of the Rubylith, the pattern is transferred to a high-resolution glass photographic plate.

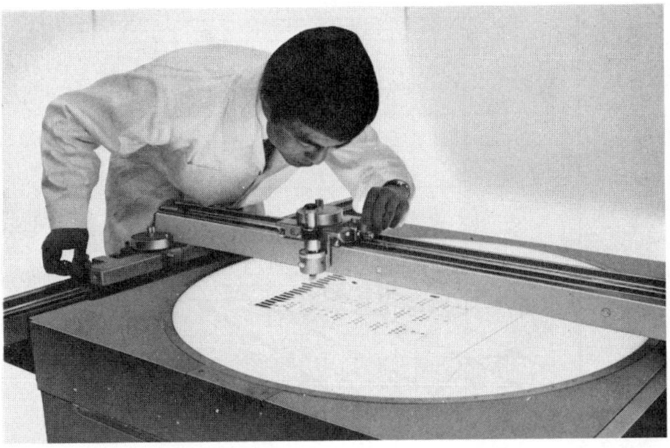

Fig. 10–13. *Example of a coordinatograph in use. (Courtesy Owen Jones Equipment Sales, national distributor for Mutoh Micro/Plotter Coordinatographs and accessories.)*

The glass plate becomes the final mask used with the wafer of Fig. 10–2. Because a few hundred to a few thousand circuits are processed simultaneously, the pattern on the Rubylith is repeated so that the mask covers the complete wafer. This is accomplished on a *step-and-repeat camera.*

Mask Aligner

Since the wafer is successively exposed to (typically) five masks, it is necessary that they always be in perfect alignment with the wafer. The *mask aligner* is used for this operation. On each glass mask is an alignment mark, called a *fiducial.* The operator peers through the aligner's microscope and adjusts the position of the wafer to ensure that the fiducial on the wafer from its exposure to the previous mask aligns with the fiducial of the new mask.

10.7 Oxidation

An apparatus for growing silicon dioxide is shown in simplified form in Fig. 10–14. Steam is introduced into an oxidation furnace, which is generally held between 1100°C and 1200°C. The wafer, in a quartz boat, is exposed to the steam, and a layer of SiO_2 is formed. Curves showing the rate of oxide growth for different temperatures are given in Fig. 10–15.

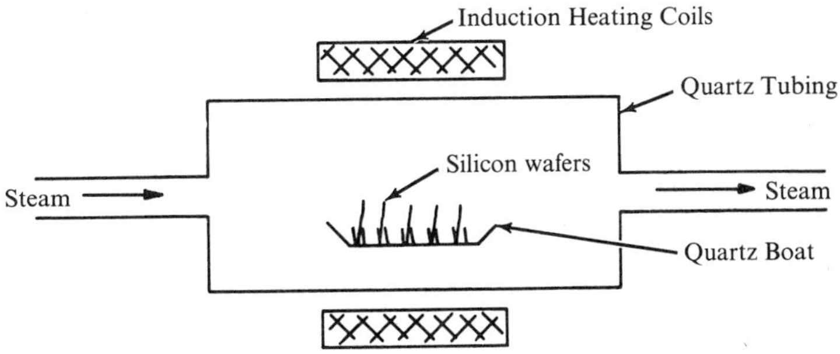

Fig. 10–14. *Apparatus used for growing SiO_2.*

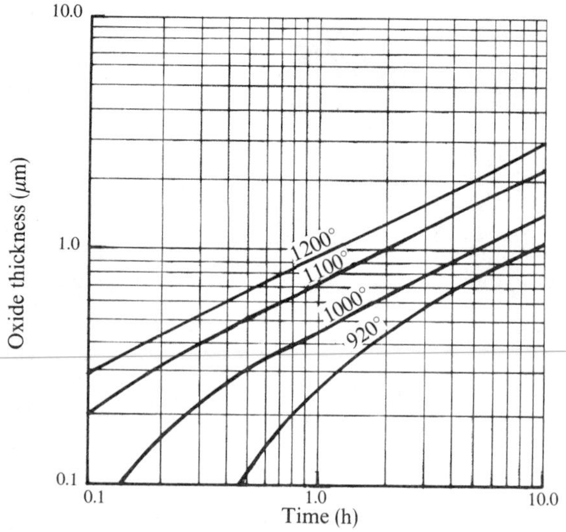

Fig. 10–15. *Steam oxidation curves for determining the growth of SiO_2.*

EXAMPLE 10–2.

Using steam at 1100°C, from the curves of Fig. 10–15, estimate the time to grow a

(a) 0.5-μm (1 μm $= 10^{-4}$ cm) layer of SiO_2.
(b) 1-μm layer of SiO_2.

Solutions:

From the 1100°C curve,

(a) $t = 0.5$ hour.
(b) $t = 2$ hours.

10.8 Photoresist

A few drops of photoresist, such as Kodak Photo Resist (KPR), are applied to the wafer which is held by vacuum on a *spinner*. The wafer is spun at a few thousand revolutions per minute for 10–30 seconds. This ensures a uniform distribution and thickness of the resist with a minimum of pinholes.

This operation, as well as others, is performed in a *clean room*. A *clean room* is an environment maintained at optimum temperature and humidity and free of dust particles. Specks of dust adhere to the photoresist, reducing the useful processing area of the wafer.

10.9 Diffusion

As described earlier, the diffusion process brings a high concentration of P- or N-type dopant atoms in contact with a silicon wafer. This is accomplished in a *diffusion furnace*, which is similar to the oxidation furnace of Fig. 10–14. Under the influence of heat (typically, 1100°C–1200°C), the dopant atoms penetrate through the open windows of the wafer. The depth and concentration of the impurity depend on the specific dopant used, the temperature, time, and how the dopant is introduced. The maximum amount of dopant that can be dissolved in silicon is called the *solid solubility* of the dopant.

Assume that the concentration of the dopant, N_o atoms/cm^3, at the surface of the wafer is always *constant*. The concentration N_x as a function of distance x in a silicon wafer for different times t is shown in Fig. 10–16. Note that the concentration at the surface is constant and equal to N_o. For longer times of diffusion, the impurity concentration is increased. Infinite time is required to achieve a uniform concentration of dopant in a wafer.

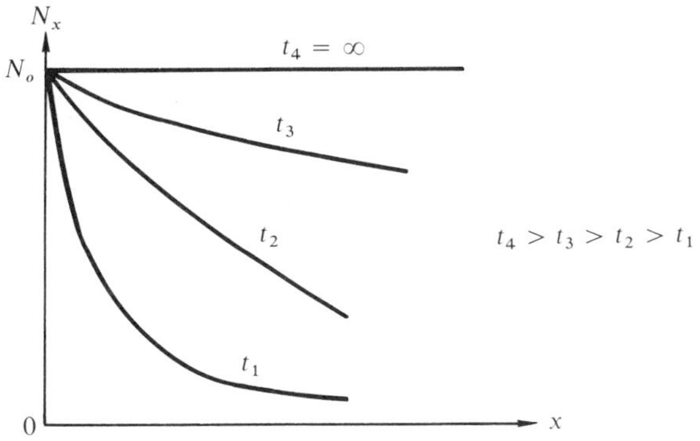

Fig. 10–16. *Dopant concentration distribution in silicon for a wafer exposed to a constant dopant source, N_o, for different times, t.*

If the concentration of the dopant at the surface of the wafer is a *fixed amount*, a more uniform distribution of impurity is obtained in the silicon. This is desirable for base diffusion, for example. The concentration N_x as a function of distance and time for a fixed amount of impurity is illustrated in Fig. 10–17. Time t_1 refers to the initial concentration. For longer time intervals, the impurity concentration becomes more uniform.

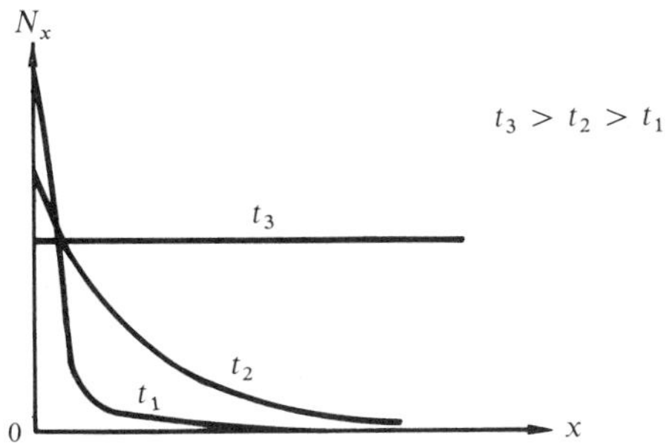

Fig. 10–17. *Dopant concentration distribution in silicon for a wafer exposed to a fixed amount of dopant for different times, t.*

The two kinds of impurity distributions just described may be represented by well-known mathematical functions which are plotted in Fig. 10–18. The first, where the concentration N_o is constant at the surface of the wafer, is called an *error function, erf*. In practice, it is convenient to describe the distribution by the *complementary error function, erfc*, which equals 1 − *erf*. The complementary error function is plotted in Fig. 10–18.

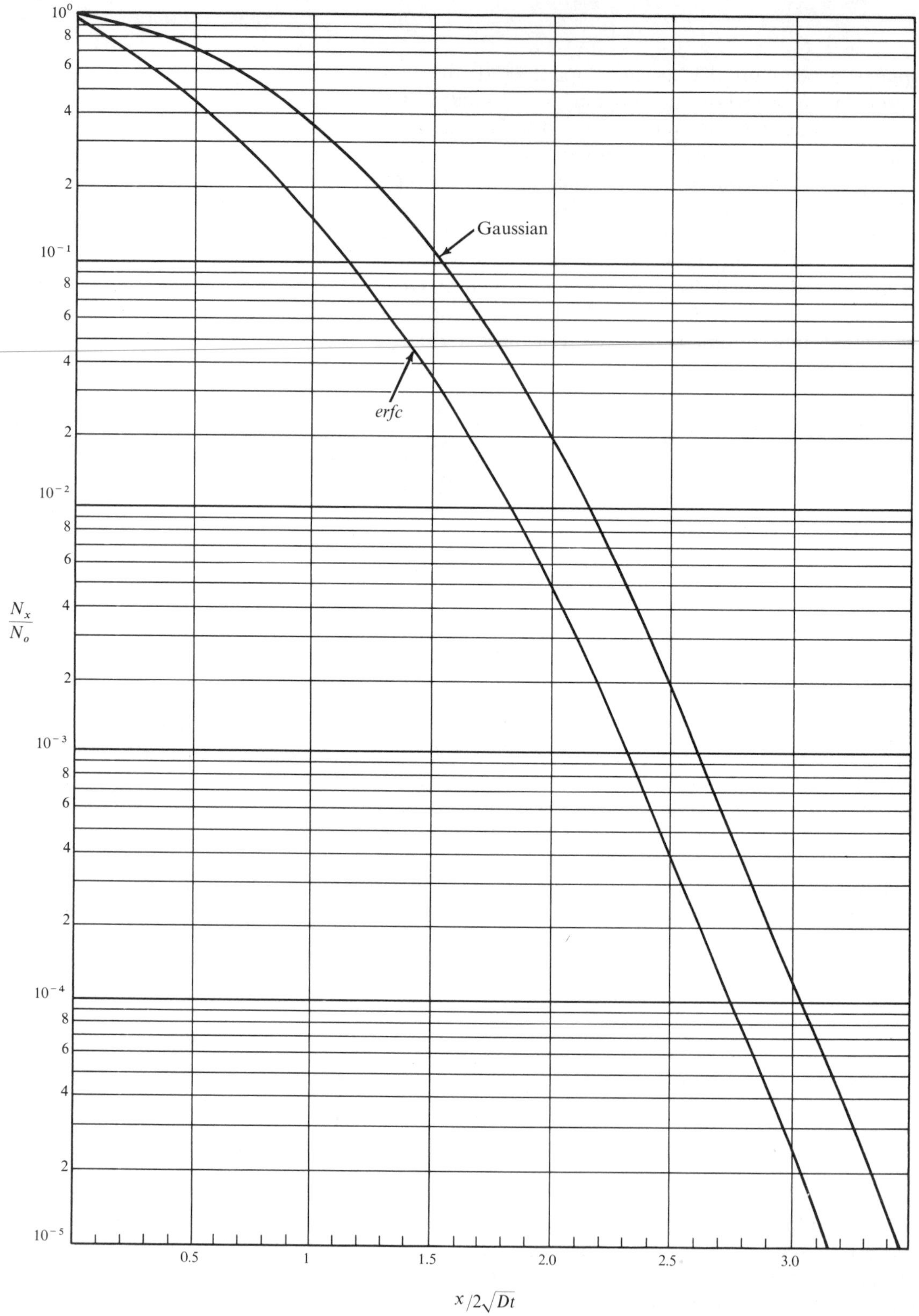

Fig 10–18. *Plots of erfc and Gaussian distribution curves.*

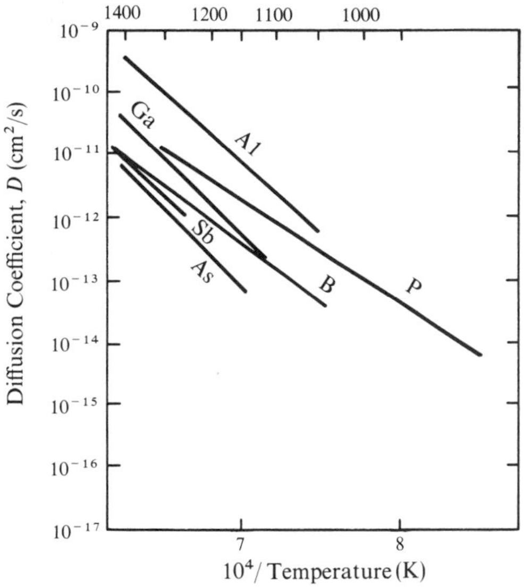

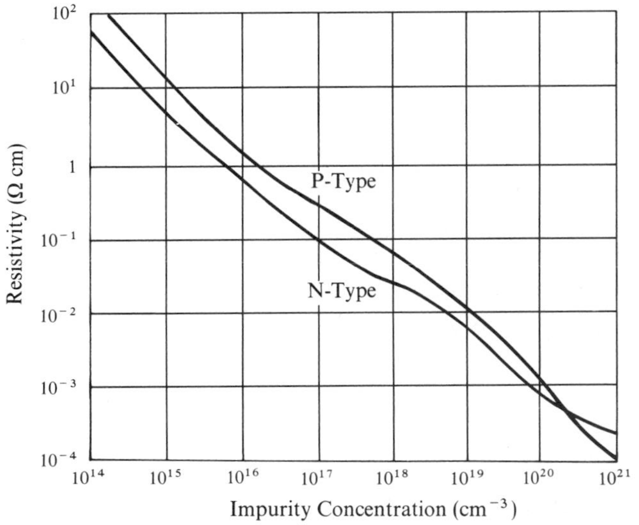

Fig. 10–19. (Above) *Diffusion coefficients as a function of temperature for various dopants.*

Fig. 10–20. (Below) *Resistivity curves for P- and N-type silicon at room temperature.*

The second distribution, where the dopant is a fixed amount, is called a *Gaussian* distribution. This, too, is plotted in Fig. 10–18. The term $x/2\sqrt{Dt}$, where D is the *diffusion coefficient*, x is the depth of penetration of the dopant from the surface, and t is time, is plotted along the abscissa.

A useful set of curves is shown in Fig. 10–19: plots of diffusion coefficient as a function of temperature for different dopants. The diffusion coefficient (cm^2/s) indicates how fast impurity atoms diffuse through a cross-section of material. The diffusion coefficient increases with rising temperature. Other curves of practical value are plots of resistivity versus impurity concentration for P- and N-type impurity in silicon (Fig. 10–20). Applications of these and other curves considered in this section are illustrated in the next group of examples.

EXAMPLE 10–3.

A silicon substrate has an N-type impurity concentration, of 10^{16} atoms/cm^3 (*background concentration*, N_B). We wish to form a PN junction 5 μm from the surface of the silicon, as shown in Fig. 10–21. To achieve this, a *constant* source of boron, $N_o = 5 \times 10^{20}$ atoms/cm^3, is used as the P dopant. The diffusion temperature is 1200°C. Determine time t required to form the PN junction.

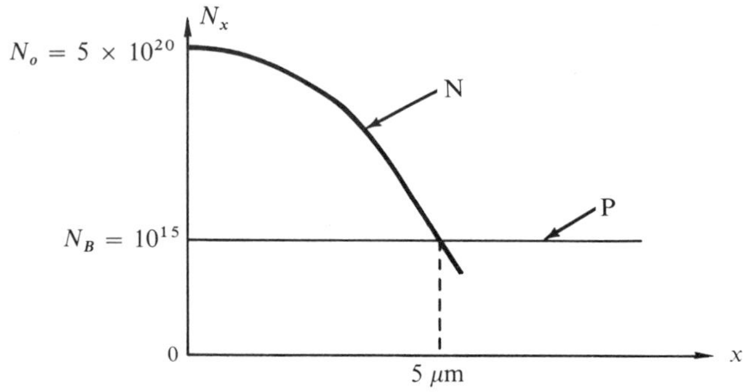

Fig. 10–21. *Dopant distribution curves (impurity profile) for the formation of a PN junction 5 µm from the silicon surface. (See Example 10–3.)*

Solution:

Because a constant source of boron is used, the distribution follows the *erfc* curve of Fig. 10–18. From Fig. 10–19 for boron (B), $D \simeq 10^{-12}$ cm^2/s. The PN junction is formed when N_x equals the background concentration: $N_x = N_B = 10^{16}$ atoms/cm^3. Hence,

$$\frac{N_B}{N_o} = \frac{10^{16}}{5 \times 10^{20}} = 0.2 \times 10^{-4}$$

From the *erfc* curve, for $N_x/N_o = N_B/N_o = 0.2 \times 10^{-4}$, $x/2\sqrt{Dt} = 3.05$. Squaring both sides of the expression yields $x^2/4Dt = 9.3$. Substituting $x = 5\ \mu\text{m} = 5 \times 10^{-4}$ cm and $D = 10^{-12}$ cm^2/s in the squared expression, we get

$$\frac{(5 \times 10^{-4})^2}{4 \times 10^{-12} t} = 9.3$$

Solving for t, $t = 6720$ s. Dividing by 3600 s/h, $t = 1.87$ h.

EXAMPLE 10–4.

A fixed number of boron atoms are deposited on an N-type silicon wafer such that $N_B/N_o = 10^{-1}$. Diffusion takes place for 2 h (7200 s) at 1100°C. What is the depth of the formed PN junction?

Solution:

Because a fixed amount of boron is deposited on the wafer, we have a Gaussian distribution. From the Gaussian curve of Fig. 10–18, for $N_B/N_o = 10^{-1}$, $x/2\sqrt{Dt} = 1.5$. In Fig. 10–19, $D \simeq 3 \times 10^{-13}$. Substituting these values and solving for x, we obtain $x = 1.4 \times 10^{-4}$ cm $= 1.4\,\mu$m.

EXAMPLE 10–5.

A uniformly doped P-type silicon wafer has a resistivity of $1\,\Omega$-cm. The wafer is exposed to phosphorus at a *constant* surface concentration of $N_o = 10^{18}$ atoms/cm^3. The wafer is in a diffusion furnace for one hour. If the depth of the formed PN junction is $2\,\mu$m from the surface, at what temperature did the diffusion take place?

Solution:

From Fig. 10–20, $N_B = 1.7 \times 10^{16}$; hence, $N_B/N_o = 1.7 \times 10^{-2}$. Referring to the *erfc* curve of Fig. 10–18, $x/2\sqrt{Dt} = 1.7$. Solving for D, we obtain $D = 2.4 \times 10^{-13}$. From the diffusion curve for phosphorus of Fig. 10–19, for the value of D calculated, $T \simeq 1050°$C.

EXAMPLE 10–6.

Figure 10–22 is an impurity profile of an integrated NPN transistor.

(a) What manufacturing process is associated with each curve?
(b) Why is curve (3) a straight line?
(c) What is the depth of the emitter from the surface?
(d) What is the base thickness?
(e) What is the maximum depth that contains N-type impurity atoms?

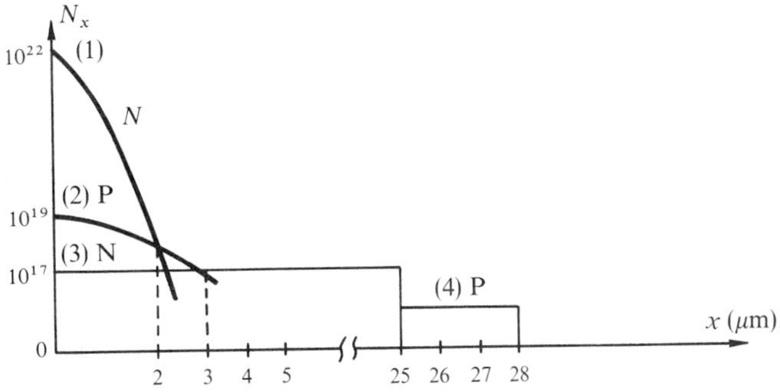

Fig. 10–22. *Impurity profile of an integrated transistor. (See Example 10–6.)*

Solutions:

(a) Curve (1) represents emitter diffusion, (2) base diffusion, (3) epitaxial growth, and (4) substrate diffusion.
(b) Curve (3) represents epitaxial growth and is therefore a straight line.

(c) Depth of emitter from surface equals 2 μm.
(d) Base thickness equals $3 - 2 = 1\ \mu$m.
(e) Maximum depth containing N-type impurity is 25 μm.

Ion Implantation

The ion implantation technique permits precise control of doping. It is ideal for shallow diffusion of impurities, such as is required for high-value resistors. The process is performed in a vacuum at or near room temperature. P- or N-type impurity ions are generated in an ion source and accelerated to energy levels up to 300,000 eV. The ions bombard the silicon wafer, and the penetration in silicon is a function of their energy.

10.10 LSI and MSI

LSI and *MSI* refer to *large-scale* and *medium-scale integration*, respectively. Presently, LSI circuits have a component density of more than 1000 components per chip; MSI has a component density somewhat in excess of 100 components per chip.

The basic processes used in the manufacture of simple integrated circuits are also employed in the manufacture of LSI and MSI circuits. Because of the huge number of components on a single chip, however, some defective components always exist. A method for detecting the defective components and eliminating them when interconnecting the good components is needed. For this purpose, there are two general methods, *discretionary wiring* and *fixed interconnection patterns*.

Discretionary Wiring

More identical circuits, called *unit cells*, than actually are required are integrated, for example, in logic gates and semiconductor memories. The reason for integrating more circuits than required is that, upon completion of fabrication, some of the circuits will be found to be defective.

The unit cells are tested by an automatic tester coupled to a digital computer which "remembers" the good cells. The computer generates an interconnection pattern only for good cells. Since the location of defective cells will be different, the testing and generation procedure is repeated for each chip.

Fixed Interconnection Pattern

In this method, the basic unit cell is complex and has a useful function by itself. The complex cell is called a *polycell*. An automatic tester and computer keep track of the good polycells. The polycells are connected by a fixed interconnection pattern which is simpler than that used for interconnecting unit cells.

10.11 Characteristics of Diffused Elements

Bipolar Junction Transistor (BJT)

An integrated bipolar junction transistor (BJT) exhibits values of short-circuit current gain, h_{fe}, as high as 300 and gain-bandwidth product, f_T, up to 500 MHz. A limitation on h_{fe} is the width of the base; h_{fe} may be increased by decreasing the base width. The resistance of the N island, which serves as the collector of the transistor, limits f_T. This resistance can be decreased by using a *buried* N^+ *layer.*

In Fig. 10–23, a heavily doped region (N^+ buried layer) is diffused between the P-type substrate and the bottom of the N island. The net collector resistance is reduced because the N^+ layer is effectively in parallel with the N island.

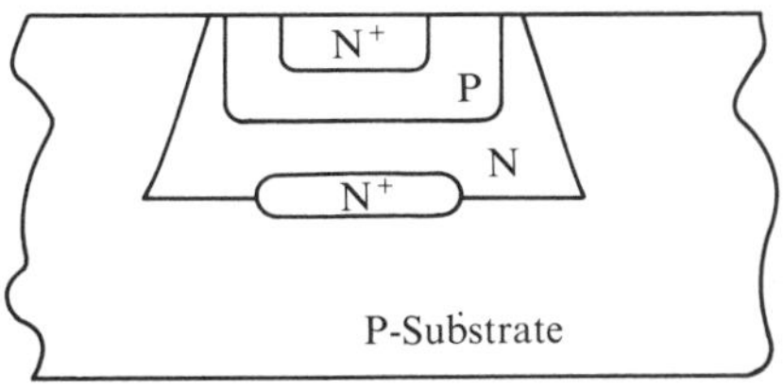

Fig. 10–23. *A buried N+ layer reduces collector resistance of an integrated transistor.*

Lateral PNP Transistor

For practical reasons, NPN transistors are ideal for the manufacture of monolithic ICs. Sometimes, however, a PNP transistor is needed in addition to the NPN type. The processing of PNP transistors must be compatible with the processing of NPN devices.

A suitable configuration is the PNP lateral transistor of Fig. 10–24. Note that emitter current I_E flows *laterally* from the emitter to the collector. The effective base width of the lateral PNP transistor is greater than for the diffused transistor. This results in the PNP device having a low short-circuit current gain, in the order of 5 to 10.

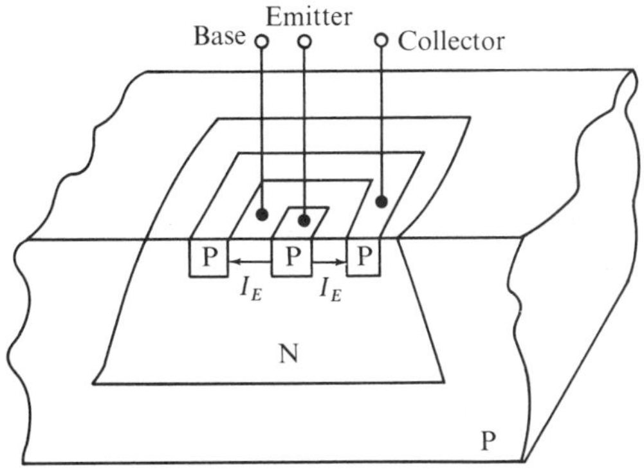

Fig. 10–24. *Basic geometry of a lateral PNP transistor.*

FET

Generally, MOSFETs are preferred over JFETs for monolithic integration. One important reason for the preference is that a MOSFET requires no electrical isolation. To see this, refer to the cross-section of an N-channel enhancement-type MOSFET of Fig. 10–25. Because the gate and drain are positive with respect to the P substrate (which is returned to ground), reverse-biased PN junctions exist, and electrical isolation is obtained.

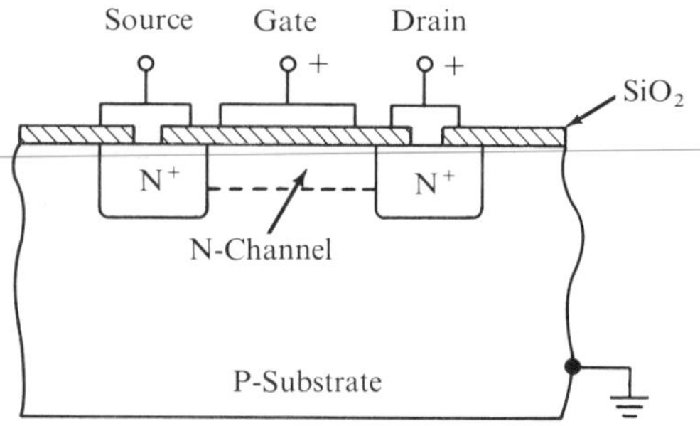

Fig. 10–25. *Cross-section of an N-channel enhancement-type MOSFET.*

Although the frequency response and switching speed for a MOSFET are not as good as those for a BJT, the MOSFET is superior in other respects. In addition to the "built-in" electrical isolation, it has fewer diffusion processing steps, and the packing density (devices/cm^3) is much greater. The MOSFET can also be connected to function as a resistor.

Resistors

Integrated resistors are normally realized by P-type diffusion, as described earlier in this chapter. A view of a diffused resistor is given in Fig. 10–26. The resistance of any material is expressed by

$$R = \frac{\rho l}{A} \qquad \textbf{(10–1)}$$

where ρ = resistivity of the material (Ω-cm),
l = length (cm),
A = cross-sectional area (cm^2).

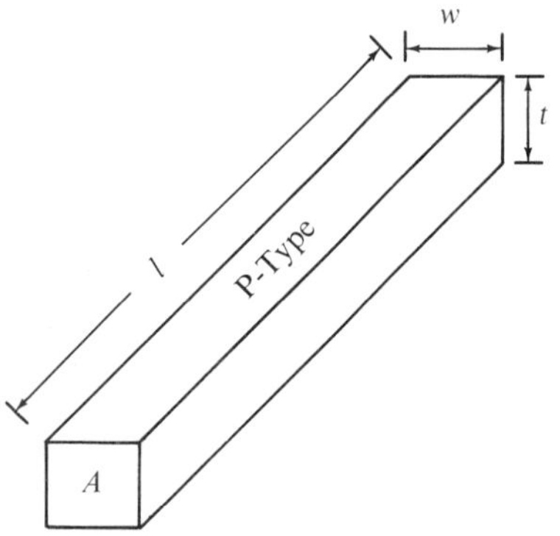

Fig. 10–26. *Basic geometry of a diffused resistor.*

But A is equal to the product of width w and thickness t of the resistor; hence, Eq. (10–1) may be expressed as

$$R = \left(\frac{\rho}{t}\right)\left(\frac{l}{w}\right) \qquad \textbf{(10–2)}$$

If length l is equal to width w, we have a *square* of material. A reasonable assumption is that the thickness of a given diffused resistor is constant. Letting $l = w$ in Eq. (10–2), we obtain an expression for the *sheet resistance*, R_S, in *ohms/square*:

$$R_S = \frac{\rho}{t} \qquad (10\text{–}3)$$

The concept of sheet resistance is very useful. *Regardless of the dimensions of the square, for a given thickness, the sheet resistance is a constant.* To find the resistance value of a diffused resistor of any length and width, the sheet resistance is multiplied by the length-to-width ratio, l/w:

$$R = R_S\left(\frac{l}{w}\right) \qquad (10\text{–}4)$$

Ratio l/w is called the *aspect ratio.*

EXAMPLE 10–7.

It is required to diffuse a resistor of 1500 Ω. The sheet resistance $R_S = 200\,\Omega$/square.

(a) Determine the aspect ratio.

(b) If $w = 2\,\mu$m, what is the length of the resistor in centimeters?

Solutions:

(a) By Eq. (10–4),

$$\frac{R}{R_S} = \frac{l}{w} = \frac{1500}{200} = 7.5:1$$

(b) Length $l = 7.5 \times 2\,\mu\text{m} = 15\,\mu\text{m}$. Since $1\,\mu\text{m} = 10^{-4}$ cm, $l = 15 \times 10^{-4}$ cm.

The practical range of P-diffused resistors is from approximately 20 Ω to 30 kΩ. For values less than 20 Ω, N^+ diffused resistors may be fabricated. The absolute tolerance of diffused resistors is poor; it can be as high as ±25 percent. The tolerance of the ratio of diffused resistors, however, can be less than ±2 percent.

Four-Point Probe

The four-point probe of Fig. 10–27 is widely used in measuring sheet resistance of a silicon specimen. The points are spaced about 0.1 cm apart. A dc source, V_i, in series with resistance, R_i, simulates a *current source.* Possible values are $V_i = 10$ V and $R_i = 100$ kΩ. The sheet resistance is obtained from the following simple relation if the dimensions of the specimen are much greater than the point spacing:

$$R_S = \frac{4.5\text{ V}}{I} \qquad (10\text{–}5)$$

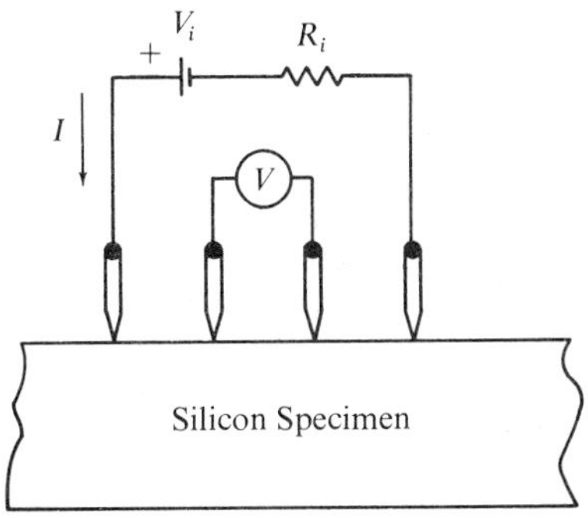

Fig. 10–27. *Four-point probe used to measure the sheet resistance of silicon.*

Diodes

Monolithic diodes are generally produced from a diffused transistor. Two examples of connecting a transistor to function as a diode are shown in Fig. 10–28. Figure 10–28A is an emitter-base junction diode with the collector connected to the base. The collector-base junction diode with the emitter unconnected is shown in Fig. 10–28B. The emitter-base diode exhibits a typical junction depletion capacitance of 0.6 pF and a breakdown voltage of 6 V. The collector-base diode has, typically, a 0.8-pF junction capacitance and a 40-V breakdown voltage.

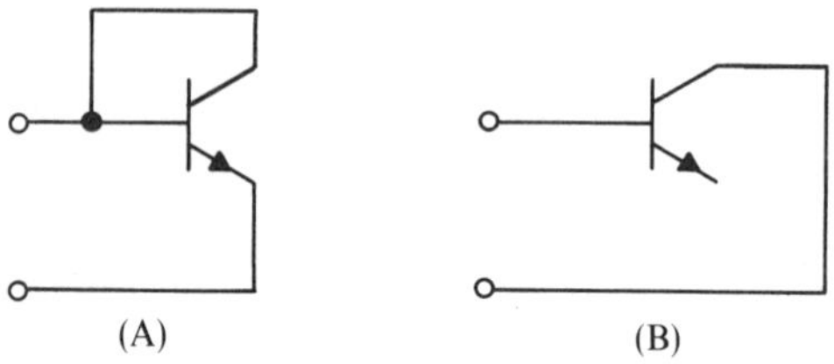

Fig. 10–28. *Using a diffused transistor as a diode. (A) Base-emitter junction diode. (B) Collector-base junction diode.*

Capacitors

Two basic capacitor structures used in monolithic fabrication are the *junction* and *thin-film* capacitors illustrated in Fig. 10–29. The junction capacitor is formed by diffusing a P region in an N island, as for base diffusion. The result is a PN junction diode with junction J formed between the N island and the P-diffused region. The capacitance value is adjusted by reverse biasing the PN junction, as for the varactor considered in Chapter 4.

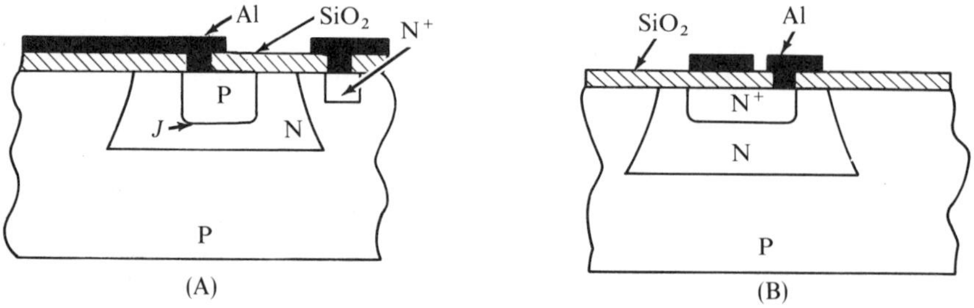

Fig. 10–29. *Two types of monolithic capacitors. (A) Junction. (B) Thin-film.*

In the thin-film capacitor, an N^+ region is diffused in an N island. The N^+ region, which acts as one plate of a capacitor, is separated from the aluminum metallized area, which acts as the other plate of the capacitor, by an SiO_2 layer. The SiO_2 layer serves as the dielectric of the capacitor.

The maximum useful value of monolithic capacitors is approximately 200 pF. Because capacitors occupy a large area on the chip, thereby reducing the packing density, they are avoided wherever possible. As of this date, there is no method available for diffusing practical inductors.

10.12 Parasitics

PN junction isolation results in undesirable circuit elements, called *parasitics*. In this section, we shall examine the origin of parasitic elements with the aid of two examples.

Figure 10–30A illustrates two diffused transistors, Q_1 and Q_2, sharing the same substrate (chip). Because substrate S is generally grounded and collectors C_1 and C_2 are returned to a positive potential, PN junction isolation is obtained. Electrically, this may be represented by depletion diode capacitance, C, in parallel with the reverse diode resistance, R, between each collector and the substrate (Fig. 10–30B).

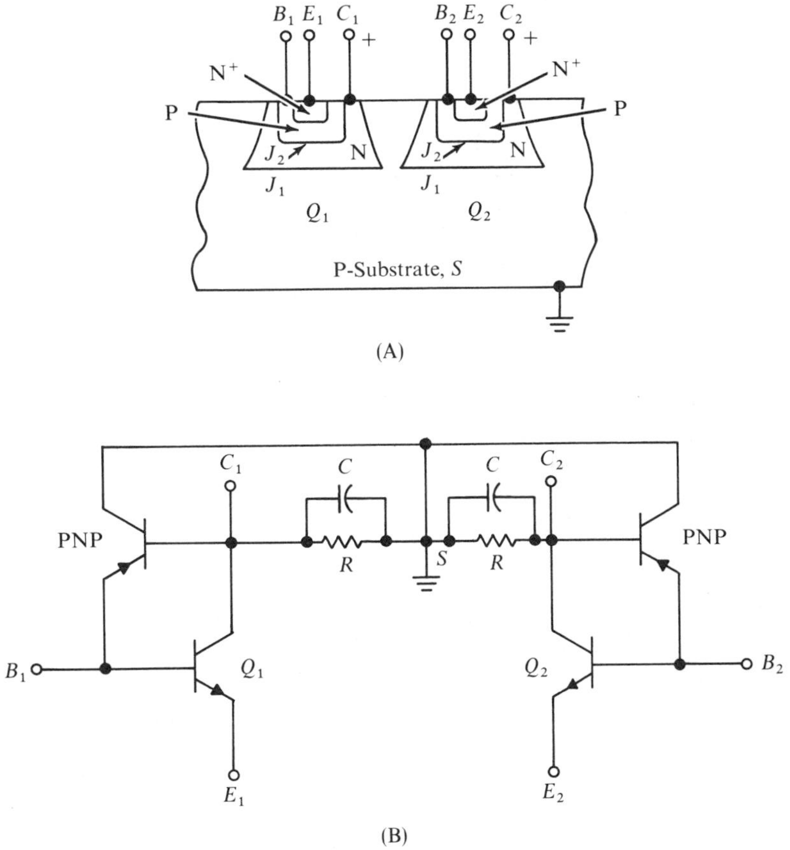

Fig. 10–30. *Two diffused transistors, Q_1 and Q_2, occupying a silicon chip. (A) Cross-section. (B) Resultant circuit illustrating parasitic elements.*

In addition, the substrate and the N island form a collector-base junction (J_1), and the N and P regions form a base-emitter junction (J_2). These two junctions result in the parasitic PNP transistors shown in Fig. 10–30B. Fortunately, the width of the N island, which serves as the base for the PNP transistor, is a few micrometers. The width of an efficient transistor is a fraction of a micrometer. Consequently, the gain of the parasitic transistor is only in the order of one or two. Such a low-gain device does not affect the operation of the integrated circuit to any great degree.

As a second example, consider the diffused resistor of Fig. 10–31A. The parasitics are shown in Fig. 10–31B. In addition to the parasitic transistor, Q_P, there exist R_1C_1 and R_2C_2 parallel networks, since junctions J_1 and J_2 are reverse biased. The capacitors and resistors are actually *distributed*, indicated by the horizontal bars below resistor R and surrounding R_P. Resistance R_P is the ohmic (bulk) resistance of the N region.

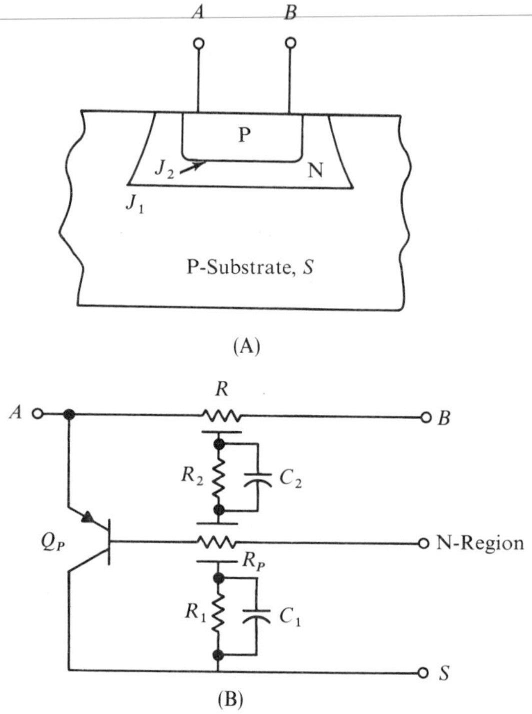

Fig. 10–31. *Diffused resistor. (A) Cross-section. (B) Origin of parasitic elements.*

10.13 Summary of Important Characteristics

Based on the preceding discussion, we can summarize some of the important characteristics of diffused components. They are the following:

1. The absolute tolerance of diffused resistors can be as high as ± 25 percent; the ratio of diffused resistor values can be held to less than ± 2 percent.
2. The use of capacitors should be avoided, or at least minimized.
3. Diffused inductors are not practical.
4. Parasitics limit the high-frequency performance of diffused elements.
5. Monolithic fabrication is best suited for high-volume production of integrated circuits.

10.14 Thin-Film Technology

Thin-film processing provides high-precision resistors and capacitors, in addition to the interconnection conductor pattern. We have already seen that the conductor pattern for the monolithic IC is a thin-film deposit of metal, generally aluminum. The term *thin film* implies a layer thickness from about 5 Å (1 Å = 10^{-8} cm) to 1 μm (10^{-4} cm). Thick films range from approximately 0.1 μm upwards. Thin-film transistors (TFTs) are not available commercially.

Thin films may be deposited on oxidized silicon, ceramic, or glass substrates. Two widely used methods for depositing thin films on a substrate are *vacuum evaporation* and *cathode sputtering.*

Vacuum Evaporation

A basic vacuum evaporation system is illustrated in Fig. 10–32. In a highly evacuated bell jar where the air pressure is approximately 10^{-5} torr (1 torr = 1 mm of mercury) is placed a tungsten element and a substrate. The material to be evaporated, such as aluminum, is placed in the element. Upon passage of 20–25 A of current through the tungsten, the material is quickly vaporized and deposited on the substrate. The substrate is placed at a considerable distance from the element. To aid in the adhesion of the vaporized material, the substrate is sometimes heated.

Cathode Sputtering

A sputtering system is shown in Fig. 10–33. An inert gas, such as argon, is introduced in the bell jar until the pressure

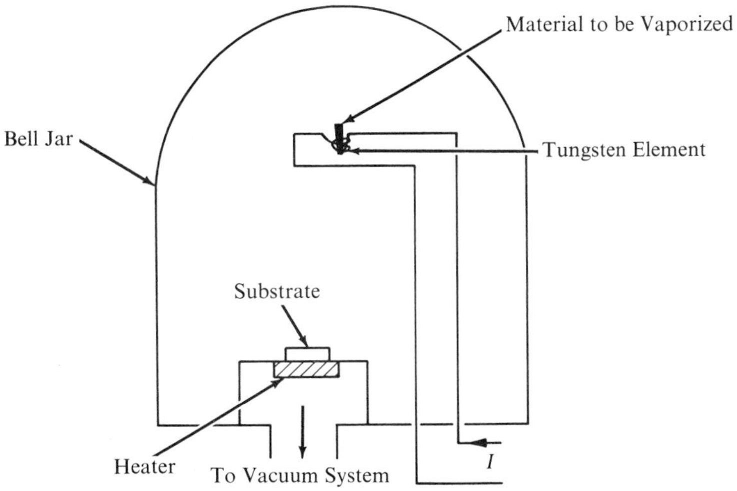

Fig. 10–32. *Basic vacuum evaporation system.*

rises to about 0.05 torr. (The bell jar is also connected to a vacuum system, as in evaporation.) The material to be deposited on the substrate acts like a *cathode*, and the stand on which the substrate is mounted acts like an *anode*, of a gas discharge tube.

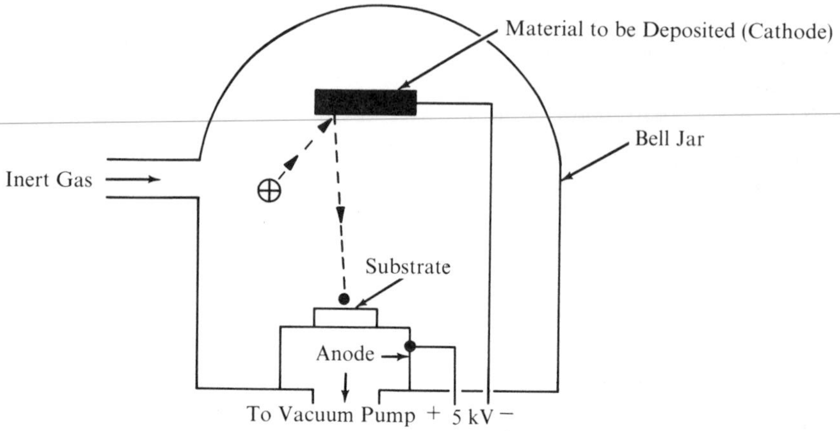

Fig. 10–33. *Basic cathode sputtering system.*

A glow discharge is initiated when a voltage of about 5 kV is impressed across the cathode and anode. Argon positive ions (Ar^+), produced by the discharge, accelerate toward the cathode. Upon striking the cathode, the Ar^+ ions liberate atoms of the material to be deposited. The material diffuses toward the anode and coats the substrate with a thin film. Cathode sputtering is slower than vacuum evaporation. It is used for the deposition of materials with high melting temperatures, such as tantalum, which cannot be readily evaporated.

Measuring Film Thickness

A convenient method for measuring the thickness of deposited films uses a quartz crystal. The quartz determines the frequency of oscillation of a quartz crystal oscillator. Mounted in the bell jar, the crystal is located near the substrate. The same material deposited on the substrate also coats the crystal, resulting in an increase in mass of the crystal and a reduction in the frequency of oscillation. The crystal oscillator is calibrated to read film thickness.

Thin-Film Patterns

The application of photoresist, as in monolithic processing, is commonly employed for obtaining conductor, resistor, and capacitor thin-film patterns. After the substrate is coated with a thin film, it is covered with photoresist. Through a suitable mask, it is then exposed to ultraviolet light. The exposed areas that become polymerized are resistant to etchants; the unexposed areas are etched away. The procedure is repeated until the desired circuit configuration is achieved.

10.15 Thin-Film Components

Resistors

Materials commonly used for thin-film resistors include nichrome ($R_S = 10 - 400\,\Omega$/square) and tantalum nitride ($R_S = 50 - 500\,\Omega$/square). The higher resistance values quoted are realized with thin deposits of material. Low resistance values are obtained with heavy deposits of material. The tolerance of thin-film resistors is better than ± 10 percent.

For very large-value resistors, a *folded geometry* is used, as illustrated in Fig. 10–34. A folded resistor is also called a *meander* resistor.

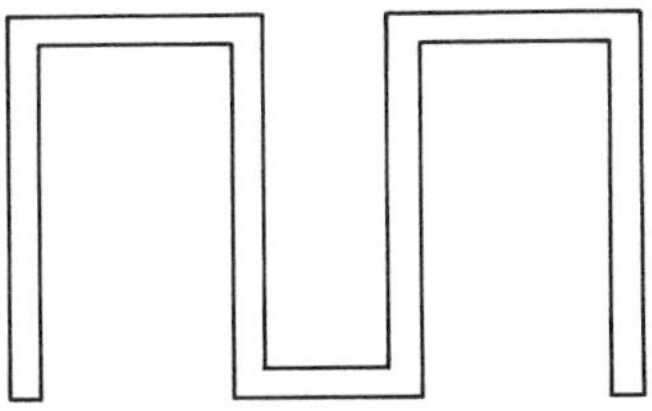

Fig. 10–34. *Example of a folded (meander) resistor.*

Capacitors

A cross-section of a thin-film capacitor is shown in Fig. 10–35. The bottom and top electrodes are generally evaporated aluminum. A number of materials can be used for the dielectric. These include silicon dioxide (dielectric constant $k = 4$) and hafnium dioxide ($k = 80$). Practical values for thin-film capacitors are in the order of 1000 pF maximum.

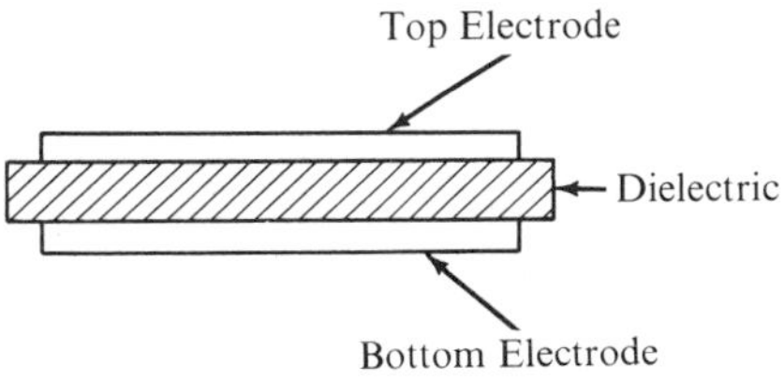

Fig. 10–35. *Cross-section of a thin-film capacitor.*

Trimming Thin-Film Components

Values of thin-film resistors can be increased by abrading, oxidation, and use of a laser beam. These methods reduce the cross-section of the thin-film resistor, thereby increasing its resistance. In abrading, the cross-section of the resistor is reduced with a fine *sandblast* tool. An equivalent effect may be achieved by using an *ultrasonic* trimmer.

In the oxidation method, the substrate is heated in an oven to a high temperature. Oxidation of the resistor surface material occurs, and the cross-section is reduced. In laser trimming, the laser beam is focused on the resistor to be trimmed. The energy of the beam evaporates some of the resistor material, reducing its cross-section.

Capacitance values can be decreased by reducing the area of the top electrode (Fig. 10–35). This generally can be done by abrasion or etching. In some cases, however, a new mask for the top electrode may be required.

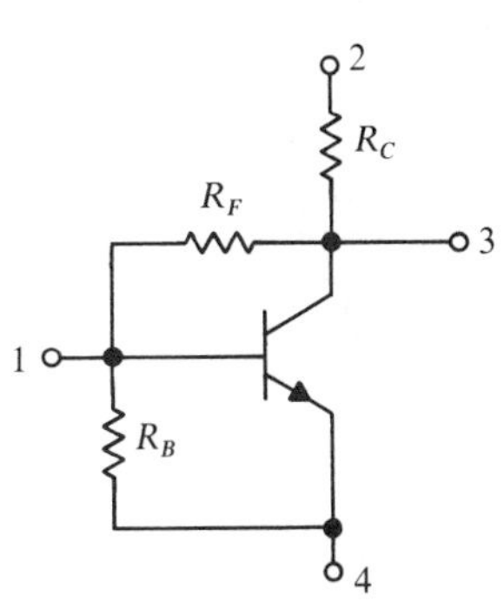

Fig. 10–36. *Transistor amplifier to be converted to a thin-film hybrid. (See Example 10–8.)*

EXAMPLE 10–8.

Lay out a thin-film circuit for the transistor amplifier of Fig. 10–36. The resistor values are such that $R_F > R_B > R_C$.

Solution:

A possible thin-film layout, which would also be the same for a thick-film circuit, is shown in Fig. 10–37. Note the need to provide *contact pads* for the connection of the transistor to the circuit. Contact of resistors with conductors is made by letting the thin-film resistor *overlap* the conductor pad. The completed circuit is an example of a thin-film hybrid IC.

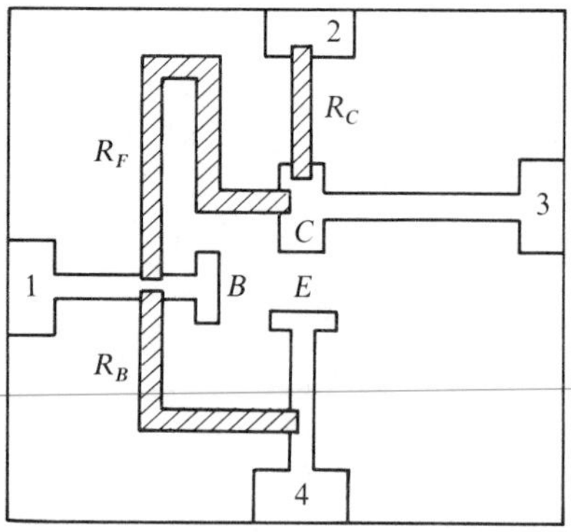

Fig. 10–37. *Thin-film layout of the amplifier of Fig. 10–36.*

10.16 Thick-Film Technology

Thick-film technology is based on a process for depositing conductors, resistors, and capacitors on a ceramic substrate, a process that has been used in the printing industry for more than a century. The process is called *silk screening.* Capital equipment and operator skill required for thick-film technology are much less than needed for monolithic or thin-film work. For these reasons, thick-film processing is very attractive for the manufacture of integrated circuits in moderate quantities.

Silk-Screen Printing

In silk-screen printing, the required circuit pattern is printed on a stainless steel or nylon screen (Fig. 10–38). The screen

Fig. 10–38. *Circuit pattern on a stainless steel screen. (Courtesy the Sel-Rex Company.)*

mesh count ranges from approximately 100 to 325 openings per inch. A suitable light-sensitive material is applied to the screen mesh. A direct-emulsion screen is obtained which is widely used in thick-film work.

The screen is then exposed to ultraviolet light through a mask containing the circuit pattern to be transferred onto the ceramic substrate. Exposed screen areas are polymerized; unexposed areas are dissolved. An exposed screen containing two resistor patterns is illustrated in Fig. 10–39. The shaded area represents polymerized photoresist.

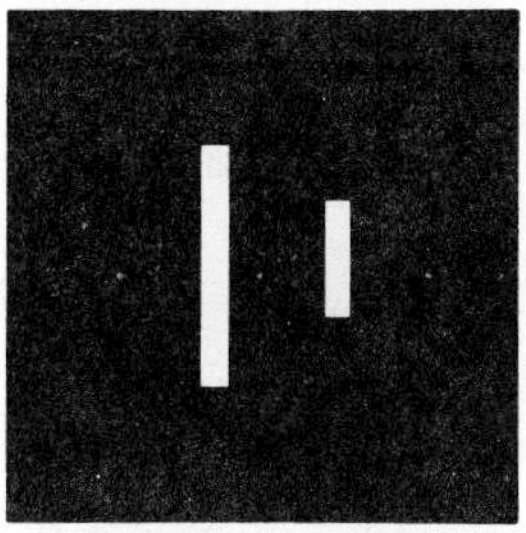

Fig. 10–39. *Exposed screen containing two resistor patterns.*

Resistor and Conductor Inks

Inks (*pastes*) contain an organic resinous filler to carry them through the screen mesh and a solvent to control their viscosity. Precious metals are used for conductors because they have low resistivity and do not oxidize. They include gold, silver, gold-palladium, silver-palladium, and platinum-gold.

Palladium-based inks are most often used for resistors. A typical resistor material is a composition of palladium silver and palladium oxide. A mixture of metals and oxides is sometimes called a *cermet*. Resistor materials are available with sheet resistances of 1 Ω/square–1 MΩ/square for a film thickness of 1 mil (1 mil $= 2.54 \times 10^{-3}$ cm).

Dielectrics for thick-film capacitors are often mixtures of glass and a ferroelectric, such as barium titanate or titanium dioxide. For low-frequency applications, barium titanate may be used, and for high frequencies, titanium dioxide. For good insulation resistance, the dielectric thickness is usually greater than 50 μm.

Contact Printing

The exposed screen is placed close to the substrate, as shown in Fig. 10–40. A conductor or resistor ink is applied to the screen. A squeegee is rolled over the screen, forcing the ink through the screen openings, coating the substrate with a thick-film pattern of ink. In practice, a *screen printer*

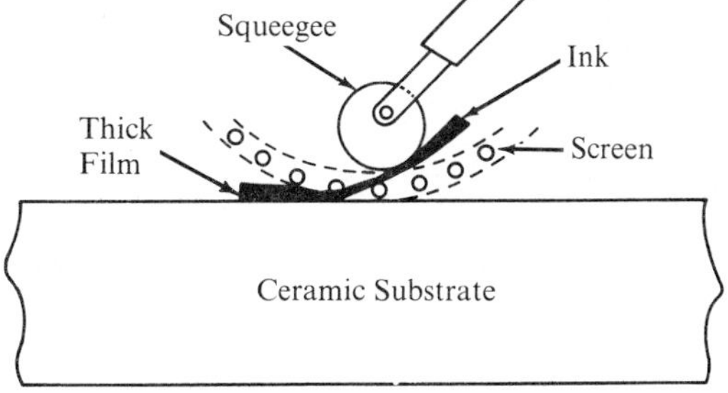

Fig. 10–40. *Applying a thick film on a ceramic substrate.*

(Fig. 10–41) is used. This equipment ensures good alignment of the screen with the substrate and provides uniform pressure and motion of the squeegee over the screen.

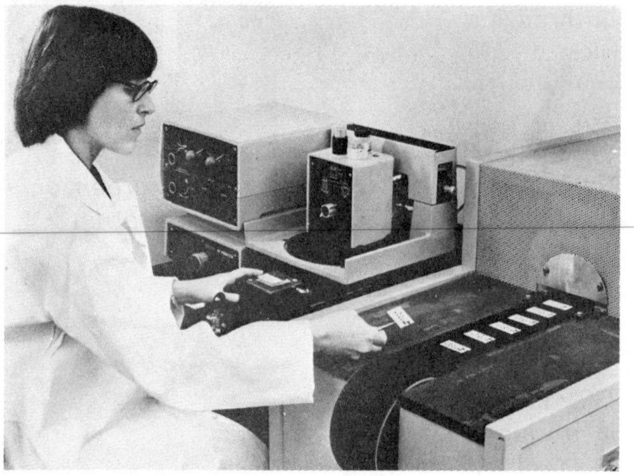

Fig. 10–41. *A screen printer ensures thick-film circuits having uniform characteristics. (Courtesy the Sel-Rex Company.)*

Drying and Firing

After contact printing has been completed, the ink is allowed to settle and is then dried to remove the solvents. Drying is done at 100°C–150°C for approximately 10 min. The substrate is then placed in a furnace at approximately 850°C for 15–30 min to decompose the organic filler. This step is called *firing*. The furnace temperature is generally controlled to within ±2°C.

10.17 Thick-Film Components

Resistors

Resistance values can range from a few ohms to many megohms. Their tolerance, at best, is ±10 percent. By using trimming, tolerances as low as ±0.1 percent can be realized.

Capacitors

A practical limit for thick-film capacitors is 400 pF. For larger values, chip capacitors are attached to contact pads, just as transistors are connected to the circuit.

SUMMARY

Integrated circuits can be classified as being monolithic, thin-film, or thick-film. For large-volume production, monolithic technology is the most economical. In terms of capital equipment, thick-film technology is least expensive.

All three IC technologies share some common features. These include circuit layout, mask cutting, photoreduction, application of photoresist, and exposure to ultraviolet light. For monolithic processing, oxidation and diffusion are two important fabrication steps. Vacuum evaporation or cathode sputtering is necessary for thin-film circuits, and screen printing is needed for thick-film circuits.

The most common and economical method of electrical isolation in the monolithic IC is PN junction isolation. Because of junction isolation, however, parasitic elements limit the frequency response of the circuit. Dielectric and beam-lead isolation minimize greatly the existence of parasitics in an integrated circuit.

Because capacitors occupy appreciable area, they are either minimized or eliminated in the design of integrated circuits. This is especially true for the monolithic IC.

Further Reading

Agnew, Jeremy. *Thick-Film Technology Fundamentals and Applications in Microelectronics.* Rochelle Park, N.J.: Hayden Publishing Company, Inc., 1973.

Ghaznavi, C., and A. H. Seidman. *Electronic Circuit Analysis.* New York: Macmillan Company, 1972, Chapter 16.

Hamer, D. W., and J. V. Biggers. *Thick-Film Hybrid Microcircuit Technology.* New York: Wiley-Interscience, 1972.

Kaufman, M., and A. H. Seidman, eds. *Handbook for Electronics Engineering Technicians.* New York: McGraw-Hill Book Company, 1976, Chapter 9.

Millman J., and C. C. Halkias. *Integrated Electronics: Analog and Digital Circuits and Systems.* New York: McGraw-Hill Book Company, 1972, Chapter 7.

Oldham, W. G., and S. E. Schwarz. *An Introduction to Electronics.* New York: Holt, Rinehart and Winston, 1972, Chapter 7.

RCA. *Linear Integrated Circuits.* Harrison, N.J.: RCA Corporation, 1967, Chapter 1.

Texas Instruments. *Understanding Solid-State Electronics.* Dallas, Texas: Texas Instruments Learning Center, 1972, Chapters 10, 11, and 12.

Tocci, Ronald J. *Fundamentals of Electronic Devices.* 2nd ed. Columbus, Ohio: Charles E. Merrill Publishing Company, 1975, Chapter 17.

REVIEW QUESTIONS

10.1 Identify the two major types of integrated circuits.

10.2 What three methods are used to isolate electrically the circuit elements in a monolithic IC? Which method is most common?

10.3 What is the principal difference between a thin-film and thick-film hybrid IC?

10.4 Why does a silicon wafer have a flattened edge?

10.5 What purity level of silicon is necessary to manufacture discrete or IC devices?

10.6 Describe the zone refining method for obtaining highly pure silicon.

10.7 What is the difference between single-crystal and polycrystalline silicon?

10.8 Explain how single-crystal silicon is obtained by Czochralski pulling.

10.9 For what purposes is SiO_2 formed on top of a silicon wafer?

10.10 What are the properties of polymerized photoresist?

10.11 Describe the diffusion process of introducing impurities into silicon. What factors influence the depth of penetration of impurities in silicon?

10.12 What is meant by epitaxial growth?

10.13 Describe the steps in manufacturing a monolithic IC using PN junction isolation. Specify the types and number of masks required.

10.14 What is the principle of PN junction isolation? To what potential should the substrate, collector, and N island be returned? Why?

10.15 What are two useful guidelines for determining the number of isolation pockets (islands) required in manufacturing an integrated circuit?

10.16 Describe what is meant by
(a) Dielectric isolation.
(b) Beam-lead isolation.

10.17 How is a crossover point made?

10.18 For what is a coordinatograph used?

10.19 Describe the composition of the mask material. What is the trade name for a commonly used mask material?

10.20 What is the purpose of a step-and-repeat camera?

10.21 Describe the use of a mask aligner.

10.22 What is meant by a clean room? Why is a clean room important in the processing of integrated circuits?

10.23 Define solid solubility of a dopant in silicon.

10.24 What is the difference between the error function and Gaussian distributions of impurities?

10.25 Define complementary error function, *erfc*.

10.26 Explain what is meant by ion implantation of impurities.

10.27 What is the difference between LSI and MSI?

10.28 Describe briefly the discretionary wiring and fixed interconnection pattern methods for the manufacture of LSI circuits.

10.29 Draw a cross-section of a buried N^+ layer in a diffused transistor. What is the purpose of the buried layer?

10.30 Compare a diffused lateral PNP transistor with a diffused conventional (vertical) NPN transistor.

10.31 In what respects is a MOSFET superior to a BJT? What are the disadvantages of a MOSFET with respect to a BJT?

10.32 Define
(a) Sheet resistance.
(b) Aspect ratio.

10.33 Why is the concept of sheet resistance useful?

10.34 Describe how a four-point probe is constructed and used to measure sheet resistance.

10.35 What are the differences between a junction and thin-film capacitor?

10.36 For what reasons does a parasitic PNP transistor have a low current gain?

10.37 How does the absolute tolerance of diffused resistors compare with tolerance of the ratio of diffused resistors?

10.38 Describe briefly
(a) Vacuum evaporation.
(b) Cathode sputtering.

10.39 When may cathode sputtering be required instead of vacuum evaporation?

10.40 How may the thickness of a deposited film be measured?

10.41 What materials are commonly used for thin-film resistors?

10.42 What is meant by a meander resistor? Give an example.

10.43 List three methods for trimming resistors.

10.44 How are thin-film (or thick-film) resistors connected to the contact pads?

10.45 On what process is thick-film technology based?

10.46 What are the constituents of a thick-film paste? What function do the constituents serve?

10.47 Define cermet.

10.48 Describe briefly the drying and firing steps in making a thick-film circuit.

PROBLEMS

P10–1 The circuit of Fig. 10–42 is to be integrated.
(a) Draw a layout for the circuit.
(b) Based on your layout, develop a set of masks needed for monolithic processing.

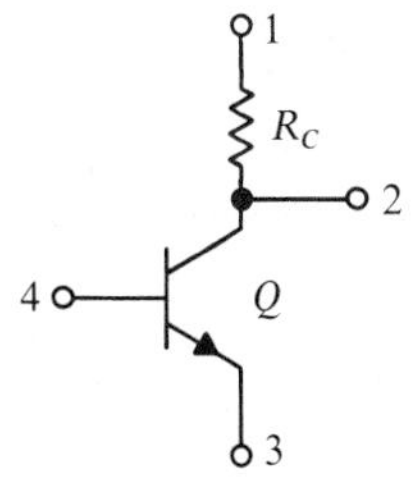

Fig. 10–42.

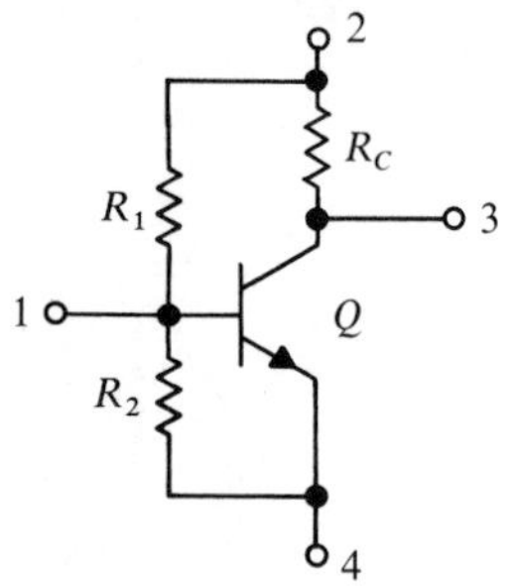

Fig. 10–43.

P10–2 Repeat prob. P10–1 for the circuit of Fig. 10–43.

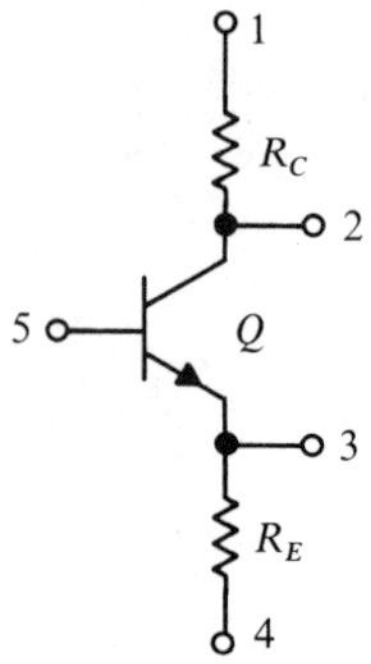

Fig. 10–44.

P10–3 Repeat prob. P10–1(a) for the circuit of Fig. 10–44.

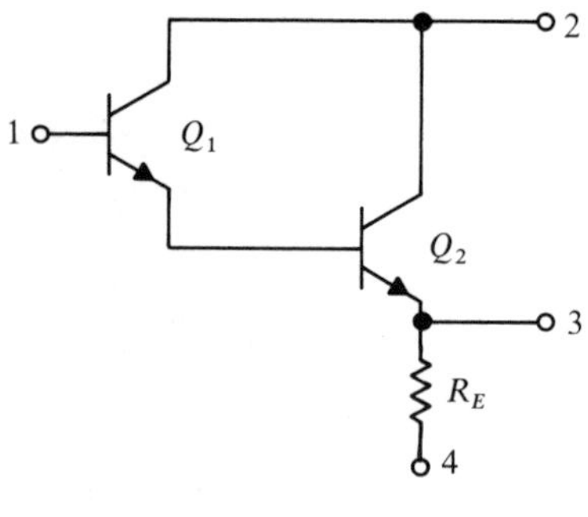

Fig. 10–45.

P10–4 Repeat prob. P10–1(a) for the circuit of Fig. 10–45.

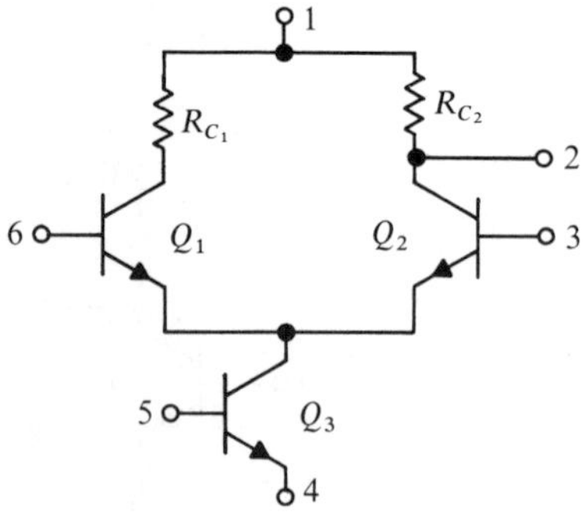

Fig. 10–46.

P10–5 Repeat prob. P10–1(a) for the circuit of Fig. 10–46.

P10–6 Using the curves of Fig. 10–15 and steam at 1200°C, estimate the time needed to grow the following:
(a) A 0.7-μm layer of SiO_2.
(b) A 1-μm layer of SiO_2.

P10–7 Repeat prob. P10–6 for steam at 1000°C.

P10–8 A silicon substrate has an N-type impurity concentration of 10^{16} atoms/cm^3. A PN junction is to be formed 3 μm from its surface. To achieve this, a constant source of boron, $N_o = 5 \times 10^{19}$ atoms/cm^3, is used as the P dopant. If the diffusion temperature $T = 1100$°C, determine the time required to form a PN junction.

P10–9 Repeat prob. P10–8 for a diffusion temperature of 1200°C.

P10–10 A fixed number of boron atoms are deposited on an N-type silicon wafer such that $N_B/N_o = 10^{-2}$. Diffusion takes place for 1.5 h at 1150°C. What is the depth of the formed PN junction?

P10–11 Repeat prob. P10–10 for $N_B/N_o = 10^{-3}$.

P10–12 A uniformly doped P-type silicon wafer has a resistivity of 10 Ω-cm. It is placed in a diffusion furnace and exposed to a constant source of phosphorus, $N_o = 10^{19}$ atoms/cm^3. The wafer is in a diffusion furnace for 0.3 h. If the depth of the formed PN junction is 3 μm from the surface, at what temperature did the diffusion occur?

P10–13 Repeat prob. P10–12 for a uniformly doped P-type silicon wafer having a resistivity of 5 Ω-cm.

P10–14 A uniformly doped P-type silicon wafer having a resistivity of 8 Ω-cm is placed in a diffusion furnace at 1200°C. It is exposed to a constant source of phosphorous, $N_o = 10^{19}$ atoms/cm^3. How long does it take to form a PN junction 1.5 μm away from the surface?

P10–15 Repeat prob. P10–14 for a PN junction formed 2.5 μm away from the surface.

P10–16 From the impurity profile for an integrated transistor in Fig. 10–47, determine
(a) Base width.
(b) Maximum depth of N-type impurity atoms.
(c) Thickness of substrate.

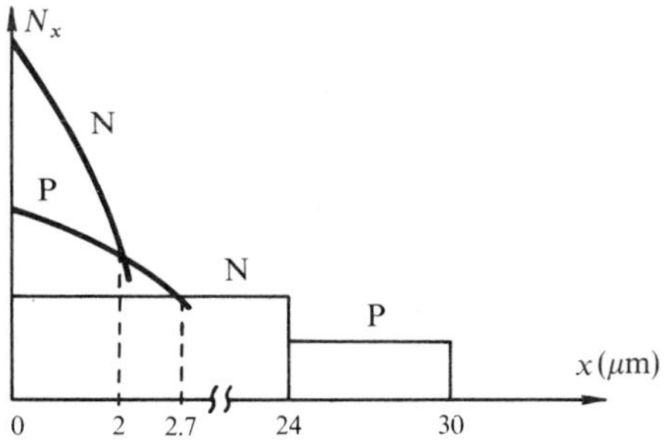

Fig. 10–47.

P10–17 For a diffused resistor of 200 Ω, the sheet resistance is 150 Ω/square.
(a) What is the aspect ratio?
(b) If the width of the resistance is 3 μm, what is the length in centimeters?

P10–18 Repeat prob. P10–17 for a sheet resistance of 250 Ω/square.

P10–19 Figure 10–28 illustrates two ways a diffused transistor can be used as a junction diode. Show three other connections of a transistor functioning as a diode.

P10–20 Lay out a thin-film (or thick-film) circuit for the amplifier of Fig. 10–42.

P10–21 Repeat prob. P10–20 for the amplifier of Fig. 10–43.

P10–22 Repeat prob. P10–20 for the amplifier of Fig. 10–44.

P10–23 Repeat prob. P10–20 for the amplifier of Fig. 10–45.

P10–24 Repeat prob. P10–20 for the amplifier of Fig. 10–46.

11

The Operational Amplifier

One may classify integrated circuits (ICs) as being either *linear* or *nonlinear*. Linear ICs are used for processing *analog* signals, such as in the amplification of voice and music. Nonlinear ICs are used for processing *digital* signals, such as switching pulses in a computer. In this chapter, our concern is with the linear IC. The nonlinear IC is the subject of later chapters.

The workhorse of linear ICs is the operational amplifier (op amp). With suitable negative feedback, the op amp finds wide use in high-gain dc amplifiers, summers, integrators, active filters, and in countless other applications. The basic circuits comprising the op amp are well known. With the introduction of monolithic IC technology, it became possible to fabricate these circuits on a silicon chip having dimensions in the order of 0.13 cm $\times$ 0.13 cm.

Our objectives in this chapter are to define the characteristics and limitations of the op amp, to analyze its basic circuits, and to examine some examples of commercial IC op amps. Chapter 12 covers the applications of op amps.

11.1 Op Amp Characteristics

In the preceding chapter, the basic processing steps in the manufacture of a monolithic IC were considered. As a result of monolithic technology,

1. Devices with almost identical parameters and current-voltage characteristics may be constructed.
2. Because of their close proximity on a chip, the temperature of devices is approximately the same. If, therefore, the temperature of a chip changes, the device parameters vary by approximately the same amount. This behavior is referred to as *good thermal tracking*.
3. Transistors occupy the least space on a chip.
4. NPN transistors are natural for the monolithic process. PNP devices also can be fabricated along with NPN transistors, but with some compromise in their performance.
5. Diffused resistors usually occupy more area on a chip than does a transistor. Individual tolerances of resistors are relatively poor. The tolerance of their ratios, however, is good—as low as ± 2 percent. Values of

diffused resistors are generally in the range of 200 Ω–30 kΩ.

6. Capacitors are restricted to very small values, in the order of 10 pF–30 pF.
7. Inductors are not practical in a monolithic IC.

Design Philosophy

Because of the characteristics of diffused components mentioned above, the design philosophy for integrated circuits differs markedly from that for discrete circuits. These differences are the following:

1. Because transistors occupy the least area on a chip, they are used freely.
2. The NPN transistor is preferred to the PNP type.
3. Because capacitors are restricted to very low values, direct coupling (dc) is used for cascading transistor stages.
4. Resistors of low values are preferred because they occupy less space on a chip.
5. Because the ratios of resistor values can be held to close tolerance, the performance of circuits should be dependent upon resistance ratios wherever possible.

Basic Op Amp

The symbol for the basic op amp is illustrated in Fig. 11–1. For simplicity, power supply and other connections have been omitted. Shown are two input terminals and an output terminal. Terminal 1, the *inverting* (−) input, denotes that the output signal is 180° out of phase with the input signal. If a signal is applied to terminal 2, the *noninverting* (+) input, the output voltage is in phase with the signal. If signals are applied simultaneously to inputs 1 and 2, the output is proportional to their *difference*. The availability of two inputs enhances the usefulness of the op amp.

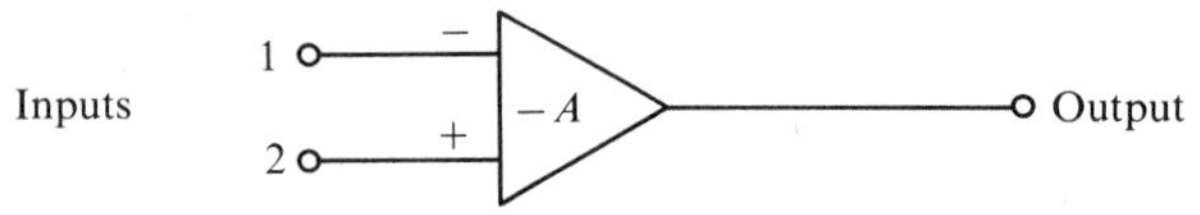

Fig. 11–1. *Electrical symbol for an op amp.*

An *ideal* op amp would exhibit infinite input resistance, zero output resistance, infinite negative gain, infinite bandwidth, and, for zero input signal, the output is also zero. Practical op amps can be made to approximate some of these ideal characteristics to a remarkable degree.

Block Diagram of an Op Amp

Figure 11–2 shows a block diagram of an op amp. The input stage is a *differential amplifier* (*difference amplifier*), which is the heart of the op amp. It provides inverting and noninverting inputs, high input resistance and gain, and small drift. (*Drift* refers to changes in the Q point of an

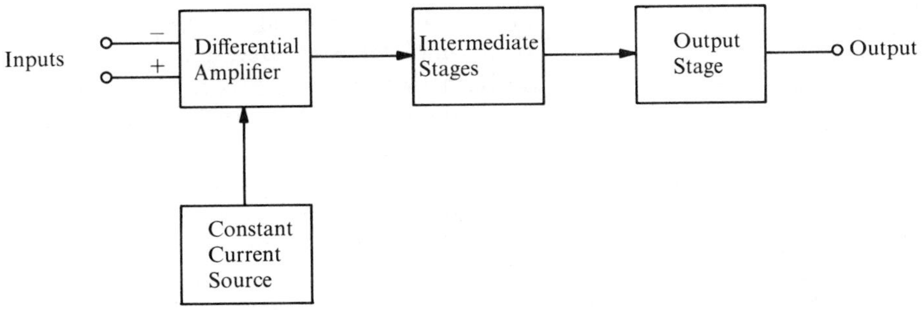

Fig. 11–2. *Block diagram of an op amp.*

amplifier with temperature, etc.) For optimum performance, the constant current source (to be described later) is essential.

The intermediate stages provide additional gain, dc level shifting (to ensure that the output is zero for zero input signal), and drive for the output stage. An emitter follower is used often for the output stage; however, other configurations are also employed. In the remainder of this chapter, the operation of these circuits is explained and analyzed.

11.2 The Differential Amplifier

The basic differential amplifier is illustrated in Fig. 11–3. Note the *symmetry* of the circuit. Two transistors, Q_1 and Q_2, are *emitter coupled.* Their emitters are connected and returned to signal ground through a large-value emitter resistor, R_E. Input signals may be applied to Q_1 and Q_2. Outputs are available from the collector of Q_1 (V_{o_1}) and the collector of Q_2 (V_{o_2}). In monolithic IC technology, the transistors and resistors are diffused simultaneously and are in close physical proximity. Therefore, their individual characteristics are very similar. In our analyses, we shall assume that they are identical.

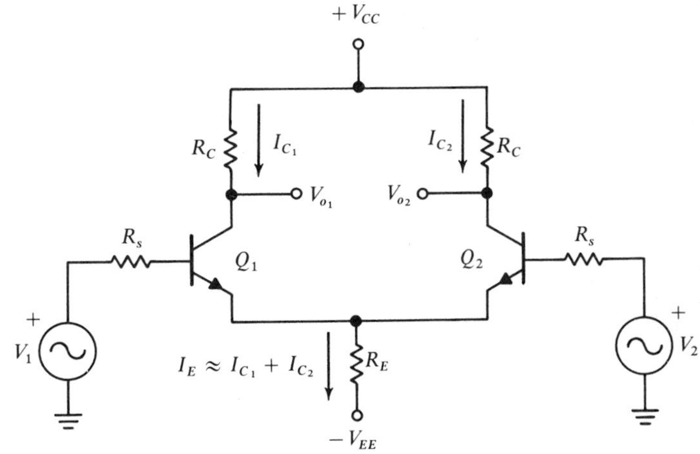

Fig. 11–3. *Basic differential amplifier.*

To understand its operation, we view the differential amplifier as a bridge, similar to a Wheatstone bridge. Viewed in this manner, collector resistors R_C and transistors Q_1 and Q_2 form four arms of the bridge. The difference output voltage is $V_{o_1} - V_{o_2}$.

If $V_1 = V_2$, the circuit is balanced. Currents I_{C_1} and I_{C_2} are equal, and the net voltage between the collectors, $V_{o_1} - V_{o_2}$, is zero. Let, for example, $V_1 > V_2$. For this condition, $I_{C_1} > I_{C_2}$, and the bridge is unbalanced. Collector voltage V_{o_1} is now less than V_{o_2}, and $V_{o_1} - V_{o_2} \neq 0$.

Common-Mode and Difference-Mode Signals

Signals V_1 and V_2 may be thought of as each containing two components: a *common-mode* and a *difference-mode* signal. Suppose $V_1 = 550\,\mu V$ and $V_2 = 450\,\mu V$. We can express these values as

$$V_1 = 500 + 50 = 550\,\mu V$$
$$V_2 = 500 - 50 = 450\,\mu V$$

The 500-μV component represents the common-mode signal, and the difference, $550 - 450 = 100\,\mu V$, the difference-mode signal. A common-mode signal, as implied by its name, is common to both inputs. Sources of common-mode signals include power supply hum, temperature variations, and noise. The difference-mode signal is to be amplified. A differential amplifier, however, also responds to the common-mode signal.

Let the common-mode signal be designated as V_c and the difference-mode signal as V_d. Using the values given in the preceding illustration, we can write

$$V_c = \frac{550 + 450}{2} = 500\,\mu V$$

$$V_d = 550 - 450 = 100\,\mu V$$

In general terms,

$$V_c = \frac{V_1 + V_2}{2} \qquad \textbf{(11–1a)}$$

$$V_d = V_1 - V_2 \qquad \textbf{(11–1b)}$$

Solving Eq. (11–1) for V_1 and V_2 in terms of the common- and difference-mode signals, we obtain

$$V_1 = V_c + \frac{V_d}{2} \qquad \textbf{(11–2a)}$$

$$V_2 = V_c - \frac{V_d}{2} \qquad \textbf{(11–2b)}$$

EXAMPLE 11–1.

Impressed across the inputs of a differential amplifier are

(a) $V_1 = 2\,mV$, $V_2 = 1\,mV$.
(b) $V_1 = 1\,mV$, $V_2 = -1\,mV$.

Determine the difference- and common-mode signal components in each case.

Solutions:

(a) By Eq. (11–1),

$$V_d = 2 - 1 = 1\,\text{mV}$$

and

$$V_c = \frac{2 + 1}{2} = 1.5\,\text{mV}$$

(b) As in part (a),

$$V_d = 1 - (-1) = 2\,\text{mV}$$

$$V_c = \frac{1 - 1}{2} = 0\,\text{mV}$$

Common-Mode Rejection Ratio

Let the voltage gain for the common-mode signal be denoted by A_{vc} and for the difference-mode signal by A_{vd}. We can define a figure of merit for the differential amplifier, as well as for the op amp, called the *common-mode rejection ratio*, CMRR. The common-mode rejection ratio is defined as the ratio of A_{vd} to A_{vc}:

$$\text{CMRR} = \frac{A_{vd}}{A_{vc}} \qquad \textbf{(11–3)}$$

The greater the value of CMRR, the better is the performance of the amplifier. For an ideal differential amplifier, the common-mode gain would be zero and CMRR infinite.

EXAMPLE 11–2.

From measurements made on a differential amplifier, it was found that $A_{vd} = -100$ and $A_{vc} = -0.1$. Express CMRR as a numeric and in decibels.

Solution:

By Eq. (11–3),

$$\text{CMRR} = \frac{-100}{-0.1} = 1000$$

In decibels,

$$\text{CMRR} = 20\log(1000) = 20 \times 3 = 60\,\text{dB}$$

Analysis

Because of its symmetry, the differential amplifier is relatively simple to analyze. In the analysis, low- and mid-frequency operation are assumed. This enables us to obtain useful results without the necessity of considering the inherent transistor and parasitic capacitances and resistances of diffused devices. Inclusion of these elements yields a very complex model whose solution is best obtained on a computer.

First, we shall derive an expression for the common-mode voltage gain, A_{vc}. It is reasonable to neglect h_{re} and to assume that $1/h_{oe} \gg R_C$. For the common-mode signal, $V_d = 0$, and, by Eq. (11–2), $V_1 = V_2 = V_c$. Because of its symmetry, we may divide Fig. 11–3 down the middle into two equal parts. When this is done, however, emitter resistor R_E has to be replaced by two resistors, each equal to $2R_E$ as illustrated in Fig. 11–4A. This is necessary because $(2R_E)\|(2R_E) = R_E$. The resultant half-circuit is given in Fig. 11–4B and its small-signal model in Fig. 11–5.

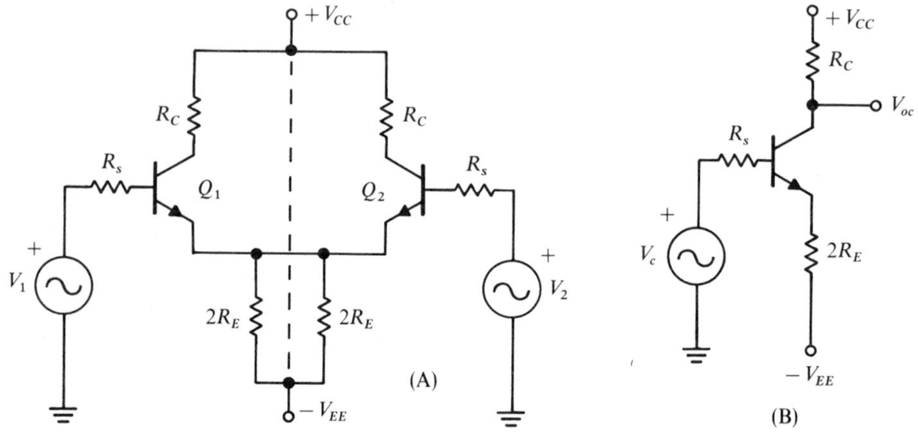

Fig. 11–4. *Because of its symmetry, the differential amplifier may be simplified for analysis. (A) Dividing the circuit into halves. (B) Simplified circuit for common-mode signals.*

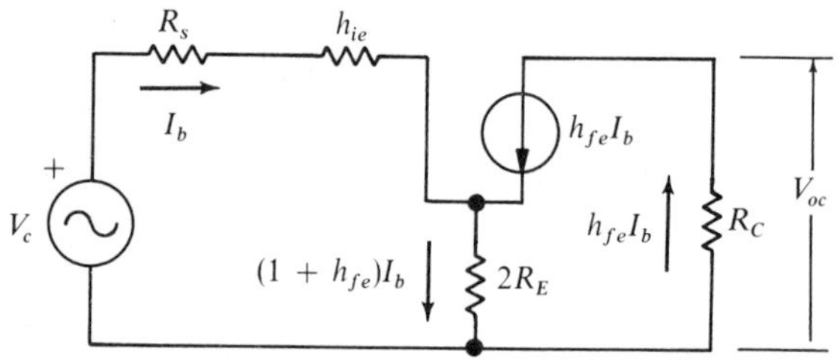

Fig. 11–5. *Small-signal model of Fig. 11–4B for finding the common-mode voltage gain, A_{vc}.*

For the input side of Fig. 11–5, we can write

$$V_c = [R_s + h_{ie} + (1 + h_{fe})2R_E]I_b$$

Solving for I_b,

$$I_b = \frac{V_c}{R_s + h_{ie} + (1 + h_{fe})2R_E} \tag{11–4}$$

For the output side, we have

$$V_{oc} = -h_{fe}I_bR_C \tag{11–5}$$

Substituting Eq. (11–4) for I_b in Eq. (11–5) and solving for V_{oc}/V_c, we obtain the common-mode voltage gain:

$$A_{vc} = \frac{V_{oc}}{V_c} = \frac{-h_{fe}R_C}{R_s + h_{ie} + (1 + h_{fe})2R_E} \tag{11–6}$$

If $(1 + h_{fe})2R_E \gg R_s + h_{ie}$ and $1 + h_{fe} \simeq h_{fe}$, both reasonable assumptions, then Eq. (11–6) reduces to

$$A_{vc} \simeq \frac{-R_C}{2R_E} \tag{11–7}$$

Remember that for a high common-mode rejection ratio, A_{vc} should be as low as possible. From Eq. (11–7), we see that if R_C is reduced or R_E increased, the common-mode gain decreases. Because R_C must be reasonably large for good difference-mode gain, we must increase R_E. How this is accomplished in a practical and efficient manner, using a constant current source, will be considered in the next section.

To find the difference-mode gain, A_{vd}, the common-mode voltage is set to zero. By Eq. (11–2), therefore, $V_1 = V_d/2$ and $V_2 = -V_d/2$. For $V_1 = V_d/2$, collector current I_{c1} increases; for $V_2 = -V_d/2$, collector current I_{c2} decreases. Using matched components, the increase in I_{c1} equals the decrease in I_{c2}. Because the base current may be assumed to be negligible with respect to the collector current, $I_e = I_{c1} + I_{c2}$ is therefore zero. This fact permits us to draw one-half of the circuit as in Fig. 11–6A, where the emitter resistor is shorted out. The small-signal model is given in Fig. 11–6B.

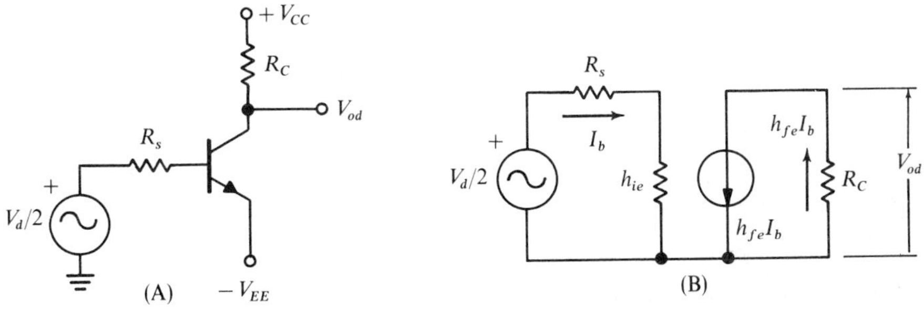

Fig. 11–6. *Determining the difference-mode voltage gain, A_{vd}. (A) Simplified circuit. (B) Small-signal model.*

In Fig. 11–6B, base current I_b is

$$I_b = \frac{\frac{V_d}{2}}{R_s + h_{ie}} \tag{11–8}$$

Output voltage V_{od} is

$$V_{od} = -h_{fe}I_bR_C \tag{11–9}$$

Substituting Eq. (11–8) in Eq. (11–9) and solving for V_{od}/V_d, the difference-mode gain, we have

$$A_{vd} = \frac{-h_{fe}R_C}{2(R_s + h_{ie})} \tag{11–10}$$

If the derived expressions for A_{vd} and A_{vc} are substituted in Eq. (11–3), we may express the common-mode rejection ratio by

$$\text{CMRR} = \frac{h_{fe}R_E}{R_s + h_{ie}} \tag{11–11}$$

EXAMPLE 11–3.

For the differential amplifier of Fig. 11–3, $h_{ie} = 2\,\text{k}\Omega$, $R_s = 3\,\text{k}\Omega$, $R_C = R_E = 5\,\text{k}\Omega$, $h_{fe} = 100$, and $h_{re} = h_{oe} = 0$. Find the values of

(a) A_{vc}.
(b) A_{vd}.
(c) CMRR.

Solutions:

(a) By Eq. (11–7),

$$A_{vc} = -\frac{5000}{2 \times 5000} = -0.5$$

(b) By Eq. (11–10),

$$A_{vd} = \frac{-100 \times 5\,\text{k}\Omega}{2(3\,\text{k}\Omega + 2\,\text{k}\Omega)} = -50$$

(c) By Eq. (11–3),

$$\text{CMRR} = \frac{-50}{-0.5} = 100$$
$$= 20 \log(100) = 40\,\text{dB}$$

Biasing the Differential Amplifier

We now calculate the dc quiescent operating (Q) point for the transistors in the differential amplifier. Again taking advantage of its symmetry, we need only analyze one-half the circuit, as we did in studying the signal performance of the amplifier. For dc analysis, the signal sources V_1 and V_2 are set to zero. The circuit of Fig. 11–4B is therefore redrawn as shown in Fig. 11–7.

Because we are concerned here with dc quantities, dc current gain, h_{FE}, is used instead of signal gain, h_{fe}. All subscripts are capitalized to remind us that we are dealing with dc voltages and currents.

For the input side of Fig. 11–7, we have

$$V_{EE} - V_{BE} = I_B[R_s + 2R_E(1 + h_{FE})]$$

Solving for I_B,

$$I_B = \frac{V_{EE} - V_{BE}}{R_s + 2R_E(1 + h_{FE})} \tag{11–12}$$

If $2R_E(1 + h_{FE}) \gg R_s$ and $h_{FE} + 1 \simeq h_{FE}$, Eq. (11–12) reduces to

$$I_B = \frac{V_{EE} - V_{BE}}{2h_{FE}R_E} \tag{11–13}$$

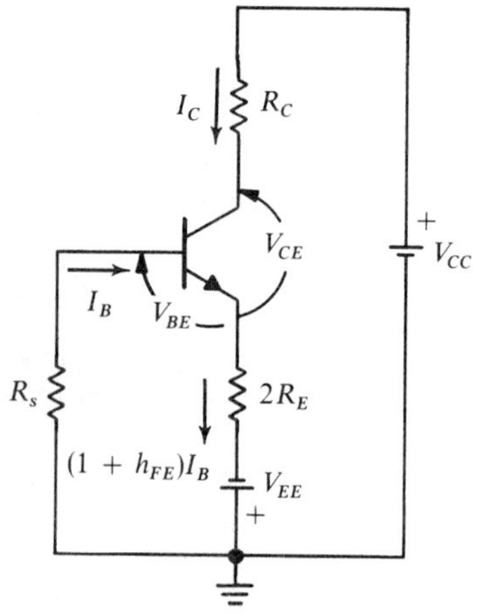

Fig. 11–7. *Model of differential amplifier used for determining its Q point.*

Collector current $I_C = h_{FE}I_B$; therefore,

$$I_C = \frac{V_{EE} - V_{BE}}{2R_E} \qquad \textbf{(11–14)}$$

From Fig. 11–7, the collector-emitter voltage, V_{CE}, is

$$V_{CE} = V_{CC} + V_{EE} - R_C I_C - 2R_E(1 + h_{FE})I_B \qquad \textbf{(11–15)}$$

Letting $(1 + h_{FE})I_B \simeq I_C$ and substituting Eq. (11–14) for I_C in Eq. (11–15), we obtain

$$V_{CE} = V_{CC} + V_{EE} - \frac{R_C}{2R_E}(V_{EE} - V_{BE}) \qquad \textbf{(11–16)}$$

In terms of resistance values, V_{CE} depends on the ratio of the collector and emitter resistances. This is desirable since ratios of diffused resistance values can be held to ± 2 percent.

11.3 Constant Current Source

In our analysis of the common-mode gain, we saw that for a low value of A_{vc}, the emitter resistance must be increased. If R_E is increased, greater values of bias supply sources, V_{CC} and V_{EE}, are required to ensure the same Q point. The power dissipated in R_E, which is wasted as heat, also increases. To overcome these objections, a constant current source is generally used in place of an emitter resistor. A constant current source simulates a high emitter resistance, in the order of several hundred kilohms, for the signal.

The symbol for a constant current source is the current generator, I_o, shown connected between the emitters of Q_1 and Q_2 and V_{EE} in Fig. 11–8. Because the transistors are well matched, the quiescent collector currents, I_{C_1} and I_{C_2}, are equal, and $I_{C_1} = I_{C_2} = I_o/2$. The constant current source is also referred to as a *current sink*.

A diode-biased constant current source is illustrated in Fig. 11–9. The collector and base of Q_1 are tied together.

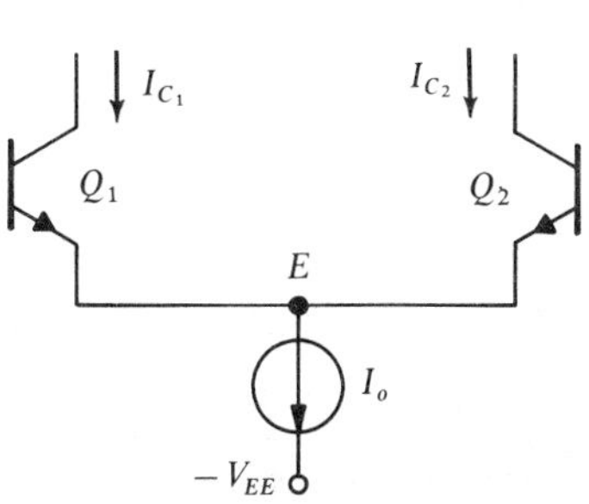

Fig. 11–8. *Constant current source, I_o, replacing an emitter resistor in a differential amplifier.*

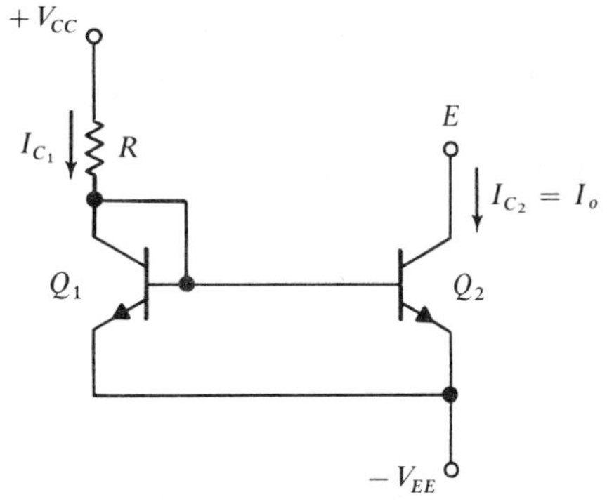

Fig. 11–9. *Diode-biased constant current source.*

Transistor Q_1, therefore, acts like a diode. Assume that both transistors have the same geometry. Because the base-emitter voltage of Q_2 is the same for Q_1, collector current I_{C_2} equals I_{C_1}.

If the emitter area of Q_1 is A_{E_1} and that of Q_2 is A_{E_2}, the ratio of I_{C_2} to I_{C_1} is related to their respective emitter areas by

$$\frac{I_{C_2}}{I_{C_1}} = \frac{A_{E_2}}{A_{E_1}}$$

In terms of the notation of Fig. 11–9, $I_o = I_{C_2}$; hence,

$$I_o = \frac{I_{C_1} A_{E_2}}{A_{E_1}} \quad \textbf{(11–17)}$$

Current I_{C_1}, neglecting the base-emitter voltage of Q_1, is equal to $(V_{CC} + V_{EE})/R$. For a given value of I_{C_1}, therefore, I_o depends primarily on the emitter areas of Q_1 and Q_2. This provides a very stable current source.

Figure 11–10 is another example of a constant current source. The circuit is basically a transistor amplifier with an unbypassed emitter resistor, R_3. Diode D cancels the base-emitter voltage, V_{BE}, thereby ensuring stable operation with temperature. In some cases, two or three diodes may be strung in series to provide optimum operation.

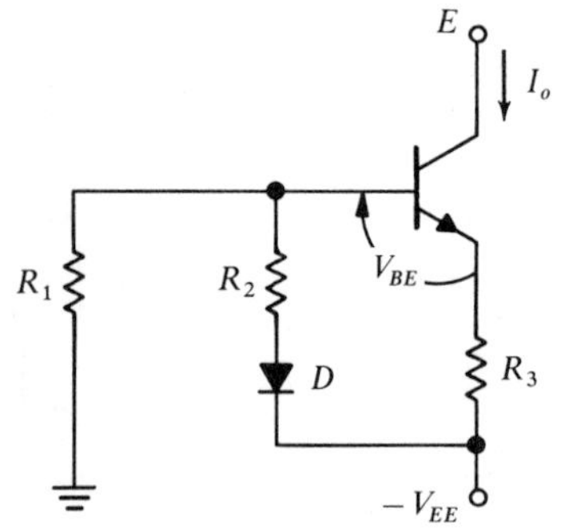

Fig. 11–10. *Another example of a constant current source.*

11.4 Effects of I_o

We begin an analysis of the differential amplifier in terms of the constant current, I_o. In Chapter 8, we found that the transconductance, g_m, is related to h_{fe} and $r_{b'e}$ by

$$g_m = \frac{h_{fe}}{r_{b'e}} \quad \textbf{(8–7)}$$

Also, by Eq. (8–13),

$$g_m = \frac{qI_C}{kT} \quad \textbf{(8–13)}$$

Substituting Eq. (8–13) in Eq. (8–7) and solving for $r_{b'e}$, we have

$$r_{b'e} = \frac{kTh_{fe}}{qI_C} \quad \textbf{(11–18)}$$

Returning to Eq. (11–10) for the differential-mode gain and neglecting, for simplicity, source resistance, R_s,

$$A_{vd} = -\frac{h_{fe}R_C}{2h_{ie}} \tag{11–19}$$

Because $r_{b'e} \simeq h_{ie}$, substitution of Eq. (11–18) in Eq. (11–19) yields

$$A_{vd} = -\frac{qI_C R_C}{2kT} \tag{11–20a}$$

Letting $I_C = I_o/2$, Eq. (11–20a) becomes

$$A_{vd} = -\frac{qI_o R_C}{4kT} \tag{11–20b}$$

Expression (11–20b) is significant because it states that the difference-mode gain varies *directly* with I_o.

To calculate the input resistance for difference-mode signals, R_{id}, we refer to Fig. 11–6B. For the input side, neglecting R_s,

$$I_b = \frac{V_d}{2h_{ie}}$$

Dividing V_d by I_b gives us R_{id}:

$$R_{id} = 2h_{ie}$$

Substitution of Eq. (11–18) for h_{ie} and replacing I_C by $I_o/2$ yields

$$R_{id} = \frac{4kTh_{fe}}{qI_o} \tag{11–21}$$

According to Eq. (11–21), R_{id} varies *inversely* with I_o. From Eq. (11–20b), we found that A_{vd} varies directly with I_o. There is a conflict, and a compromise in values for A_{vd} and R_{id} must be made by the circuit designer.

EXAMPLE 11–4.

Determine R_{id} and A_{vd} of a differential amplifier at room temperature if

(a) $I_o = 1$ mA.

(b) $I_o = 0.1$ mA.

Assume that $h_{fe} = 100$ and $R_C = 4\,\text{k}\Omega$. At room temperature, $kT/q \simeq 25\,\text{mV}$.

Solutions:

(a) By Eq. (11–21),

$$R_{id} = \frac{4 \times 0.025 \times 100}{10^{-3}} = 10\,\text{k}\Omega$$

By Eq. (11–20b),

$$A_{vd} = -\frac{4 \times 10^3 \times 10^{-3}}{4 \times 0.025} = -40$$

(b) Similar to part (a),

$$R_{id} = 10 \times 10{,}000 = 100\,\text{k}\Omega$$
$$A_{vd} = 0.1(-40) = -4$$

11.5 Darlington Pair

The *Darlington pair* is a circuit for realizing high input resistance. In one version, shown in Fig. 11–11, the circuit consists of two cascaded emitter followers. The emitter of Q_1 is connected directly to the base of Q_2. Resistance R_B provides bias, and the output is taken across emitter resistance R_E.

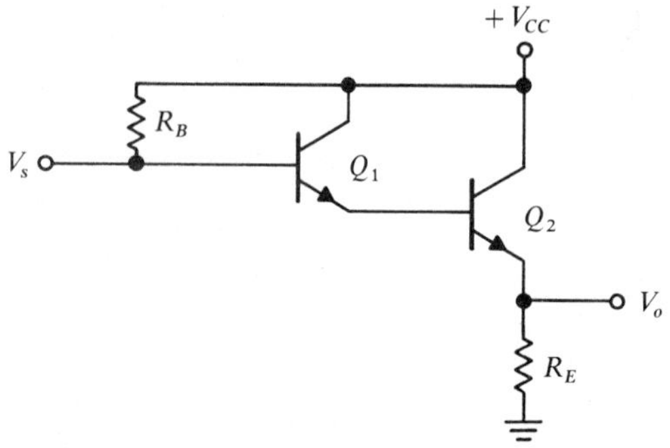

Fig. 11–11. *Darlington pair with output taken across the emitter.*

The input resistance of Q_2, as shown in Chapter 6, may be approximated by

$$R_{i_2} \simeq h_{fe}R_E$$

But R_{i_2} may be thought of as the "emitter resistor" for Q_1; hence, the input resistance to the circuit, R_i, is

$$R_i \simeq h_{fe}^2 R_E \tag{11–22}$$

Because of the presence of R_B, the actual input resistance is $R_i \| R_B$.

Because of the cascaded emitter followers, the overall voltage gain of the Darlington pair of Fig. 11–11 is less than one. The current gain of each stage is approximately equal to h_{fe}. The overall current gain, therefore, is h_{fe}^2.

EXAMPLE 11–5.

If, in the Darlington pair of Fig. 11–11, $h_{fe} = 100$ for each transistor and $R_E = 100\,\Omega$, find the input resistance to the circuit.

Solution:

By Eq. (11–22),

$$R_i = 100^2 \times 100 = 1\,\text{M}\Omega$$

In another version of the Darlington pair, the output is taken across the collector, as shown in Fig. 11–12. An analysis for the circuit shows that $R_i \simeq h_{fe}h_{ie}$, $A_i \simeq h_{fe}^2$, and $A_v \simeq h_{fe}R_C/h_{ie}$. An example of a Darlington-connected differential amplifier using the collector-connected pair is

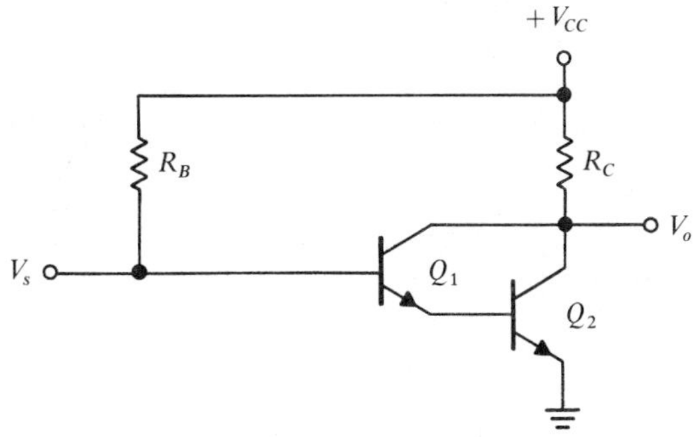

Fig. 11–12. *Darlington pair with output taken across the collector.*

shown in Fig. 11–13. Another method for realizing high input resistance is to use field-effect transistors for the differential amplifier.

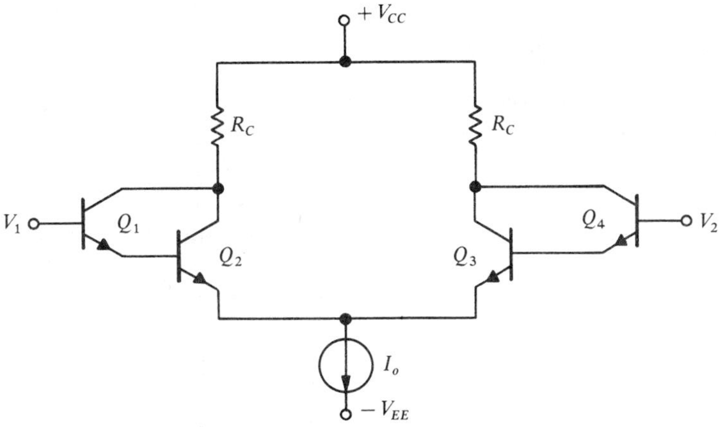

Fig. 11–13. *Darlington-pair connected differential amplifier.*

11.6 Intermediate Stages

Often the gain obtained from a single differential amplifier is inadequate to satisfy the overall gain requirements of an op amp. To achieve greater gain, another differential amplifier may be connected in cascade, as illustrated in Fig. 11–14. The cascaded stage provides a balanced load for the first (input) differential amplifier stage.

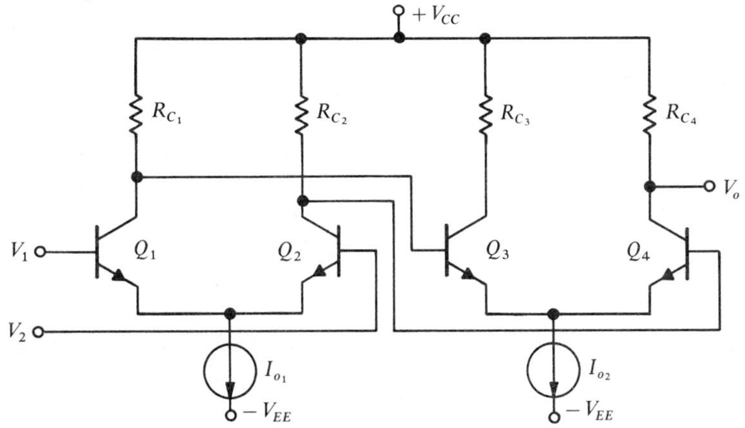

Fig. 11–14. *Cascading differential amplifier stages.*

Output voltage, V_o, is obtained from the collector of Q_4. Because a single output is usually required, the collector resistor of Q_3 may be omitted. Another simplification is the replacement of the constant current source in the cascaded stage by an emitter resistor. These modifications result in the simplified cascaded stage shown in Fig. 11–15.

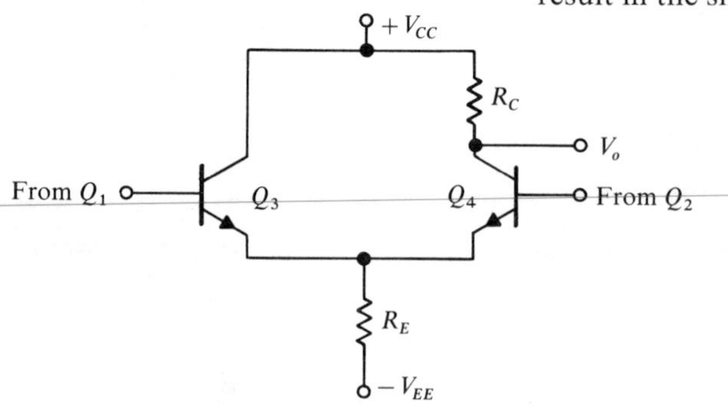

Fig. 11–15. *Simplified cascaded differential amplifier stage.*

Another technique for increasing gain is illustrated in Fig. 11–16. The collectors of Q_1 and Q_2 are directly coupled to the bases of Q_3 and Q_4, respectively. Transistor Q_4 constitutes the intermediate stage. To achieve balanced operation, $R_1 = R_2$ and $R_3 = R_4$.

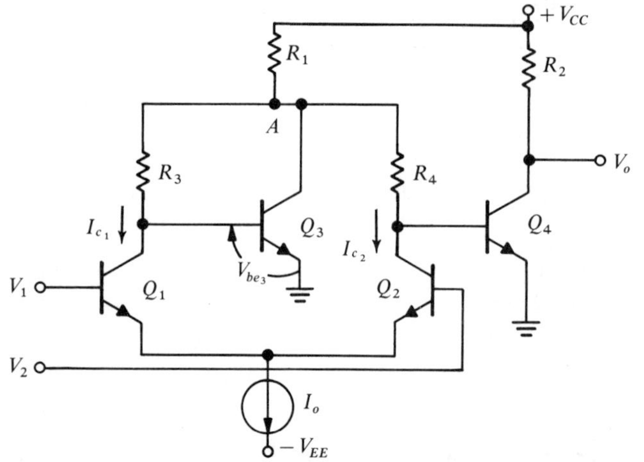

Fig. 11–16. *Circuit for increasing voltage gain of a differential amplifier.*

Assume that I_{c_1} increases and I_{c_2} decreases by equal amounts. Consequently, the collector voltage of Q_1 falls, and the collector voltage of Q_2 rises. The net voltage across the base-emitter junction of Q_3, V_{be_3}, tends to decrease. This decrease produces a greater change in collector voltage of Q_3 because of its amplification. The voltage at point A is therefore increased.

Looking at the base of Q_4, we see two effects occurring simultaneously; at the base of Q_4, we see:

1. A rising voltage because of the decrease in I_{c2}.
2. A rising voltage because of the increase of voltage at point A.

These two effects effectively double the gain of Q_4. An example of this circuit in a commercial op amp is given later in this chapter.

11.7 Level Shifters

Because of direct coupling in an op amp, as we proceed from the input to the output stage, a positive voltage buildup, or translation, occurs. This means that for a zero input signal, a dc voltage is present at the output. Compensation is required to ensure that zero output is obtained for zero input. A circuit for accomplishing this is called a *dc level shifter.*

A simple dc level shifter is illustrated in Fig. 11–17A. Transistor Q_1 is a modified emitter follower where the output is taken at the junction of two emitter resistors in series, R_{E_1} and R_{E_2}. The dc voltage dropped in the circuit, which is made equal to the positive voltage buildup, is

$$\text{Voltage dropped} = V_{BE_1} + I_{E_1}R_{E_1} \qquad \textbf{(11–23)}$$

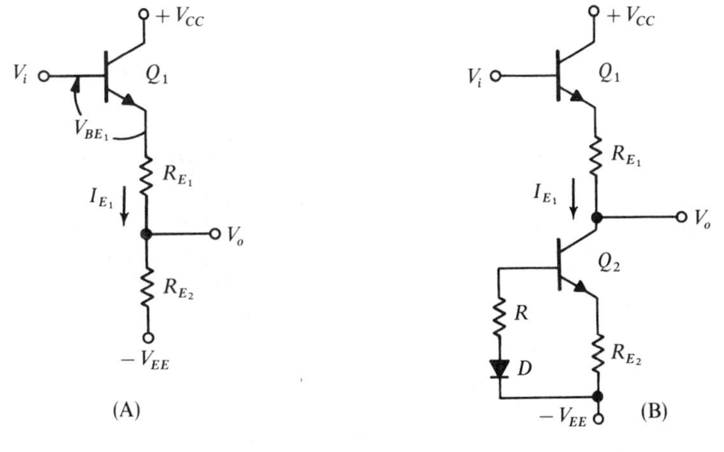

Fig. 11–17. *Examples of dc level shifters. (A) Modified emitter follower. (B) Using a constant current source.*

Because the voltage gain is much less than one for the modified emitter follower, an improved circuit is shown in Fig. 11–17B. Transistor Q_2 acts as a constant current source (see Fig. 11–10). The dc voltage drop across the base-emitter junction of Q_1 and R_{E_1} is the same as given by Eq. (11–23); the voltage gain, however, is close to unity.

11.8 Output Stage

The last stage of an op amp is the *output stage.* Requirements for a good output stage include:

1. Sufficient power to drive the load to which it is connected.
2. Low output impedance.

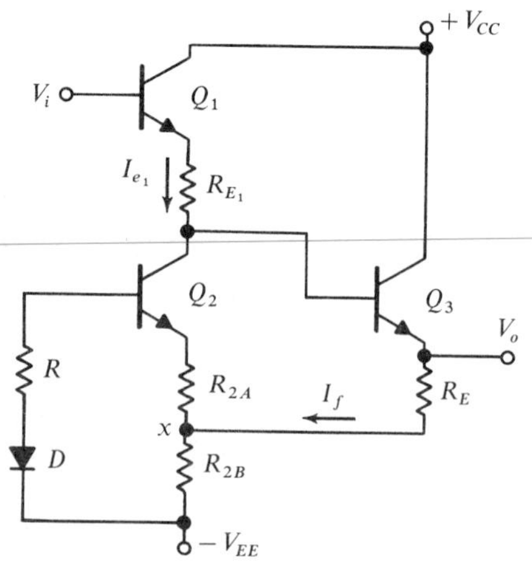

Fig. 11–18. *Transistors Q_1 and Q_2 form a dc level shifter. Transistor Q_3 serves as an emitter follower output stage. Emitter resistor R_E is returned to point x to provide a voltage gain greater than unity for the emitter follower.*

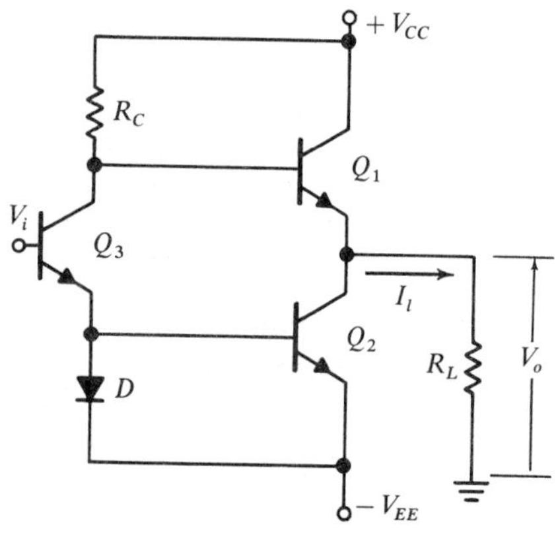

Fig. 11–19. *Transistors Q_1 and Q_2 form a totem-pole output stage. Transistor Q_3 serves as a phase splitter.*

3. Output voltage capable of swinging from zero volts for zero input signal to a voltage limited by the supply voltages for a maximum input signal.

The simplest output stage is an emitter follower. A variation of this circuit is shown is Fig. 11–18. Transistors Q_1 and Q_2 constitute the dc level shifter of Fig. 11–17B, with the exception that resistor R_{E_2} has been replaced by two resistors in series, R_{2A} and R_{2B}. Transistor Q_3 is an emitter-follower output stage. Emitter resistor R_E, instead of being returned to ground, is returned to point x. This connection provides *positive feedback* which increases the gain of the emitter follower output stage to between two and three.

Feedback current I_f is in phase with emitter current I_{e_1} flowing in the level shifter. Current I_f is added to I_{e_1}, thereby increasing the voltage drop across R_{2B}. Because the supply voltages V_{CC} and V_{EE} are fixed, the voltage across R_{E_1} is reduced. This results in an increase in signal voltage across the base of the emitter follower, Q_3. The output voltage is therefore greater than if no feedback were used.

For high-level signals, the emitter follower has a serious disadvantage. The dc power dissipated in the emitter resistor is excessive. To achieve higher power capability, the circuits of either Fig. 11–19 or Fig. 11–20 are employed.

In Fig. 11–19, the emitter resistor has been replaced by transistor Q_2. Both Q_1 and Q_2 are operating as class *A* amplifiers, and diode *D* provides biasing. This configuration is sometimes called a *totem-pole amplifier.*

Assume that the signal to transistor Q_3 decreases. The collector voltage of Q_3 and, because of its direct connection, the base voltage of Q_1, increase. At the same time, the voltages between emitter and ground of Q_3 and between base and ground of Q_2 decrease because of the reduced current in Q_3. As a result, Q_1 conducts more current than Q_2, and the difference current, I_l, is the load current.

The circuit containing Q_3 acts as a *phase splitter.* The voltage at the collector is out of phase and the voltage at the emitter is in phase with respect to the input signal.

The phase splitter used in the previous circuit is eliminated in the circuit of Fig. 11–20. In this configuration, Q_1 is an NPN transistor and Q_2 a PNP transistor. Such a circuit is called a *complementary pair amplifier.* Both Q_1 and Q_2 function as emitter followers.

Because Q_1 is NPN, during the positive half-cycle of the input signal, its base is forward biased, and the transistor conducts. Current, therefore, flows in Q_1 through the load resistor. Since Q_2 is PNP, it is cut off. On the negative half-cycle, Q_2 now conducts, and Q_1 is cut off. Current therefore flows in the opposite direction in R_L, and the output signal is completed.

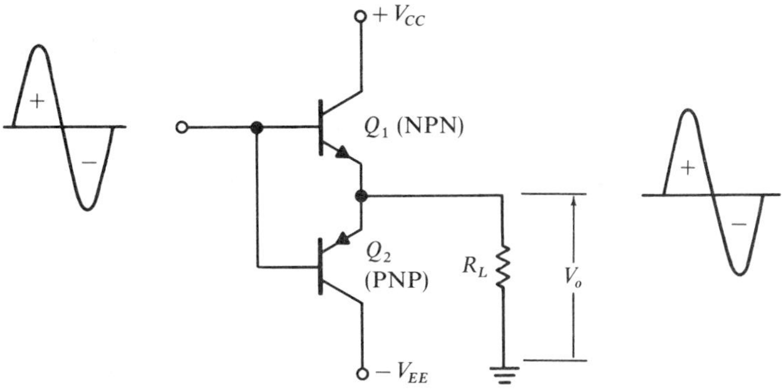

Fig. 11–20. *Example of a complementary pair output stage.*

11.9 Examples of Op Amps

We now can see how the building blocks analyzed in this chapter are used in op amps. Two examples of commercial op amps are considered.

EXAMPLE 11–6.

Figure 11–21 is a schematic of the Fairchild μA-702A op amp. Identify its circuits.

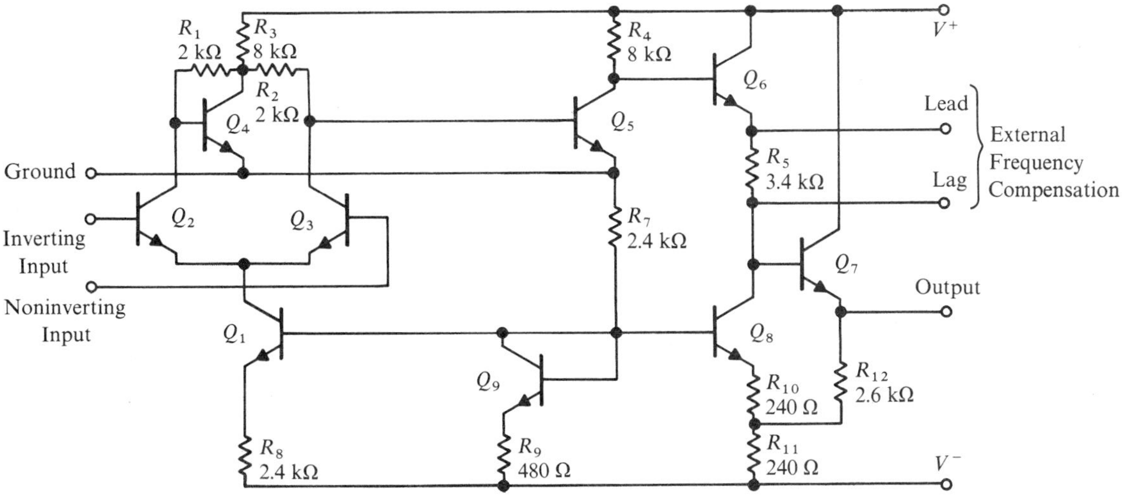

Fig. 11–21. *Schematic of a Fairchild μA-702A op amp which is analyzed in Example 11–6. (Courtesy Fairchild Camera and Instrument Corp.)*

Solution:

Transistors Q_2 and Q_3 constitute the differential amplifier. Transistor Q_1 serves as a constant current source and Q_9, connected as a diode, provides dc bias stabilization. The intermediate stage is composed of Q_4 and Q_5, similar to Fig. 11–16.

Level shifter, Q_6 and Q_8, drives the emitter follower output stage, Q_7. Positive feedback is achieved by returning emitter resistor, R_{12}, to the junction of R_{10} and R_{11}.

Note that the resistor values used in the op amp range from only 240 Ω to 8 kΩ. Very low as well as very high value resistors have been avoided. This is good practice in the design of monolithic IC amplifiers.

EXAMPLE 11–7.

The Motorola MC-1530 op amp is illustrated in Fig. 11–22. Identify its circuits.

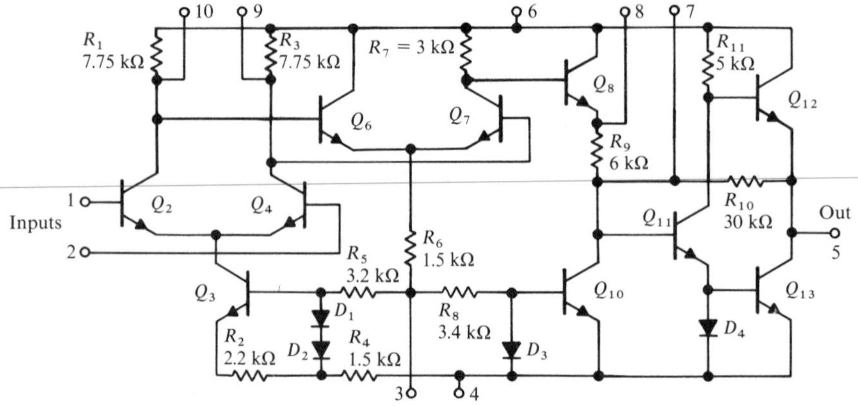

Fig. 11–22. *Schematic of a Motorola MC-1530 op amp which is analyzed in Example 11–7.*

Solution:

Transistor pairs Q_2–Q_4 and Q_6–Q_7 are cascaded differential amplifier stages. Transistor Q_3 serves as a constant current source for Q_2–Q_4, and emitter resistor R_6 for Q_6–Q_7.

Transistors Q_8 and Q_{10} constitute a dc level shifter. Transistor Q_{11} is a phase splitter which drives the totem-pole amplifier, consisting of Q_{12} and Q_{13}.

The calculation of dc operating voltages for transistors in an integrated circuit is sometimes required. The procedure is illustrated in the next example.

EXAMPLE 11–8.

Figure 11–23 illustrates a three-stage, direct-coupled amplifier. If the dc voltage across the emitter of Q_3 is 1 V, deter-

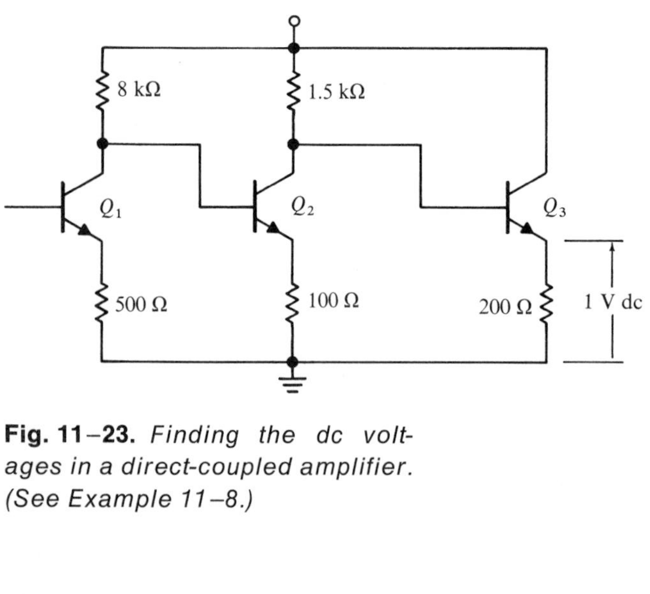

Fig. 11–23. *Finding the dc voltages in a direct-coupled amplifier. (See Example 11–8.)*

mine the collector, base, and emitter voltages of Q_2 and Q_1 with respect to ground. Assume that for each transistor, $V_{BE} = 0.7\,V$ and the base current is negligible.

Solution:

The collector voltage of Q_2 with respect to ground, V_{C_2}, is equal to the sum of the base-emitter voltage and emitter voltage of Q_3. Hence,

$$V_{C_2} = 0.7 + 1 = 1.7\,V$$

Collector current I_{C_2} is

$$I_{C_2} = \frac{V_{CC} - V_{C_2}}{R_{C_2}} = \frac{6 - 1.7}{1.5\,k\Omega} = 2.87\,mA$$

Hence,

$$V_{E_2} \simeq R_{E_2} I_{C_2} = 0.1 \times 2.87 \simeq 0.29\,V$$

Collector voltage $V_{C_1} = V_{B_2}$ is

$$V_{C_1} = V_{B_2} = V_{BE_2} + V_{E_2} = 0.29 + 0.7 \simeq 1\,V$$

Collector current I_{C_1} is

$$I_{C_1} = \frac{6 - 1}{8\,k\Omega} = 0.625\,mA$$

and

$$V_{E_1} = 0.5 \times 0.625 \simeq 0.31\,V$$
$$V_{B_1} = 0.7 + 0.31 \simeq 1\,V$$

SUMMARY

The most versatile linear IC is the operational amplifier. Major building blocks of an op amp include the differential amplifier, constant current source, one or more cascaded stages, dc level shifter, and an output stage. A useful figure of merit for the op amp is the common-mode rejection ratio, CMRR. A high CMRR indicates that the op amp responds primarily to the difference-mode signal and only slightly to the common-mode signal.

The differential amplifier offers inverting and noninverting inputs to the op amp. A constant current source simulates a large-value emitter resistor which is necessary for a high CMRR. Cascaded stages provide additional gain. A cascaded stage may be another differential amplifier.

Level shifting is required to compensate for the dc voltage buildup in an op amp. The level shifter is generally a modified emitter follower. Possible output stages include the emitter follower, totem-pole, and complementary pair amplifiers.

Further Reading

Ghaznavi, C., and A. H. Seidman. *Electronic Circuit Analysis.* New York: Macmillan Company, 1972, Chapter 16.

Kahn, Michael. *The Versatile Op Amp.* New York: Holt, Rinehart and Winston, 1970.

Kaufman, M., and A. H. Seidman, eds. *Handbook for Electronics Engineering Technicians.* New York: McGraw-Hill Book Company, 1976, Chapter 13.

Millman, J., and C. C. Halkias. *Integrated Electronics: Analog and Digital Circuits and Systems.* New York: McGraw-Hill Book Company, 1972, Chapter 15.

Oldham, W. G., and S. E. Schwarz. *An Introduction to Electronics.* New York: Holt, Rinehart and Winston, 1972, Chapter 12.

RCA. *Linear Integrated Circuits.* Harrison, N.J.: RCA Corporation, 1967.

REVIEW QUESTIONS

11.1 Explain the difference between a linear and a nonlinear IC.

11.2 What is meant by thermal tracking?

11.3 Discuss the design philosophy for integrated circuits. How does this philosophy differ from that for discrete circuits?

11.4 Describe the characteristics of an ideal op amp.

11.5 Explain the function of each of the blocks in Fig. 11–2.

11.6 What is a striking feature of the differential amplifier?

11.7 Define
(a) Common-mode signals.
(b) Difference-mode signals.

11.8 Define common-mode rejection ratio (CMRR).

11.9 Why is a constant current source preferable to an emitter resistor for a differential amplifier?

11.10 What are the characteristics of a Darlington pair?

11.11 Why is a dc level shifter required in an op amp?

11.12 What are the requirements for an output stage of an op amp?

11.13 Draw a schematic diagram of a totem-pole amplifier.

11.14 Describe the operation of a phase splitter.

11.15 Describe the operation of the complementary pair amplifier of Fig. 11–20.

PROBLEMS

P11–1 Impressed across the inputs of a differential amplifier are $V_1 = 4\,\text{mV}$ and $V_2 = 2\,\text{mV}$. Determine
(a) The difference-mode signal.
(b) The common-mode signal.

P11–2 Repeat prob. P11–1 for $V_1 = 3\,\text{mV}$ and $V_2 = 0\,\text{V}$.

P11–3 Express the CMRR as a numeric and in decibels if $A_{vd} = -1000$ and $A_{vc} = -1$.

P11–4 Repeat prob. P11–3 for $A_{vd} = -2000$ and $A_{vc} = -0.3$.

P11–5 Derive Eq. (11–6).

P11–6 Derive Eq. (11–11).

P11–7 In the differential amplifier of Fig. 11–3, $h_{ie} = 2\,\text{k}\Omega$, $h_{fe} = 80$, and h_{re} and h_{oe} are negligible. If $R_s = R_C = 5\,\text{k}\Omega$ and $R_E = 100\,\Omega$, calculate
(a) A_{vc}.
(b) A_{vd}.
(c) CMRR.

P11–8 Repeat problem P11–7 for $R_E = 2\,\text{k}\Omega$.

P11–9 For the constant current source in Fig. 11–24, determine the value of I_o. Neglect the base current and assume that $I_o = I_E$ and $V_{BE} = V_D = 0.7\,\text{V}$.

P11–10 For a differential amplifier at room temperature, $h_{fe} = 60$, $R_C = 10\,\text{k}\Omega$, and $kT/q = 25\,\text{mV}$. Calculate the values of R_{id} and A_{vd} if
(a) $I_o = 2\,\text{mA}$.
(b) $I_o = 0.2\,\text{mA}$.

P11–11 For the Darlington pair of Fig. 11–12, show that
(a) $R_i \simeq h_{fe}h_{ie}$.
(b) $A_i \simeq h_{fe}^2$.
(c) $A_v \simeq -h_{fe}R_C/h_{ie}$.
In your analysis, neglect h_{oe} and h_{re}. Assume R_B is very large, h_{fe} is much greater than one, and the transistors are identical.

P11–12 Identify the circuits of the op amp illustrated in Fig. 11–25.

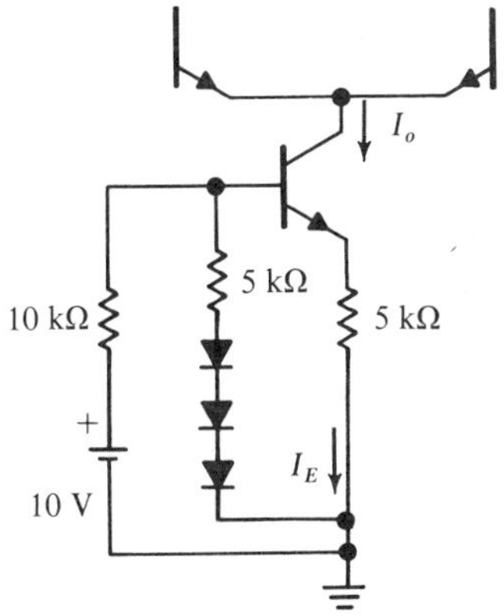

Fig. 11–24.

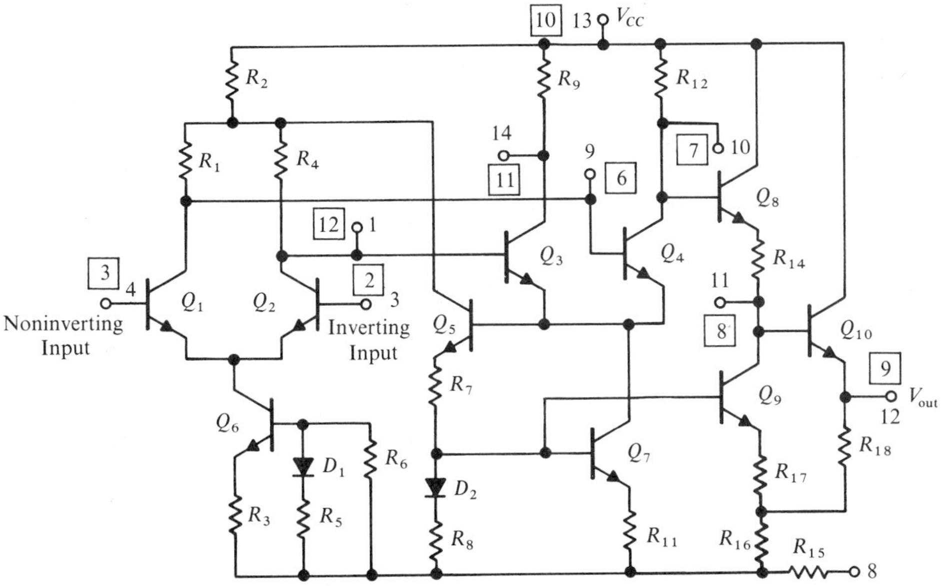

Fig. 11–25. *(Courtesy RCA Solid State Division.)*

P11–13 Repeat prob. P11–12 for the op amp of Fig. 11–26.

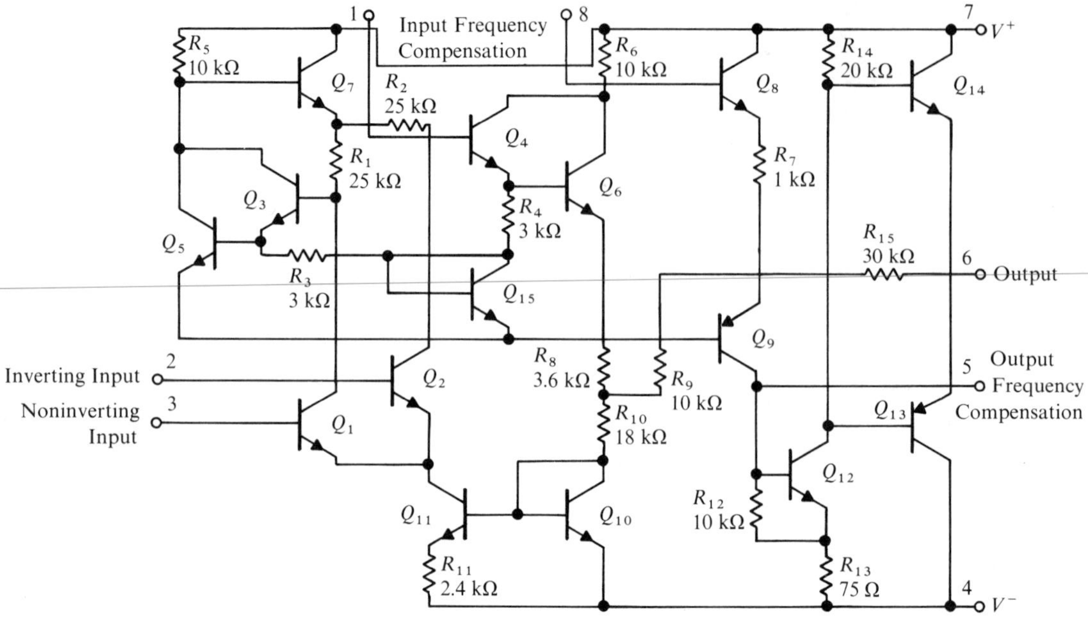

Fig. 11–26. *(Courtesy Fairchild Camera and Instrument Corp.)*

P11–14 In Fig. 11–27, $V_{CC} = 5\,\text{V}$. Determine the collector, base, and emitter voltages of Q_1 and Q_2 with respect to ground. Assume that $V_{BE} = 0.7\,\text{V}$ and the base current is negligible.

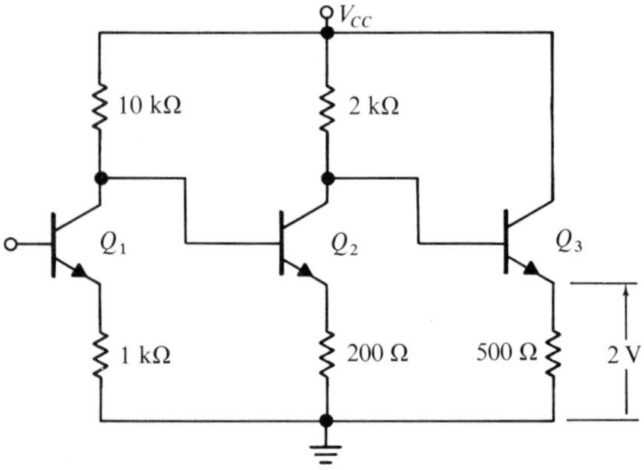

Fig. 11–27.

P11–15 Repeat prob. P11–14 for $V_{CC} = 12\,\text{V}$.

P11–16 For the amplifier of Fig. 11–28, assume that $V_{CC} = 12\,\text{V}$. Letting $h_{FE} = 100$ and $V_{BE} = 0.7\,\text{V}$, determine

(a) Quiescent collector and base currents for each transistor.

(b) Quiescent collector voltage with respect to ground of Q_1 and Q_2.

(c) Quiescent emitter voltage with respect to ground of Q_3 and Q_4.

(d) Total dc input power to the circuit, neglecting base current.

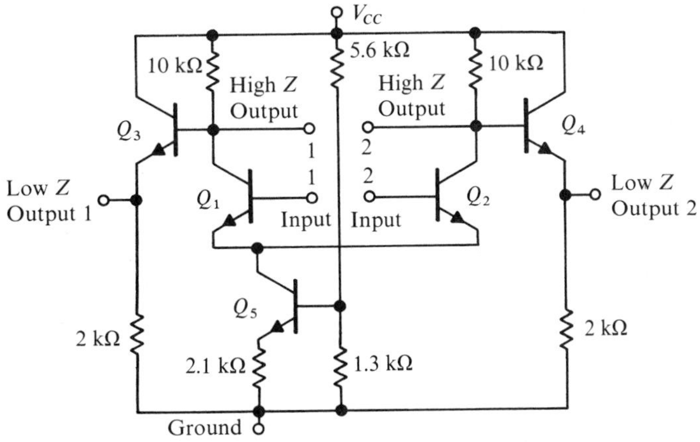

Fig. 11–28. *(Courtesy Fairchild Camera and Instrument Corp.)*

P11–17 Repeat prob. P11–16 for $V_{CC} = 18$ V.

12

Using the Op Amp

In the previous chapter, we studied the basic circuits that make up an operational amplifier (op amp). In this chapter, we shall learn how the op amp is used in the processing of analog (continuously varying) signals.

In this chapter, we shall learn how the op amp is used for amplification, mathematical operations, and active filters. We shall also learn how to compensate the op amp to ensure that it always behaves as a stable and precise device. Before we delve into these areas, however, we must examine the manufacturers' specifications (specs) given on their data sheets and make sure that we understand them.

12.1 What the Specs Mean

Typical data sheets for an op amp (Fairchild Semiconductor μA-709C) are illustrated in Fig. 12–1. Information generally found on data sheets for an op amp may be summarized as follows:

1. On top of the sheet is a brief description of the amplifier, its type number, and a listing of some of the specs, such as power consumption, noise, etc.
2. A general description of the circuit is given in some detail.
3. Absolute maximum ratings, *which should never be exceeded*, are listed.
4. A schematic of the op amp is shown.
5. Physical dimensions of the package are given.
6. A pin connection diagram is provided.
7. Electrical characteristics (parameter values) for *specified test conditions*, and their range of variation, are listed.
8. Additional diagrams, tables, and curves provide information on frequency compensation, frequency response, gain, etc.

Some of the more frequently used parameters for characterizing an op amp include:

Open-loop voltage gain—The dc voltage gain, without external feedback, between the inverting or noninverting input and output terminals.

μA709C

HIGH PERFORMANCE OPERATIONAL AMPLIFIER

FAIRCHILD LINEAR INTEGRATED CIRCUITS

GENERAL DESCRIPTION - The μA709C is a high-gain operational amplifier constructed on a single silicon chip using the Fairchild Planar epitaxial process. It features low offset, high input impedance, large input common mode range, high output swing under load and low power consumption. The device displays exceptional temperature stability and will operate over a wide range of supply voltages with little degradation of performance. The amplifier is intended for use in DC servo systems, high impedance analog computers, in low-level instrumentation applications and for the generation of special linear and nonlinear transfer functions. For full temperature range operation (-55°C to +125°C) see μA709 or μA709A data sheet.

ABSOLUTE MAXIMUM RATINGS

Supply Voltage		± 18 V
Internal Power Dissipation	(Note 1)	250 mW
Differential Input Voltage		± 5.0 V
Input Voltage		± 10 V
Output Short-Circuit Duration	(T_A = 25°C)	5 sec
Storage Temperature Range	TO-99	-65°C to + 150°C
	Dual-In-Line	-55°C to +125°C
Operating Temperature Range		0°C to +70°C
Lead Temperature	TO-99 (Soldering, 60 sec)	300°C
	Dual-In-Line (Soldering, 10 sec)	260°C

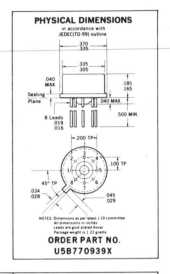

PHYSICAL DIMENSIONS

in accordance with JEDEC(TO-99) outline

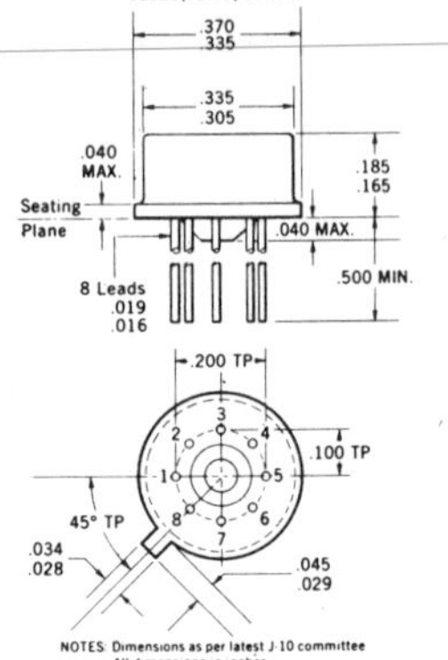

NOTES: Dimensions as per latest J-10 committee
All dimensions in inches
Leads are gold-plated Kovar
Package weight is 1.22 grams

ORDER PART NO.
U5B770939X

SCHEMATIC DIAGRAM

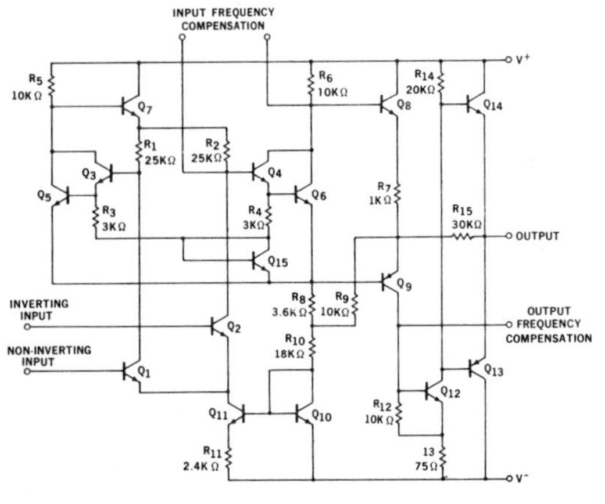

CONNECTION DIAGRAM

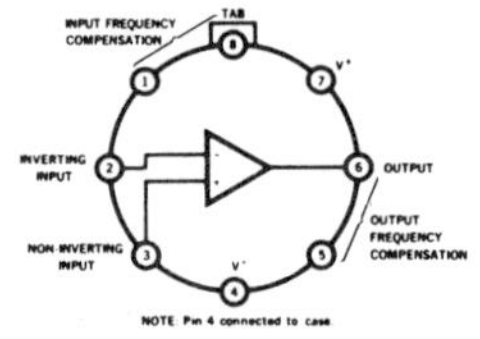

(Top View)

CONNECTION DIAGRAM

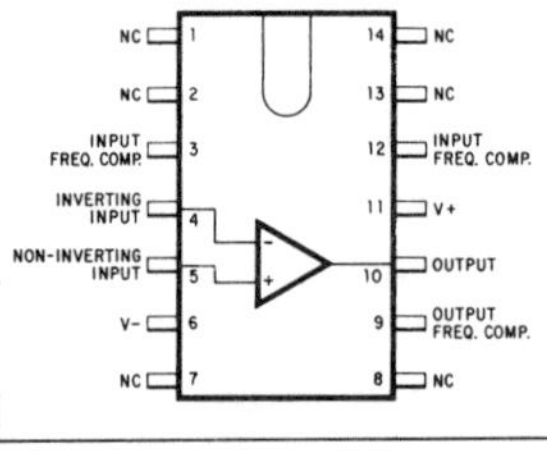

PHYSICAL DIMENSIONS

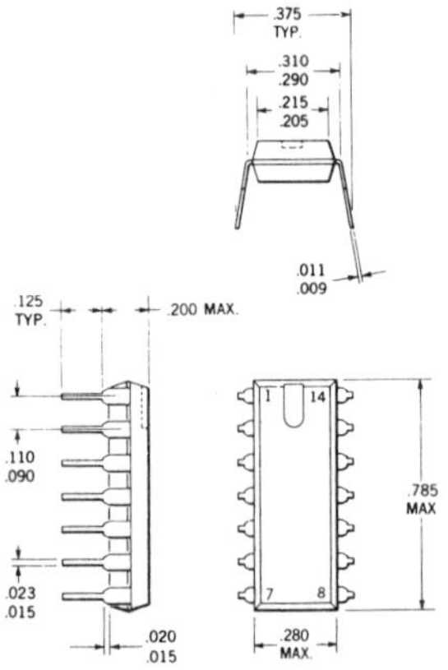

NOTES: All dimensions in inches

ORDER PART NO.
U6E7709393

NOTE 1: Rating applies for ambient temperatures to +70°C.

Fig. 12–1. *Typical data sheets for an op amp. (Courtesy Fairchild Camera and Instrument Corp.)* →

ELECTRICAL CHARACTERISTICS (V_S = ± 15 V, T_A = 25°C unless otherwise specified)

Parameter	Conditions	Min.	Typ.	Max.	Units
Input Offset Voltage	$R_S \leq 10\ k\Omega$, $\pm 9\ V \leq V_S \leq \pm 15\ V$		2.0	7.5	mV
Input Offset Current			100	500	nA
Input Bias Current			0.3	1.5	μA
Input Resistance		50	250		kΩ
Output Resistance			150		Ω
Large-Signal Voltage Gain	$R_L \geq 2\ k\Omega$, $V_{out} = \pm 10\ V$	15,000	45,000		
Output Voltage Swing	$R_L \geq 10\ k\Omega$	±12	±14		V
	$R_L \geq 2\ k\Omega$	±10	±13		V
Input Voltage Range		±8.0	±10		V
Common Mode Rejection Ratio	$R_S \leq 10\ k\Omega$	65	90		dB
Supply Voltage Rejection Ratio	$R_S \leq 10\ k\Omega$		25	200	μV/V
Power Consumption			80	200	mW
Transient Response	V_{in} = 20 mV, R_L = 2 kΩ,				
Risetime	C_1 = 5000 pF, R_1 = 1.5 kΩ,		0.3		μs
	C_2 = 200 pF, R_2 = 50 Ω				
Overshoot	$C_L \leq 100$ pF		10		%
The following specifications apply for $0°C \leq T_A \leq +70°C$					
Input Offset Voltage	$R_S \leq 10 k\Omega$, $\pm 9\ V \leq \pm 15\ V$			10	mV
Input Offset Current				750	nA
Input Bias Current				2.0	μA
Large-Signal Voltage Gain	$R_L \geq 2 k\Omega$, $V_{out} = \pm 10\ V$	12,000			
Input Resistance		35			kΩ

GUARANTEED ELECTRICAL CHARACTERISTICS

VOLTAGE GAIN

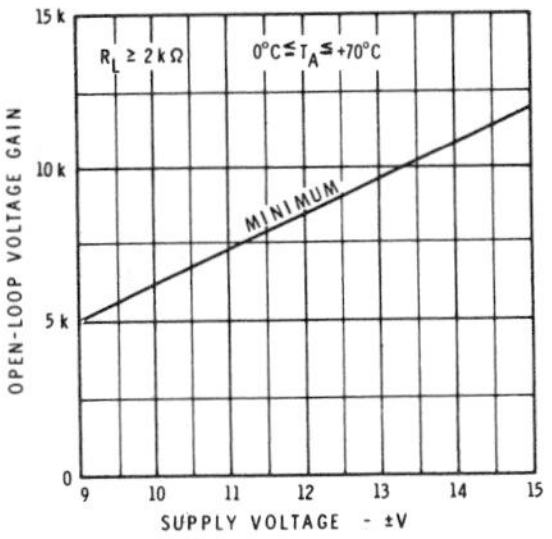

OUTPUT VOLTAGE SWING

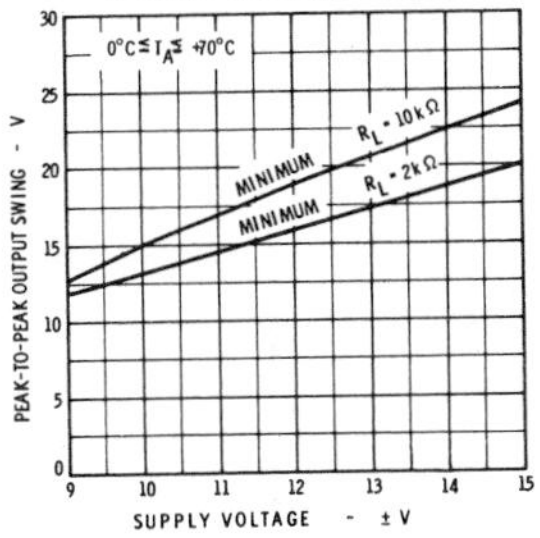

INPUT COMMON MODE VOLTAGE RANGE

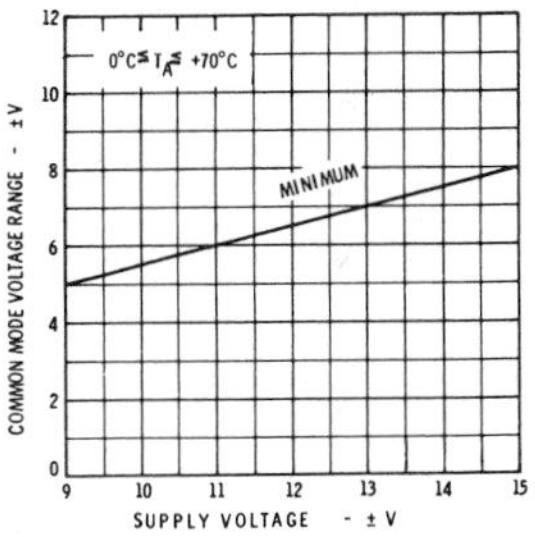

TYPICAL PERFORMANCE CURVES

VOLTAGE TRANSFER CHARACTERISTIC

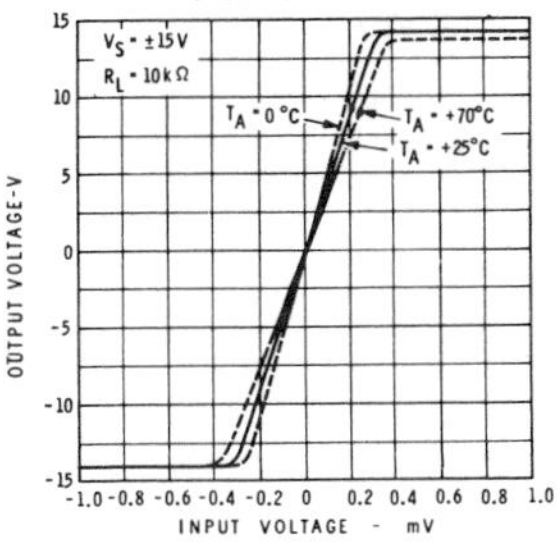

FREQUENCY COMPENSATION CIRCUIT

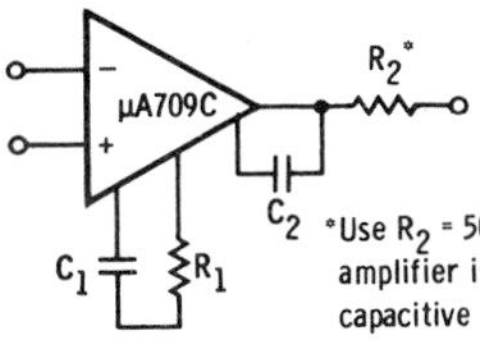

*Use R_2 = 50 Ω when the amplifier is operated with capacitive loading.

FREQUENCY RESPONSE FOR VARIOUS CLOSED-LOOP GAINS

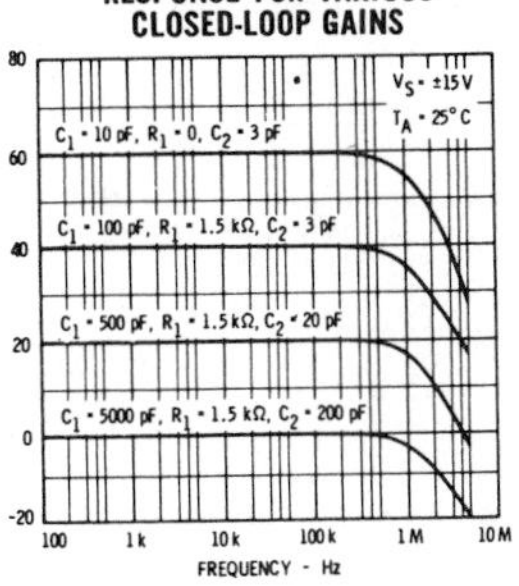

Input offset current (I_{io})—The difference in the dc bias currents, $I_{B_1} - I_{B_2}$, entering the inverting and noninverting inputs for zero output (Fig. 12–2).

Input offset voltage (V_{io})—The voltage applied across the inverting and noninverting input terminals for zero output (Fig. 12–2).

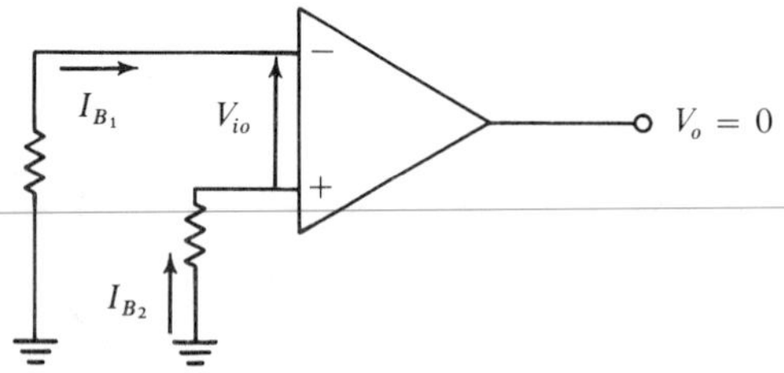

Fig. 12–2. *Illustrating the definitions of I_{io} and V_{io}.*

Input offset current drift—The rate of change in input offset current as a function of temperature: $\Delta I_{io}/\Delta T$.

Input offset voltage drift—The rate of change in the input offset voltage as a function of temperature: $\Delta V_{io}/\Delta T$.

Common-mode rejection ratio (*CMRR*)—The ratio of the differential-mode gain to the common-mode gain.

Slew rate—An indication of how well an op amp follows a rapidly changing signal, sometimes referred to as a *transient*. In Fig. 12–3, a rising waveform (V_o) is shown as a function of time, t. The *slew rate*, *SR*, is the ratio of the change in output voltage, ΔV_o, to a change in time, Δt:

$$SR = \frac{\Delta V_o}{\Delta t} \tag{12–1}$$

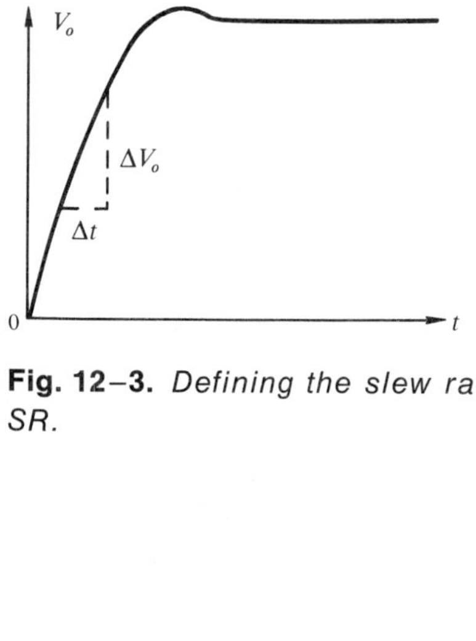

Fig. 12–3. *Defining the slew rate, SR.*

Table 12–1 provides a summary of parameter values for typical IC op amps.

TABLE 12–1. Typical operating characteristics of operational amplifiers.

Open-loop gain, A_{vo}: −1500– −50,000
Unity gain crossover frequency, f_c: 0.2 MHz–11 MHz
Input offset voltage, V_{io}: 1 mV–5 mV
Input offset current, I_{io}: 1 nA–100 nA
Slew rate, SR: 0.25 V/μs–5 V/μs
Input offset voltage drift, $\Delta V_{io}/\Delta T$: 1 μV/°C–20 μV/°C
Input offset current drift, $\Delta I_{io}/\Delta T$: 0.05 nA/°C–1 nA/°C
Common-mode rejection ratio, CMRR: 70 dB–110 dB
Input resistance, R_i: 10 kΩ–20 MΩ
Output resistance, R_o: 25 Ω–100 Ω

Techniques used for the correction of input offset voltage and bias currents are deferred until later in the chapter. Frequency compensation and its realization are also considered later.

12.2 Amplifiers

An important application for an op amp is its use as a feedback amplifier. In this section, we shall consider four widely used circuits. These are the inverting, noninverting, voltage follower, and difference amplifiers.

The basic symbol for an op amp is shown in Fig. 12–4A. In considering its signal performance, we show only the inverting (−) and noninverting (+) input and output terminals. A simplified model of an op amp is illustrated in Fig. 12–4B. The input side is represented by an equivalent input resistance, R_i, and the output side by a Thevenin equivalent circuit. Dependent voltage source, $A_{vo}V_i$ (where A_{vo} is the open-loop gain and V_i the voltage across R_i), is in series with the output resistance of the amplifier, R_o.

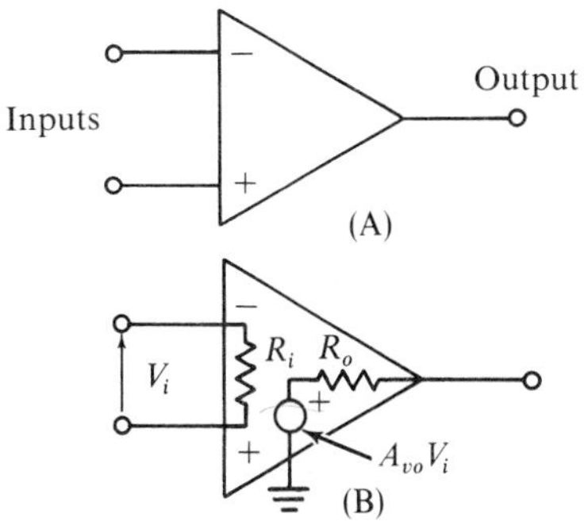

Fig. 12–4. *Representation of an op amp. (A) Basic electrical symbol. (B) Simplified model.*

Inverting Amplifier

An op amp circuit that enjoys wide application is the *inverting amplifier* of Fig. 12–5. It is an example of a voltage-feedback, shunt-input amplifier considered in Chapter 9.

If we apply the results obtained for the FET amplifier of Fig. 9–12 with R_1 in place of R_s, Eq. (9–23) becomes

$$B = \frac{R_1}{R_1 + R_F} \tag{12–2a}$$

In general, $R_1 \ll R_F$; hence,

$$B \simeq \frac{R_1}{R_F} \tag{12–2b}$$

Because the open-loop gain typically is at least −1500 for an op amp (see Table 12–1), by Eq. (9–6), $A_{vf} \simeq -1/B$. Therefore,

$$A_{vf} \simeq \frac{-R_F}{R_1} \tag{12–3}$$

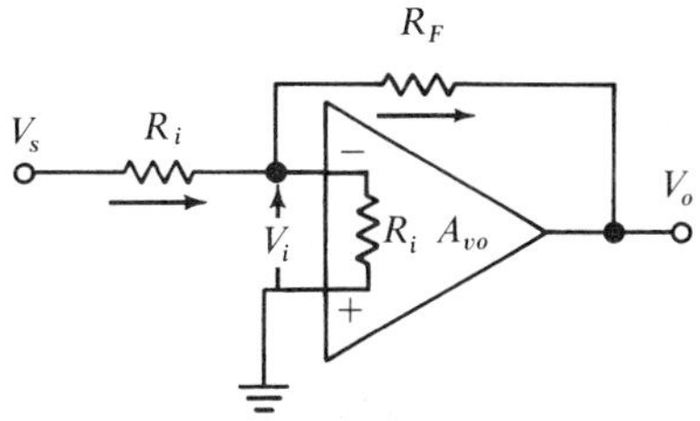

Fig. 12–5. *Inverting amplifier.*

We now derive expression (12–3) in a direct manner which is instructive and useful for our understanding of other op amp configurations. In Fig. 12–5, the algebraic sum of currents at the inverting terminal is

$$\frac{V_s - V_i}{R_1} + \frac{V_i}{R_i} = \frac{V_i - V_o}{R_F} \tag{12–4}$$

But $V_i = V_o/A_{vo}$. Substituting this expression for V_i in Eq. (12–4) and simplifying, we obtain

$$\frac{V_s}{R_1} - \frac{V_o}{R_1 A_{vo}} + \frac{V_o}{R_i A_{vo}} = \frac{V_o}{R_F A_{vo}} - \frac{V_o}{R_F}$$

or

$$\frac{V_s}{R_1} = \frac{V_o}{A_{vo}}\left[\frac{1}{R_1} - \frac{1}{R_i} + \frac{1}{R_F}\right] - \frac{V_o}{R_F} \tag{12–5}$$

Because A_{vo} is at least -1500 and R_1, R_i, and R_F are typically 10 kΩ or more, the bracketed term multiplied by $1/A_{vo}$ is, for all practical purposes, equal to zero. Hence, solving Eq. (12–5) for V_o/V_s,

$$A_{vf} = \frac{V_o}{V_s} = -\frac{R_F}{R_1} \tag{12-6}$$

which is identical to Eq. (12–3).

The preceding results could also have been derived by recognizing that, because of the large value of open-loop gain, the input voltage across the inverting and noninverting terminals, V_i, is virtually zero. For example, if the output is 1 V and the open-loop gain of the op amp is 10,000, $V_i = 1/10{,}000 = 0.1$ mV. Because V_i is so low, it may be taken as zero.

If we set V_i to zero in Eq. (12–4) and solve for V_o/V_s, the result is identical to Eq. (12–6). In future considerations of op amp applications, we shall assume that $V_i = 0$.

EXAMPLE 12–1.

Using an op amp with an open-loop gain of $-10{,}000$, design an amplifier having three precisely defined voltage gains of -10, -50, and -100. Assume that feedback resistor $R_F = 100$ kΩ.

Solution:

A possible design for such an amplifier is given in Fig. 12–6. Because of a high open-loop gain of $-10{,}000$, Eq. (12–6) may be used. Substituting R_x for R_1 in Eq. (12–6), we obtain $R_x = -100/A_{vf}$. For $A_{vf} = -10$,

$$R_{x_1} = -\frac{100\text{ k}\Omega}{-10} = 10\text{ k}\Omega$$

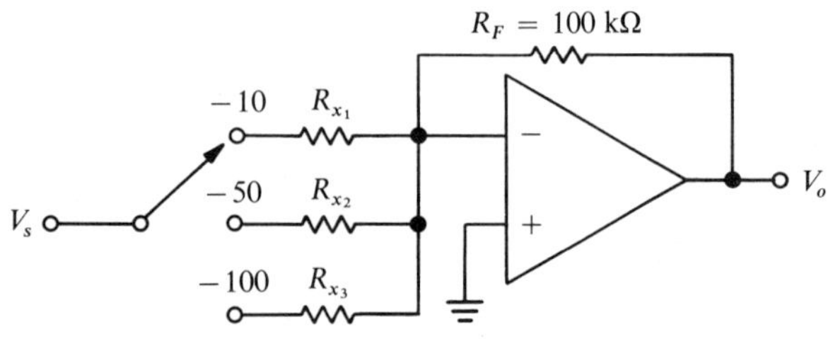

Fig. 12–6. *Design of a multigain voltage amplifier. (See Example 12–1.)*

For $A_{vf} = -50$,

$$R_{x_2} = -\frac{100\text{ k}\Omega}{-50} = 2\text{ k}\Omega$$

Lastly, for $A_{vf} = -100$,

$$R_{x_3} = -\frac{100\text{ k}\Omega}{-100} = 1\text{ k}\Omega$$

Noninverting Amplifier

An op amp used as a *noninverting amplifier* is illustrated in Fig. 12–7. Because $V_i = 0$, the voltage at the inverting (−) terminal equals V_s. Summing currents at this terminal,

$$\frac{V_s}{R_1} + \frac{V_s - V_o}{R_F} = 0$$

Solving for V_o/V_s,

$$A_{vf} = \frac{V_o}{V_s} = 1 + \frac{R_F}{R_1} \qquad \textbf{(12–7)}$$

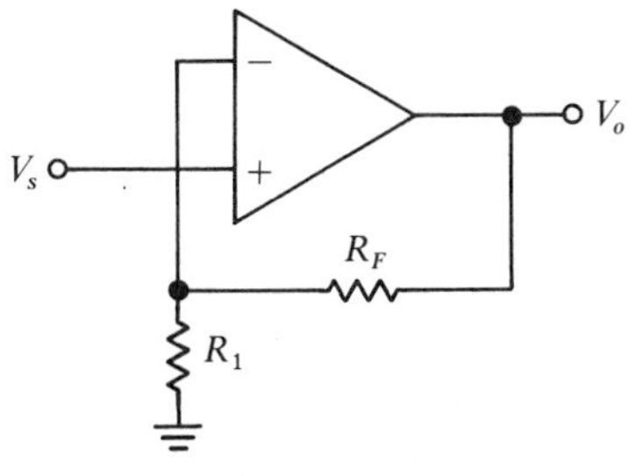

Fig. 12–7. *Noninverting amplifier.*

EXAMPLE 12–2.

Using an op amp and a 0-V–10-V voltmeter, design a multirange electronic voltmeter having voltage ranges of 0–0.1, 1, and 10 V.

Solution:

With a high-gain op amp as a noninverting amplifier, the proposed electronic voltmeter is illustrated in Fig. 12–8. A reasonable value for R_1 is 1 kΩ. For the 0.1-V range, the gain with feedback must be 100 in order to obtain 10 V full scale on the voltmeter (0.1 × 100 = 10). Hence, by Eq. (12–7),

$$100 = 1 + \frac{R_{F_1}}{1\,\text{k}\Omega}$$

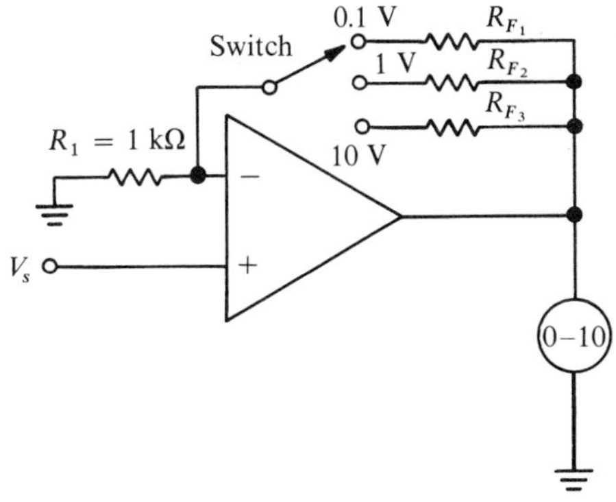

Fig. 12–8. *Example of a multirange electronic voltmeter. (See Example 12–2.)*

Solving, $R_{F_1} = 99\,\text{k}\Omega$. For the 1-V range, $A_{vf} = 10$, and by Eq. (12–7), $R_{F_2} = 9\,\text{k}\Omega$. Finally, for the 10-V range, $A_{vf} = 1$ and $R_{F_3} = 0$.

Voltage Follower

If, in the noninverting amplifier of Fig. 12–7, feedback resistor $R_F = 0$ and R_1 is removed, the new circuit appears as drawn in Fig. 12–9. This circuit is called a *voltage follower*, or *buffer*. Letting $R_F = 0$ in Eq. (12–7), we find that $A_{vf} = 1$.

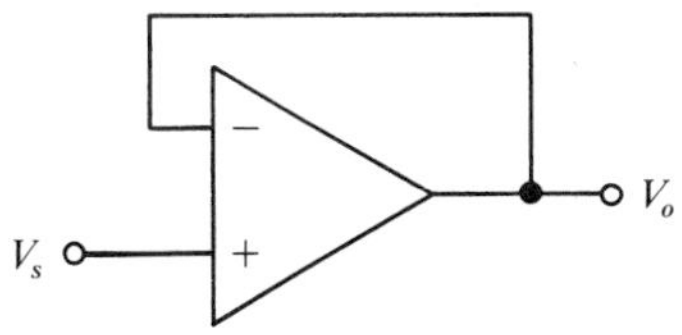

Fig. 12–9. *Voltage follower (buffer).*

The voltage follower therefore has unity voltage gain. Its output resistance is in the order of 0.001 Ω. One important application for this amplifier, as for the emitter and source followers, is as a buffer between a large source resistance and a low resistance load. (See Chapter 5, Example 5–3.)

Difference Amplifier

An op amp functioning as a *difference amplifier* is illustrated in Fig. 12–10. The output is proportional to the difference between the signals applied to the inverting (−) and non-inverting (+) terminals.

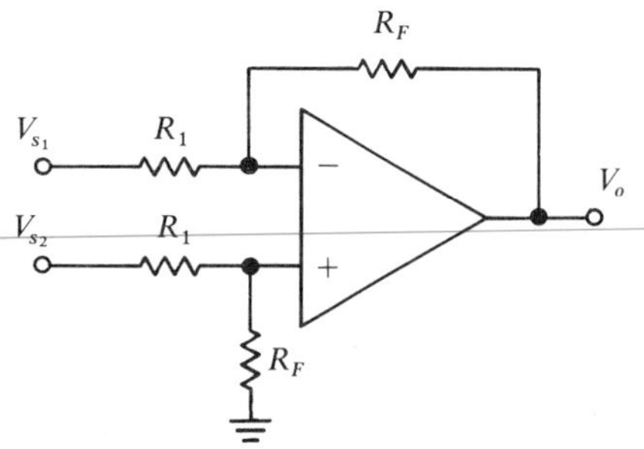

Fig. 12–10. *Difference amplifier.*

The principle of superposition will be used in analyzing the circuit. Setting V_{s_2} to zero, output V_{o_1} due to input V_{s_1} is

$$V_{o_1} = -\left(\frac{R_F}{R_1}\right)V_{s_1}$$

Setting V_{s_1} to zero, output V_{o_2} due to V_{s_2} is

$$V_{o_2} = \frac{V_{s_2}R_F}{R_1 + R_F}\left(\frac{R_1 + R_F}{R_1}\right) = \frac{V_{s_2}R_F}{R_1}$$

Adding V_{o_1} and V_{o_2},

$$V_o = \left(\frac{R_F}{R_1}\right)(V_{s_2} - V_{s_1}) \qquad \textbf{(12–8)}$$

Note that the output voltage is proportional to the difference in the input signals.

EXAMPLE 12–3.

For the difference amplifier of Fig. 12–10, assume that $R_F/R_1 = 10$, the supply voltages to the op amp are ± 15 V, and $V_{s_2} = 5$ V. What is the maximum value of V_{s_1} that can be applied to the amplifier for reliable operation?

Solution:

The output voltage can never exceed the difference in the supply voltages, which, in this example, is $15 - (-15) = 30$ V. Hence, by Eq. (12–8),

$$V_o = 30 = 10(5 - V_{s_1})$$

Solving, $V_{s_1} = 2$ V maximum.

EXAMPLE 12–4.

Because of the 60-Hz hum in an input signal, the output of an op amp has −1 V of hum. The gain of the amplifier is −10. How can the hum be minimized or reduced to zero?

Solution:

One method is to use the difference amplifier of Fig. 12–10. For a gain of −10, the input component for a −1-V output is $-1/(-10) = 0.1$ V. Therefore, if a 0.1-V, 60-Hz signal of the same phase as the hum in the input signal is applied to the noninverting input, by Eq. (12–8), $V_{s_2} - V_{s_1} = 0$. Consequently, V_o for the hum is also zero.

12.3 Mathematical Operations

Historically, the op amp gained prominence in World War II when it was used to perform calculations in guiding anti-aircraft missles to their targets. Since then, it has become the major component of the *analog computer*. In an analog computer, voltage is used to represent physical quantities such as force and velocity. The analog computer is used to simulate and optimize physical systems.

A detailed discussion of analog computation needs a separate text. We shall, however, demonstrate how the op amp is used to perform mathematical operations.

Summer

An example of a summer, having three inputs, is shown in Fig. 12–11. Summing the currents at the inverting terminal, we obtain

$$\frac{V_1}{R_1} + \frac{V_2}{R_2} + \frac{V_3}{R_3} = -\frac{V_o}{R_F}$$

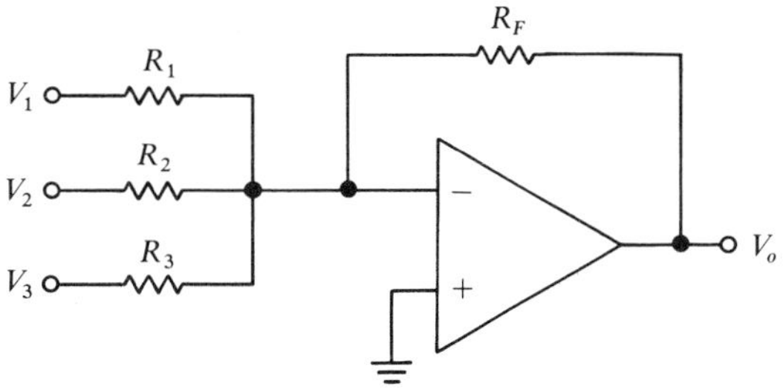

Fig. 12–11. *Example of a three-input summing amplifier.*

Solving for V_o and simplifying, we have

$$V_o = -\left(\frac{R_F}{R_1}V_1 + \frac{R_F}{R_2}V_2 + \frac{R_F}{R_3}V_3\right) \qquad \textbf{(12–9)}$$

Ratios R_F/R_1, R_F/R_2, and R_F/R_3 are the *coefficients*, or *scale factors*, of input variables V_1, V_2, and V_3, respectively. Typical values of coefficients are 10 and 1. In summers for analog computers, five or six inputs are often available to the user.

EXAMPLE 12–5.

In the summer of Fig. 12–11, $R_F = 100\,\text{k}\Omega$, $R_1 = R_2 = 10\,\text{k}\Omega$, and $R_3 = 100\,\text{k}\Omega$. If $V_1 = 0.1\,\text{V}$, $V_2 = 0.5\,\text{V}$, and $V_3 = 0.8\,\text{V}$, what is the output voltage?

Solution:

By Eq. (12–9),

$$\begin{aligned} V_o &= -\frac{100\,\text{k}\Omega}{10\,\text{k}\Omega}0.1 - \frac{100\,\text{k}\Omega}{10\,\text{k}\Omega}0.2 - \frac{100\,\text{k}\Omega}{100\,\text{k}\Omega}0.8 \\ &= -10 \times 0.1 - 10 \times 0.2 - 1 \times 0.8 \\ &= -(1 + 2 + 0.8) = -3.8\,\text{V} \end{aligned}$$

Sign Changer (Inverter)

From the results of Example 12–5, we see that the output of a summer has a negative sign. This is an inherent characteristic of summers. If a positive result is required, the output is fed to a *sign changer*, or *inverter* (Fig. 12–12). Because $R_F = R_1$, $V_o = -V_s$. If in Example 12–5 the output of the summer is fed to a sign changer, the output of the sign changer is $(-3.8)(-1) = +3.8$ V.

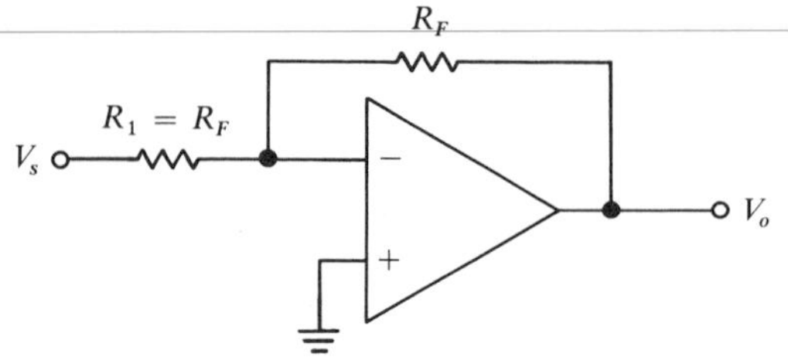

Fig. 12–12. *Sign changer (inverter).*

Integrator*

In an integrator, feedback resistor R_F of an inverting amplifier is replaced by capacitor C as shown in Fig. 12–13. Summing the currents at the inverting terminal, and remembering that the current in a capacitor is $C(dv/dt)$, we have

$$\frac{v_s}{R_1} = -C\left(\frac{dv_o}{dt}\right) \qquad \textbf{(12–10)}$$

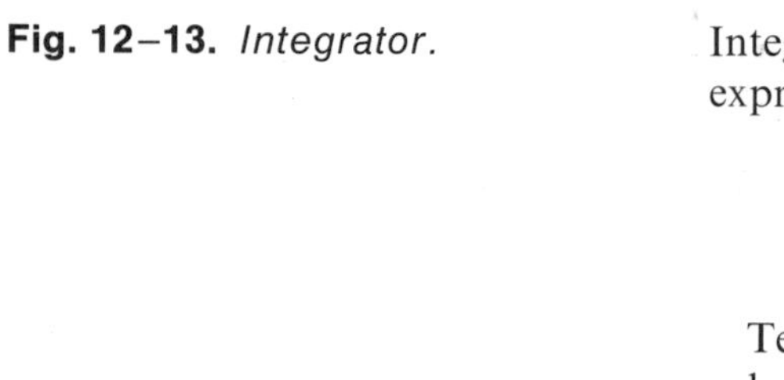

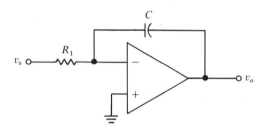

Fig. 12–13. *Integrator.*

Integrating Eq. (12–10) with respect to time, we obtain an expression for v_o:

$$v_o = -\frac{1}{R_1 C}\int_0^t v_s\,dt + V_0 \qquad \textbf{(12–11)}$$

Term V_0 is a constant of integration and represents the value of v_o at $t = 0$. This is called an *initial condition*. In a computer, the value of V_0 is introduced by applying a dc voltage in series with a resistor to charge capacitor C to V_0 volts.

* If the reader has not been exposed to the concepts of elementary calculus, this and the section on the differentiator may be omitted.

EXAMPLE 12–6.

The waveform of Fig. 12–14A, called a *unit step*, is denoted by $\mu_{-1}(t)$. For time less than zero, $\mu_{-1}(t) = 0$; for time greater than zero, $\mu_{-1}(t) = 1$.

Assume that a negative unit step, $-\mu_{-1}(t)$, is applied to the integrator of Fig. 12–13 and $V_0 = 0$. Plot the output voltage, v_o, for $t > 0$. Let $R_1C = 1$ s.

Solution:

For $t > 0$, we may express $-\mu_{-1}(t)$ by $v_i = -1$. Substituting this value and $R_1C = 1$ in Eq. (12–11), we obtain

$$v_o = -\frac{1}{1}\int_0^t -1\,dt + 0$$

or $v_o = +t$. The result is called a *ramp function*, which is an equation of a straight line beginning at $t = 0$ and having a positive slope of 1. A plot of the ramp function is given in Fig. 12–14B.

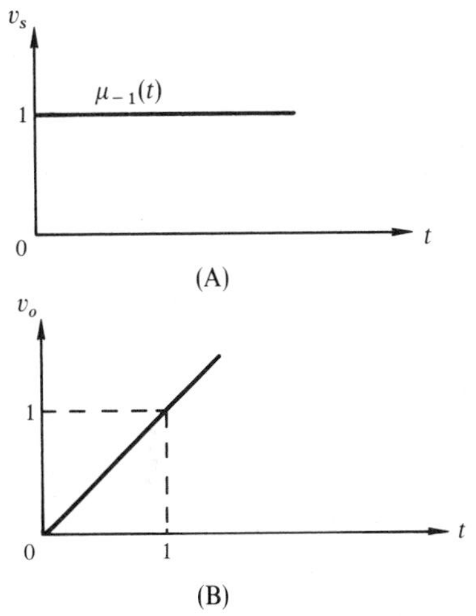

Fig. 12–14. *Example 12–6. (A) A unit step, $\mu_{-1}(t)$. (B) A positive ramp function is obtained when integrating a negative unit step.*

Differentiator

If in Fig. 12–13 the capacitor and resistor are interchanged, a *differentiator*, shown in Fig. 12–15, is obtained. Summing currents at the inverting terminal,

$$C\frac{dv_s}{dt} = -\frac{v_o}{R_1}$$

or

$$v_o = -R_1C\frac{dv_s}{dt} \tag{12–12}$$

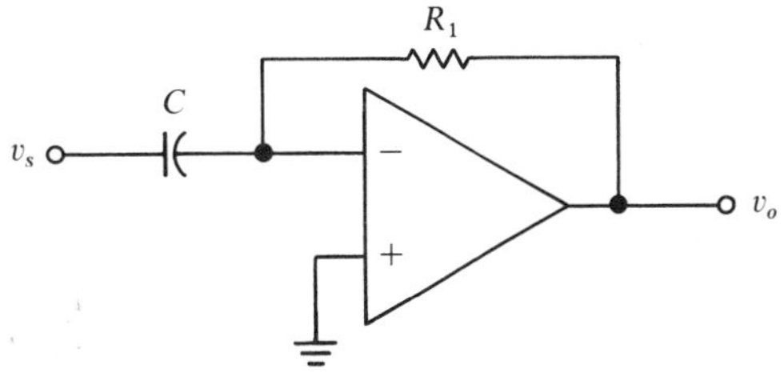

Fig. 12–15. *Differentiator.*

Thus, the output voltage is proportional to the time derivative of the input voltage. Because the differentiator is susceptible to noise and instability, it is seldom used for analog calculations. It is possible, for virtually all simulation problems, to obtain a solution by using integrators only.

Logarithmic Multiplier

One method of multiplying two numbers is to take their logarithms, form a sum, and then take the antilogarithm of the sum. For example, using natural logs (ln) to multiply

X and Y, the product, Z, is

$$Z = \ln X + \ln Y \qquad \textbf{(12–13)}$$

Taking the antilogarithm, product XY is obtained:

$$\ln^{-1}(Z) = \ln^{-1}(\ln X + \ln X) = XY \qquad \textbf{(12–14)}$$

The basic component of a logarithmic multiplier is the *logarithmic amplifier* of Fig. 12–16. A diode has replaced the feedback resistor of an inverting amplifier. From Chapter 2, the diode current, I_D, at room temperature is

$$I_D \simeq I_s\epsilon^{39V_D} \qquad \textbf{(12–15)}$$

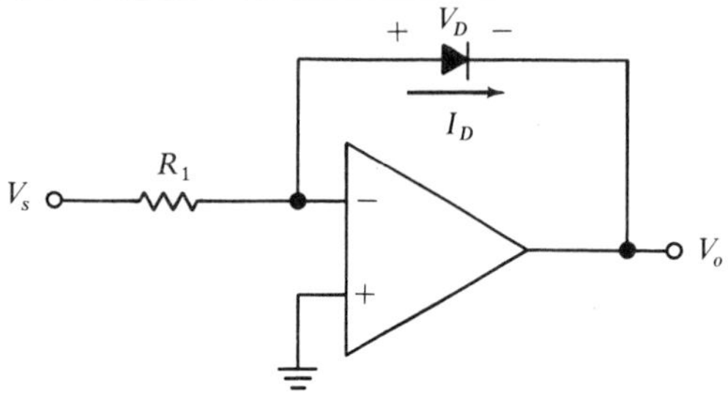

Fig. 12–16. *Logarithmic amplifier.*

where I_s is the reverse saturation current and V_D is the forward voltage across the diode. Summation of currents at the inverting terminal yields

$$\frac{V_s}{R_1} = I_s\epsilon^{39V_D} \qquad \textbf{(12–16)}$$

Taking the natural log of Eq. (12–16),

$$\ln\frac{V_s}{R_1} = \ln I_s + 39V_D$$

Output voltage V_o is equal to the negative of the voltage across the diode, $-V_D$. Substituting for $V_D = -V_o$ and solving,

$$V_o = -\frac{1}{39}\left(\ln\frac{V_s}{R_1} - \ln I_s\right) \qquad \textbf{(12–17)}$$

From Eq. (12–17), we see that the output voltage is proportional to the natural log of the input voltage. In practical circuits, a transistor is often used in place of a diode. In such a circuit, the effect of I_s is negligible.

A basic *antilog amplifier* is illustrated in Fig. 12–17. A comparison of this circuit with the logarithmic amplifier of

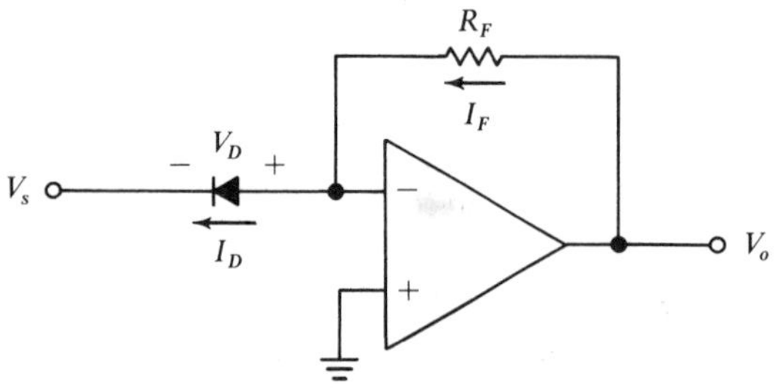

Fig.12–17. *Antilog amplifier.*

Fig. 12–16 shows that the diode and resistor have switched roles. Diode current, I_D, is

$$I_D = I_s \epsilon^{39V_D}$$

But $V_D = -V_s$; hence,

$$I_D = I_s \epsilon^{-39V_s}$$

At the inverting terminal, $I_D = I_F$:

$$I_D = I_s \epsilon^{-39V_s} = -\frac{V_o}{R_F}$$

If $V_s = \ln Z$, then

$$\begin{aligned} V_o &= -I_s R_F \epsilon^{-39(\ln Z)} \\ &= -I_s R_F \epsilon^{-39} \epsilon^{(\ln Z)} \\ &= -kZ \qquad \textbf{(12–18)} \end{aligned}$$

where $k = I_s R_F \epsilon^{-39}$.

The antilog amplifier of Fig. 12–17, therefore, takes the antilog of a function. A block diagram of a complete logarithmic multiplier which satisfies Eqs. (12–13) and (12–14) is illustrated in Fig. 12–18.

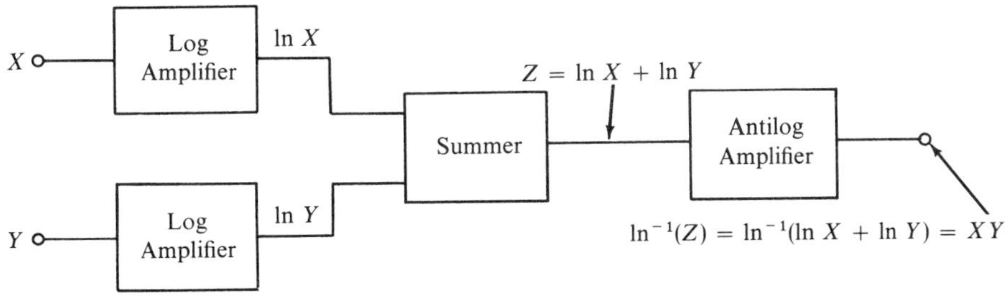

Fig. 12–18. *Block diagram of a logarithmic multiplier.*

12.4 Active Filters

In the previous two chapters, we saw that integrated inductors are not practical in IC technology. Another consideration is that for low frequencies, *LC* filters become bulky because of the large physical size of inductors. Filters, as well as inductors, may be realized by using an op amp and *RC* networks. The resulting configuration is called an *active*, or *inductorless*, *filter*. Because capacitors are, in general, smaller in size than inductors, the active filter is more compact than an *LC* filter.

In the inverting amplifier of Fig. 12–19, resistors R_1 and R_F of Fig. 12–5 have been replaced by impedances Z_1 and

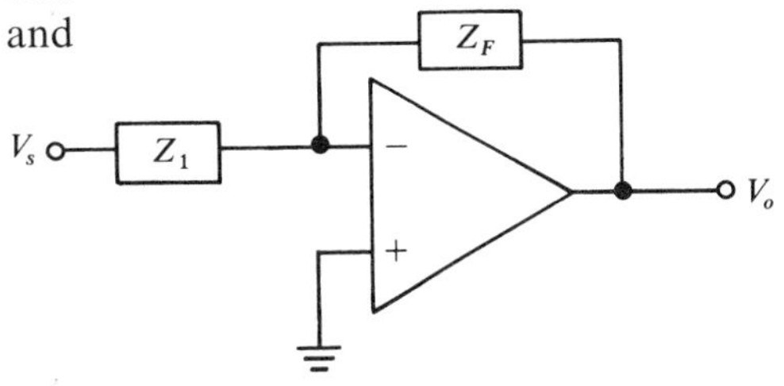

Fig. 12–19. *Inverting amplifier with impedances Z_1, Z_F, replacing resistors R_1, R_F.*

Z_F, respectively. By Eq. (12–3), we may write

$$A_{vf} = -\frac{Z_F}{Z_1} \tag{12–19}$$

An example of an active low-pass filter having voltage gain is shown in Fig. 12–20A. In the circuit, $Z_1 = R_1$ and $Z_F = R_F \| (1/j\omega C_F)$, or

$$Z_F = \frac{R_F}{1 + j\omega R_F C_F}$$

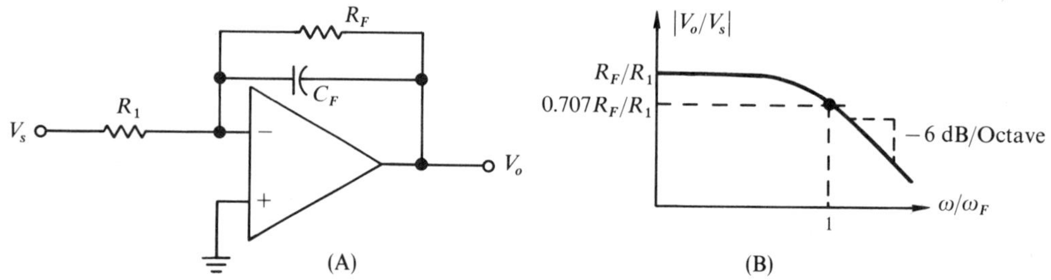

Fig. 12–20. *Example of a low-pass active filter. (A) Circuit. (B) Frequency response curve.*

Let the upper −3-dB frequency be

$$\omega_F = \frac{1}{R_F C_F} \tag{12–20a}$$

Hence,

$$Z_F = \frac{R_F}{1 + \dfrac{j\omega}{\omega_F}}$$

Substitution of the expression for Z_1 and Z_F in Eq. (12–19) yields

$$\frac{V_o}{V_s} = -\frac{R_F}{R_1}\left(\frac{1}{1 + \dfrac{j\omega}{\omega_F}}\right) \tag{12–20b}$$

Coefficient R_F/R_1 is the low-frequency gain of the filter. The expression in parentheses is identical to that of the low-pass filter discussed in Chapter 8. The frequency response curve for the low-pass active filter is given in Fig. 12–20B.

EXAMPLE 12–7.

For the low-pass active filter of Fig. 12–20A, the gain is −10, and $\omega_F = 100$ rad/s. If $R_F = 100\,\text{k}\Omega$, determine

(a) R_1.
(b) C_F.

Solutions:

(a) By Eq. (12–3),

$$R_1 = -\frac{R_F}{A_{vf}} = -\frac{100\,\text{k}\Omega}{-10} = 10\,\text{k}\Omega$$

(b) By Eq. (12–20a),

$$C_F = \frac{1}{\omega_F R_F} = \frac{1}{10^2 \times 10^5} = 0.1\,\mu\text{F}$$

A 0.1-μF capacitor is small for a -3-dB frequency of $100/2\pi = 15.9$ Hz.

12.5 dc Offset Voltage and Current

Figure 12–21A is a plot of output voltage versus input voltage for an ideal op amp. Such a curve is called the *voltage transfer characteristic* of an amplifier. The slope of the linear region equals the open-loop voltage gain. Beyond input voltages V_1 and $-V_1$, the output saturates at a value limited by the power supply voltages.

Note that the linear region of the transfer characteristic intersects the origin. Therefore, for zero input signal, the output signal is also zero. As you recall, this is an attribute only of an ideal op amp. For a practical op amp, because of device differences, an output voltage V'_o exists for zero input signal, as shown in Fig. 12–21B. For zero output, a dc voltage equal and opposite to the *input offset voltage*, V_{io}, must be applied to the amplifier input.

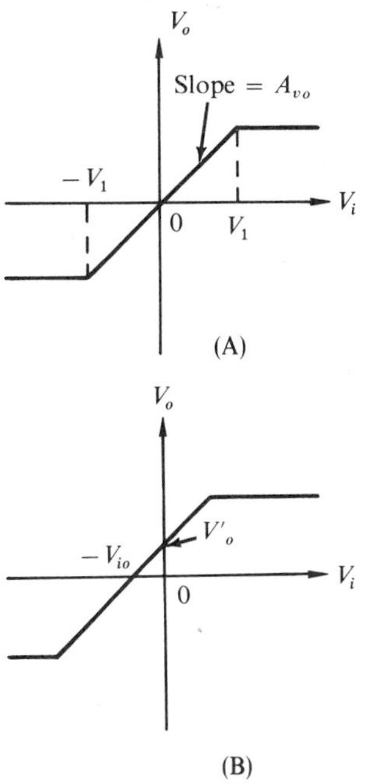

Fig. 12–21. *Voltage transfer characteristics of an op amp. (A) Ideal. (B) Practical.*

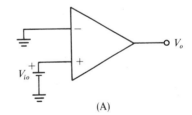

Offset Voltage Compensation

Mathematically, the linear region of the transfer characteristics is a straight line. It may therefore be described by the equation $y = mx + b$. In this case, $y = V_o$, m, the slope, is equal to A_{vo}, $x = V_i$, and b is the y-intercept, V'_o. Hence, the linear region of a practical op amp may be described by

$$V_o = A_{vo} V_i + V'_o \qquad \textbf{(12–21)}$$

From Fig. 12–21B, output voltage $V_o = 0$ for $V_i = -V_{io}$. Substitution of this value in Eq. (12–21) yields

$$0 = -A_{vo} V_{io} + V'_o$$

or

$$V'_o = A_{vo} V_{io}$$

Replacing V'_o by $A_{vo} V_{io}$ in Eq. (12–21), we obtain

$$V_o = A_{vo}(V_i + V_{io}) \qquad \textbf{(12–22)}$$

To compensate for the offset voltage in an inverting amplifier, we apply a dc voltage equal and opposite to V_{io} to the noninverting input, as shown in Fig. 12–22A. This is called *offset nulling*. Substituting $V_i = -V_{io}$ in Eq. (12–22) yields $V_o = 0$. The amplifier is thereby compensated for the input offset voltage.

Instead of using a separate bias source for V_{io}, we use the circuit of Fig. 12–22B. Resistors R_A and R_B form a voltage divider, with voltage V_{io} developed across R_B. The

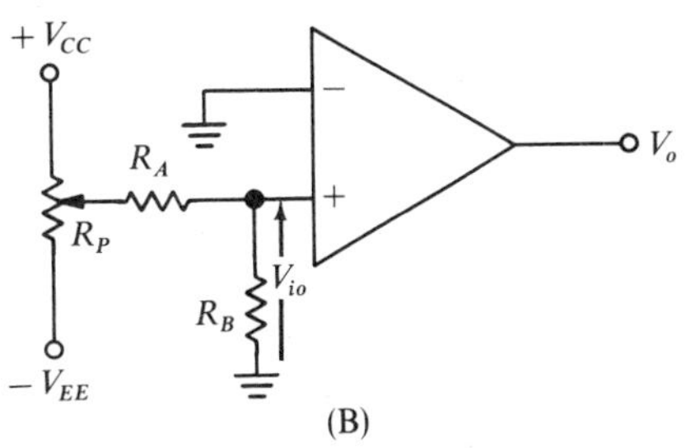

Fig. 12–22. *Offset voltage compensation. (A) Using a separate bias source. (B) Practical circuit using the supply voltages.*

arms of the potentiometer, R_P, are connected to the positive and negative supply voltages. This type of connection provides both positive and negative voltages for offset voltage compensation. Typically, the resistance of the potentiometer is in the order of $10\,k\Omega$–$20\,k\Omega$, and R_A is between $100\,k\Omega$ and $200\,k\Omega$. Resistance R_B is selected to give the value of V_{io} needed for cancellation of the offset voltage.

EXAMPLE 12–8.

In Fig. 12–22B, $R_P = 10\,k\Omega$, $R_A = 100\,k\Omega$, and $R_B = 0.1\,k\Omega$. If $V_{CC} = V_{EE} = 5\,V$, find the range of variation in V_{io} developed across R_B.

Solution:

The maximum equivalent resistance of the potentiometer occurs when the wiper arm is located at its electrical center. For this condition, it is equal to $(10/2)\|(10/2) = 2.5\,k\Omega$. The value of $2.5\,k\Omega$ is much less than $R_A = 100\,k\Omega$ and can be neglected in the calculation. The maximum variation in V_{io}, ΔV_{io}, therefore, is

$$\Delta V_{io} = \pm 5 \frac{0.1}{100.1} \simeq \pm 5\,\text{mV}$$

Offset Current Compensation

Because of differences in device parameters, the bias current for the inverting and noninverting inputs of an op amp are unequal. As defined earlier, the difference in bias currents is the offset bias current, I_{io}. The effect of I_{io} is the generation of an equivalent input offset voltage.

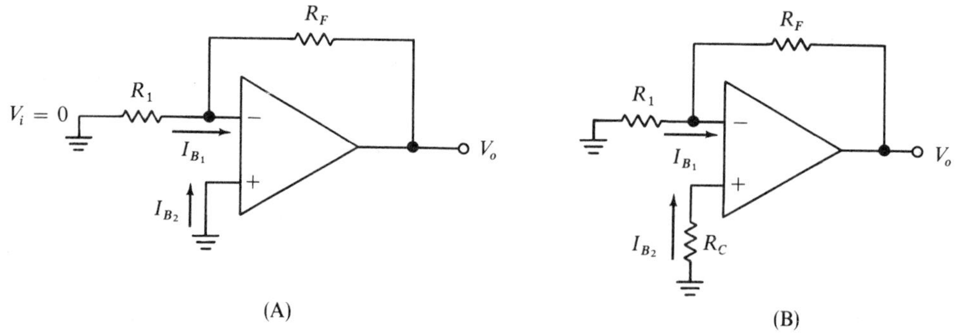

Fig. 12–23. *Offset current compensation. (A) Bias currents flowing in inverting and noninverting terminals. (B) Addition of resistor R_C for cancellation of offset current.*

Consider the inverting amplifier of Fig. 12–23A with input signal $V_i = 0$. Indicated in the diagram are bias currents I_{B_1} and I_{B_2}. Because the output resistance of an op amp is in the order of $50\,\Omega$ (see Table 12–1), the effective resistance across the inverting input and ground is $R_1 \| R_F$. Assuming $R_1 \ll R_F$, the equivalent offset voltage due to I_{B_1} is $-I_{B_1}R_1$. The effect of I_{B_1} may be cancelled by inserting a resistor R_C

between the noninverting input and ground (Fig. 12–23B). For cancellation,

$$R_1 I_{B_1} = R_C I_{B_2} \tag{12–23}$$

Practical circuits for compensating voltage and current offsets for inverting and noninverting amplifiers are shown in Fig. 12–24. For either circuit, with V_i set to zero, a dc voltmeter is connected between the output terminal and ground. The potentiometer is adjusted until the voltmeter reads zero volts, indicating that the amplifier is compensated.

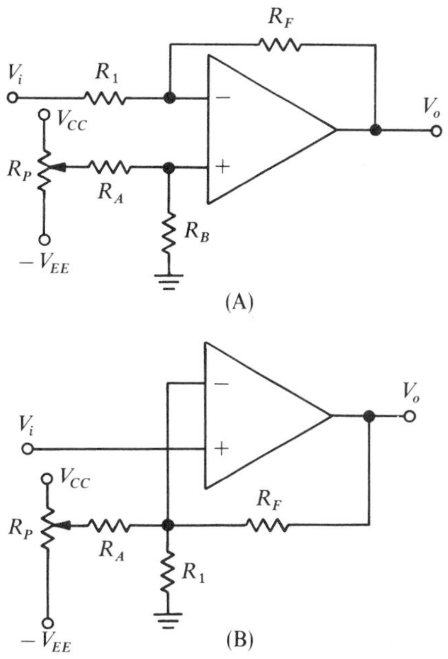

Fig. 12–24. *Practical offset compensation circuits. (A) For an inverting amplifier. (B) For a noninverting amplifier.*

Drift

Both the input offset voltage and the current vary with temperature. Manufacturers specify drift (variation in the operating point) either by curves, such as shown in Fig. 12–25, or by noting its maximum value. Because of the effects of drift, an op amp is compensated only at the temperature the potentiometer was set for zero output. At other temperatures, there exists a minute output (the *error voltage*).

EXAMPLE 12–9.

Assume that for the op amp to be compensated, the lower curve of Fig. 12–25A applies. The closed-loop gain of the amplifier is -100. For simplicity, I_{io} is neglected. At room temperature (25°C), the amplifier is compensated to yield zero output for zero input signal. What is the output voltage at 125°C with the signal set to zero?

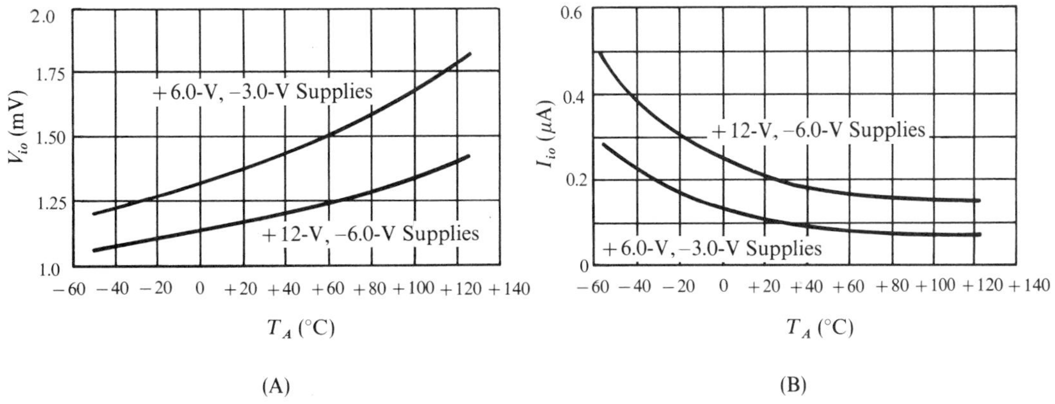

Fig. 12–25. *Examples of variation in (A) input offset voltage and (B) input offset current with temperature.*

Solution:

In the lower curve of Fig. 12–25A, the offset voltage has increased from approximately 1.15 mV at 25°C to 1.4 mV at 125°C. The net change is $1.4 - 1.15 = 0.25$ mV. Because the compensation was performed at room temperature, an error voltage exists at 125°C for zero input signal. In this example, the error voltage is $-100 \times 0.25 = -25$ mV.

12.6 Frequency Compensation

In our examples of op amp applications, we saw that negative feedback provided the desired amplifier characteristics. When feedback is employed, the possibility exists that the amplifier may break into oscillation (see Chapter 9). In this section, we shall consider how an op amp can be stabilized.

Because of internal shunt capacitances, the frequency response curve of an op amp generally has three break frequencies, illustrated in the Bode plot of Fig. 12–26. A Bode plot is a straight-line approximation of the actual response curve. The first break frequency, f_1, essentially determines the useful bandwidth of the amplifier. At each break frequency, the curve becomes steeper by an additional $-6\,\text{dB}/\text{octave}$ (or $-20\,\text{dB}/\text{decade}$). (An octave is a twofold increase in frequency; a decade is a tenfold increase in frequency.)

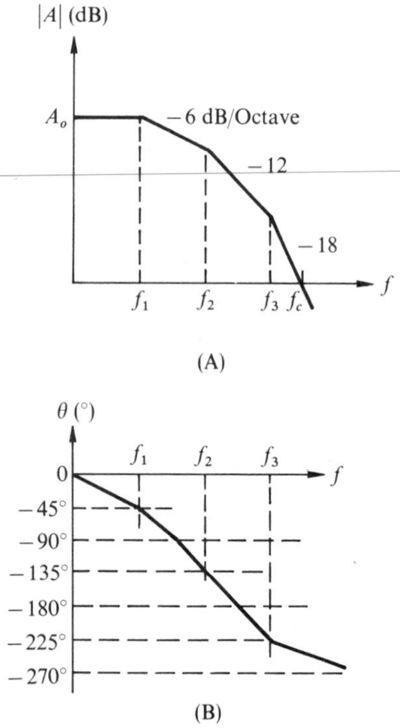

Fig. 12–26. *Open-loop response of a typical op amp. (A) Amplitude. (B) Phase angle.*

An amplifier having three break frequencies may be expressed by

$$A_{vo} = \frac{A_o}{\left(1 + \dfrac{jf}{f_1}\right)\left(1 + \dfrac{jf}{f_2}\right)\left(1 + \dfrac{jf}{f_3}\right)} \qquad \textbf{(12–24)}$$

where A_o is the gain at mid frequencies.

From Chapter 9, the loop gain is defined as the product of the feedback factor, B, and the open-loop gain, A_{vo}:

$$\text{Loop gain} = BA_{vo}$$

From the loop gain, we can predict the stability of a feedback amplifier. When $BA_{vo} = 1\angle 180^\circ$, the amplifier becomes unstable and breaks into oscillation.

In terms of decibels (dB), the loop gain of $1 = 20\log(1) = 0\,\text{dB}$. In Fig. 12–27A, the curve intersects the frequency axis

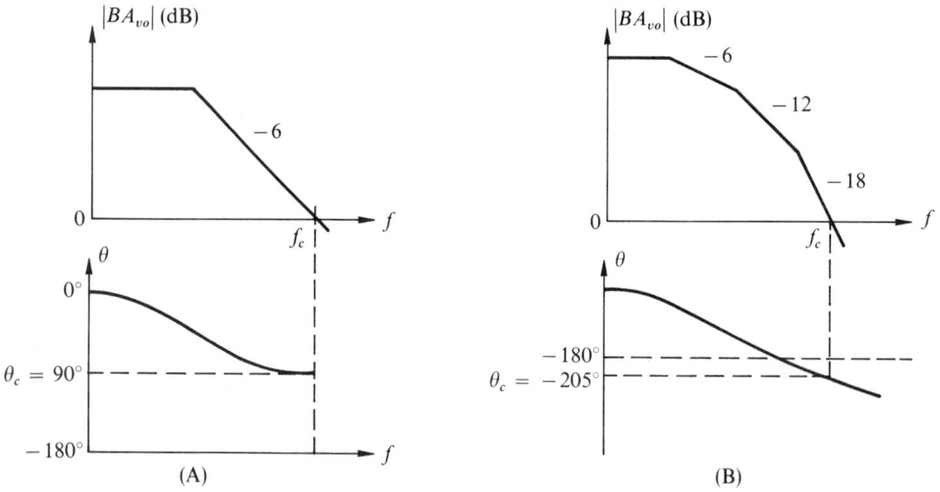

Fig. 12–27. *Response curves of two amplifiers. (A) Stable. (B) Unstable. (See Example 12–10.)*

at *unity gain crossover frequency*, f_c, when the loop gain is 0 dB. If the phase angle corresponding to f_c is $-180°$, or is more negative, the amplifier oscillates; if it is less negative than $-180°$, the amplifier is stable.

In Fig. 12–27A, the phase angle corresponding to f_c, designated by θ_c, is $-90°$. This is less negative than $-180°$, and the amplifier is stable. In Fig. 12–27B, the angle corresponding to f_c is $\theta_c = -205°$. This is more negative than $-180°$, and the amplifier is unstable.

One can define a term called *phase margin*, θ_{PM}, as

$$\theta_{PM} = \theta_c + 180° \qquad \textbf{(12–25)}$$

If the phase margin is positive, the amplifier is stable; if zero or negative, the amplifier is unstable.

EXAMPLE 12–10.

Determine the phase margins from the plots of Fig. 12–27.

Solution:

By Eq. (12–25), for Fig. 12–27A,

$$\theta_{PM} = -90° + 180° = 90°$$

For Fig. 12–27B,

$$\theta_{PM} = -205° + 180° = -25°$$

If the phase margin is zero, the amplifier will oscillate. If the phase margin is only a few degrees positive, the amplifier is potentially unstable. A reasonable value of phase margin for stable operation is 30°.

One can formulate general guidelines for predicting the stability of an op amp with feedback. They include the following.

1. If the slope of the amplitude response curve is -18 dB/octave at the crossover frequency, the amplifier is unstable.
2. If the slope is -12 dB/octave at crossover, it is conditionally stable; that is, the amplifier may break into oscillation.
3. If the slope is -6 dB/octave at crossover, the amplifier is absolutely stable.

Phase Compensation

By use of the *phase lag network* of Fig. 12–28, it is possible to stabilize an op amp. Resistance R_a represents an internal equivalent resistance of the op amp. The external components added to the amplifier, therefore, are compensating capacitor, C_c, in series with compensating resistance, R_c. In practice, the manufacturer specifies the values of R_c and C_c for different frequency response curves, as indicated in Fig. 12–1. To show how compensation is achieved, however, we will analyze the circuit of Fig. 12–28.

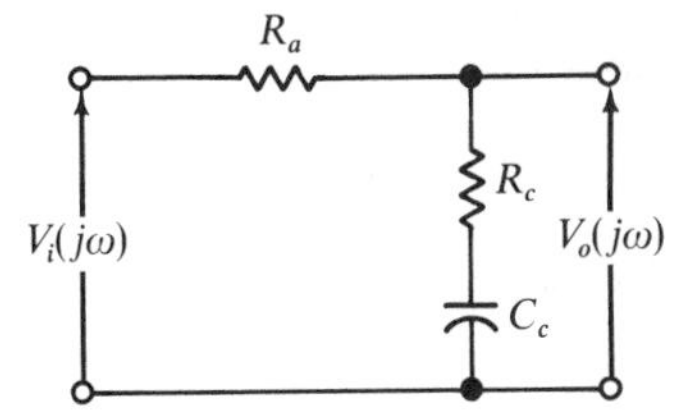

Fig. 12–28. *Example of a phase lag network.*

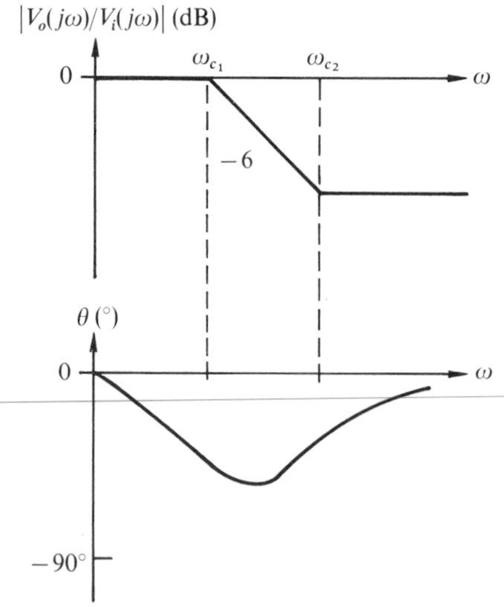

Fig. 12–29. *Amplitude and phase angle response curves of a phase lag network.*

By voltage division, output voltage $V_o(j\omega)$ is

$$V_o(j\omega) = \frac{\left(R_c + \dfrac{1}{j\omega C_c}\right)V_i(j\omega)}{R_a + R_c + \dfrac{1}{j\omega C_c}}$$

Multiplying the numerator and denominator by $j\omega C_c$ and dividing the result by $V_i(j\omega)$, we obtain

$$\frac{V_o(j\omega)}{V_i(j\omega)} = \frac{1 + j\omega R_c C_c}{1 + j\omega C_c(R_a + R_c)} \qquad \textbf{(12–26)}$$

Letting $1/(R_a + R_c)C_c = \omega_{c1}$ and $1/R_c C_c = \omega_{c2}$, where $\omega_{c2} > \omega_{c1}$, Eq. (12–26) may be expressed by

$$\frac{V_o(j\omega)}{V_i(j\omega)} = \frac{1 + \dfrac{j\omega}{\omega_{c2}}}{1 + \dfrac{j\omega}{\omega_{c1}}} \qquad \textbf{(12–27)}$$

The Bode plot of Fig. 12–28 is illustrated in Fig. 12–29.

The effect of a phase lag network connected to an op amp is shown in Fig. 12–30. In this example, for the uncompensated op amp, the response curve intersects the ω-axis with a slope of -12 dB/octave. By adding the phase lag network, the response curve of the compensated op amp is "pulled down" and intersects the ω-axis with a slope of -6 dB/octave. This condition represents absolute stability.

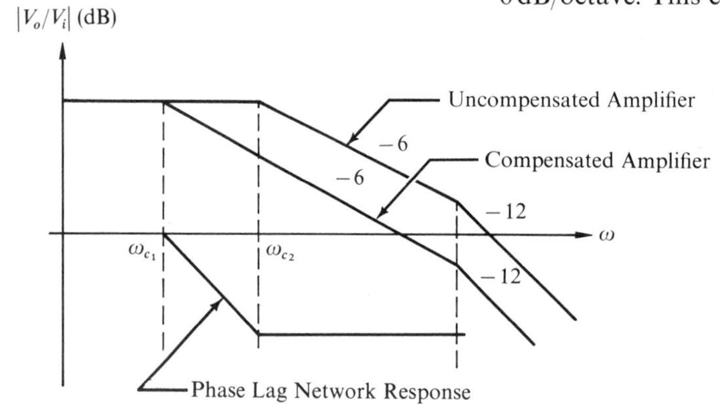

Fig. 12–30. *The effect of a phase lag network is to "pull down" the response curve of an uncompensated amplifier.*

SUMMARY

Before an op amp is used, its data sheet should be consulted. Valuable information obtained from data sheets includes circuit description, maximum ratings, connection diagram, open-loop gain, common-mode rejection ratio, and frequency compensation methods.

Because of its high open-loop gain, the connected feedback network determines the operating characteristics of an op amp circuit. By suitable choice of feedback components, one may use the op amp as an amplifier, summer, integrator, differentiator, multipler, active filter, and in many other circuits. The application areas for the op amp are vast, only limited by the ingenuity of the user.

For reliable and stable operation of an op amp circuit, voltage and current offset compensation, as well as frequency compensation, are required. Offset compensation ensures that the output is zero for zero input. Frequency compensation ensures that the op amp circuit does not break into oscillation.

Further Reading

Ghaznavi, C., and A. H. Seidman. *Electronic Circuit Analysis.* New York: Macmillan Company, 1972, Chapter 16.

Kahn, Michael. *The Versatile Op Amp.* New York: Holt, Rinehart and Winston, 1970, Chapters 4–9.

Millman J., and C. C. Halkias. *Integrated Electronics: Analog and Digital Circuits and Systems.* New York: McGraw-Hill Book Company, 1972, Chapters 15 and 16.

Oldham, W. G., and S. E. Schwarz. *An Introduction to Electronics.* New York: Holt, Rinehart and Winston, 1972, Chapter 12.

Roberge, James K. *Operational Amplifiers.* New York: John Wiley and Sons, 1975, Chapters 11 and 12.

Senturia, S. D., and B. D. Wedlock. *Electronic Circuits and Applications.* New York: John Wiley and Sons, 1975, Chapter 5.

REVIEW QUESTIONS

12.1 Identify at least seven distinct items of information provided on a manufacturer's data sheet for an op amp.

12.2 Define
(a) Open-loop voltage gain.
(b) Input offset current.
(c) Input offset voltage.
(d) Input offset current and voltage drift.
(e) Slew rate.

12.3 What is the significance of slew rate?

12.4 Draw schematic diagrams of
(a) An inverting amplifier.
(b) A noninverting amplifier.
What is the principal difference between the two amplifiers?

12.5 Draw a schematic diagram of a voltage follower. What are its electrical characteristics?

12.6 Draw a schematic diagram of a difference amplifier. To what is its output voltage proportional?

12.7 On what basic principle does the analog computer operate?

12.8 To what does the scale factor refer in a summer?

12.9 What is the function of a sign changer?

12.10 Define, in words, a unit step function.

12.11 Define, in words, a ramp function.

12.12 What function is performed by a logarithmic amplifier?

12.13 What does the antilog amplifier accomplish?

12.14 How does an active filter compare with an *LC* filter?

12.15 Describe the procedure for determining offset compensation of an op amp.

12.16 Define error voltage of an op amp.

12.17 What is a Bode plot?

12.18 Define crossover frequency.

12.19 Define phase margin of an amplifier.

12.20 State three guidelines for predicting the stability of an op amp with feedback.

12.21 Draw a schematic diagram of a phase lag network. What are its electrical characteristics?

PROBLEMS

P12–1 Using an op amp with an open-loop voltage gain of $-50{,}000$, design an amplifier having three defined voltage gains of -5, -25, and -75. Assume that $R_F = 150\,\text{k}\Omega$.

P12–2 Repeat prob. P12–1 for $R_F = 200\,\text{k}\Omega$.

P12–3 Using an op amp and a 0-V–5-V voltmeter, design a multirange electronic voltmeter having full-scale ranges of 0–0.2, 1.5, and 3 V. Assume $R_1 = 2\,\text{k}\Omega$.

P12–4 Repeat prob. P12–3 using a 0-V–15-V voltmeter.

P12–5 Assume that $R_F/R_1 = 15$ in the difference amplifier of Fig. 12–10. If the supply voltages to the op amp are ± 10 V, what is the maximum value of V_{s_2} if $V_{s_1} = 1$ V?

P12–6 Repeat prob. P12–5 for $V_{s_1} = 3$ V.

P12–7 Because of a 400-Hz hum on an input signal, the output of a noninverting amplifier is 2 V. If the gain of the amplifier is 20, how can the hum be reduced to zero?

P12–8 Referring to three-input summer of Fig. 12–11, assume that $R_F = 120\,\text{k}\Omega$, $R_1 = 12\,\text{k}\Omega$, $R_2 = 24\,\text{k}\Omega$, and $R_3 = 60\,\text{k}\Omega$. Determine the output voltage if $V_1 = 0.1$ V, $V_2 = 0.2$ V, and $V_3 = -1$ V.

P12–9 Repeat prob. P12–8 for $V_1 = V_2 = 0.2$ V and $V_3 = -0.5$ V.

P12–10 The gain of the active low-pass filter of Fig. 12–20 is -20, and the upper -3-dB frequency is 60 Hz. If $R_F = 200\,\text{k}\Omega$, determine

(a) R_1.

(b) C_F.

P12–11 Repeat prob. P12–10 for an upper −3-dB frequency of 100 Hz.

P12–12 Referring to Fig. 12–22B, $R_P = 15\,\text{k}\Omega$, $R_A = 150\,\text{k}\Omega$, and $R_B = 200\,\Omega$. If $V_{CC} = V_{EE} = 6\,\text{V}$, what is the variation in V_{io} developed across R_B?

P12–13 Repeat prob. P12–12 for $V_{CC} = V_{EE} = 10\,\text{V}$.

P12–14 An op amp has a closed-loop gain of −50. At room temperature, the op amp is compensated to yield zero output for zero input signal. Assuming that the upper curve of Fig. 12–25A applies to the op amp, determine the output voltage at 125°C for no input signal.

P12–15 Repeat prob. P12–14 for a closed-loop gain of −75.

P12–16 Show that −6 dB/octave is approximately equal to −20 dB/decade.

P12–17 Determine the phase margin from each of the plots in Fig. 12–31.

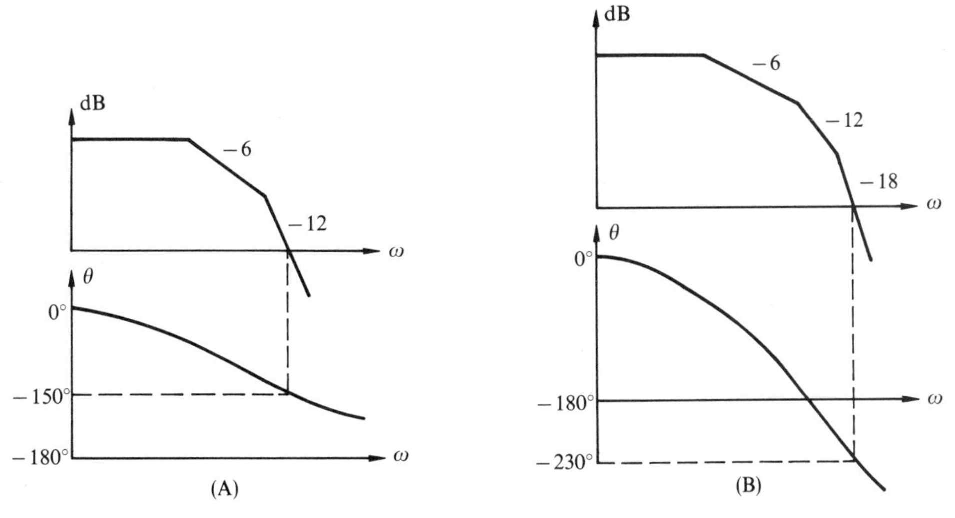

Fig. 12–31.

part iii

LARGE-SIGNAL OPERATION

This part of the text is concerned with the amplification of power. Unlike small-signal amplifiers, power amplifiers present problems not encountered previously.

To this point, we have treated amplifiers as linear circuits and semiconductors as linear devices. These approximations were valid because of the small-signal swings that were handled by these amplifiers. On the other hand, the effectiveness of a power amplifier is largely dependent on the magnitude of the input applied to it. Hence, large-signal swings are unavoidable. For this reason, power amplifiers are called *large-signal* amplifiers. Linear approximations become invalid for power amplifiers, and other methods of analysis, such as graphical analysis, must be used.

The large swings in voltage and current in power amplifiers invariably yield substantial amounts of distortion. Distortion and methods for minimizing it are considered in Chapter 13.

In the following two chapters, various types of power amplifiers are introduced, stressing the audio power amplifier. The different classes of operation are depicted, and examples of practical power amplifiers are given.

With large signals also comes the problem of heat generation and dissipation within the transistor. Types of heat dissipators and methods of heat sink design are introduced in Chapter 14. The use of IC power amplifiers is also considered.

13

Power Amplifiers

Power amplifiers play an important role in many types of electronic systems. The power amplifier often is used as the final amplifier stage in a system. Its prime purpose is to drive a transducer, such as a motor or a loudspeaker.

Consider the sound system found in a home. The power amplifier is used to generate sufficient power to drive a loudspeaker. The loudspeaker converts electrical energy into acoustical energy. Driving the power amplifier is a preamplifier, which is a small-signal voltage amplifier.

Another example of the use of power amplifiers is found in communication systems. The transmitter generates large amounts of radio-frequency (rf) power which is transmitted through space. Again, a power amplifier is employed in a system.

Power amplifiers are generally built as discrete and hybrid circuits. Monolithic power ICs are available in moderate power ratings.

13.1 Modes of Operation

Power amplifiers may be categorized by their mode of operation, not by the type of connection they represent (*C-E*, *C-B*, or *C-C*) as shown earlier with small-signal amplifiers. The four fundamental modes of operation for power amplifiers are class *A*, *AB*, *B*, and *C*. These designations are related to the location of the *Q* point on the characteristics for the device. Because power amplifiers are generally designed with BJTs, the BJT is the only active device we shall consider in this chapter.

As explained in Chapter 5 and reviewed here, class *A* amplifiers are biased so the transistor conducts for the full duration (360°) of the input signal. This mode of operation is used in small-signal amplifiers considered in previous chapters.

In class *AB* operation, the transistor is biased to conduct for greater than 180° but less than 360° of the input signal. A class *B* amplifier conducts current for 180° of the cycle. In class *C* operation, the amplifier conducts for less than 180°.

Class *A* amplifiers are used in applications in which high-power levels are not required and distortion is to be kept at a minimum. Class AB and B amplifiers have the capacity to deliver large amounts of power with tolerable levels of distortion when connected in push-pull. (Push-pull operation is described later in this chapter.)

Class C amplifiers, which can deliver large amounts of power, produce high levels of distortion. They are used primarily in rf applications where the output load is a tuned circuit adjusted to the frequency of the input signal. Unwanted frequencies due to the distorted waveform in class C operation are thereby rejected.

13.2 Class *A* Power Amplifiers

A common-emitter, class A, large-signal (power) amplifier is shown in Fig. 13–1A. The circuit is called a *series-fed*

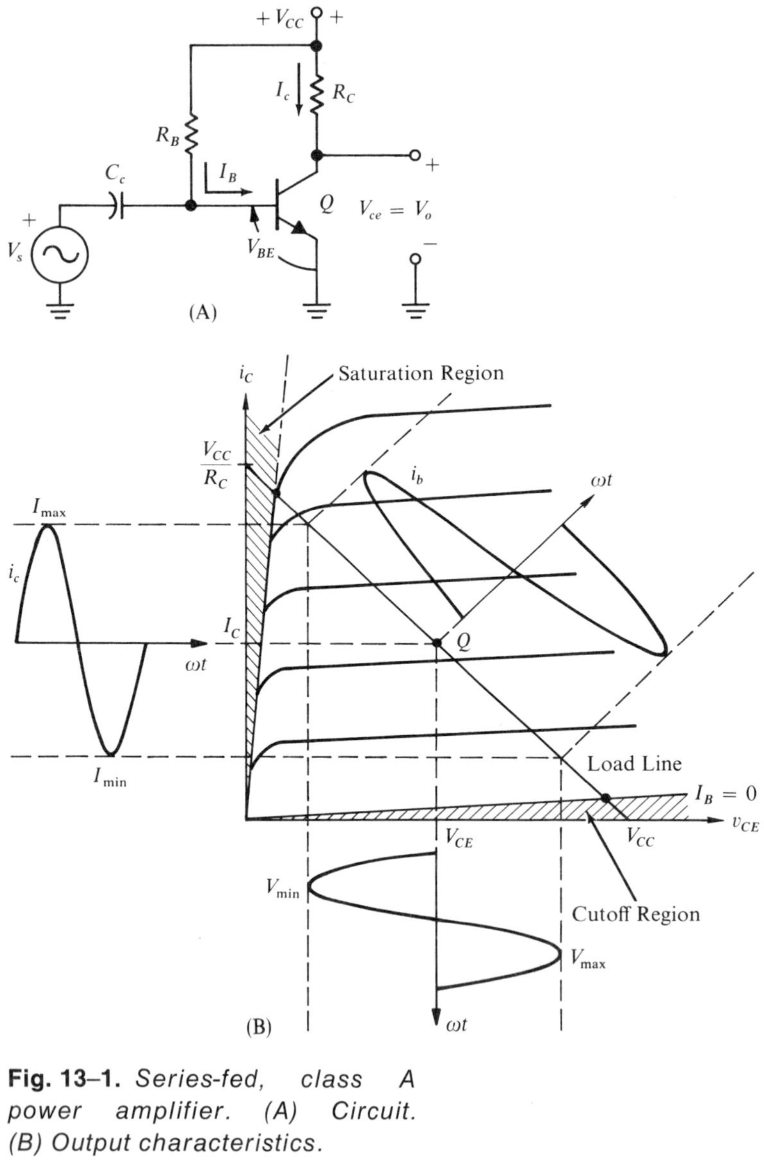

Fig. 13–1. *Series-fed, class A power amplifier. (A) Circuit. (B) Output characteristics.*

power amplifier because the load, R_C, is in series with the output (collector) terminal of the transistor. Resistor R_C acts as the dc as well as the ac load. Therefore, the dc and ac load lines are the same.

The ac power, P_o, delivered to the load equals the product of the rms values of the collector voltage (V_{ce}) and current (I_c) waveforms:

$$P_o = V_{ce} I_c \qquad \textbf{(13–1)}$$

In terms of the maximum and minimum values of the output waveforms, Fig. 13–1B shows that

$$V_{ce} = \frac{V_{max} - V_{min}}{2\sqrt{2}} \qquad \textbf{(13–2)}$$

and

$$I_c = \frac{I_{max} - I_{min}}{2\sqrt{2}} \qquad \textbf{(13–3)}$$

Substituting Eqs. (13–2) and (13–3) in Eq. (13–1) and simplifying, we obtain

$$P_o = \frac{(V_{max} - V_{min})(I_{max} - I_{min})}{8} \qquad \textbf{(13–4a)}$$

Because the waveforms are generally reasonably symmetrical,

$$I_c = \frac{I_{max}}{\sqrt{2}}$$

and

$$V_{ce} = \frac{V_{max}}{\sqrt{2}}$$

where I_{max} and V_{max} are the maximum (peak) values of the current and voltage waveforms, respectively. Then,

$$P_o = \frac{V_{max} I_{max}}{2} \qquad \textbf{(13–4b)}$$

$$= \frac{I_{max}^2 R_C}{2} \qquad \textbf{(13–4c)}$$

$$= \frac{V_{max}^2}{2R_C} \qquad \textbf{(13–4d)}$$

From the resulting power equations, it becomes apparent that the ac output power is a function of V_{max} and I_{max}, which depend on the input signal. We may conclude that the larger the input signal, the greater is the output power delivered to the load.

The maximum available output power from a class *A* power amplifier is now determined. A careful examination of Fig. 13–1B reveals that maximum signal swing is obtained by locating the *Q* point at the center of the load line. For this condition, the *Q* point is at $v_{CE} = V_{CC}/2$ and $i_C = V_{CC}/2R_C$. Theoretically, the signal can swing through the entire length of the load line. The collector voltage swings from zero to V_{CC} and the collector current from zero to V_{CC}/R_C. By Eq. (13–4a),

$$P_{o(\max)} = \frac{(V_{CC} - 0)\left(\frac{V_{CC}}{R_C} - 0\right)}{8}$$

$$= \frac{V_{CC}^2}{8R_C} \qquad \textbf{(13–5)}$$

From the collector characteristics of Fig. 13–1B, we see that the maximum signal swing is limited by the *saturation* and *cutoff* regions of the transistor. In saturation, the collector current does not follow the base current. Consequently, the relation $I_c = h_{fe}I_b$ is no longer valid. Further, the collector-emitter voltage, v_{CE}, is approximately zero when the transistor is saturated. The current and voltage swings, therefore, are not linearly amplified in this region of operation.

The cutoff region extends below the characteristic curve for $I_B = 0$. In this region, the collector does not amplify any input current below $I_B = 0$. A portion of the input wave, therefore, does not appear at the output.

Because of the saturation and cutoff regions of a transistor, maximum current and voltage swings unavoidably produce a distorted output waveform. For this reason, it is good practice to operate a class *A* power amplifier as close to the load line extremes as possible, while avoiding the saturation and cutoff regions.

In our concern with maximum power, we may be overlooking an important criterion, namely, the efficiency of a power amplifier. No system is 100 percent efficient. We must, therefore, know the amount of input power needed for a desired output. The total power, P_{it}, supplied to an amplifier, has three components. Expressed mathematically,

$$P_{it} = P_i + I_B V_{CC} + I_C V_{CC} \qquad \textbf{(13–6)}$$

where P_i = ac input signal power,
$I_B V_{CC}$ = dc power supplied to the base,
$I_C V_{CC}$ = dc power supplied to the collector.

In practice, P_i and $I_B V_{CC}$ are negligible compared with $I_C V_{CC}$. Neglecting these terms, Eq. (13–6) reduces to the dc collector power, $P_{it} = P_{dc}$:

$$P_{dc} = V_{CC} I_C \qquad \textbf{(13–7)}$$

With the Q point located in the center of the load line, $I_C = V_{CC}/2R_C$. Substitution of this quantity in Eq. (13–7) yields

$$P_{dc} = \frac{V_{CC}^2}{2R_C} \qquad \textbf{(13–8)}$$

The efficiency, η, of any system, calculated on a percentage basis, is given by

$$\eta = \frac{\text{output power}}{\text{input power}} \times 100\% \qquad \textbf{(13-9)}$$

For an amplifier, the efficiency is defined as the ratio of the ac power delivered to the load to the dc power supplied to the collector circuit. The *maximum* efficiency of a series-fed, class *A* amplifier may be calculated by substituting Eq. (13–5) and Eq. (13–8) in Eq. (13–9), yielding

$$\eta_{max} = \frac{\dfrac{V_{CC}^2}{8R_C}}{\dfrac{V_{CC}^2}{2R_C}} \times 100\% = 25\% \qquad \textbf{(13-10)}$$

The actual efficiency (*collector efficiency*) of a class *A* power amplifier may be expressed by

$$\eta = \frac{V_{max}I_{max}}{V_{CC}^2} R_C \times 100\% \qquad \textbf{(13-11)}$$

EXAMPLE 13–1.

In the power amplifier of Fig. 13–1A, $V_{CC} = 12\,\text{V}$, $R_C = 100\,\Omega$, $h_{FE} = 60$, and $V_{BE} = 0.7\,\text{V}$. Determine

(a) The value of R_B that locates the Q point in the center of the load line.

(b) The maximum output power.

Solutions:

(a) For the Q point to be in the center of the load line,

$$V_{CE} = \frac{V_{CC}}{2} = \frac{12}{2} = 6\,\text{V}$$

and

$$I_C = \frac{6}{100} = 60\,\text{mA}$$

Because $I_B = I_C/h_{FE}$,

$$I_B = \frac{60}{60} = 1\,\text{mA}$$

Writing a voltage equation for the base circuit, we have

$$V_{CC} = I_B R_B + V_{BE}$$

Solving for R_B,

$$R_B = \frac{V_{CC} - V_{BE}}{I_B} = \frac{12 - 0.7}{1} = 11.3\,\text{k}\Omega$$

(b) By Eq. (13–5),

$$P_{o(\max)} = \frac{V_{CC}^2}{8R_C}$$

$$= \frac{12^2}{8 \times 100} = 180\,\text{mW}$$

The power dissipated in a transistor, P_D, is equal to the product of the quiescent collector voltage (V_{CE}) and current (I_C). In the previous example,

$$P_D = V_{CE}I_C = 6\,\text{V} \times 60\,\text{mA} = 360\,\text{mW}$$

In the absence of an input signal, maximum power is dissipated as heat in the collector of a transistor operating class *A*. Care must be exercised, therefore, to ensure that the maximum power rating of a transistor is not exceeded under "no-input" conditions.

EXAMPLE 13–2.

When an input signal is applied to the amplifier of Example 13–1, the ac voltage measured across the load is 4 V maximum (Fig. 13–2). Determine

(a) The output power delivered to the load.
(b) The collector efficiency of the amplifier.

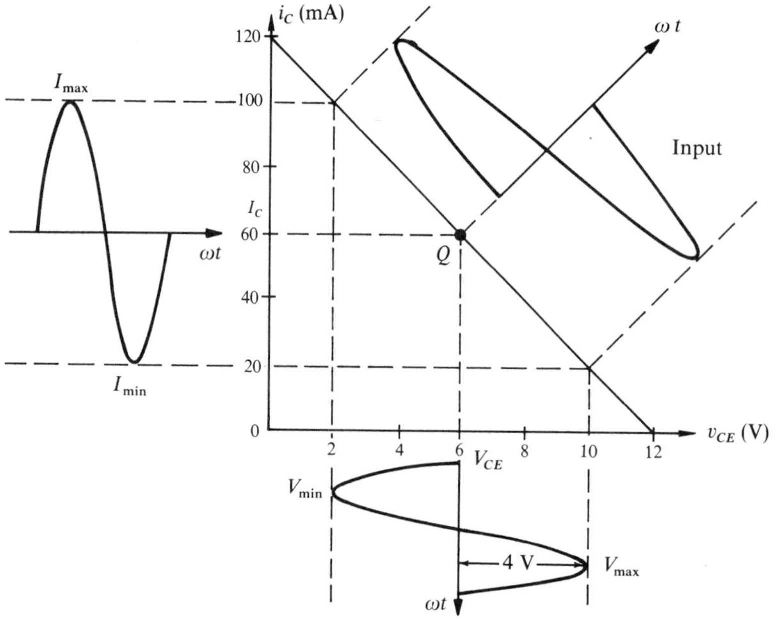

Fig. 13–2. *Determining output power and collector efficiency of a series-fed, class A power amplifier. (See Example 13–2.)*

Solutions:

(a) By Eq. (13–4d),

$$P_o = \frac{V_{\max}^2}{2R_C}$$

$$= \frac{4^2}{2 \times 100} = 80\,\text{mW}$$

(b) Based on Eq. (13–9),

$$\eta = \left(\frac{P_o}{P_{dc}}\right) \times 100\%$$

From the data of Example 13–1, $P_{dc} = 12\,\text{V} \times 60\,\text{mA} = 720\,\text{mW}$. Hence,

$$\eta = \left(\frac{80}{720}\right) \times 100\% = 11.1\%$$

The same result can also be obtained by Eq. (13–11), assuming the Q point is located in the center of the load line. From Fig. 13–2, $I_{max} = 40\,\text{mA}$ and $V_{max} = 4\,\text{V}$; therefore,

$$\eta = \frac{4 \times 40}{12^2} \times 10^{-3} \times 100 \times 100\% = 11.1\%$$

It is apparent from the preceding example that although the load line was well utilized, the efficiency was only 11.1 percent. One may conclude that, in general, the series-fed, class *A* power amplifier is inefficient.

Transformer-Coupled Power Amplifier

A more efficient class *A* power amplifier is realized by using a transformer to couple the load to the collector of the transistor. The resulting circuit, called a *transformer-coupled amplifier*, is shown in Fig. 13–3A. In this circuit, the dc collector current *does not* flow through the load, and it therefore operates more efficiently.

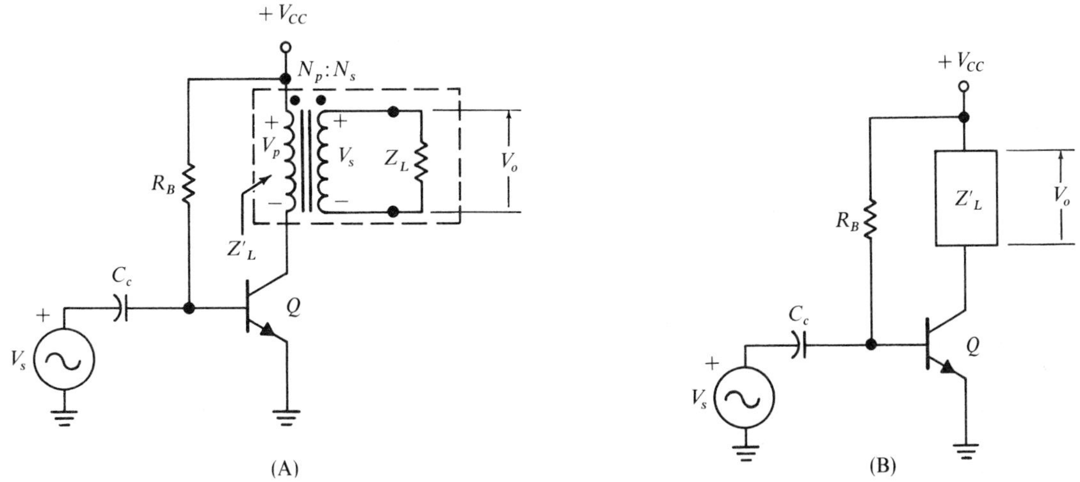

Fig. 13–3. *Transformer-coupled, class A power amplifier. (A) Basic circuit. (B) Simplified equivalent circuit.*

Figure 13–3B provides an equivalent circuit of the amplifier in which the load is reflected in the collector circuit. Impedance Z'_L is the reflected load impedance "seen by" the collector. Its value may be calculated by

$$Z'_L = \left(\frac{N_p}{N_s}\right)^2 \times Z_L \qquad \textbf{(13–12)}$$

where N_p/N_s is the primary-to-secondary turns ratio of the transformer and Z_L is the load impedance.

The transformer used in a transformer-coupled amplifier is a *step-down* transformer. Hence, $N_p > N_s$ (or $N_p/N_s > 1$). For this condition, by Eq. (13–12), $Z'_L > Z_L$. The value of Z'_L is made greater than Z_L, so the collector "sees" a larger impedance, delivering more power to the load.

To study the power relations in the circuit, we once again use graphical analysis. The output characteristic curves are given in Fig. 13–4. The dc load line is determined as usual by the values of V_{CC} and the dc collector resistance, R_C. A glance at Fig. 13–3A reveals that there is no collector resistor. In fact, the only dc collector resistance is the resistance of the transformer primary, R_p; hence, $R_C = R_p$.

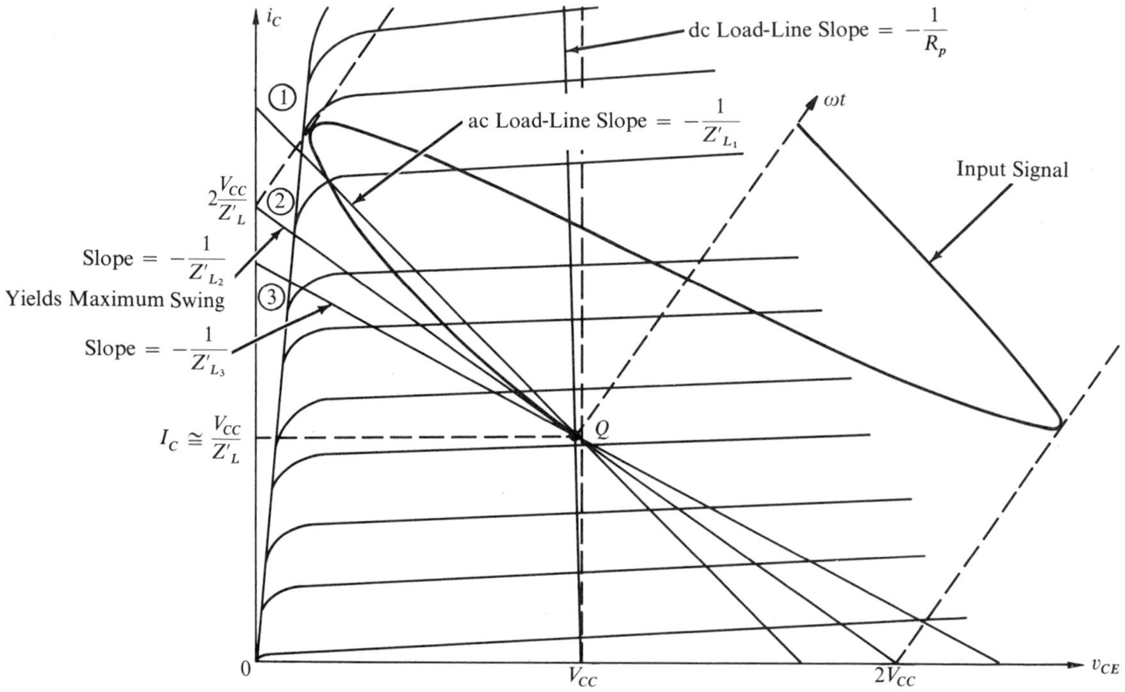

Fig. 13–4. *Output (collector) characteristics for a transformer-coupled, class A power amplifier. Different ac load lines are drawn for various values of Z'_L, illustrating that load line 2 provides maximum output power.*

Because the dc resistance of the primary is usually very low, the dc load line is nearly vertical. For an ideal transformer, $R_p = 0$, and the dc load line is exactly vertical, intersecting the v_{CE}-axis at V_{CC} volts. In a practical case, the slope of the dc load line is equal to $-1/R_p$.

Since the dc and ac loads are not the same, a second (ac) load line is constructed. The slope of the ac load line, also called the *dynamic load line*, has the value of $-1/Z'_L$. The procedure for constructing an ac load line is as follows:

1. First, locate the Q point on the dc load line from the biasing conditions.
2. Using this point as a coordinate for the ac load line, draw the ac load line through the point with a slope of $-1/Z'_L$.

The transformer is used as an impedance matching element. With the selection of the proper turns ratio, any load can be reflected in the collector circuit to achieve a desired value of Z'_L. Maximum power is delivered to the load when the ac load line intersects the v_{CE}-axis at $2V_{CC}$ and the i_C-axis at $2V_{CC}/Z'_L$ (see Fig. 13–4). When this condition is satisfied, the Q point divides the ac load line into two equal segments, and the dc collector current may be expressed by

$$I_C = \frac{V_{CC}}{Z'_L} \tag{13–13}$$

At this point, we ask, How is it possible for the output to reach $2V_{CC}$ volts when the collector supply voltage is only V_{CC} volts? The answer is that the transformer primary, being an inductor, can store energy which contributes to the output voltage. The instantaneous primary voltage can, therefore, reach $2V_{CC}$ volts.

To calculate output power, we use Eq. (13–4a), which is also valid for a transformer-coupled amplifier. The maximum possible output is obtained by substituting the currents and voltages in Fig. 13–4 for the ac load line in Eq. (13–4a):

$$P_{o(\text{max})} = \frac{(2V_{CC} - 0)\left(\dfrac{2V_{CC}}{Z'_L} - 0\right)}{8}$$

$$= \frac{V_{CC}^2}{2Z'_L} \tag{13–14}$$

The dc input power supplied to the collector circuit for maximum output is given by

$$P_{\text{dc}} = V_{CC}I_C = V_{CC}\frac{V_{CC}}{Z'_L}$$

$$= \frac{V_{CC}^2}{Z'_L} \tag{13–15}$$

The maximum obtainable efficiency for a transformer-coupled, class A amplifier is calculated as the ratio of $P_{o(\text{max})}$ to P_{dc}:

$$\eta_{\text{max}} = \frac{V_{CC}^2/2Z'_L}{V_{CC}^2/Z'_L} \times 100\% = 50\% \tag{13–16}$$

In conclusion, the theoretical maximum output power is obtained when a transformer is used to couple the load to the collector of a transistor operating class A.

Output power of a transformer-coupled, class A amplifier also may be calculated from the voltage and current across the primary and secondary of the transformer. In terms of rms quantities, it is given by

$$P_o = \frac{V_{p(\text{rms})}^2}{Z'_L} = \frac{V_{s(\text{rms})}^2}{Z_L} \tag{13–17a}$$

and

$$P_o = I_{p(\text{rms})}^2 Z'_L = I_{s(\text{rms})}^2 Z_L \tag{13–17b}$$

In practice, a transformer-coupled, class A power amplifier is designed to have an efficiency of 35%–40%. Such a design avoids operation in the nonlinear region of the collector characteristics. The efficiency of a practical circuit may be calculated from the following expression:

$$\eta = \frac{V_{max} - V_{min}}{V_{max} + V_{min}} \times 50\% \tag{13–18}$$

EXAMPLE 13–3.

For the power amplifier of Fig. 13–5A and the collector characteristics of Fig. 13–5B,

(a) Construct the dc and ac load lines.

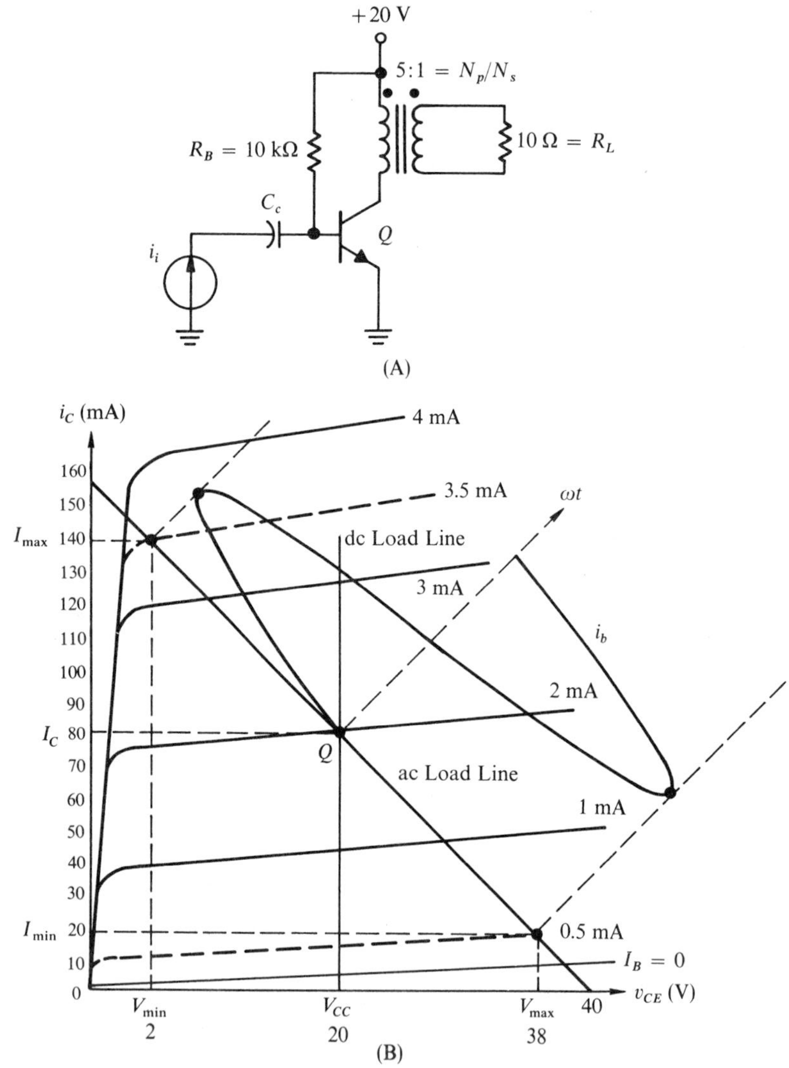

Fig. 13–5. *Diagram for Example 13–3. (A) Circuit. (B) Collector characteristics.*

(b) Calculate the ac output power for a peak-to-peak input current of 3 mA.
(c) Determine the collector efficiency of the circuit.

Solutions:

(a) Assuming that the transformer is ideal, $R_C = R_p = 0$. We therefore draw the dc load line as a vertical line originating at $v_{CE} = V_{CC}$.

To construct the ac load line, we first find the reflected load impedance, Z'_L. Because $N_p/N_s = 5:1$, by Eq. (13–12),

$$Z'_L = 5^2 \times 10 = 250\,\Omega$$

The slope of the ac load line is $-1/Z'_L = -1/250 = -4\,\text{mA/V}$.

The Q point is determined by finding I_B and locating it on the dc load line. The value of I_B is

$$I_B = \frac{20 - 0.7}{10} = 1.93\,\text{mA} \simeq 2\,\text{mA}$$

From the collector characteristics, an I_B of 2 mA corresponds to an I_C of 80 mA.

To locate the i_C-intercept of the ac load line, the change in collector-emitter voltage, ΔV_{CE}, and the change in collector current, ΔI_C, must be determined. Quantity ΔV_{CE} is

$$\Delta V_{CE} = V_{CC} = 20\,\text{V}$$

Quantity ΔI_C is found from the value of the slope of the ac load line. Because $\Delta I_C/\Delta V_{CE} = -4\,\text{mA/V}$, then

$$\Delta I_C = \left(\frac{-1}{Z'_L}\right)(\Delta V_{CE})$$
$$= -(-4)(20) = 80\,\text{mA}$$

The second coordinate for the ac load line is $2 \times 80\,\text{mA} = 160\,\text{mA}$ and 0 V. The v_{CE}-intercept is 40 V ($2V_{CC}$). Note that in this particular example, the maximum voltage swing is $2V_{CC}$ volts. This is not true for a load line having a different slope.

(b) For a 3-mA peak-to-peak signal, the base current swings from $I_B = 0.5\,\text{mA}$ to $I_B = 3.5\,\text{mA}$. The corresponding collector current swing is from 20 mA to 140 mA. Hence, $I_{c(\text{rms})} = (140 - 20)/2\sqrt{2} \simeq 42.5\,\text{mA}$. By Eq. (13–17b),

$$P_o = (42.5 \times 10^{-3})^2 \times 250 = 0.452\,\text{W}$$

(c) The collector efficiency, by Eq. (13–18), is

$$\eta = \frac{38 - 2}{38 + 2} \times 50\% = 45\%$$

In the preceding example, the transformer was assumed to be 100 percent efficient. In practice, a transformer efficiency of 75 percent is typical.

Dissipation Curve

In our discussion of power amplifiers thus far, the power limitations of the transistor have not been considered. It is important that the transistor be capable of dissipating the necessary power over the entire range of amplifier operation. For safe operation of the transistor, three important ratings are provided in data sheets:

1. The maximum power that the device can dissipate, $P_{D(\max)}$.
2. Maximum collector current, $I_{C(\max)}$.
3. Collector-emitter breakdown voltage with base unconnected, BV_{CEO}.

Knowing these ratings, we can draw a *maximum collector dissipation* curve, as illustrated in Fig. 13–6.

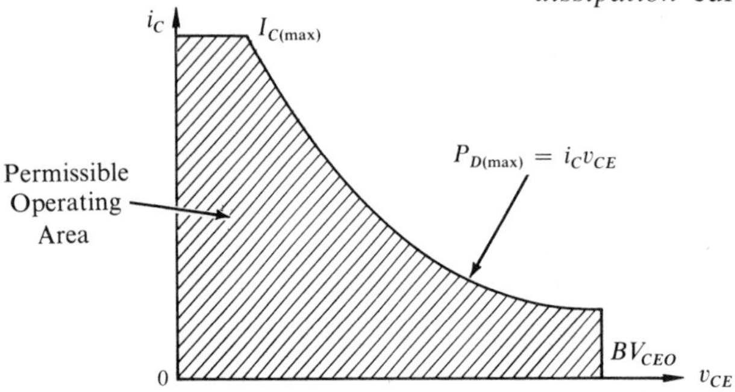

Fig. 13–6. *Collector dissipation curve.*

The dissipation curve is generated by choosing values of v_{CE} and i_C such that their product equals $P_{D(\max)}$. Generally, only three pairs of values of v_{CE} and i_C are needed for the curve, which turns out to be a hyperbola. The dissipation curve is superimposed on the collector characteristics. Safe device operation is realized only in the shaded area bounded by the curve.

One of the advantages of a transformer-coupled amplifier is that no dc flows through the load. Consequently, no dc power is wasted in the load as in the case of a series-fed amplifier.

A general drawback of either a series-fed or transformer-coupled, class *A* amplifier is that the transistor dissipates maximum power under no-load conditions. This may be demonstrated by writing a power equation for the transformer-coupled amplifier. The total dc power, P_{dc}, is equal to the sum of the dissipated power, P_D, and the output power supplied to the load, P_o:

$$P_{dc} = P_D + P_o \qquad \textbf{(13–19a)}$$

Solving for P_D, we have

$$P_D = P_{dc} - P_o \qquad \textbf{(13–19b)}$$

When the load is removed or the input signal is zero, $P_o = 0$. This results in $P_D = P_{dc}$, or the total supply power is dissipated in the transistor (which may damage the transistor). For this reason, it is always recommended *not* to operate such an amplifier under a no-load condition.

13.3 Distortion in Power Amplifiers

Distortion in an amplifier is said to exist when the output waveform is not a faithful reproduction of the input waveform. Three types of distortion are common in power amplifiers. They are *frequency, phase, and nonlinear* distortion.

Frequency distortion exists when an amplifier is unable to amplify equally signals at all frequencies having the same amplitude. This kind of distortion may be reduced with proper design techniques, such as negative feedback (see Chapter 9).

Phase distortion is defined as a phase shift in the output signal which is not proportional to its frequency. This type of distortion also may be minimized by the use of negative feedback.

Nonlinear distortion is present when the shape of the output wave is not the same as the shape of the input wave. It is a result of operation over the nonlinear regions of the collector characteristics. Other components, such as a transformer operating in a nonlinear mode, also distort the signal.

Nonlinear distortion also is called *amplitude* and *harmonic* distortion. A mathematical analysis, known as *Fourier analysis*, reveals that such a distorted wave is composed of an infinite number of frequency components. It contains a *dc* component, a *fundamental* component which is a sinusoidal wave of the same frequency as the input signal, plus *harmonic* components. A harmonic component has a frequency which is a whole multiple (2, 3, 4, . . .) of the fundamental.

Mathematically, a distorted waveform may be expressed by the following *Fourier series*:

$$i_C = A_0 + A_1\cos\omega_0 t + A_2\cos 2\omega_0 t + A_3\cos 3\omega_0 t + \cdots \tag{13-20}$$

where
A_0 = the dc term,
ω_0 = the fundamental frequency in rad/s,
$A_1\cos\omega_0 t$ = the fundamental component,
$A_2\cos 2\omega_0 t$ = the second harmonic component,

and so on. The Fourier series components are plotted against frequency in Fig. 13–7. A laboratory instrument called a *spectrum analyzer* displays on its screen the plot of Fig. 13–7 when an amplitude-distorted waveform is connected to its input terminals.

A typical transfer characteristic of a transistor where collector current is plotted as a function of base current is

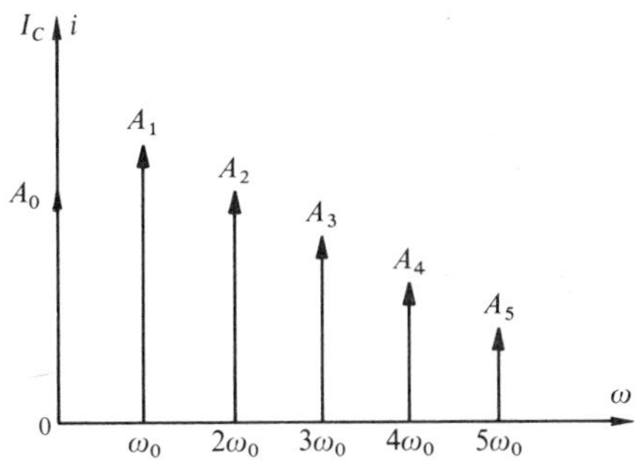

Fig. 13–7. *Frequency spectrum plot illustrating Fourier components.*

shown in Fig. 13–8. Also plotted are the collector and base current waveforms. The coefficients of the terms in Eq. (13–20) may be obtained from Fig. 13–8:

$$A_0 = \frac{1}{6}(I_{\max} + 2I_x + 2I_y + I_{\min}) - I_{C_Q} \quad \textbf{(13–21a)}$$

$$A_1 = \frac{1}{3}(I_{\max} + I_x - I_y - I_{\min}) \quad \textbf{(13–21b)}$$

$$A_2 = \frac{1}{4}(I_{\max} - 2I_{C_Q} + I_{\min}) \quad \textbf{(13–21c)}$$

$$A_3 = \frac{1}{6}(I_{\max} - 2I_x + 2I_y - I_{\min}) \quad \textbf{(13–21d)}$$

$$A_4 = \frac{1}{12}(I_{\max} - 4I_x + 6I_{C_Q} - 4I_y + I_{\min}) \quad \textbf{(13–21e)}$$

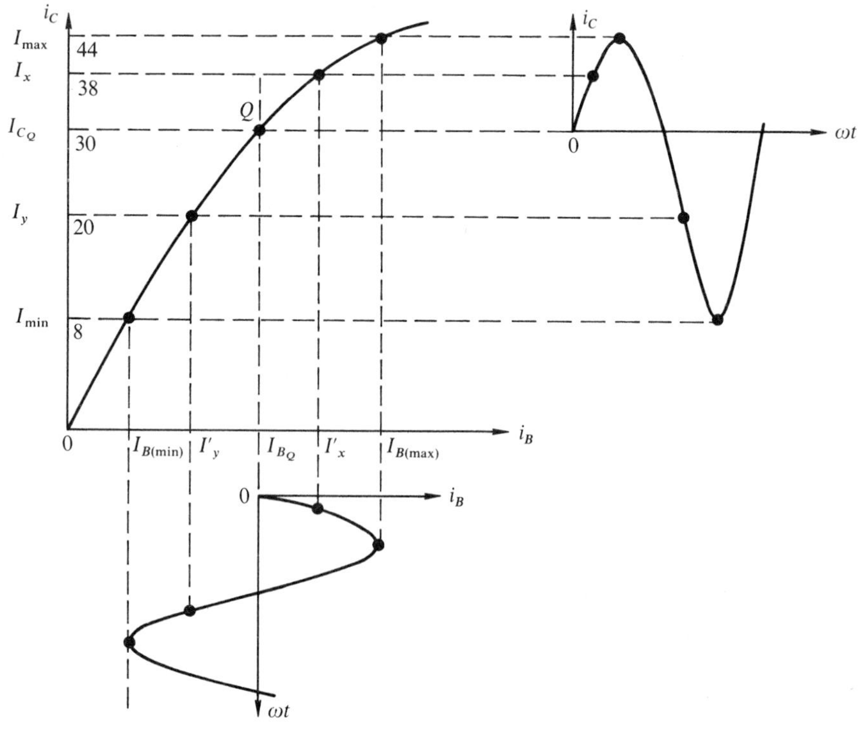

Fig. 13–8. *Distorted output current waveform obtained from the transfer characteristics of a transistor. (See Example 13–4.)*

The magnitude of the ratio of each coefficient to A_1 is defined as *harmonic distortion.* For example,

$$\text{Second harmonic distortion, } D_2 = |A_2/A_1| \quad \textbf{(13–22a)}$$

$$\text{Third harmonic distortion, } D_3 = |A_3/A_1| \quad \textbf{(13–22b)}$$

$$\text{Fourth harmonic distortion, } D_4 = |A_4/A_1| \quad \textbf{(13–22c)}$$

The *total distortion, D_T,* is given by

$$D_T = \sqrt{D_2^2 + D_3^2 + D_4^2 + \cdots} \quad \textbf{(13–23a)}$$

Expressed as a percentage,

$$\%D_T = D_T \times 100\% \quad \textbf{(13–23b)}$$

EXAMPLE 13–4.

Determine the second harmonic distortion from the plot of Fig. 13–8.

Solution:

By Eq. (13–21b) and Eq. (13–21c),

$$A_1 = \frac{1}{3}(44 + 38 - 20 - 8) = 18\,\text{mA}$$

$$A_2 = \frac{1}{4}(44 - (2)(30) + 8) = -2\,\text{mA}$$

Substituting the values of A_1 and A_2 in Eq. (13–22a),

$$D_2 = \left| -\frac{2}{18} \right| = 0.11 = 11\%$$

The second harmonic component contributes 11 percent distortion.

13.4 Transformer-Coupled Push-Pull Amplifiers

Because of the excessive distortion they introduce, class-B operated amplifiers containing a single transistor are not practical in most applications. When used in a circuit containing two transistors, each one conducting for 180°, the distortion is minimized. Such a circuit is called a *push-pull* amplifier, illustrated in Fig. 13–9.

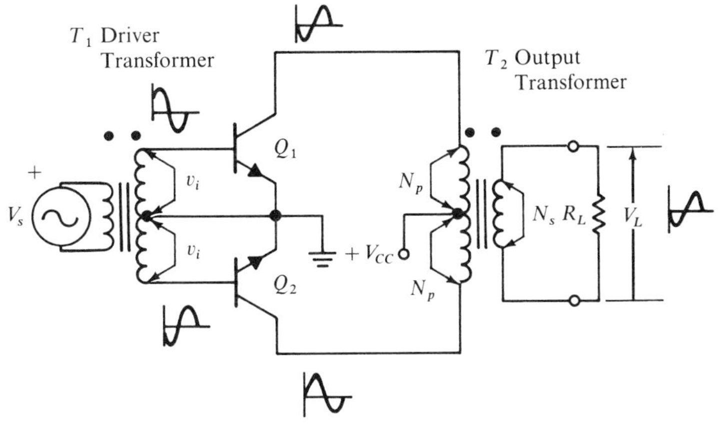

Fig. 13–9. *Transformer-coupled, class B, push-pull power amplifier.*

Push-pull amplifiers have many advantages over single-ended class A amplifiers, considered in the previous sections. Mainly, they are more efficient. In class B operation, both transistors are biased at cutoff. Hence, very little power is dissipated in the transistors with no input signal. Maximum transistor dissipation occurs near maximum output power.

The push-pull amplifier also delivers to the load much greater power than the power dissipated in its transistors.

In fact, maximum power delivered to the load can be five times the power dissipated in each transistor.

Figure 13–9 shows two transistors excited by a center-tapped transformer, called a *driver transformer*. This transformer is used to deliver an equal, but out-of-phase, signal to the bases of the transistors. A center-tapped output transformer is used to impedance match the load to the output circuit and to isolate the load from the dc circuit.

One serious drawback hampers class *B*, push-pull operation. Because it is biased at cutoff, the output signal is always distorted. The distortion is due to the most non-linear portion of the collector characteristics. It begins at the origin where the transistor starts to conduct current and extends through the turn-on, or threshold, voltage.

The resulting distortion, called *crossover distortion*, is illustrated in Fig. 13–10. The output waveform is obtained graphically from the *composite transfer characteristic* curve. This curve is generated by plotting the algebraic sum of the transfer characteristics of both transistors.

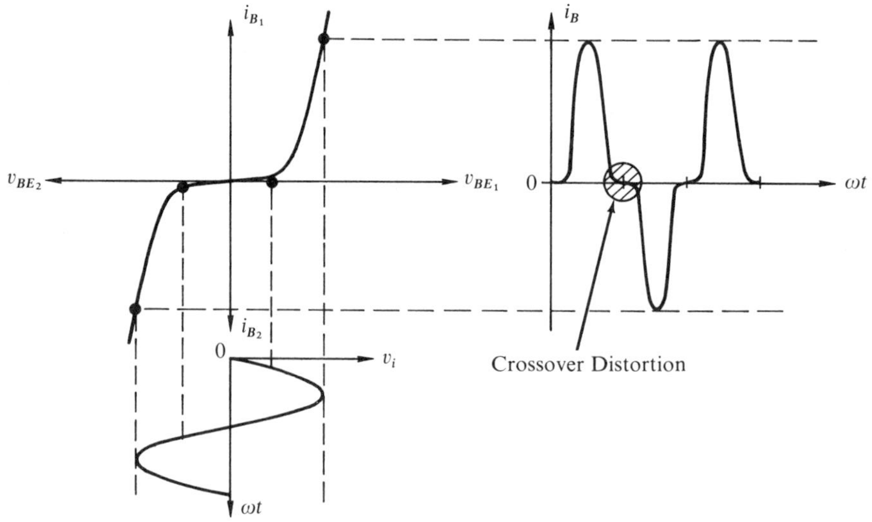

Fig. 13–10. *Composite transfer characteristics of a class B, push-pull amplifier for determining crossover distortion.*

To minimize crossover distortion, the transistors are biased so that they are conducting slightly, or ON. This eliminates operation below the turn-on point. Such biasing provides signal conduction for more than 180°, resulting in class *AB* operation. The circuit of a class *AB*, push-pull amplifier is similar to that of a class *B*, push-pull circuit with a biasing network added.

An example of a class *AB*, push-pull amplifier is shown in Fig. 13–11A. Resistors R_1 and R_2 provide the correct biasing current to keep transistors Q_1 and Q_2 turned ON. Connected to each emitter is resistor R_E. In the order of $10\,\Omega$–$20\,\Omega$, resistor R_E provides negative feedback that helps to stabilize the Q point and reduce distortion.

An alternate biasing circuit is illustrated in Fig. 13–11B. This circuit is superior to that in Fig. 13–11A because the

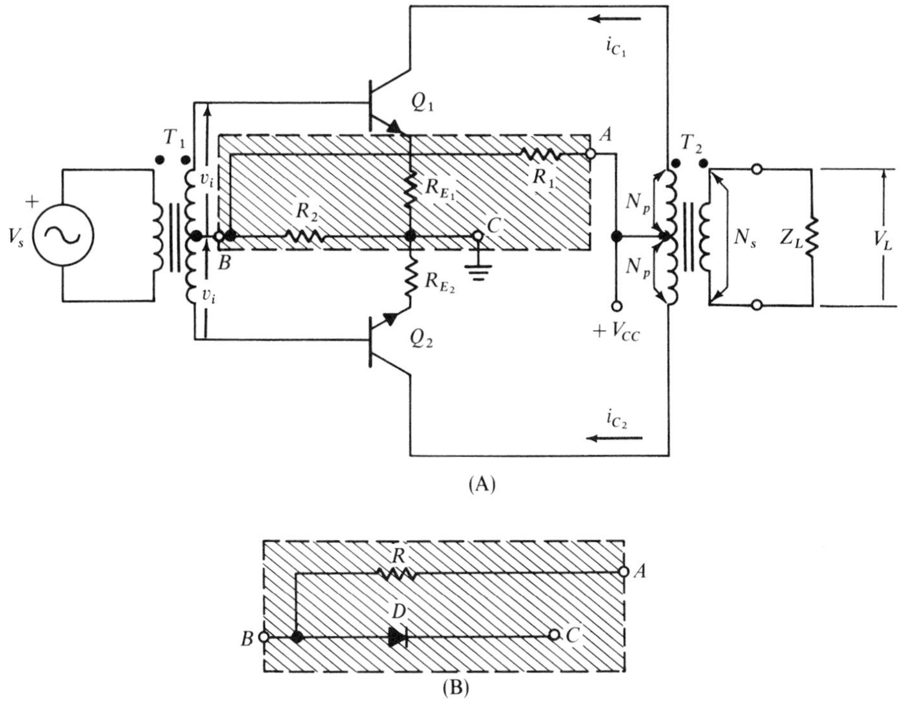

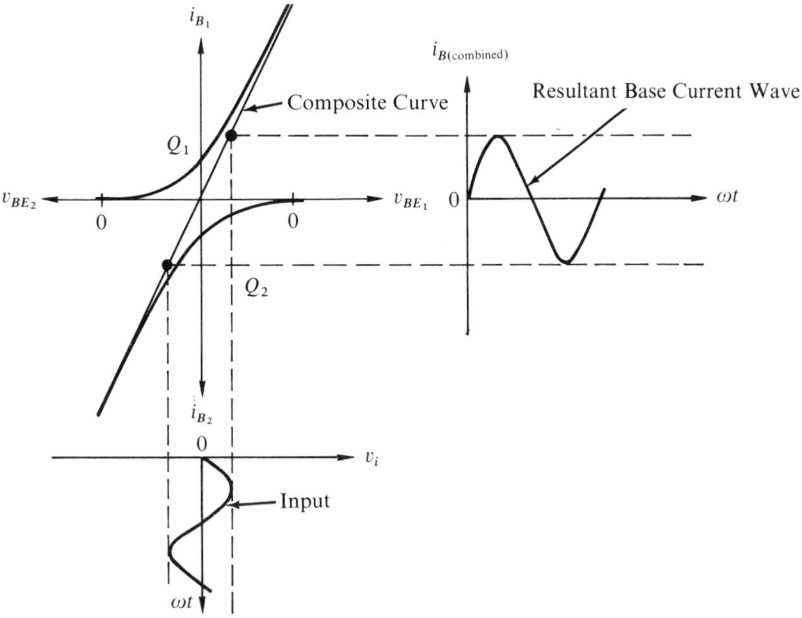

Fig. 13–11. (Above) *Transformer-coupled, class AB, push-pull power amplifier. (A) Basic circuit. (B) Alternate bias network.*

Fig. 13–12. (Below) *Composite transfer curve for class AB, push-pull operation illustrating the elimination of crossover distortion.*

diode establishes a constant biasing level. In addition, the diode provides temperature stabilization. The diode is affected by temperature in a manner that cancels the change in V_{BE} of the transistor.

To illustrate how crossover distortion is eliminated in class *AB* operation, a composite transfer curve is constructed in Fig. 13–12. The transfer characteristics for each transistor are also shown. Note that they are shifted on the v_{BE}-axis to indicate their relative bias points. Whereas the individual transistor transfer curves are nonlinear, the composite curve is linear, resulting in linear amplification and an undistorted base current.

Because of its symmetrical operation, the push-pull amplifier exhibits other advantages not mentioned previously. Since the two collector currents flow in opposite directions through the transformer, the following advantages are realized:

1. Any ripple that might be present in the power supply is cancelled.
2. Opposing dc currents in the primary windings prevent the transformer core from saturating. Additional nonlinearities are thereby avoided. This property permits the use of smaller output transformers.
3. Even harmonic components cancel, reducing the amount of distortion. The second harmonic component is generally a major contributor to the overall distortion in a power amplifier.

These advantages are realized only if the components of the amplifier are perfectly matched.

The power delivered to the load is calculated with the aid of Eq. (13–4b):

$$P_o = \frac{I_{max} V_{max}}{2} = I^2_{p(rms)} Z'_L = \frac{V^2_{p(rms)}}{Z'_L} \qquad \textbf{(13–24)}$$

where $I_{p(rms)}$ is the primary rms current and $V_{p(rms)}$ is the primary rms voltage. The maximum power that can be delivered by a push-pull amplifier can be shown to be

$$P_{o(max)} = \frac{V^2_{CC}}{2Z'_L} \qquad \textbf{(13–25)}$$

The collector efficiency of a class B, push-pull amplifier is

$$\eta = 0.785\left(1 - \frac{V_{min}}{V_{max}}\right) \times 100\% \qquad \textbf{(13–26)}$$

Equation (13–26) may be used as an approximation for a class AB amplifier. For class B operation, $V_{min} = 0$; hence, the maximum efficiency for a class B, push-pull amplifier is 78.5 percent.

EXAMPLE 13–5.

A push-pull class AB audio amplifier is operated from a 12-V dc source. It supplies 1.5 W of power to an 8-Ω loudspeaker. Determine

(a) The output transformer specifications assuming a typical output transformer efficiency of 75 percent.
(b) The ratings $I_{C(max)}$ and BV_{CEO} the transistors should have.

Solutions:

(a) Because the transformer is 75 percent efficient, the power that must be delivered to the primary of the transformer, P_{pri}, is

$$P_{pri} = \frac{1.5}{0.75} = 2\,\text{W}$$

By rearranging Eq. (13–25), Z'_L can be determined:

$$Z'_L = \frac{V_{CC}^2}{2P_{o(\max)}} = \frac{12^2}{2 \times 2} = 36\,\Omega$$

The value of Z'_L calculated is the nominal impedance for one-half the primary winding. The full primary impedance is four times $Z'_L(4 \times 36 = 144\,\Omega)$ because of the squared relationship of the turns ratio. Hence, the transformer is specified as a 144-Ω–8-Ω center-tapped transformer.

(b) The maximum current in each transistor is

$$I_{C(\max)} = \frac{V_{CC}}{Z'_L} = \frac{12}{36} = 0.33\,\text{A}$$

The transistors must be capable of handling a collector current of at least 0.33 A.

Each of the transistors experiences an output voltage swing of $2V_{CC} = 2 \times 12 = 24\,\text{V}$. Therefore, transistors with a minimum $BV_{CEO} = 24\,\text{V}$ should be used.

13.5 Variations in Push-Pull Amplifier Circuits

In this section, we consider how the push-pull circuits of Figs. 13–9 and 13–11 may be modified to overcome some inherent shortcomings. The major problem with these circuits lies in the use of transformers. Transformers are frequency-sensitive components which affect the overall frequency response and linearity of an amplifier.

The primary purpose of the driver transformer is to deliver two signals of the same amplitude, 180° out of phase with respect to each other. A transformerless circuit that performs this function is the *phase splitter* (or *phase inverter*) of Fig. 13–13. In this circuit, advantage is taken of the

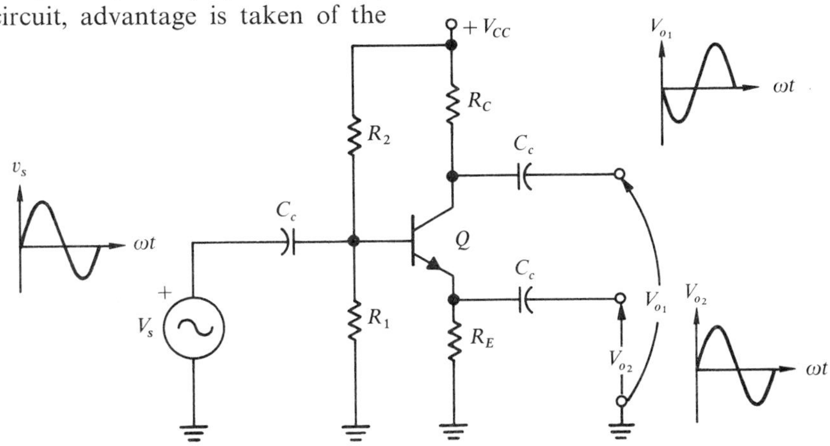

Fig. 13–13. *Basic phase splitter (phase inverter).*

inherent phase shift in a transistor. The outputs are taken from the collector and emitter which are 180° out of phase.

The phase splitter is by no means a perfect circuit. Because the outputs are taken from different terminals of the transistor, the signals are derived from unequal source impedances. This results in an imbalance in the overall operation of the amplifier. With additional (emitter-follower) circuitry, the two impedances can be equalized.

Another type of phase-splitting circuit, the emitter-coupled phase splitter, is illustrated in Fig. 13–14. This circuit utilizes a differential amplifier (see Chapter 11) to achieve the 180° phase difference between the outputs.

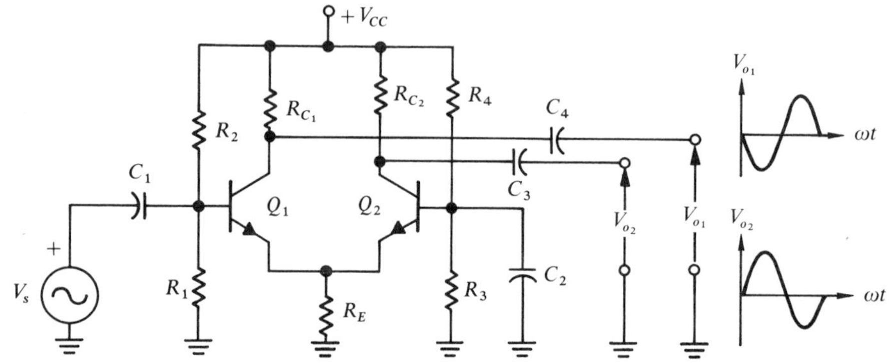

Fig. 13–14. *Emitter-coupled phase splitter.*

The output transformer suffers from the same shortcomings as the driver transformer. In addition, because of the transformer, the transistors must be capable of withstanding a voltage of $2V_{CC}$ volts. Transformerless power amplifiers are described in the following chapter.

13.6 Class *C* Power Amplifiers

In class *C* operation, the transistor conducts for less than 180°, and the collector quiescent current is zero. It is the most efficient mode of operation. Because the output of a class *C* amplifier is badly distorted in comparison with the input signal, it is not suitable for audio applications. It is used extensively, however, as radio-frequency (rf) power amplifiers with tuned circuit (*tank*) loads.

A class *C* power amplifier is illustrated in Fig. 13–15. Resistor R_E reverse biases the base-emitter junction. This is required to keep the transistor OFF when there is no input signal. The time constant, $R_E C_E$, should be at least ten times as large as a half-period of the signal. The tank circuit is tuned to the frequency of the input signal.

Collector efficiencies of a class *C* amplifier can approach 100 percent. In practice, they operate at about 85 percent efficiency.

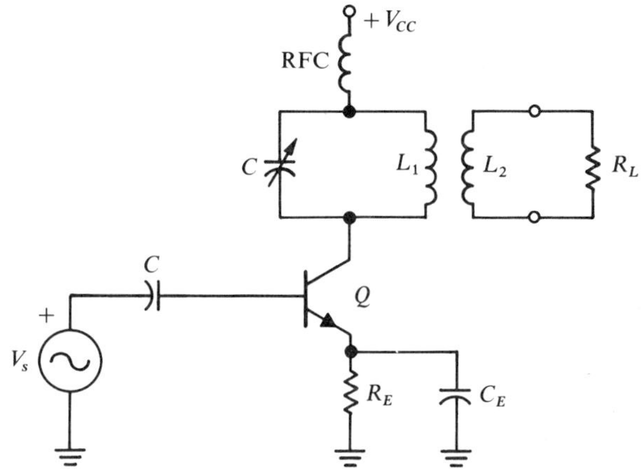

Fig. 13–15. *Example of a class C power amplifier. Inductor RFC is a radio-frequency choke. It prevents rf from reaching the dc power supply,* V_{CC}.

SUMMARY

The primary function of a power amplifier is to supply maximum signal power to a load with good efficiency and minimum distortion. Power amplifiers may be classified in terms of their biasing. The class *AB* push-pull amplifier is the most desirable of the amplifiers considered, where good efficiency, large amounts of power, and low distortion are essential.

Class *A* amplifiers are capable of delivering moderate amounts of power and are the least efficient. Class *B* amplifiers produce a high amount of distortion and are not suitable as audio amplifiers unless connected in a push-pull circuit. Class *C* amplifiers are most efficient and are used primarily in rf applications.

Further Reading

Cowles, L. G. *Transistor Circuits and Applications.* Englewood Cliffs, N.J.: Prentice-Hall, 1968, Chapter 6.

Manera, Anthony S. *Solid State Electronic Circuits for Engineering Technology.* New York: McGraw-Hill Book Company, 1973, Chapter 12.

Millman, J., and C. C. Halkias. *Integrated Electronics: Analog and Digital Circuits and Systems.* New York: McGraw-Hill Book Company, 1972, Chapter 18.

Motorola. *Semiconductor Power Circuits Handbook.* Phoenix, Ariz.: Motorola Semiconductor Products, Inc., 1968.

Pierce, J. F., and T. J. Paulus. *Applied Electronics.* Columbus, Ohio: Charles E. Merrill Publishing Company, 1972, Chapter 12.

RCA. *Solid State Power Circuits.* (Technical Series SP-52). Somerville, N.J.: RCA Corporation, 1971.

Texas Instruments. *Audio and AM/FM Circuit Design Handbook.* Dallas, Tex.: Texas Instruments, Inc., 1966, Chapters 1–6.

REVIEW QUESTIONS

13.1 Describe the four basic modes of operation of power amplifiers.

13.2 Why are class *C* amplifiers not used in audio applications?

13.3 What type of power amplifier is required if low distortion and high output power are desired?

13.4 Define collector efficiency.

13.5 What is the maximum efficiency of a class *A* series-fed amplifier?

13.6 Why is a transformer-coupled amplifier more efficient than a series-fed amplifier?

13.7 Explain how a transformer is used as an impedance-matching device.

13.8 Under what circuit conditions is an ac load line identical to the dc load line?

13.9 What is the efficiency of a typical output transformer?

13.10 What transistor specifications are necessary to construct a maximum collector dissipation curve?

13.11 Define
(a) Phase distortion.
(b) Frequency distortion.
(c) Harmonic distortion.

13.12 What is the function of a spectrum analyzer?

13.13 What type of distortion is eliminated if a class *AB* push-pull amplifier is used instead of a class *B* push-pull amplifier?

13.14 Discuss the merits of a push-pull amplifier.

13.15 What is the purpose of a phase splitter?

13.16 Define transfer characteristics.

13.17 Explain why a driver transformer is necessary in the push-pull amplifier of Fig. 13–9.

13.18 For what applications is the class *C* power amplifier most suited?

13.19 How will the output of the circuit in Fig. 13–11A be affected if transistor Q_1 burns out (acts like an open circuit)?

13.20 What is the effect on the output of the circuit in Fig. 13–14 if R_{C_1} and R_{C_2} are unequal?

PROBLEMS

P13–1 A 10-V peak-to-peak signal swing is developed across $R_C = 100\,\Omega$ in the class *A* series-fed amplifier of Fig. 13–1A. Determine the ac power delivered to R_C.

P13–2 Repeat prob. P13–1 for a 15-V peak-to-peak signal swing.

P13–3 In Fig. 13–1A, what is the maximum theoretical ac power developed across $R_C = 500\,\Omega$ if $V_{CC} = 20\,\text{V}$?

P13–4 Repeat prob. P13–3 for $R_C = 2\,\text{k}\Omega$.

P13–5 For the power amplifier of Fig. 13–1A, $R_C = 500\,\Omega$, $R_B = 100\,\text{k}\Omega$, $h_{FE} = 100$, $V_{BE} = 0.7\,\text{V}$, and $V_{CC} = 25\,\text{V}$. Find
(a) The maximum possible output signal swing.
(b) The maximum possible output power.

P13–6 Repeat prob. P13–5 for $V_{CC} = 40\,\text{V}$.

P13–7 For the amplifier of prob. P13–5, calculate
(a) The output power when the ac signal measured across R_C is 10 V peak-to-peak.
(b) The collector efficiency for the output power found in (a).

P13–8 Find the reflected load impedance Z'_L in the circuit of Fig. 13–3A if $Z_L = 4\,\Omega$ and the following transformer turns ratios, N_p/N_s are present:
(a) 4:1.
(b) 10:1.
(c) 100:1.

P13–9 Repeat prob. P13–8 for $Z_L = 10\,\Omega$.

P13–10 For the amplifier of Fig. 13–5A, $R_B = 5.6\,\text{k}\Omega$, $R_L = 4\,\Omega$, $V_{CC} = 12\,\text{V}$, and $N_p/N_s = 8:1$. Assume that the transformer is ideal. Using the collector characteristics of Fig. 13–5B, find
(a) The ac output power for a 1-mA peak-to-peak input current.
(b) The collector efficiency of the amplifier.
Assume a transformer efficiency of 80 percent.

P13–11 In prob. P13–10, what value of R_L will consume 0.1 W of power?

P13–12 Design a class *A* transformer-coupled amplifier to deliver 0.2 W of power to a 5-Ω load from a 2-mA peak-to-peak source. The collector characteristics for the transistor are provided in Fig. 13–5B, and the circuit is powered by a 20-V source.

P13–13 Repeat prob. P13–12 for a 8-Ω load.

P13–14 Construct a maximum collector dissipation curve for a transistor with the following specifications: $I_{C(\text{max})} = 1\,\text{A}$, $BV_{CEO} = 40\,\text{V}$, and $P_{D(\text{max})} = 5\,\text{W}$.

P13–15 From the power dissipation curve constructed in prob. P13–14, determine the maximum allowable collector current, I_C, for the following values of collector-emitter voltage, V_{CE}:
(a) 1 V.
(b) 10 V.
(c) 30 V.

P13–16 Using the curves of Fig. 13–8,
(a) Find the fourth harmonic distortion.
(b) Solve for the total distortion ($\%D_T$) using the fourth harmonic as the highest term.

P13–17 The push-pull amplifier of Fig. 13–9 is operated from $V_{CC} = 40\,\text{V}$. What is the maximum power that the circuit can deliver to an equivalent load of $Z'_L = 100\,\Omega$? Assume the transformer is ideal.

P13–18 Repeat prob. P13–17 for $Z'_L = 64\,\Omega$.

P13–19 The following measurements were taken across the primary of the output transformer in a class *B* push-pull amplifier: $V_{max} = 20\,\text{V}$, $V_{min} = 2\,\text{V}$. Calculate the efficiency of the amplifier if the transformer efficiency is
(a) 100 percent.
(b) 72 percent.

P13–20 A push-pull class *AB* amplifier operates from a 20-V dc supply and delivers ac power to a 12-Ω load. The transformer is 80 percent efficient and is specified as a 300-Ω–12-Ω transformer. Calculate the maximum power delivered to the load.

P13–21 Determine the $I_{C(max)}$ and BV_{CEO} ratings for the transistors in prob. P13–20.

P13–22 Design a class *B* push-pull amplifier to deliver 2 W of power to a 4-Ω load. The circuit is operated from a 12-V dc source. Make all necessary assumptions in your design.

P13–23 Repeat prob. P13–22 for a 20-V dc source.

P13–24 Draw a schematic diagram of a PNP class *AB* push-pull amplifier using a phase-splitter input circuit.

14

Transformerless Power Amplifiers and Heat Sinks

In Chapter 13, we showed that in order to supply large amounts of power to a load, power (large-signal) amplifiers must be employed. In analyzing these amplifiers, we made use of graphical techniques rather than the analytical methods used for small-signal amplifiers. Small-signal ac models, such as the hybrid model, are not valid for power amplifiers because of the large signal current and voltage swings encountered. In the previous chapter, we also concluded that the greater the input signal, the greater is the power delivered to the load by an amplifier.

Power amplifiers which use transformer coupling were shown to be most efficient. We saw, however, that they have some severe shortcomings, stemming from the use of transformers in respect to distortion and frequency response. Transformers are frequency-sensitive and do not exhibit uniform characteristics over a wide range of frequencies.

In this chapter, we shall demonstrate that it is possible to construct transformerless power amplifiers that are efficient and can deliver large amounts of power to a low-impedance load. In addition, these amplifiers are designed to have low distortion and wide frequency response. Discrete as well as IC power amplifiers will be examined.

IC power amplifiers are available in monolithic and hybrid types. Hybrids have greater power handling capabilities than the monolithic IC. (See Chapter 10 for a discussion of IC technology.)

Heat dissipation in transistors becomes a major factor in the design of power amplifiers. The power demanded from a power amplifier can be very high. Proper care must be exercised to ensure that the transistors delivering large amounts of power do not overheat and burn out.

Thermal behavior of semiconductors will be discussed, and proper methods of controlling the heat developed in transistors considered. Control of semiconductor junction temperature is achieved through the use of *heat sinks*. Heat sinks increase the power handling capabilities of semiconductor devices by transferring the developed heat to the surrounding environment.

14.1 Series-Output Amplifiers

Transformerless power amplifiers are high-efficient, low-distortion amplifiers. Two examples of class *B*, push-pull amplifiers which are transformerless are shown in Fig. 14–1. In each circuit, the inputs are 180° out of phase to the output transistors. To eliminate an input transformer, a phase splitter is used (see Chapter 13).

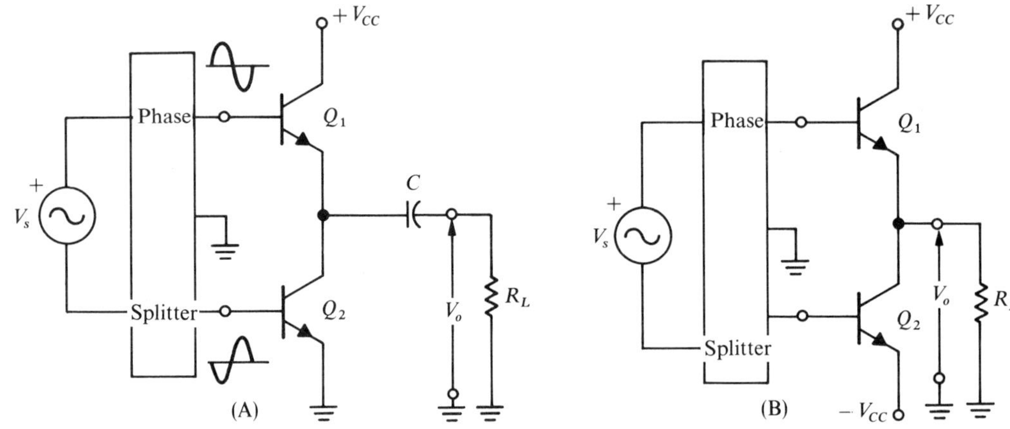

Fig. 14–1. *Series-output, class B, transformerless power amplifiers. (A) Capacitor coupled, using a single dc source. (B) Direct coupled, using a split dc source.*

The output transistors are connected in series; in Fig. 14–1A, the load is coupled to the amplifier through coupling capacitor *C*. (Series-connected transistors are sometimes called a *totem-pole* configuration.) In order to achieve good low-frequency response, the value of the coupling capacitor must be large.

The coupling capacitor may be eliminated when the circuit is powered from a *split dc source*, as shown in Fig. 14–1B. Essentially, two power supplies, one positive and one negative with respect to ground, are used. We assume the transistors are matched to yield a zero dc level across the load.

Because of the out-of-phase signals at their bases, each output transistor conducts for alternate halves of the cycle. This action results in a reconstructed waveform at the load. Crossover distortion also is present in a transformerless class *B* amplifier unless it is biased for class *AB* operation.

A complete circuit of a push-pull, series-output, class *AB* amplifier is illustrated in Fig. 14–2. The differential amplifier, comprised of transistors Q_1 and Q_2, serves as a phase splitter and driver for output transistors Q_3 and Q_4. Resis-

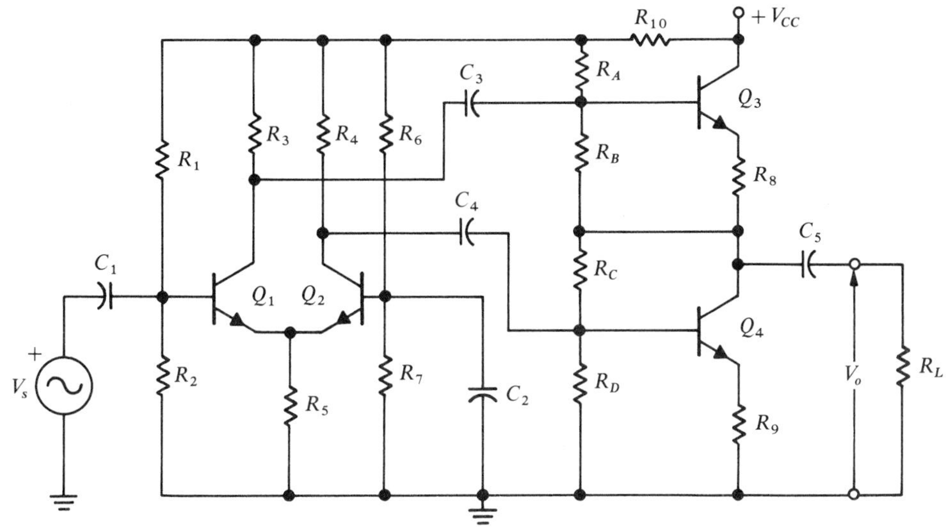

tors R_A, R_B, R_C, and R_D bias the output transistors for class *AB* operation.

Fig. 14–2. *Example of a series-output, class AB, transformerless power amplifier.*

14.2 Complementary Symmetry Amplifiers

A *complementary symmetry*, or *complementary output*, amplifier is a series-output circuit that does not have to be driven by two out-of-phase signals. The complementary amplifier is not new to us. It was considered in Chapter 11, where it was used as an output stage of an op amp.

In Fig. 14–3, a complementary symmetry amplifier employs two output transistors: an NPN and a PNP type.

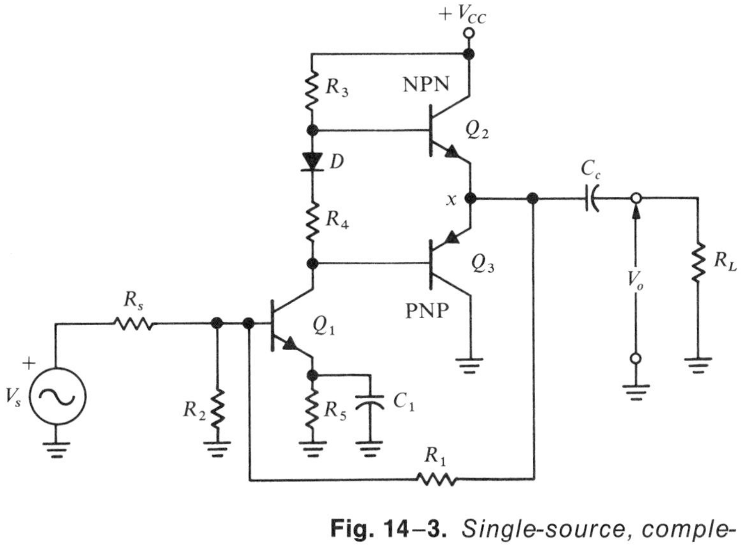

Fig. 14–3. *Single-source, complementary output amplifier.*

Their emitters are connected, and the output is taken across the emitters and ground. The load is coupled through a capacitor to the amplifier. If the circuit is powered from a split dc source, as indicated in Fig. 14–4, the load may be direct-coupled. Efficiency and power calculations for this amplifier are similar to those for the transformer-coupled, push-pull amplifier discussed in Chapter 13.

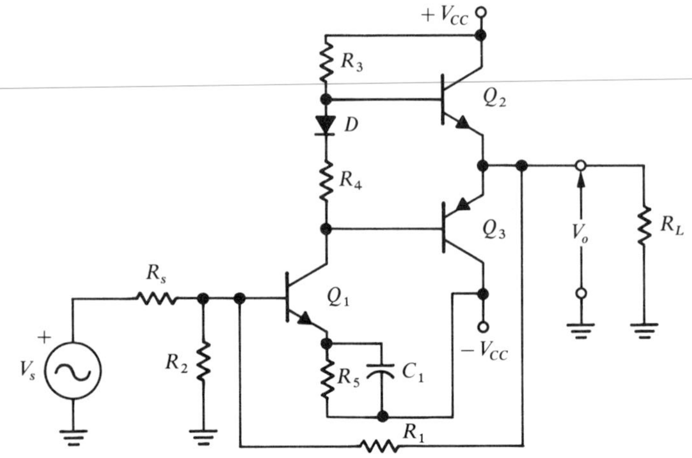

Fig. 14–4. *Split-source, complementary output amplifier.*

In the circuits of Figs. 14–3 and 14–4, transistor Q_1 functions as a class *A* driver amplifier. Its purpose is to provide voltage gain. Transistors Q_2 and Q_3 operate as emitter followers, providing good current and power gain. Emitter followers also exhibit low output impedance and distortion. Diode *D* in series with resistor R_4 keeps the output transistors slightly turned ON, resulting in class *AB* operation. By compensating for variations in junction temperature of the output transistors, the diode also provides thermal stability. In some designs, resistor R_4 is replaced by an additional diode.

Resistors R_1 and R_2 bias driver transistor Q_1 for class *A* operation. They also provide negative feedback (see Chapter 9) which stabilizes the complete amplifier.

Circuit Operation

We shall now explain in detail the operation of the amplifier of Fig. 14–3. The circuit is symmetrically biased. If we assume the transistors have identical characteristics, the voltage at point *x* is therefore equal to $V_{CC}/2$ volts. A positive-going input signal, V_s, is amplified and inverted by transistor Q_1. At the collector of Q_1, the signal is of a larger amplitude and is negative-going. A negative-going signal turns ON Q_3 and turns OFF Q_2. Because Q_3 acts as an emitter follower with a voltage gain of approximately one, the output voltage is nearly the same as the signal at the base of Q_3.

When the signal at the collector of Q_1 is positive-going, transistor Q_2 conducts, and Q_3 is cut off. The output is now positive-going. By alternate conduction of the output transistors, the full waveshape of the input signal is reconstructed at the output.

Output transistors Q_2 and Q_3 are power transistors and must be capable of handling large collector currents. Power transistors generally do not have large values of current gain; therefore, high base currents are required. Transistor Q_1 must be capable of delivering these high base-current swings. These demands on Q_1 cause large amounts of power to be dissipated in the driver stage for large-output power conditions.

EXAMPLE 14–1.

In the amplifier of Fig. 14–3, transistor Q_1 has a rated maximum collector current, $I_{C(\text{max})}$, of 100 mA, and a maximum power rating of 600 mW. What is the maximum power that may be delivered to the load if Q_2 and Q_3 have an $h_{FE} = 20$?

Solution:

If the maximum quiescent collector current in Q_1 is 100 mA, then the maximum quiescent collector-emitter voltage of Q_1, $V_{CE(\text{max})}$, is

$$V_{CE(\text{max})} = \frac{600}{100} = 6\text{ V}$$

Hence, the peak output voltage, $V_{o(\text{peak})}$, cannot exceed 6 V, because Q_2 and Q_3 function as emitter followers. Also, the peak current that Q_1 supplies to the bases of the output transistors cannot exceed $I_{C(\text{max})} = 100$ mA. The peak load current, $I_{o(\text{peak})}$, is equal, therefore, to the product of the dc current gain, h_{FE}, and base current, I_B:

$$I_{o(\text{peak})} = h_{FE} I_B = 20 \times 100\text{ mA} = 2\text{ A}$$

The maximum rms power, $P_{o(\text{max})}$, delivered to the load may be expressed by the product of the rms values of the output load current and voltage:

$$P_{o(\text{max})} = \left(\frac{I_{o(\text{peak})}}{\sqrt{2}}\right)\left(\frac{V_{o(\text{peak})}}{\sqrt{2}}\right)$$

$$= 2 \times \frac{6}{2} = 6\text{ W}$$

The preceding example demonstrated that the output power is limited by the power capabilities of the driver stage. A reduction in current demand of the driver stage may be realized when the output transistors are connected in a *Darlington pair* configuration. The single dc source circuit of Fig. 14–5 utilizes two Darlington pairs in the output stage. This circuit is the same in all other respects as that of Fig. 14–3. Transistors Q_2 and Q_3, as well as Q_4 and Q_5, form Darlington pairs. Occasionally, a Darlington pair is called a *compound transistor.*

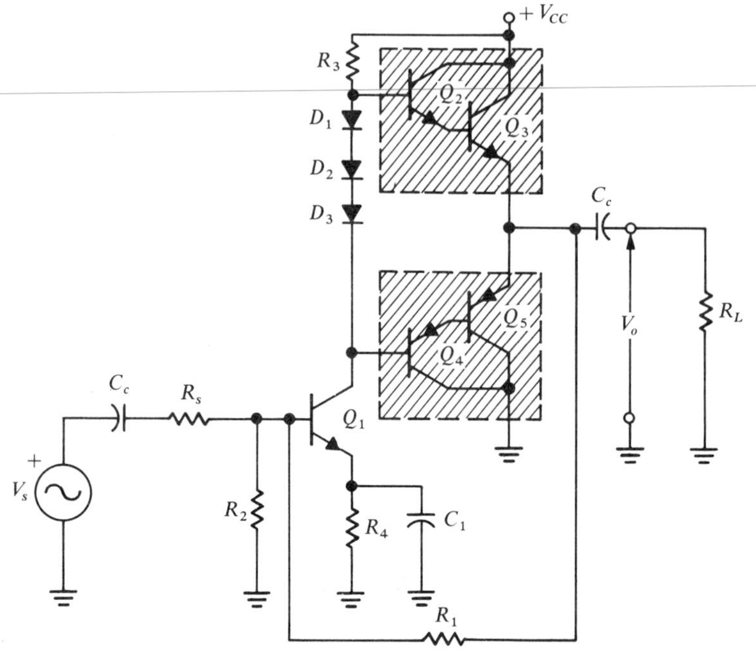

Fig. 14–5. *Complementary symmetry amplifier with Darlington-pair output.*

The advantage of a Darlington circuit is that the total power delivered to the load is increased significantly. This is achieved because transistor Q_1 is feeding transistors Q_2 and Q_4, which in turn supply current drive to Q_3 and Q_5. The output stages are still emitter followers, with Q_2 and Q_3 conducting during the positive half-cycle at the collector of Q_1. Likewise, Q_4 and Q_5 conduct during the negative half-cycle.

Three biasing diodes (D_1, D_2, and D_3) are used in the amplifier. Their purpose is to slightly forward bias the output stages for class *AB* operation and to provide temperature stability. Three diodes are required to compensate for the base-emitter voltage drops across Q_2, Q_3, Q_4, and Q_5. The current through the diodes is generally of the same value as the *idling current* (the small biasing current) in the output transistors.

As discussed in Chapter 11, the characteristics of a Darlington pair are such that the compound collector or emitter current is greater than the base current by a factor equal to the product of $h_{FE_1}h_{FE_2}$. When the two transistors have identical values of h_{FE}, then the current gain of a Darlington pair is h_{FE}^2. Hence, a small current at the base results in a large current at the collector. The current demands on tran-

volution of electronic devices: Enlarged vacuum tube, transistor, nd integrated circuit (IC). (Courtesy Western Electric.)

The first transistor: The point-contact device. (Courtesy Western Electric.)

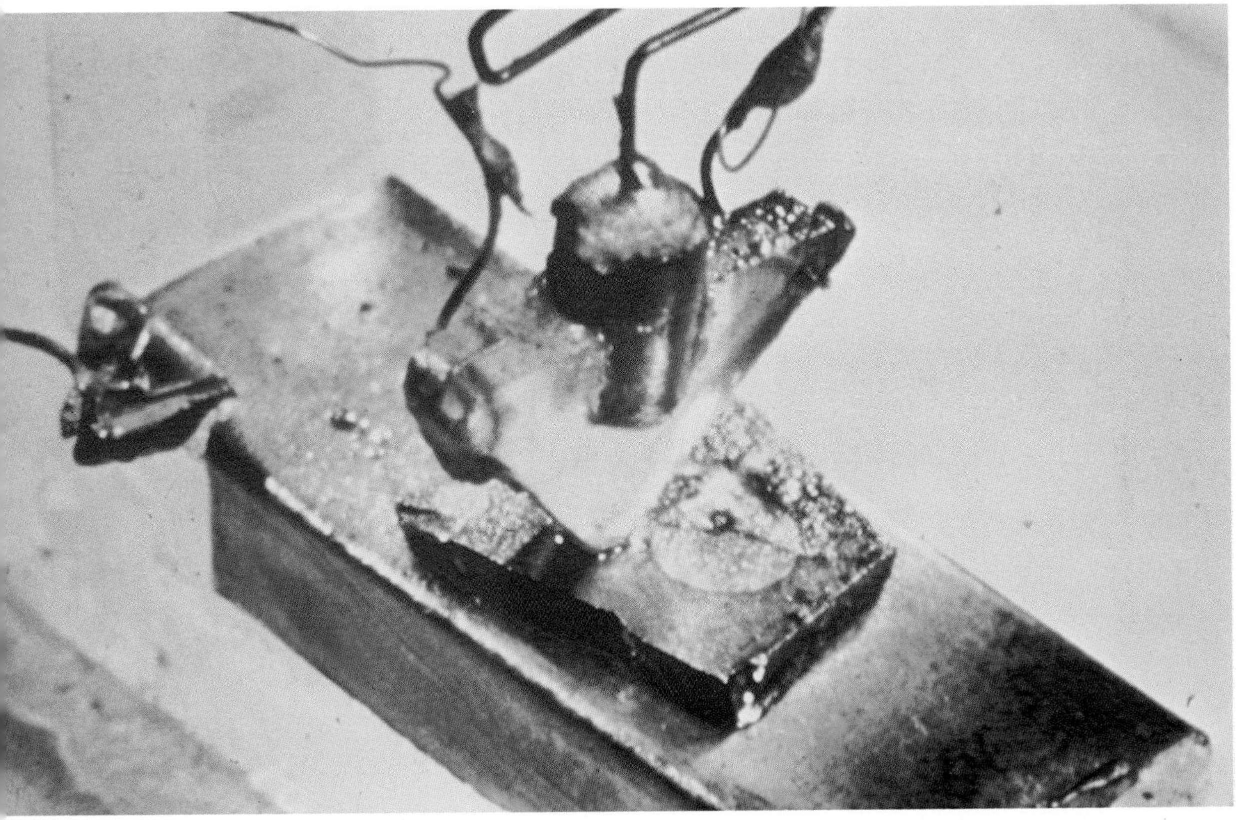

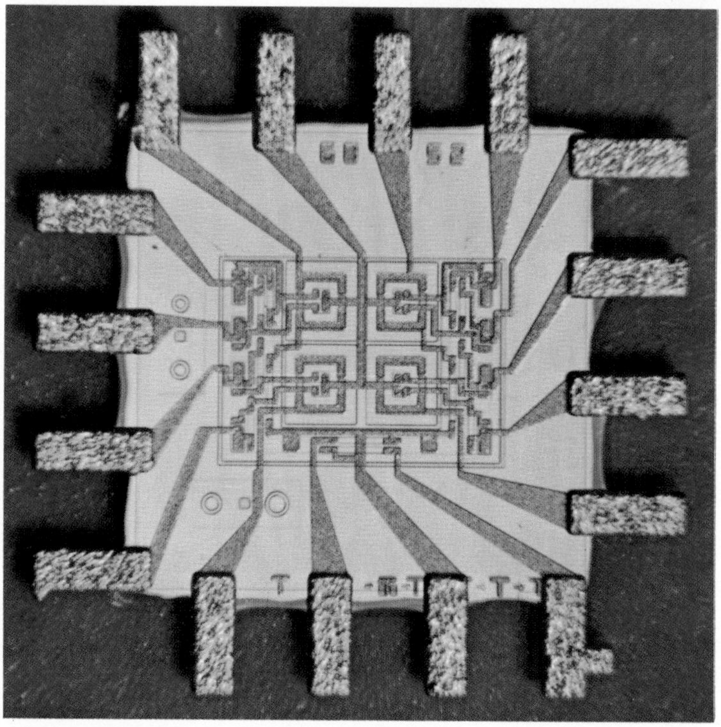

Discrete circuit on a printed circuit (PC
board. (Courtesy Western Electric.

Magnified monolithic integrated circui
(IC). (Courtesy Western Electric.)

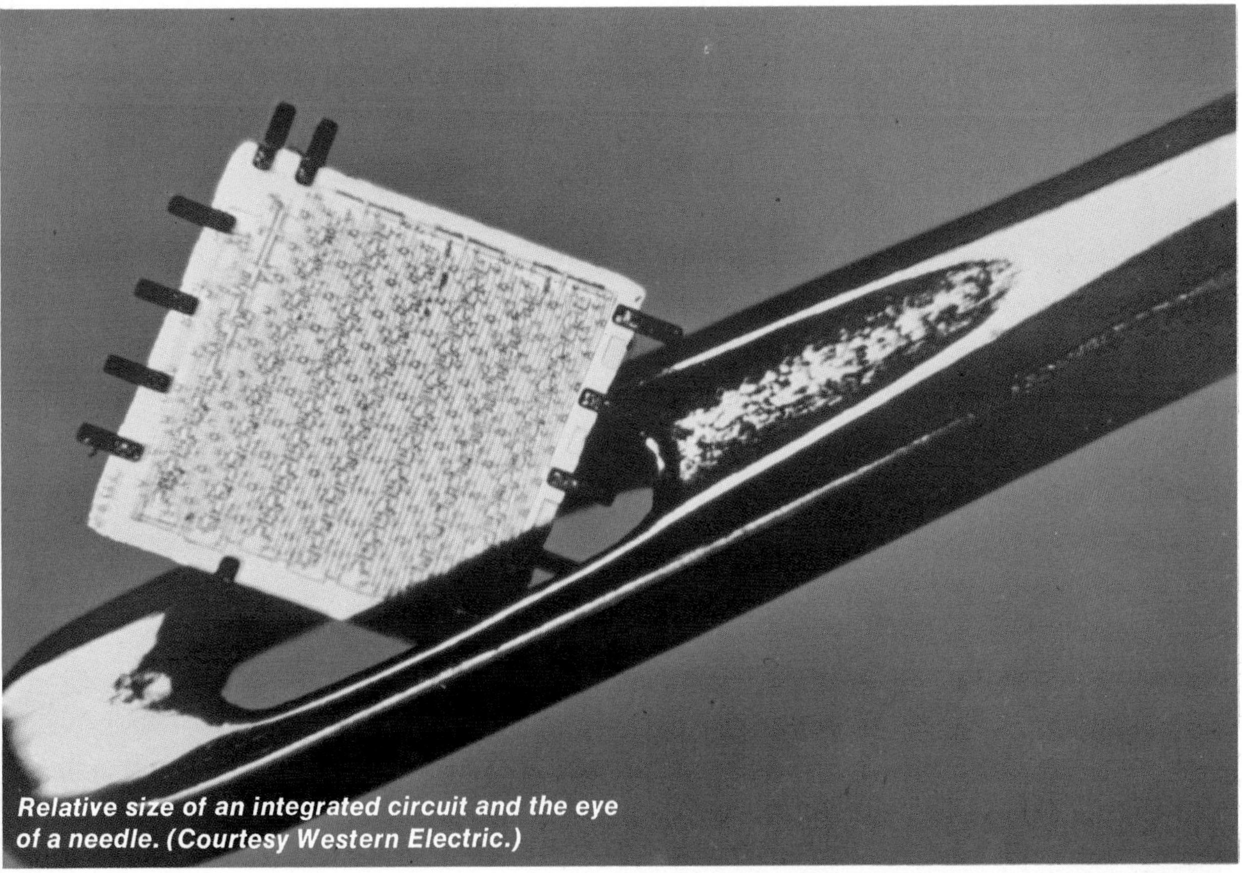

Relative size of an integrated circuit and the eye of a needle. (Courtesy Western Electric.)

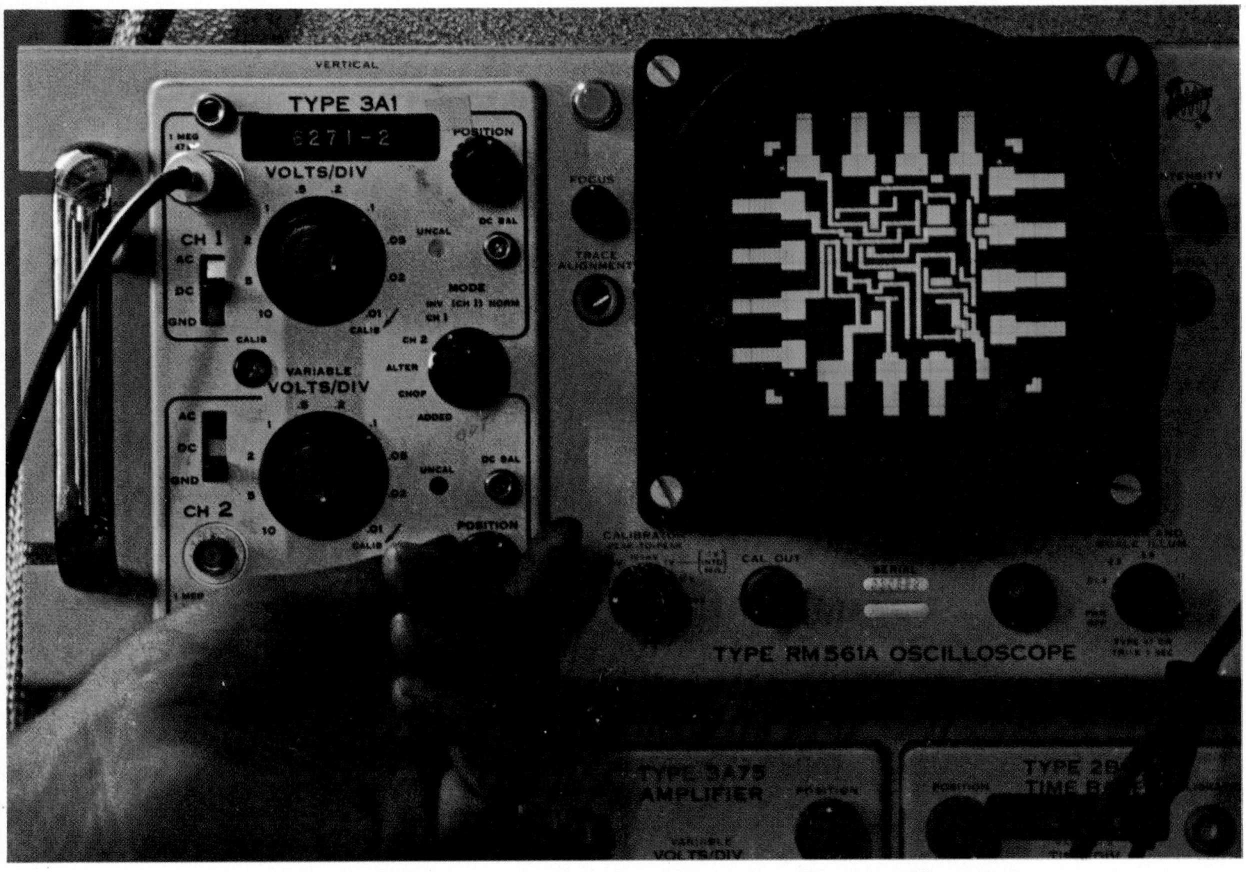

Oscilloscope display of an IC layout. (Courtesy Western Electric.)

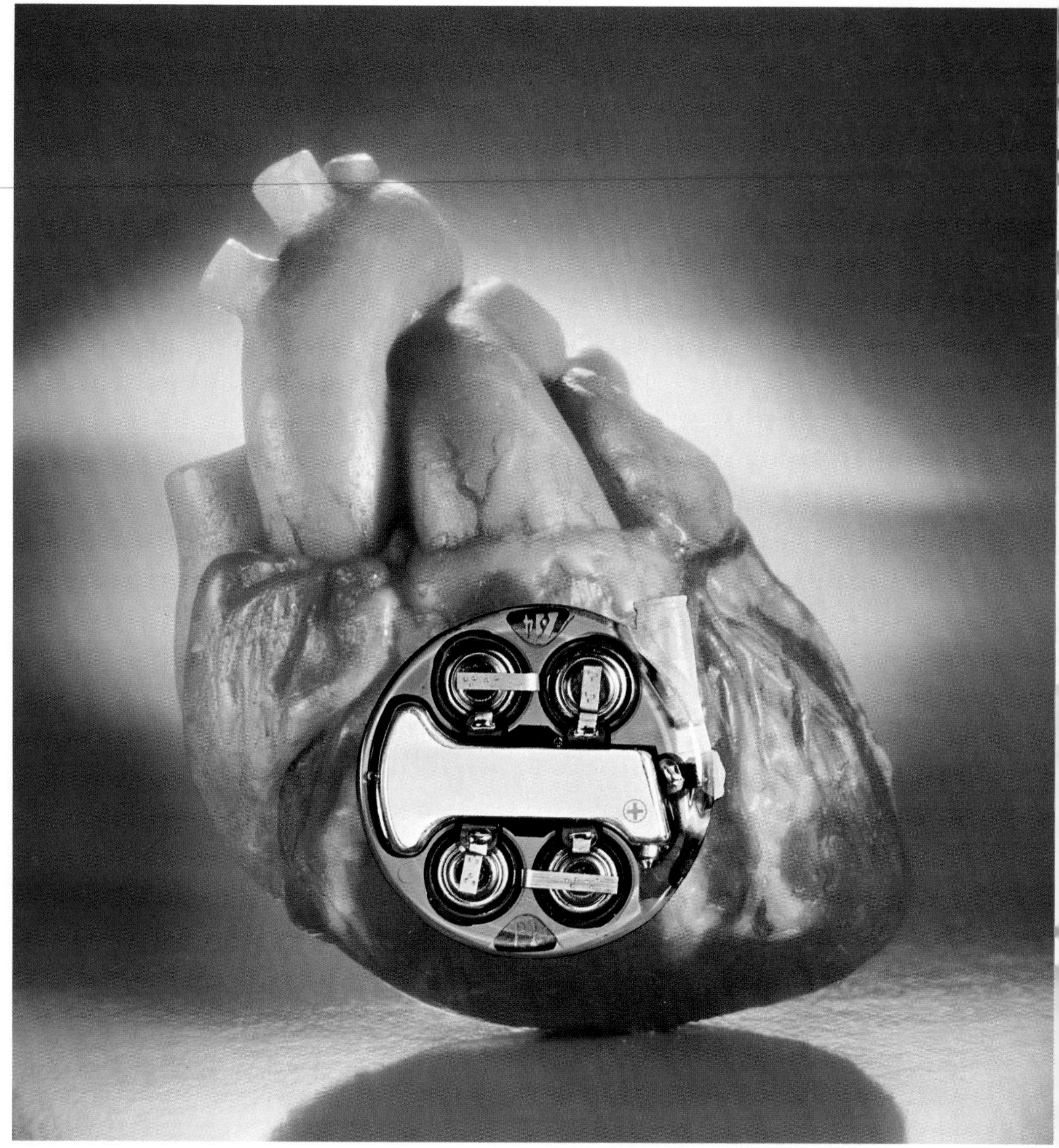

The Pacemaker: An important application of electronics to medicine.

sistor Q_1 are thereby significantly reduced. This is demonstrated in the next example.

EXAMPLE 14–2.

The amplifier of Fig. 14–5 is to deliver the same amount of power (6 W) as the amplifier in Example 14–1. Transistor Q_1 has the same specifications as in Example 14–1, and each transistor of the Darlington pair has an $h_{FE} = 20$. Determine the maximum collector current and power dissipated in Q_1.

Solution:

From Example 14–1, the peak current delivered to the load is $I_{o(\text{peak})} = 2\text{ A}$. The maximum current, $I_{C1(\text{max})}$, delivered to the Darlington pair by Q_1 is

$$I_{C1(\text{max})} = \frac{I_{o(\text{peak})}}{h_{FE}^2} = \frac{2}{20^2} = 5\text{ mA}$$

The maximum power dissipated, $P_{D(\text{max})}$, in Q_1 with a $V_{CE(\text{max})}$ of 6 V, as in the previous example, is given by the product of the maximum collector current and voltage:

$$P_{D(\text{max})} = I_{C1(\text{max})} V_{CE(\text{max})} = 5\text{ mA} \times 6\text{ V} = 30\text{ mW}$$

EXAMPLE 14–3.

Referring to Fig. 14–6, determine

(a) The dc voltage at point A.

(b) The maximum output power delivered to the load.

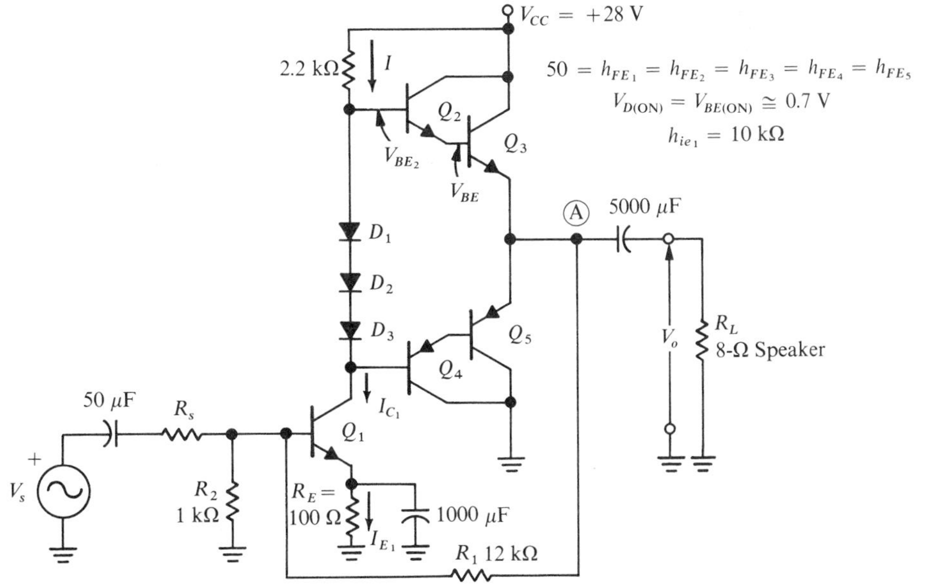

Fig. 14–6. *Complementary symmetry amplifier analyzed in Example 14–3.*

Solutions:

(a) The voltage at point A with respect to ground, V_A, is

$$V_A = 28 - (2.2I + V_{BE_2} + V_{BE_3})$$

If Q_2 and Q_3 are forward biased, then $V_{BE_2} = V_{BE_3} = 0.7\text{ V}$; hence,

$$\begin{aligned} V_A &= 28 - 2.2I - 1.4 \\ &= 26.6 - 2.2I \qquad \textbf{(14–1)} \end{aligned}$$

The voltage at the emitter of Q_1 may be expressed by

$$\begin{aligned} V_{E1} &\simeq \frac{R_2 V_A}{R_1 + R_2} - V_{BE1} \\ &= \frac{(1)V_A}{12 + 1} - 0.7 \\ &= \frac{V_A - 9.1}{13} \end{aligned}$$

The emitter current of Q_1 is

$$\begin{aligned} I_{E_1} &= \frac{V_{E1}}{R_E} \\ &= \frac{V_A - 9.1}{13 \times 100} \end{aligned}$$

Because $I_{E1} \simeq I_{C1}$, and assuming that I_{B_2} and I_{B_4} are negligible compared with I_{C1}, then

$$I_{E_1} \simeq I$$

and

$$I = \frac{V_A - 9.1}{1300} \qquad \textbf{(14–2)}$$

Substituting I in Eq. (14–1), we obtain

$$V_A = 26.6 - \frac{2.2(V_A - 9.1)}{1300}$$

Solving for V_A,

$$V_A = 15.6\text{ V}$$

Ideally, for a maximum undistorted signal swing, the voltage at point A should be $\frac{1}{2}$ of V_{CC}, or 14 V.

The biasing current I may also be calculated from Eq. (14–2). Substitution of $V_A = 15.6\text{ V}$ in the expression yields

$$I = \frac{15.6 - 9.1}{1300} = 5\text{ mA}$$

(b) Before we calculate the maximum available output power, let us list the factors that influence the output of a power amplifier. They include:

1. Supply voltage.
2. Device power limitations.

3. Biasing conditions.
4. Input signal level.

We shall concentrate on the third factor dealing with biasing conditions. From part (a), we found that the dc voltage at point A is 15.6 V. The voltage across the collector and emitter of Q_1, V_{CE_1}, from Fig. 14–6 is

$$\begin{aligned} V_{CE_1} &= V_A - (V_{BE_4} + V_{BE_5} + 100I) \\ &= 15.6 - (0.7 + 0.7 + 5 \times 10^{-3} \times 100) \\ &= 13.7\ \text{V} \end{aligned}$$

The maximum undistorted voltage swing at Q_1 is 13.7 V. With $V_{o(\text{peak})} = 13.7$ V, the output power, P_o, is the rms output voltage, $(13.7/\sqrt{2}\text{V})^2$, divided by the load resistance, 8 Ω:

$$P_o = \frac{\left(\dfrac{13.7}{\sqrt{2}}\right)^2}{8} = 11.7\ \text{W}$$

The largest undistorted power that the amplifier can deliver to the load is, therefore, 11.7 W.

14.3 Quasi-Complementary Symmetry Amplifiers

A *quasi-complementary* amplifier employs a somewhat different version of a Darlington pair output than the complementary amplifier. This circuit is illustrated in Fig. 14–7.

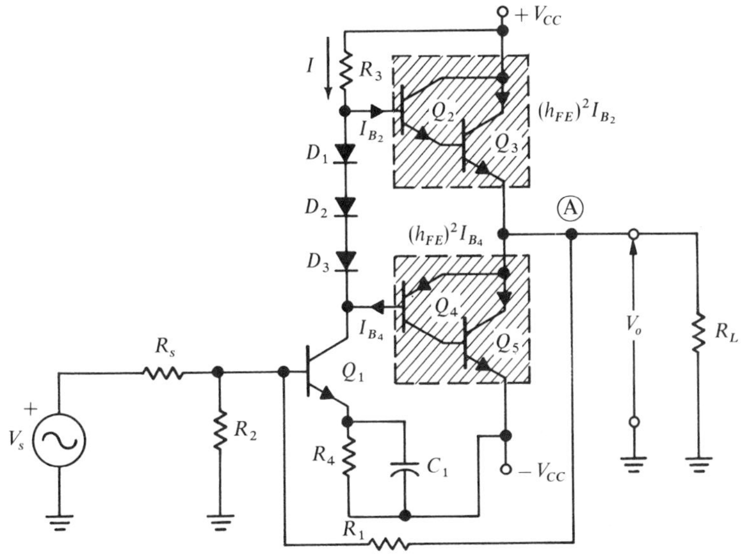

Fig. 14–7. *Quasi-complementary symmetry amplifier.*

Transistors Q_2 and Q_3 are both NPN and form a basic Darlington pair. Transistor Q_4, however, is a PNP transistor, and Q_5 an NPN device.

This type of Darlington pair is known as a *complementary Darlington circuit*. The advantage of such a configuration is that both output transistors (Q_3 and Q_5) are of the same type—NPN. This fact makes the fabrication and matching of power transistors more convenient.

In Fig. 14–7, Q_1 is again used as a driver. Transistor Q_2 provides an output in phase with its input, and Q_4 acts as an inverter, providing Q_5 with an out-of-phase signal. A comparison of the complementary Darlington circuit composed of Q_4 and Q_5 and that of Q_4 and Q_5 of Fig. 14–5 is given in Fig. 14–8. We see that each configuration effectively forms a PNP Darlington pair. The operation of both circuits can be shown to be basically the same. An increase in signal at either base produces an increase at the corresponding "effective" emitter. In both circuits, the current gain is equal to the product of their respective h_{FE}s.

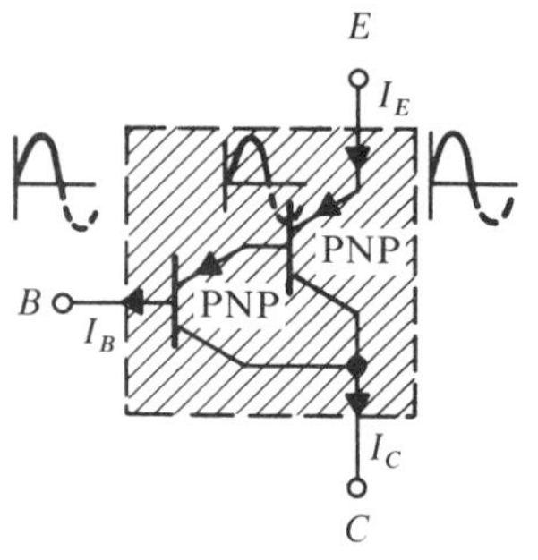

(A)

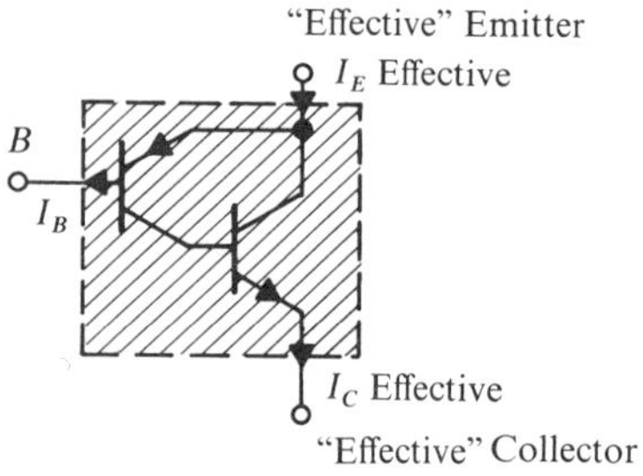

(B)

Fig. 14–8. *Darlington circuits. (A) PNP Darlington pair. (B) PNP-NPN Darlington pair.*

Note that the complementary pair of Fig. 14–8B operates as an emitter follower. The NPN transistor, however, functions as a common-emitter amplifier. In the quasi-complementary amplifier of Fig. 14–7, therefore, one-half the output circuit (Q_2, Q_3) operates as a common-collector amplifier, and the other half (Q_4, Q_5) as a common-emitter amplifier. This kind of operation results in an imbalance in output impedances during the two halves of the output waveform. This unbalance may be compensated for by introducing sufficient negative feedback around the amplifier.

An improved version of the complementary amplifier is achieved when biasing resistor R_3 in Fig. 14–5 is replaced by a constant current source. In practice, small-value resistors are also added in the emitter legs of the output transistors. This practice is also applicable to the quasi-complementary amplifier. A modified version of the quasi-complementary amplifier of Fig. 14–7 is shown in Fig. 14–9. Transistor Q_2 and its associated circuitry functions as a constant current source. Resistors R_7 and R_8 are inserted in the legs of the output transistors.

The requirement for constant current source biasing arises because biasing current I varies with changes in the signal. For example, assume that the signal at point A in Fig. 14–7 is positive-going. The voltage across R_3 decreases accordingly, since the top of R_3 is connected to V_{CC}. This, in turn, causes current I to decrease.

In some cases, the decrease in I is sufficient to turn OFF Q_1. It is obvious now that a constant current source in place of R_3 is highly desirable. Emitter resistors R_7 and R_8

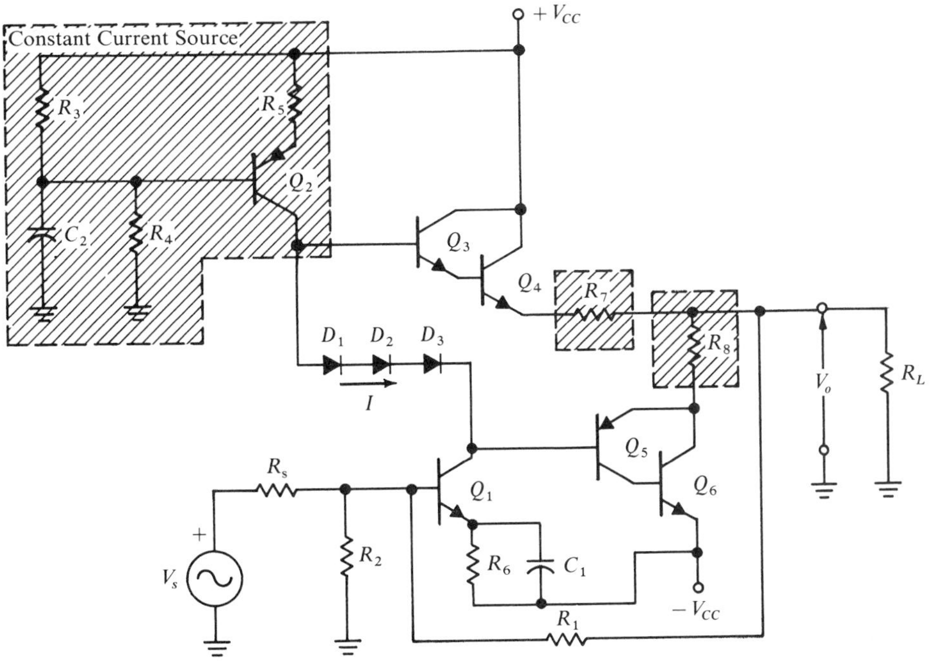

Fig. 14–9. *Quasi-complementary symmetry amplifier with constant current biasing (Q_2) and emitter resistors R_7 and R_8.*

provide negative feedback and, thereby, additional stability of the amplifier.

14.4 Short-Circuit Protection

Normally, large amounts of current flow in the load connected to a power amplifier; the danger of shorting out the load terminals always exists. Without proper protection, a short across the terminals will cause severe damage to the amplifier. Power supplies are generally fused, and in some cases, a fuse is placed in series with the load. This type of protection, however, is not always sufficient for a power amplifier.

In addition to fuses in the power and load lines (F_1 and F_2, respectively), the circuit of Fig. 14–10 utilizes short-circuit diode protection. The protection circuit is composed of diodes D_4 and D_5. Under normal operating conditions, D_4 and D_5 are reverse biased and have no effect on the circuit. When the output terminals are shorted, either D_4 or D_5 turns ON, depending on the polarity of the input signal.

If it is assumed that the signal at the collector of Q_1 is positive-going, D_5 becomes forward biased. The input to transistors Q_3 and Q_4 becomes clipped, thereby reducing the drive to the transistors. When the collector of Q_1 is negative-going, D_4 conducts, reducing the drive to transistors Q_5 and Q_6.

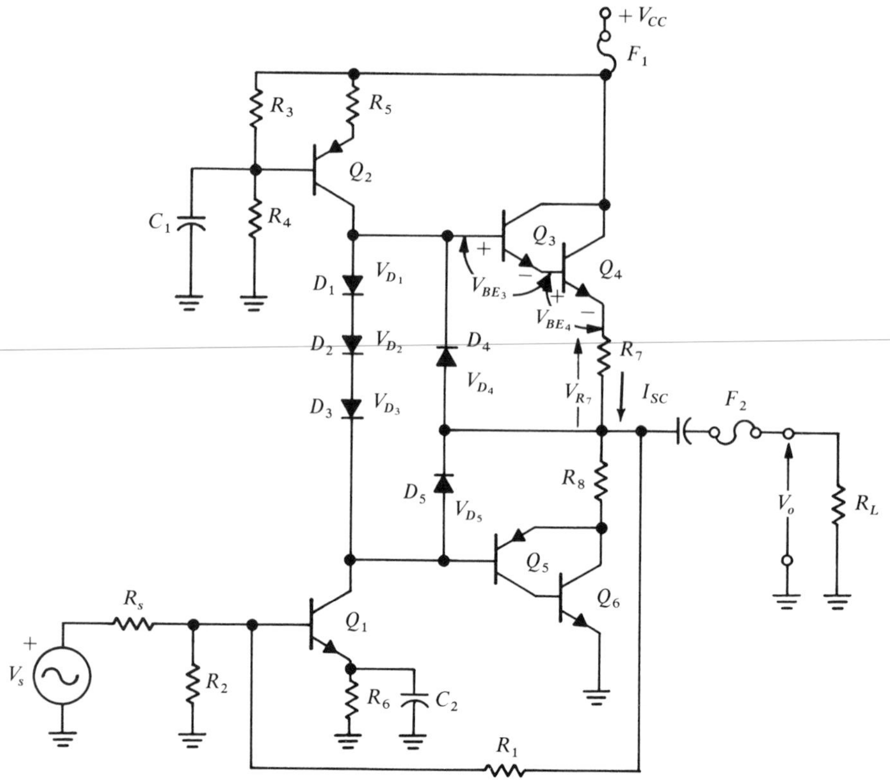

Fig. 14–10. *Quasi-complementary power amplifier with short-circuit protection provided by diodes D_4 and D_5.*

The diode short-circuit protection circuit is basically current limiting. It limits the current through the power transistors to a safe value. During the positive-going cycle, the short-circuit current, I_{SC}, is expressed by

$$I_{SC} = \frac{V_{R_7}}{R_7}$$

$$= \frac{V_{D_1} + V_{D_2} + V_{D_3} + V_{D_5} - V_{BE_4} - V_{BE_3}}{R_7} \tag{14–3}$$

where the voltages are defined in Fig. 14–10. The short-circuit current is approximately equal to two diode voltage drops divided by R_7. For silicon devices, the drop is 0.7 V across each diode and transistor. Hence,

$$I_{SC} \simeq \frac{1.4}{R_7} \tag{14–4}$$

14.5 IC Power Circuits

The elimination of transformers in discrete power amplifiers led to the development of IC power amplifiers. In general, the majority of IC power amplifiers are currently restricted to low output power levels. These are the monolithic type which are limited to about 5 W with suitable heat sinking.

Another group of monolithic circuits contains only the driver and associated circuitry. To become a true power amplifier, discrete power transistors must be used in the output stage. Various thick-film hybrid power amplifiers are available which can deliver in excess of 100 W.

The first circuit we shall examine is a monolithic IC, 2-W power amplifier. The unit, designated MFC9020, is manufactured by Motorola Semiconductor Products, Inc. It is encapsulated in a plastic package with metal fins for heat-sink mounting (Fig. 14–11A). The circuit is shown in Fig. 14–11B.

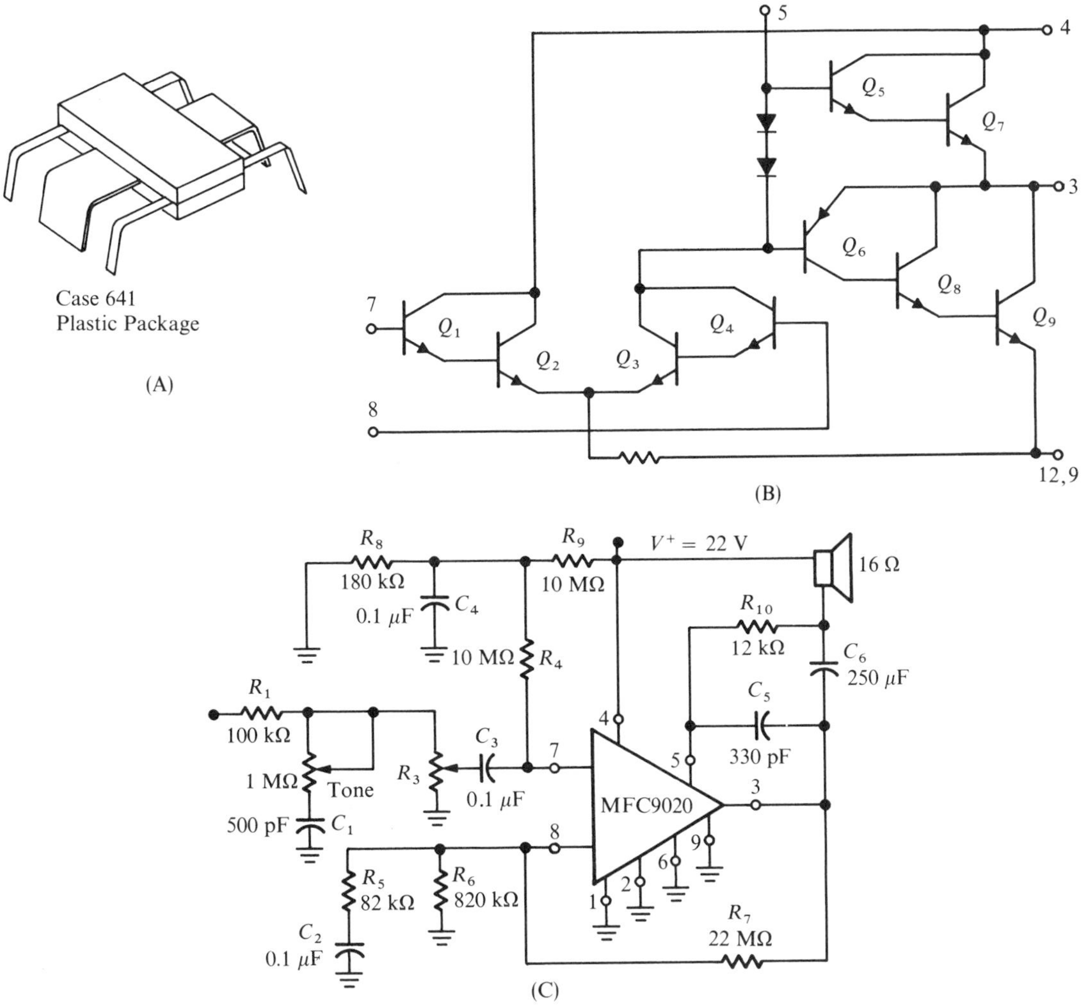

Fig. 14–11. *The MFC9020, 2-W audio amplifier. (A) Package. (B) Circuit. (C) Connected as an audio amplifier. (Courtesy Motorola Semiconductor Products, Inc.)*

The circuit consists of a differential amplifier driver which has an input impedance of 50 kΩ. The output stage is a quasi-complementary circuit. Transistor Q_6 is a PNP device. Because monolithic PNP transistors have low values of current gain, two NPN transistors are direct-coupled to Q_6 to compensate for its low current gain. A typical circuit application of this integrated circuit is shown in Fig. 14–11C. The amplifier is rated for 1 percent total harmonic distortion at full load.

A popular thick-film hybrid IC power amplifier is the RCA HC2000. The circuit schematic is provided in Fig. 14–12A. This amplifier is capable of delivering up to 100 W into a 4-Ω load. It can operate over a frequency range of from dc to 50 kHz, making it an excellent audio amplifier.

The complete circuit is mounted on a 1.2 in. × 1.6 in. substrate and operates from ±37-V split dc power supplies. This circuit, like the monolithic IC, employs a quasi-

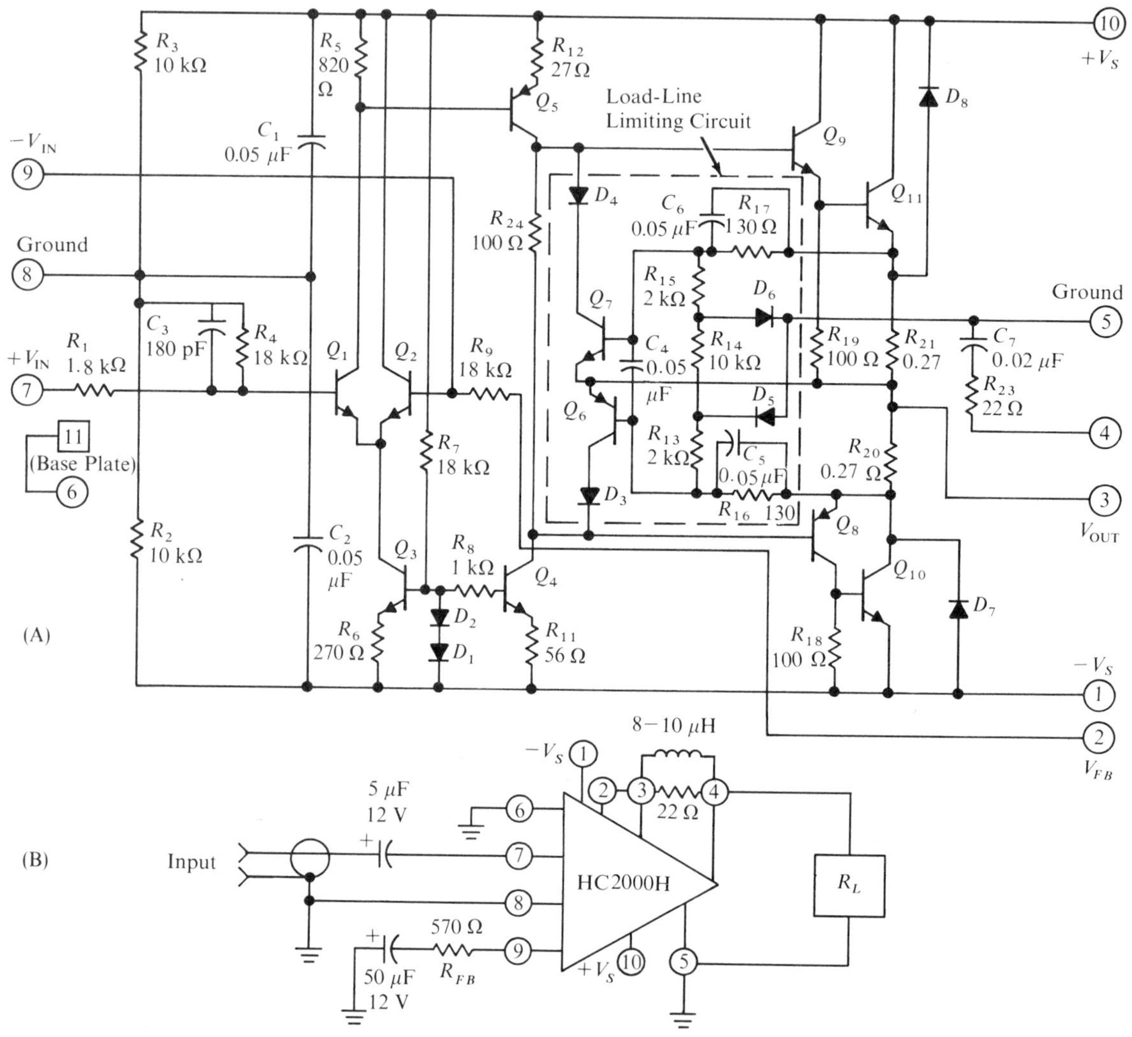

Fig. 14–12. *The HC2000 hybrid power amplifier. (A) Circuit. (B) Typical operation as an audio amplifier. (Courtesy RCA Solid State Division.)*

complementary output stage and a differential amplifier driver. It also has a very effective current limiting circuit. Typical operation of the HC2000 as a power amplifier is illustrated in Fig. 14–12B.

14.6 Thermal Behavior of Semiconductor Devices

The maximum power a semiconductor device may dissipate is limited by its maximum junction temperature. The ability to keep the operating temperature of the device low results in higher power dissipation capabilities. The most common means of heat removal is heat sinking.

In heat sinking, the device is mounted on a base that is a good conductor, such as copper or aluminum. The heat developed in the device is transferred to the heat sink. The heat is then transferred from the sink to the surrounding environment, or *ambient*.

Several phenomena may cause overheating and ultimate destruction of power transistors. *Thermal runaway* is a mechanism that leads to the destruction of a transistor. In Chapter 3, we indicated that an increase in temperature causes the reverse saturation current, I_{CO}, to increase. As a matter of fact, for each 10°C rise in junction temperature, I_{CO} doubles.

An increase in I_{CO} causes the collector current I_C to rise. An increase in I_C results in more power dissipated in the transistor, raising its operating temperature. An increase in temperature further raises I_{CO}, continuing to increase the temperature. Ultimately, the allowable dissipation of the device is exceeded. Feedback stabilizing elements, such as emitter resistors in the output stage (Figs. 13–11 and 14–9), are effective in preventing thermal runaway.

Second breakdown is a phenomenon that also may lead to the destruction of transistors. Second breakdown occurs when the energy absorbed by a transistor exceeds a maximum allowable level and *hot spots* are developed in the transistor chip. The formation of hot spots means that the collector current is not uniformly distributed over the junction area. It is greater at the hot spots than at other regions of the junction. This problem is especially acute in power transistors because of the high currents that flow in these devices. To minimize second breakdown, care is exercised in the manufacture of power devices by carefully controlling the doping to uniform levels.

Manufacturers of power transistors supply *safe-area rating curves* of collector current and voltage which define the allowable operating range. A safe-area rating curve for a 2N5190 transistor is shown in Fig. 14–13. Collector current I_C is plotted along the y-axis, and the collector-emitter voltage, V_{CE}, along the x-axis. The curve is for continuous operation; for pulsed operation, the voltage and current ratings are extended.

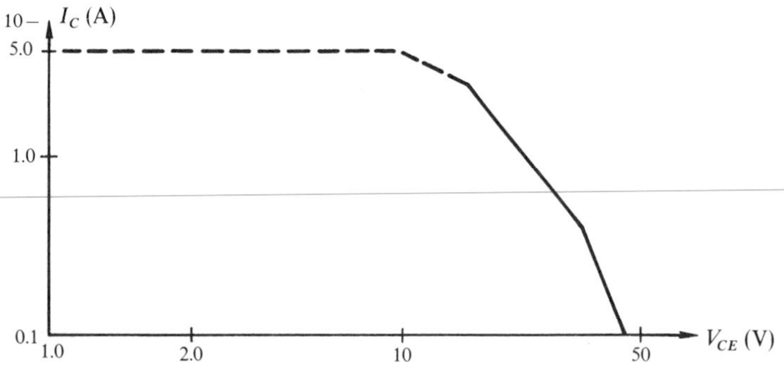

Fig. 14–13. *Safe-area rating curve for a 2N5190 transistor operating at dc.*

Power devices may also be destroyed by a mechanical type of stress called *thermal fatigue*. Temperature changes due to variations in power dissipation cause the semiconductor chip to expand and contract against the metallic material to which it is attached. These stresses can result in damage to the device.

14.7 Thermal Parameters

In our study of semiconductor devices, we have defined the power dissipated at a junction as the product of the voltage across, and the current flowing through, the junction. For transistors, the average power dissipated was given by the product of the collector-emitter voltage and collector current. As the power dissipated in a semiconductor device increases, because of an increase in current or applied voltage, the *junction temperature*, T_j, also increases.

Manufacturers supply maximum junction temperature ratings, $T_{j(\max)}$. Maximum power ratings of devices are usually based on a case (package) temperature of 25°C. When the junction temperature increases, a temperature difference is created between the junction and its case; heat flows from a higher temperature level to a lower temperature level. This flow is analogous to the flow of electric current, where the difference in temperature is equivalent to a voltage difference, and heat is equivalent to current. The temperature difference and the type of medium through which heat flows determine the rate of flow.

Based on the electrical analogy of heat flow, we may deduce that the medium acts like a *thermal resistor*. The *thermal resistance*, θ, is defined as the ratio of the temperature difference, ΔT, to the heat flow, P:

$$\theta = \frac{\Delta T}{P} \tag{14–5}$$

where the unit of θ is degrees Celsius per watt of dissipated power (°C/W). Equation (14–5) is known as Ohm's law for thermal circuits.

In a semiconductor device, the important parameter is the *junction-to-case thermal resistance*, θ_{jc}. A circuit representation of this resistance is illustrated in Fig. 14–14A. If the *case temperature*, T_c, is not the same as the *ambient* (surrounding) *temperature*, T_a, but higher, heat flows away from the case. The circuit of Fig. 14–14B represents heat flow from the junction to the case, and from the case to the ambient. The junction temperature may be computed by summing all the junction drops. From Fig. 14–14B, we have

$$T_j = P(\theta_{jc} + \theta_{ca}) + T_a \tag{14–6}$$

where θ_{ca} is the thermal resistance between the case and ambient.

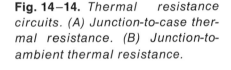

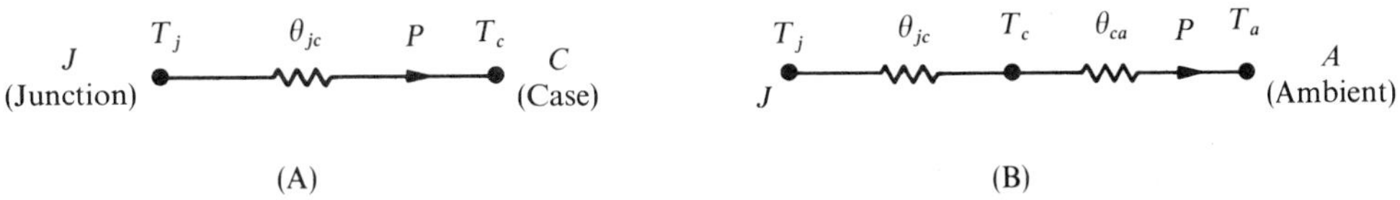

Fig. 14–14. *Thermal resistance circuits. (A) Junction-to-case thermal resistance. (B) Junction-to-ambient thermal resistance.*

Maximum power dissipation, as pointed out earlier, is specified at a case temperature of 25°C. The power rating of a device decreases with an increase in case temperature. A typical manufacturer's data sheet for a power transistor (2N5190) reads

Total power dissipated, $P_{D(\max)} = 40$ W at 25°C.
Derate 320 mW/°C above 25°C.

Based on this information, we can draw a *derating curve*, illustrated in Fig. 14–15. From this plot, we conclude that maximum power dissipation is allowed at temperatures below 25°C. At 150°C and above, the device cannot dissipate any power.

The junction-to-case thermal resistance, θ_{jc}, is the reciprocal of the derating factor. For the 2N5190, $\theta_{jc} = 1/0.320 = 3.12$°C/W.

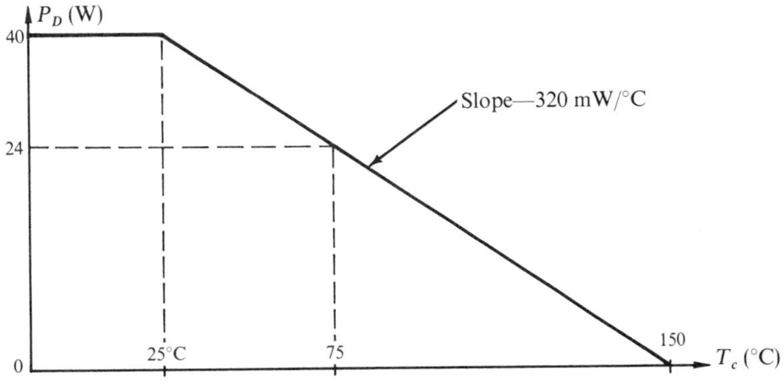

Fig. 14–15. *Power derating curve for a 2N5190 transistor.*

EXAMPLE 14–4.

Determine the maximum power that a 2N5190 transistor can dissipate if the case temperature is not to exceed 75°C.

Solution:

The case temperature of 75°C is 50°C above 25°C. At 25°C, $P_{D(\max)} = 40\ \text{W}$; hence,

$$\begin{aligned} P_D\,(75°\text{C}) &= 40\ \text{W} - (50°\text{C}) \times (0.320\ \text{W}/°\text{C}) \\ &= 40\ \text{W} - 16\ \text{W} = 24\ \text{W} \end{aligned}$$

Therefore, at a case temperature of 75°C, the transistor can only dissipate 24 W of power. The same result could have been obtained from the derating curve of Fig. 14–15.

If the transistor is not mounted on a heat sink and the ambient is air, the *thermal resistance between the case and air*, θ_{ca}, is very high. The larger the surface area of the transistor case, the more heat can flow from the transistor, and the smaller is the value of θ_{ca}. Some typical transistor packages and their respective values of θ_{ca} are indicated in Fig. 14–16. Their values are larger than the value of θ_{jc} for the 2N5190 transistor. It is desirable to make the value of θ_{ca} comparable to θ_{jc}. Increasing the case size to produce this matching of thermal resistances is not practical. Therefore, we must add external heat dissipators, called *heat sinks*.

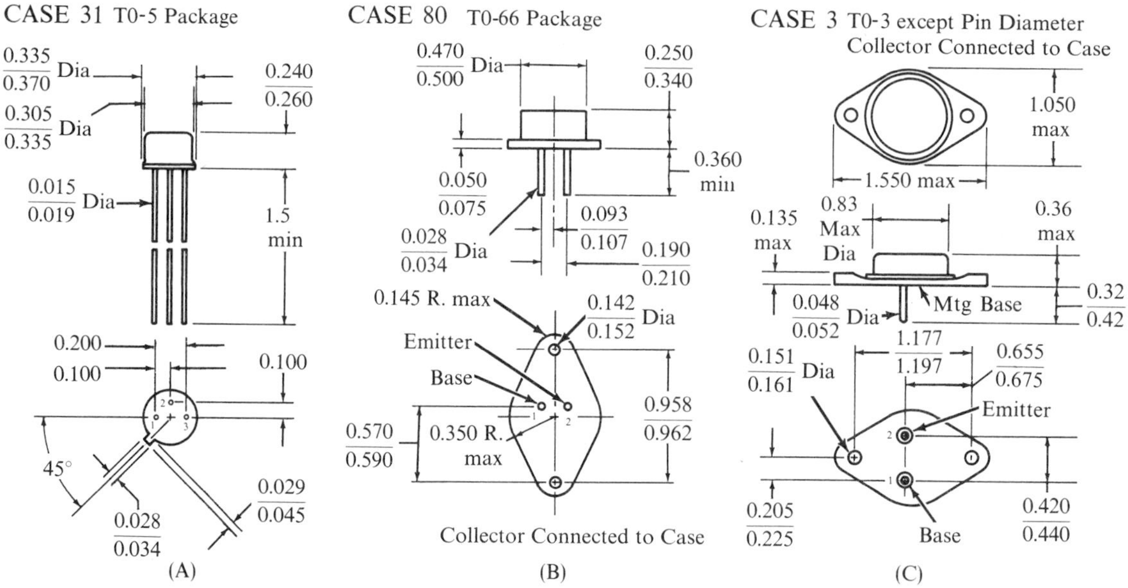

Fig. 14–16. *Typical transistor packages. (A) TO-5: $\theta_{ca} = 150°\text{C/W}$. (B) TO-66: $\theta_{ca} = 60°\text{C/W}$. (C) TO-3: $\theta_{ca} = 30°\text{C/W}$. (Courtesy Motorola Semiconductor Products, Inc.)*

14.8 Heat Sinks

Heat sinks are made of good heat-conductive materials, such as aluminum and copper, on which the transistor is mounted. Proper conditions for the transfer of heat from case to sink must be provided. Various types of heat sinks are marketed, and all have one thing in common: They provide a maximum heat dissipation area. Some of the more popular heat sink designs having fins are illustrated in Fig. 14–17. Flat areas are also used as heat sinks. In many applications, for example, power transistors are mounted directly on a metal chassis.

When using a heat sink (Fig. 14–18A), the thermal circuit may be represented as a series-resistive circuit, as shown in Fig. 14–18B. The thermal resistances in the circuit are junction-to-case, θ_{jc}; case-to-heat-sink, θ_{cs}, which is an interface resistance; and heat-sink-to-ambient, θ_{sa}. The power dissipated in the thermal circuit is

$$P = \frac{T_j - T_a}{\theta_{jc} + \theta_{cs} + \theta_{sa}} \tag{14-7}$$

Because the heat flowing in a series circuit is the same in each thermal resistance, the power dissipated in each section must also be the same. We may express Eq. (14–6), therefore, by

$$P = \frac{T_c - T_a}{\theta_{cs} + \theta_{sa}} \tag{14-8}$$

and

$$P = \frac{T_s - T_a}{\theta_{sa}} \tag{14-9}$$

where T_s is the temperature of the heat sink. From the preceding discussion, the lower the thermal resistance, the less cooling is required. In other words, a small heat sink may be used.

The interface between the transistor case and heat sink frequently must include an electrical insulator. In many power transistors, the collector is connected to the case, making it necessary to isolate electrically the case from the heat sink. Because an electrical insulator also acts as a thermal insulator, a material must be chosen which has a low value of thermal resistance.

Materials such as mica, anodized aluminum, and beryllia are most frequently used as insulating washers. All three have reasonable values of thermal resistance. Typical values of θ_{cs} are less than 0.5°C/W, with beryllia exhibiting the lowest value, 0.25°C/W. A filling compound, such as silicone grease, is also spread on the mounting area to ensure good thermal contact. An exploded view of the process of

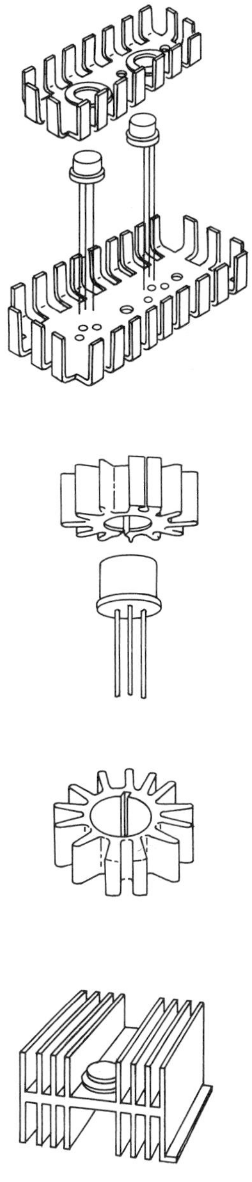

Fig. 14–17. *Examples of heat sinks with fins. (Courtesy Thermalloy, Inc.)*

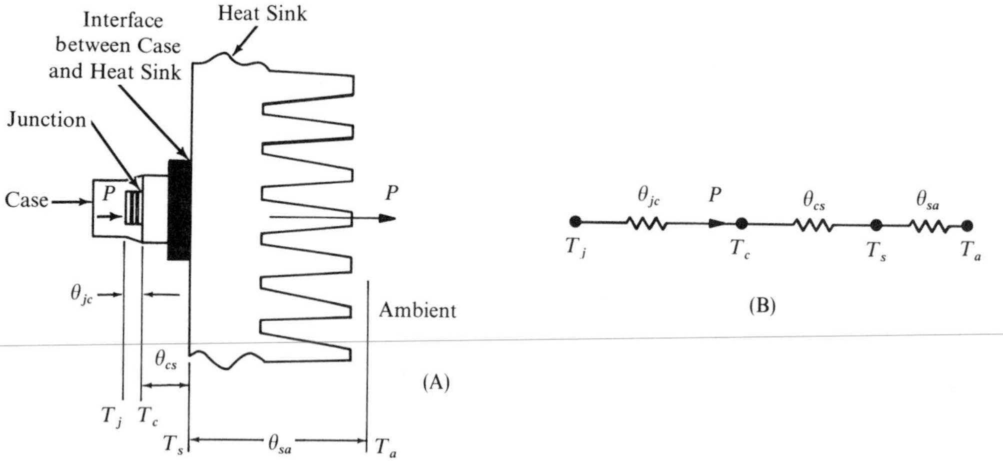

Fig. 14–18. *Semiconductor device mounted on a heat sink. (A) Mechanical details. (B) Equivalent thermal resistance circuit.*

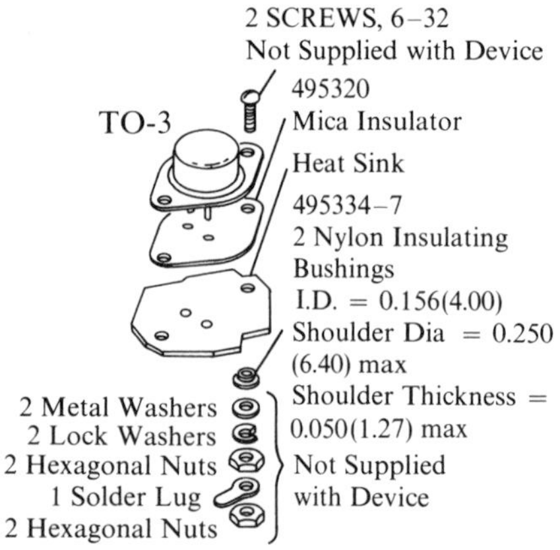

Fig. 14–19. *Heat-sink mounting diagram for a TO-3 package. (Courtesy RCA Solid State Division.)*

mounting a power transistor on a heat sink is given in Fig. 14–19.

EXAMPLE 14–5.

A power transistor in a TO-3 case has a maximum dissipation of 20 W. The manufacturer lists the following ratings for the transistor: $T_{j(\max)} = 150°\text{C}$ and $\theta_{jc} = 1.75°\text{C/W}$. The ambient temperature must not exceed 60°C. Calculate the thermal resistance of the heat sink required in this application.

Solution:

Solving for θ_{sa} from Eq. (14–7),

$$\theta_{sa} = \frac{T_j - T_a}{P} - (\theta_{jc} + \theta_{cs})$$

Assuming a beryllia washer is used, then $\theta_{cs} = 0.25°\text{C/W}$, and

$$\theta_{sa} = \frac{150 - 60}{20} - (1.75 + 0.25) = 2.5°\text{C/W}$$

The curves provided in Fig. 14–20 are useful in determining the type of heat sink needed for a specific application. The surface area of the heat sink also can be calculated from the curves.

EXAMPLE 14–6.

Using the curves of Fig. 14–20, determine the type of heat sink and its total surface area for mounting the transistor in Example 14–5.

Solution:

The thermal resistance of the heat sink was calculated in Example 14–5 to be 2.5°C/W. We shall consider the flat vertical fins and square bright aluminum of Fig. 14–20 for heat sinks.

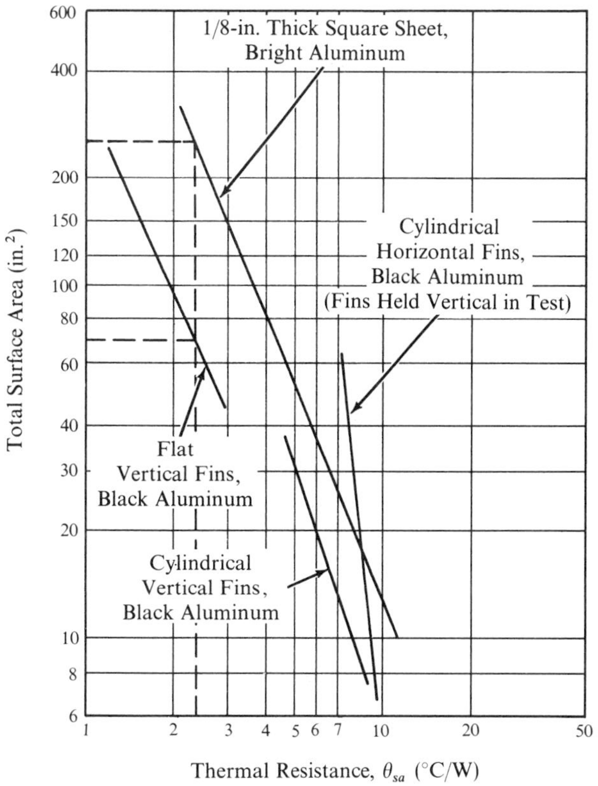

Fig. 14–20. *Graph used in determining the type and size of a heat sink for a given application.*

For $\theta_{sa} = 2.5°C/W$, the total minimum surface area for the finned sink is 60 in.^{2} and approximately 200 in.^{2} for the aluminum sheet sink. If the chassis on which the circuit is mounted has the characteristics of the aluminum, then the device may be mounted on the chassis. In all other cases, the finned-type sink should be used.

The need for a heat sink in most applications is clearly illustrated by the following example.

EXAMPLE 14–7.

A germanium power transistor in a TO-3 case has the following maximum ratings: $T_{j(\max)} = 100°C$, $\theta_{jc} = 0.8°C/W$, $\theta_{ca} = 30°C/W$, and $P_{D(\max)} = 90$ W at $T_c = 25°C$. Can the transistor dissipate 10 W safely without a heat sink?

Solution:

First we calculate the junction temperature and then compare it with the rated value of $T_{j(\max)} = 100°C$. By Eq. (14–6),

$$\begin{aligned} T_j &= P(\theta_{jc} + \theta_{ca}) + T_a \\ &= 10(0.8 + 30) + 25 = 333°C \end{aligned}$$

Because $T_{j(\max)}$ is only 100°C, we conclude that the transistor *cannot* dissipate 10 W of power unless a heat sink is provided.

SUMMARY

A number of transformerless power amplifier designs were considered in this chapter. We showed that complementary-type amplifiers have the efficiency of class *B* push-pull amplifiers discussed in Chapter 13. Because no transformers are used, they have the advantage of improved frequency response and low distortion. IC power amplifiers currently available can deliver up to 100 W of power.

Because of large current flow, short-circuit protection is often incorporated in power amplifiers. This protection is generally accomplished by the use of diodes.

Thermal considerations must be evaluated when dealing with power devices. Proper heat removal methods increase power handling capabilities of semiconductor devices. Heat removal is achieved by the use of heat sinks.

Further Reading

Cowles, L. G. *Transistor Circuits and Applications.* Englewood Cliffs, N.J.: Prentice-Hall, 1968, Chapter 6.

Kaufman, M., and A. H. Seidman, eds. *Handbook for Electronics Engineering Technicians.* New York: McGraw-Hill Book Company, 1976, Chapter 12.

Millman, J., and C. C. Halkias. *Integrated Electronics: Analog and Digital Circuits and Systems.* New York: McGraw-Hill Book Company, 1972, Chapter 18.

Motorola. *Linear Integrated Circuits Data Book.* Phoenix, Ariz.: Motorola Semiconductor Products, Inc., 1971.

———. *Semiconductor Power Circuits Handbook.* Phoenix, Ariz.: Motorola Semiconductor Products, Inc., 1968.

———. *The Semiconductor Data Book.* Phoenix, Ariz.: Motorola Semiconductor Products, Inc., 1970.

Pierce, J. F., and T. J. Paulus. *Applied Electronics.* Columbus, Ohio: Charles E. Merrill Publishing Company, 1972, Chapter 12.

RCA. *Solid State Power Circuits.* (Technical Series SP-52.) Somerville, N.J.: RCA Corporation, 1971.

Thermalloy. *Heat Sinks and Electronic Cooling.* (Catalog No. 72-HS-8.) Dallas, Tex.: Thermalloy, Inc., 1972.

Williams, Gerald. *Practical Transistor Circuit Design and Analysis.* New York: McGraw-Hill Book Company, 1973, Chapter 12.

REVIEW QUESTIONS

14.1 Explain the operation of the totem-pole amplifier.

14.2 Why is there no need for a coupling capacitor in the circuit of Fig. 14–1B?

14.3 What is the function of transistor Q_1 and its associated circuitry in Fig. 14–3?

14.4 Why is there no phase splitter in the circuits of Figs. 14–3 and 14–4?

14.5 What is the advantage in using Darlington pairs in the power amplifier of Fig. 14–5 over the complementary output circuit of Fig. 14–3?

14.6 What are the advantages of the complementary Darlington circuit of Fig. 14–7 with respect to the circuit of Fig. 14–5?

14.7 Describe the operation of the complementary pairs of Figs. 14–8A and B.

14.8 What is the purpose of the constant current source in Fig. 14–9?

14.9 Describe the function of emitter resistors R_7 and R_8 in Fig. 14–9.

14.10 In Fig. 14–10, why may a fuse placed in series with the load provide insufficient protection?

14.11 How do diodes D_4 and D_5 in Fig. 14–10 provide short-circuit protection?

14.12 What types of IC power amplifiers are available commercially?

14.13 What factor limits the maximum power that a semiconductor device can dissipate?

14.14 Describe thermal runaway.

14.15 Describe second breakdown.

14.16 Define thermal resistance.

14.17 What is the purpose of heat sinking?

14.18 What material is used as a filling compound to ensure good thermal contact between the heat sink and the device?

14.19 Identify two good heat-conductive materials used as heat sinks.

14.20 What will the effect be on the output in Fig. 14–10 if diodes D_1, D_2, and D_3 are shorted out?

PROBLEMS

P14–1 The amplifier of Fig. 14–3 delivers 2 W of power to a 100-Ω load. Determine the peak collector current flowing in transistors Q_2 and Q_3.

P14–2 Repeat prob. P14–1 for 3 W of power to the load.

P14–3 Find the ac collector current and collector-emitter voltage of transistor Q_1 in prob. P14–1 ($h_{FE_2} = h_{FE_3} = 30$).

P14–4 In the power amplifier of Fig. 14–5, the peak values of collector current and voltage are $I_{c_1} = 10\,\text{mA}$ and $V_{ce_1} = 10\,\text{V}$, respectively. Each transistor of a Darlington pair has an $h_{FE} = 30$. Calculate the power dissipated in the load.

P14–5 Repeat prob. P14–4 for an $h_{FE} = 40$.

P14–6 The amplifier in prob. P14–4 is to deliver 20 W to a load. Find the collector current in transistor Q_1 assuming that the peak value of V_{ce_1} remains at 10 V.

P14–7 Referring to Example 14–3,
(a) Calculate current I for symmetrical biasing of 14 V dc from point A to ground.
(b) Find the value of the 2.2-kΩ resistor in Fig. 14–6 to yield the new value of I calculated in (a).

P14–8 Redraw the circuit in Fig. 14–7 for PNP transistors. Transistor Q_4 will be the only NPN device in the new circuit.

P14–9 Find the approximate short-circuit current, I_{SC}, in the circuit of Fig. 14–10 if $R_7 = 1\,\Omega$.

P14–10 Repeat prob. P14–9 for $R_7 = 0.5\,\Omega$.

P14–11 Draw a derating curve for a transistor with the following specifications: $P_{D(\text{max})} = 5\,\text{W}$ at 25°C; derate 50 mW/°C above 25°C.

P14–12 Specify θ_{jc} for the transistor in prob. P14–11.

P14–13 Calculate the maximum power that the transistor of prob. P14–11 can dissipate at
(a) 50°C.
(b) 100°C.

P14–14 The manufacturer of the 2N1011 transistor supplies the following data: $P_{D(\text{max})} = 90\,\text{W}$ at 25°C, $T_{j(\text{max})} = 100°\text{C}$, and $\theta_{jc} = 0.8°\text{C/W}$. What is the maximum power that the transistor can dissipate at $T_j = 75°\text{C}$?

P14–15 Repeat prob. P14–14 for $T_j = 85°\text{C}$.

P14–16 For the transistor in prob. P14–14, calculate the maximum power that can be dissipated if a heat sink having a $\theta_{sa} = 5°\text{C/W}$ is used. The ambient temperature is 50°C. Assume a reasonable value for θ_{cs}.

P14–17 A 2N2291 power transistor has the following maximum ratings: $T_{j(\text{max})} = 110°\text{C}$, $\theta_{jc(\text{max})} = 1.2°\text{C/W}$, and $P_{D(\text{max})} = 70\,\text{W}$. Calculate the thermal resistance, θ_{sa}, of the heat sink to be used for a power dissipation of 20 W. The ambient temperature is not to exceed 45°C.

P14–18 Repeat prob. P14–17 for a maximum dissipation of 10 W at 60°C.

P14–19 For the conditions of prob. P14–17, design a heat sink using the curves of Fig. 14–20.

part iv

POWER CONVERSION

This section deals with changing electrical power from one form to another. Most electronic equipment requires dc power for its operation. Power companies supply electrical energy in the form of ac, therefore requiring conversion from ac to dc. The dc power supply, consisting of a rectifier and a filter, can provide an almost perfect dc from ac. The way in which this is accomplished is the subject of Chapter 15.

Regulated power supplies consist of a regulator circuit in addition to the basic dc supply. The regulator is a feedback circuit that, within limits, delivers a constant output regardless of variations in input voltage or load current. Regulators, in discrete and in integrated form, are considered in Chapter 16.

In many industrial applications, controlled ac power is needed. The magnitude or the frequency of the input voltage may be controlled. The thyristor in these circuits is the primary controlling element. Some conditions arise in which the only source of power is a battery, and ac equipment is to be operated. In this case, a dc-to-ac inverter is used. In other cases, a high-value dc voltage is required from a low-value dc source. For this application, a dc-to-dc converter is used. These topics are covered in Chapter 17.

15

Diode Rectifiers and Filters

In *rectification*, ac is converted to a *unidirectional*, or *pulsating*, dc, as represented by the waveforms of Figs. 15–1C and D. Two types of rectifier circuits generally used are the *half-wave* and *full-wave rectifiers*. The basic device used in these circuits is the junction diode.

The unidirectional dc is usually filtered to eliminate the fluctuations from the rectified waveform. This ensures a "clean" dc output voltage. Filter circuits discussed in this chapter include the shunt-capacitance (capacitor), L-section (choke), pi, and RC filters.

15.1 Half-Wave Rectifier

Energy supplied by the utilities in the United States is typically a sinusoidal wave of 117 V rms at a frequency of 60 Hz. The average value of a sine wave is zero, since a pure sine wave has no dc component. To obtain dc from a sine wave, its shape is altered to offset its symmetry. When this is accomplished, the resultant waveform has an average value other than zero.

The junction diode, which exhibits a unidirectional characteristic (see Chapter 2), is capable of changing a sine wave into a wave with a dc component. Consider the half-wave rectifier of Fig. 15–1A. The input to the circuit is a sine wave (Fig. 15–1B). Diode D conducts for the positive half-cycle of the input wave ($0 \leqslant \omega t \leqslant \pi$ radians). If we assume that the diode is ideal (its forward resistance is zero for the positive half-cycle, and its reverse resistance is infinite for the negative half-cycle), the current in the circuit (Fig. 15–1C) is

$$i(\omega t) = \begin{cases} (V_{\max}/R_L)\sin \omega t & \text{for} \quad 0 \leqslant \omega t \leqslant \pi \qquad \textbf{(15–1a)} \\ 0 & \text{for} \quad \pi \leqslant \omega t \leqslant 2\pi \qquad \textbf{(15–1b)} \end{cases}$$

where $V_{\max}$ is the maximum (peak) value of the input voltage.

During the negative half-cycle ($\pi \leqslant \omega t \leqslant 2\pi$ radians), the diode acts as an open circuit. No current flows in the diode, and the negative half-cycle of the input voltage is dropped across it (Fig. 15–1E). The result is an output waveform which is repetitive and of the same frequency as the input. It is, however, altered in shape to contain a dc component. The average value (same as the dc value) of the half-rectified

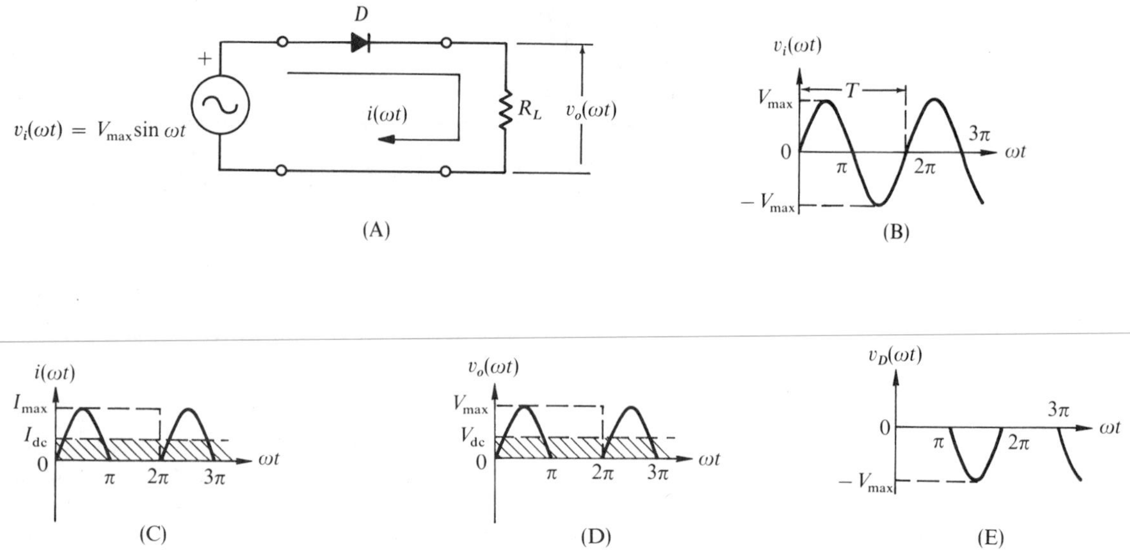

Fig. 15–1. *The half-wave rectifier. (A) Circuit. (B) Input waveform. (C), (D) Output current and voltage waveforms, indicating the dc level. (E) Voltage waveform across the diode.*

wave is found by calculating the area under the curve for one cycle and dividing it by 2π radians.

Without calculus, a descriptive approach may be taken to visualize the average value of a waveform. Imagine the wave in Fig. 15–1C as mounds of sand of the same shape and spacing. An open box, having a height equal to I_{max} (the maximum current), and length equal to 2π, encloses the waveform for 2π radians. The sand is then leveled evenly over the length of the box. This results in a rectangle of sand in the box of length 2π and a specific height. The height of the rectangle is the average value of the waveform. Its value is given by

$$I_{dc(HW)} = \frac{I_{max}}{\pi} = 0.318 I_{max} \tag{15–2}$$

and

$$V_{dc(HW)} = 0.318 I_{max} R_L = 0.318 V_{max} \tag{15–3}$$

where subscript HW denotes half-wave and $I_{max} = V_{max}/R_L$.

When the diode connections are reversed, as in Fig. 15–2A, the circuit conducts current only during the negative half-cycle. The polarity of the output voltage is therefore reversed. The waveforms of Figs. 15–2B–E illustrate the input, current, voltage, and diode voltage, respectively.

Most frequently, a transformer is used at the input of a rectifier. Its purpose is twofold. The transformer *isolates* the source from the load. (It is, therefore, sometimes called an *isolation transformer*.) A careful examination of Fig. 15–3 reveals that there is no direct connection (no dc path) between the source and the load. The primary purpose for an input transformer, however, is to increase or decrease the input voltage to ensure the desired output voltage.

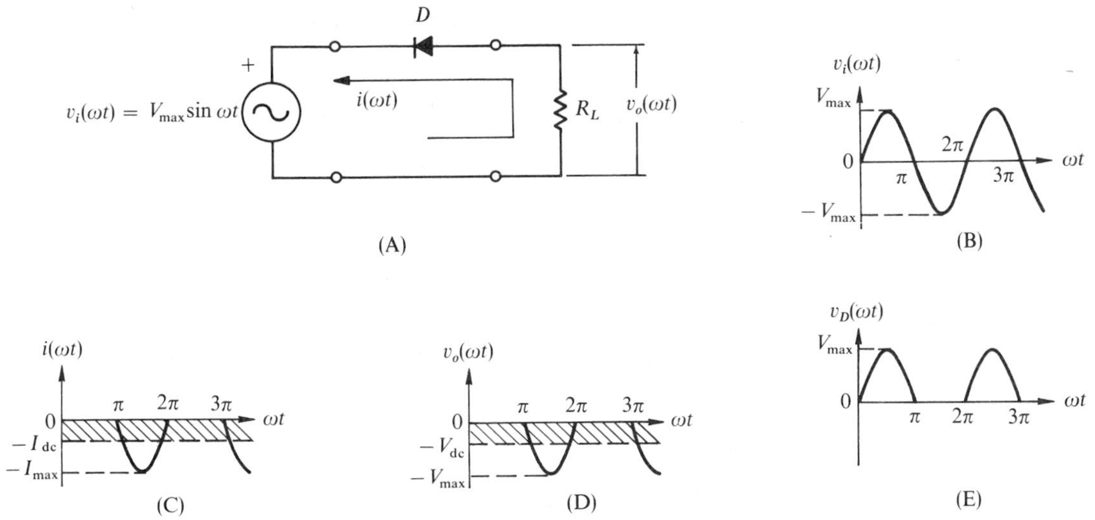

Fig. 15–2. *Half-wave rectifier with the diode connections reversed. (A) Circuit. (B) Input waveform. (C), (D) Output current and voltage waveforms. (E) Diode voltage waveform.*

EXAMPLE 15–1.

For the circuit of Fig. 15–3, calculate the direct current in the diode and the dc output voltage.

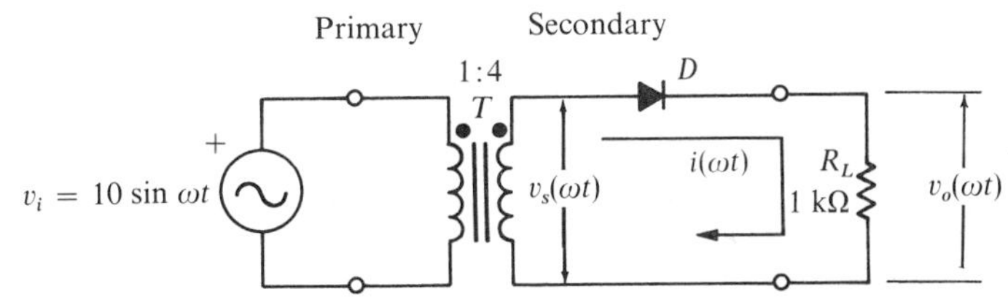

Fig. 15–3. *Transformer input half-wave rectifier. (See Example 15–1.)*

Solution:

The maximum voltage across the secondary of the transformer, $V_{s(max)}$, is

$$V_{s(max)} = 4V_{p(max)} = 4 \times 10 = 40\,\text{V}$$

where $V_{p(max)}$ is the maximum voltage across the primary winding. By Eq. (15–2),

$$I_{dc(HW)} = 0.318 I_{max}$$
$$= \frac{0.318 V_{s(max)}}{R_L} = \frac{0.318 \times 40}{1} = 12.72\,\text{mA}$$

By Eq. (15–3),

$$V_{dc(HW)} = 0.318 \times 40 = 12.72\,\text{V}$$

The dc output also can be determined from the following relationship:

$$V_{dc(HW)} = I_{dc(HW)} R_L$$
$$= 12.72 \times 1 = 12.72\,\text{V}$$

15.2 Full-Wave Rectifier

Two types of full-wave rectifiers are considered: the *center-tapped transformer* full-wave rectifier and the *bridge* rectifier. The full-wave rectifier requires more components than the half-wave circuit. A higher price is paid for higher dc output and more efficient filtering of the waveform.

The center-tapped full-wave rectifier is shown in Fig. 15–4A. The circuit may be viewed as two half-wave rectifiers having a common load resistor, R_L. At any instant, only one diode conducts current to the load. With a sine wave applied to the input (Fig. 15–4B) during the positive half-cycle, D_1 is forward biased and D_2 reverse biased. Load

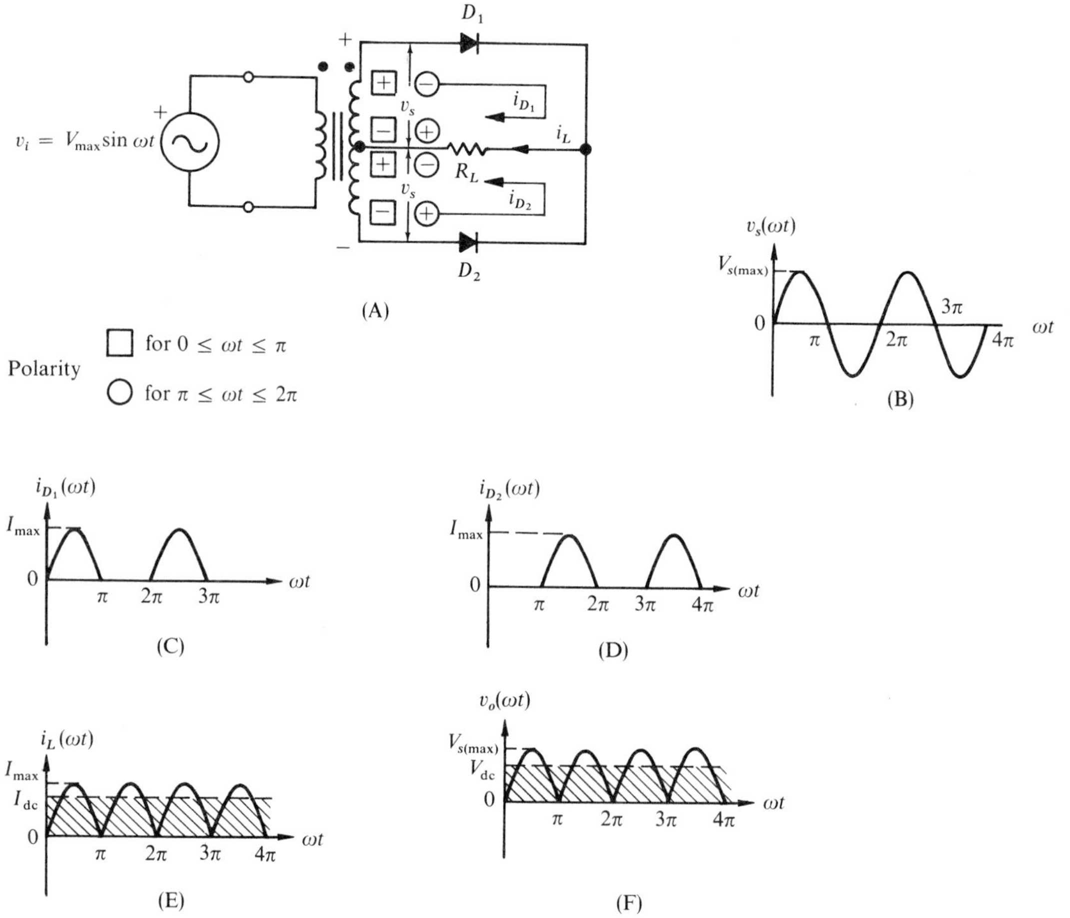

Fig. 15–4. *The full-wave rectifier. (A) Circuit. (B) Waveform across secondary winding of transformer. (C) Current in diode D_1. (D) Current in diode D_2. (E) Load current. (F) Output voltage waveform.*

current $i_L = i_{D_1}$ flows through the load (Fig. 15–4C). During the negative half-cycle, D_1 is reverse biased and D_2 forward biased; $i_L = i_{D_2}$ (Fig. 15–4D).

The direction of current in the load for both half-cycles is the same, regardless of which diode is conducting (Fig. 15–4E). The resultant waveform contains the positive portions of the input wave with double the number of positive peaks. This means that the frequency of the load current and voltage (Figs. 15–4E and F) is exactly double the frequency of the input signal. The dc load current is twice the value obtained in a half-wave rectifier:

$$I_{dc(FW)} = \frac{2I_{max}}{\pi} = 0.636 I_{max} \tag{15–4}$$

Similarly, the dc output voltage is

$$V_{dc(FW)} = 0.636 V_{s(max)} \tag{15–5}$$

where subscript FW denotes full-wave.

The *bridge rectifier* of Fig. 15–5A produces a full-wave rectified output without a center-tapped power transformer. An ac input to the circuit causes diodes D_1 and D_4 to conduct during the positive half-cycle (Fig. 15–5B). Diodes D_2 and D_3 conduct during the negative half-cycle (Fig. 15–5C). In each half-cycle, current flows through two of the four diodes.

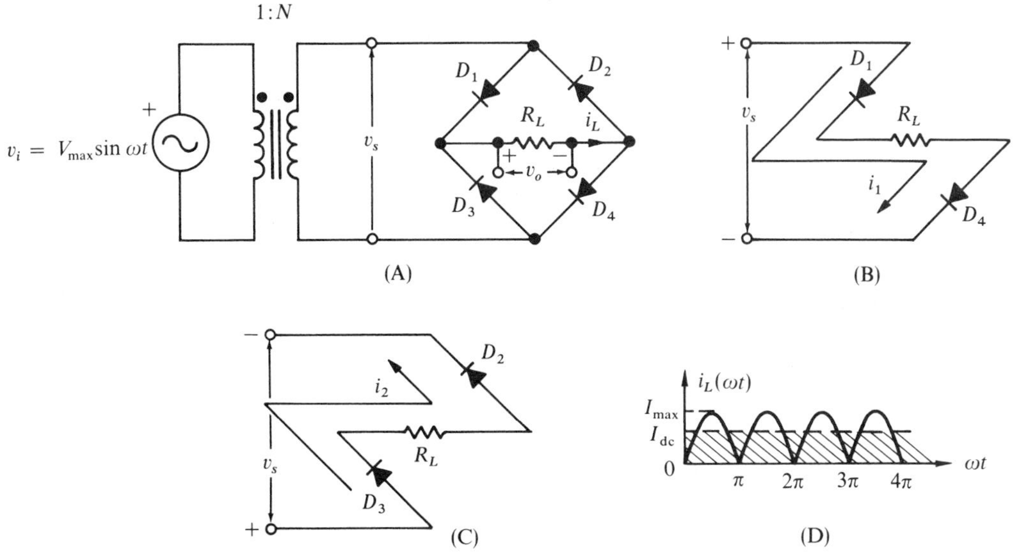

Fig. 15–5. *The bridge rectifier. (A) Circuit. (B) Circuit for the positive half-cycle. (C) Circuit for the negative half-cycle. (D) Output current waveform.*

Assuming ideal diodes, the maximum current in diode D_1 (or D_4), $I_{1(max)}$, is

$$I_{1(max)} = \frac{V_{s(max)}}{R_L} \tag{15–6a}$$

Similarly, in D_2 (or D_3),

$$I_{2(\max)} = \frac{V_{s(\max)}}{R_L} \qquad \textbf{(15–6b)}$$

Each pair of diodes (D_1 and D_4 or D_2 and D_3) conducts for one half-cycle. The total load current is illustrated in Fig. 15–5D. It has the same waveshape as that obtained for a conventional (center-tapped transformer) full-wave rectifier. The average values of the load current and voltage are therefore expressed by Eq. (15–4) and Eq. (15–5), respectively. Also, the frequency of the output waveform is twice the frequency of the input sine wave.

EXAMPLE 15–2.

For the circuit of Fig. 15–6, calculate the dc output voltage and power dissipated in the load.

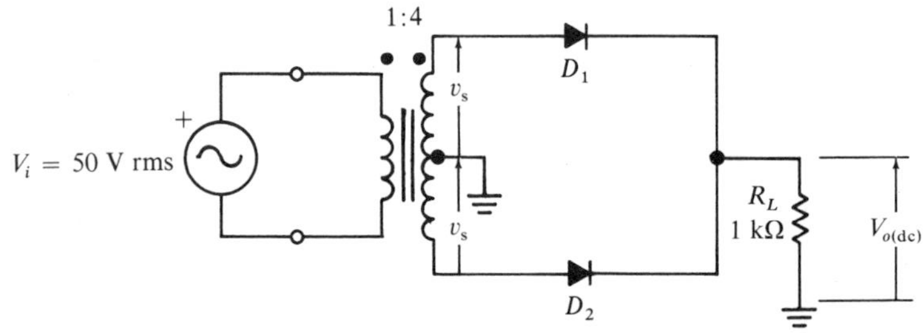

Fig. 15–6. *Full-wave rectifier circuit for Example 15–2.*

Solution:

The maximum primary voltage, $V_{p(\max)}$, is

$$V_{p(\max)} = \sqrt{2} \times 50 = 70.7\text{ V}$$

For the given transformer ratio, 4:1, the maximum secondary voltage, $V_{s(\max)}$, is

$$V_{s(\max)} = 70.7 \times 4 = 282.8\text{ V}$$

By Eq. (15–5), dropping subscript FW,

$$V_{\text{dc}} = 0.636 \times 282.8 = 179.8\text{ V}$$

The power dissipated in the load, P_D, is

$$P_D = \frac{V_{\text{dc}}^2}{R_L} = \frac{179.8^2}{1\text{ k}\Omega} = 32\text{ W}$$

EXAMPLE 15–3.

Referring to Fig. 15–5A,

(a) Find the turns ratio of the transformer for an output of 200 V dc and an input of 117 V rms at 60 Hz.

(b) What is the frequency of the output waveform?

Solutions:

(a) Solving Eq. (15–5) for $V_{s(\max)}$,

$$V_{s(\max)} = \frac{V_{dc}}{0.636}$$

$$= \frac{200}{0.636} = 315\text{ V}$$

At the input,

$$V_{p(\max)} = 117 \times \sqrt{2} = 166\text{ V}$$

Turns ratio, N, is

$$N = \frac{V_{s(\max)}}{V_{p(\max)}}$$

$$= \frac{315}{166} = 1.89$$

The transformer turns ratio should be 1:1.89.

(b) The frequency of the output waveform, f_o, is

$$f_o = 2 \times 60 = 120\text{ Hz}$$

15.3 Peak Inverse (Reverse) Voltage Rating

Diodes used for rectification are called *rectifier diodes.* Their important characteristics include the ability to

1. Conduct large amounts of current.
2. Handle peak currents which are several times greater than the average current rating.
3. Withstand large voltages across them when reverse biased. This is known as the *peak inverse voltage* (PIV) or *peak reverse voltage* (PRV) rating.

Rectifier diodes only conduct for one half-cycle of the input wave. During the nonconducting half-cycle, the diode behaves like an open circuit with a voltage reaching the peak voltage impressed across it. The PIV across a diode in a conventional full-wave rectifier is equal to twice the maximum value of the secondary voltage (the voltage from center tap to one side): PIV $= 2V_{s(\max)}$. In other words, the PIV is equal to the *total* secondary voltage. For the bridge rectifier, however, PIV $= V_{s(\max)}$. Diodes with a lower PIV rating can, therefore, be used in a bridge rectifier.

EXAMPLE 15–4.

Determine the PIV rating of diodes used in

(a) A bridge rectifier.

(b) A conventional full-wave rectifier.

The dc output voltage is 140 V.

Solutions:

(a) For the bridge rectifier,

$$V_{s(\max)} = \frac{V_{dc}}{0.636}$$
$$= \frac{140}{0.636} = 220.1 \text{ V}$$

Therefore, PIV $= V_{s(\max)} = 220.1$ V.

(b) For a conventional full-wave rectifier,

$$\text{PIV} = 2V_{s(\max)} = 2 \times 220.1 = 440.2 \text{ V}$$

15.4 Ripple Factor

When converting ac to dc, it is useful to know how much dc is obtained with respect to the ac component of the output. Such a figure of merit is the *ripple factor*, *RF*. Ideally, we would like a dc output free of any ac, or ripple ($RF = 0$). The ripple factor for any rectifier is defined as

$$RF = \frac{\text{rms value of the ac component}}{\text{dc value of the waveform}} \qquad \textbf{(15–7a)}$$

The ac component of the output voltage is called the *ripple voltage*. Expressing *RF* as a percentage, $\%RF$,

$$\%RF = \frac{\text{rms value of the ac component}}{\text{dc value of the waveform}} \times 100\% \qquad \textbf{(15–7b)}$$

The rectified load current, i_L, is composed of an ac (ripple) component, i_{ac}, and a dc component, I_{dc}:

$$i_L = i_{ac} + I_{dc}$$

Solving for i_{ac},

$$i_{ac} = i_L - I_{dc} \qquad \textbf{(15–8)}$$

The rms of the ac component, $I_{ac(rms)}$, is computed by the following method:

1. Express i_L as an rms quantity, $I_{L(rms)}$.
2. Square $I_{L(rms)}$ and I_{dc}.
3. Take the square root of their difference.

Hence,

$$I_{ac(rms)} = \sqrt{I_{L(rms)}^2 - I_{dc}^2} \qquad \textbf{(15–9)}$$

Substitution of Eq. (15–9) in Eq. (15–7a) yields

$$RF = \sqrt{\frac{I_{L(rms)}^2 - I_{dc}^2}{I_{dc}}}$$
$$= \sqrt{\left(\frac{I_{L(rms)}}{I_{dc}}\right)^2 - 1} \qquad \textbf{(15–10)}$$

In terms of voltage,

$$RF = \sqrt{\left(\frac{V_{L(\mathrm{rms})}}{V_{\mathrm{dc}}}\right)^2 - 1} \qquad \textbf{(15–11)}$$

We now shall calculate the ripple factor for the different types of rectifiers considered in this chapter. The rms load voltage of a half-wave rectifier is expressed by

$$V_{L(\mathrm{rms})} = \frac{V_{\max}}{2} \qquad \textbf{(15–12a)}$$

and the rms load current by

$$I_{L(\mathrm{rms})} = \frac{I_{\max}}{2} \qquad \textbf{(15–12b)}$$

Substituting $V_{L(\mathrm{rms})} = V_{\max}/2$ and $V_{\mathrm{dc}} = V_{\max}/\pi$ in Eq. (15–11), we have

$$RF_{\mathrm{HW}} = 1.21 \qquad \textbf{(15–13)}$$

As a percentage,

$$\%RF = 1.21 \times 100\% = 121\%$$

The high RF is clearly an indication that the half-wave rectifier produces an output with a large ac component. As a matter of fact, an $RF > 1$ is an indication that the ripple is greater than the dc.

For a full-wave and bridge rectifier,

$$V_{L(\mathrm{rms})} = \frac{V_{\max}}{\sqrt{2}} = 0.707V_{\max} \qquad \textbf{(15–14a)}$$

$$I_{L(\mathrm{rms})} = \frac{I_{\max}}{\sqrt{2}} = 0.707I_{\max} \qquad \textbf{(15–14b)}$$

and

$$RF = 0.482 \qquad \textbf{(15–15)}$$

As a percentage,

$$\%RF = 0.482 \times 100\% = 48.2\%$$

EXAMPLE 15–5.

The output of a full-wave rectifier was measured on an oscilloscope. Voltage $V_{\max} = 120\,\mathrm{V}$. Calculate

(a) The dc load voltage.

(b) The rms value of the ac component.

Solutions:

(a) The dc voltage, V_{dc}, is

$$V_{\mathrm{dc}} = 0.636 \times 120 = 76.32\,\mathrm{V}$$

(b) By Eq. (15–15), $RF = 0.482$. Substituting 0.482 in Eq. (15–7a), we have

$$0.482 = \frac{\text{rms value of the ac component}}{76.32}$$

Solving for $V_{ac(rms)}$,

$$V_{ac(rms)} = 0.482 \times 76.32 = 36.79 \text{ V}$$

15.5 Rectifier Efficiency

Another measure of rectifier performance is *rectifier efficiency*, defined as the *ratio of the dc load power to the ac power consumed by the circuit*. Rectifier efficiency indicates how much dc power is obtained from an ac source. Stated in the form of an equation,

$$\eta_R = \frac{P_{L(dc)}}{P_{i(ac)}} \qquad \textbf{(15–16a)}$$

where η_R = rectifier efficiency,
$P_{L(dc)}$ = dc power dissipated in the load,
$P_{i(ac)}$ = average ac input power.

The percentage rectifier efficiency, $\%\eta_R$, is given by

$$\%\eta_R = \frac{P_{L(dc)}}{P_{i(ac)}} \times 100\% \qquad \textbf{(15–16b)}$$

For the half-wave rectifier, neglecting transformer losses,

$$\begin{aligned} P_{L(dc)} &= I_{dc}V_{dc} \\ &= I_{dc}^2 R_L \\ &= \left(\frac{I_{max}}{\pi}\right)^2 R_L \end{aligned} \qquad \textbf{(15–17)}$$

The ac input power to a half-wave rectifier is

$$P_{i(ac)} = V_{rms}I_{rms} = I_{rms}^2 R_L$$

By Eq. (15–12b), the rms load current is $I_{max}/2$; hence,

$$P_{i(ac)} = \left(\frac{I_{max}}{2}\right)^2 R_L \qquad \textbf{(15–18)}$$

and

$$\eta_R = 0.406 \qquad \textbf{(15–19)}$$

As a percentage,

$$\%\eta_R = 40.6\%$$

Similarly, we can show that the rectifier efficiency for a conventional full-wave and bridge rectifier is

$$\eta_R = 0.812 \qquad \textbf{(15–20)}$$

and

$$\%\eta_R = 81.2\%$$

A conventional full-wave or bridge rectifier is twice as efficient as a half-wave rectifier. The characteristics of the rectifiers discussed in the preceding material are summarized in Table 15–1.

TABLE 15–1. Comparison of rectifiers.

Rectifier	V_{dc}	RF	f_{output}	η_R	PIV
Half-wave 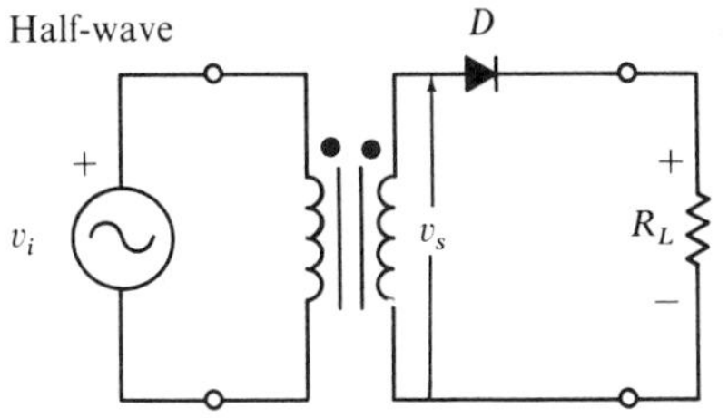	$0.318V_{s(max)}$	1.21	f_{input}	40.6%	$V_{s(max)}$
Full-wave 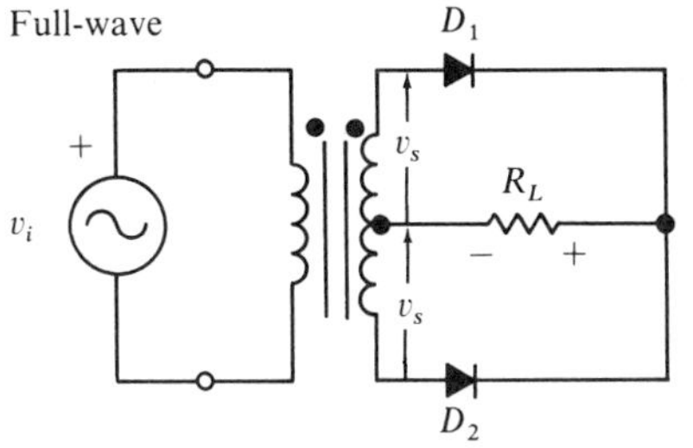	$0.636V_{s(max)}$	0.482	$2f_{input}$	81.2%	$2V_{s(max)}$
Bridge 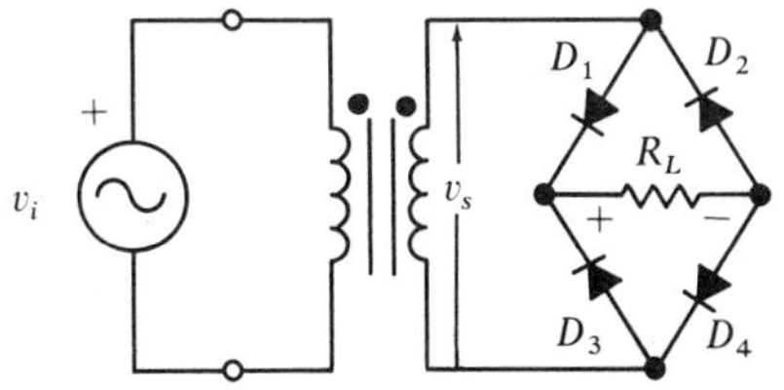	$0.636V_{s(max)}$	0.482	$2f_{input}$	81.2%	$V_{s(max)}$

EXAMPLE 15–6.

How much ac power must be supplied to a bridge rectifier if the power dissipated in the load is 10 W?

Solution:

Solving Eq. (15–16a) for $P_{i(ac)}$,

$$P_{i(ac)} = \frac{P_{L(dc)}}{\eta_R} = \frac{10}{0.812} = 12.3\text{ W}$$

15.6 Percent Load Regulation

Before our discussion of rectifiers is concluded, we must remember that certain approximations were made. In our first approximation, we assumed that the diode is ideal. This permitted us to eliminate the diode voltage drop and power dissipation from our calculations. We also assumed that no leakage current flows in a reverse-biased diode.

In reality, if we examine the diode during conduction, we measure a small voltage across the device. The voltage is a function of the current flowing, I_{dc}, and the forward resistance, r_d, of the diode. The true dc output of a rectifier is equal to the difference between the ideal dc output and the dc voltage across the diode. The diode voltage drop is equal to the product of I_{dc} and r_d. Hence, for a half-wave rectifier,

$$V_{dc} = 0.318V_{max} - I_{dc}r_d \qquad \textbf{(15–21)}$$

With no loading ($I_{dc} = 0$), the dc output voltage is that of an ideal half-wave circuit and is equal to $0.318V_{max}$ volts. As the loading increases (I_{dc} increases), the dc output voltage decreases.

A useful way to describe the changes in output voltage with loading is the *percent load regulation*, $\%LR$:

$$\%LR = \frac{V_{NL} - V_{FL}}{V_{FL}} \times 100\% \qquad \textbf{(15–22)}$$

where V_{NL} is the no-load dc voltage and V_{FL} is the full-load dc voltage. A low value of $\%LR$ denotes good regulation. It implies that only slight variations in output voltage occur with changes in loading. A high $\%LR$ is synonymous with poor regulation.

EXAMPLE 15–7.

For a given power supply, $\%LR = 2\%$. The dc voltage measured with no load is 100 V. What is the dc output voltage with load?

Solution:

Solving Eq. (15–22) for V_{FL},

$$V_{FL} = \frac{V_{NL}}{1 + \dfrac{\%LR}{100\%}}$$

$$= \frac{100}{1 + 0.02} = 98\text{ V}$$

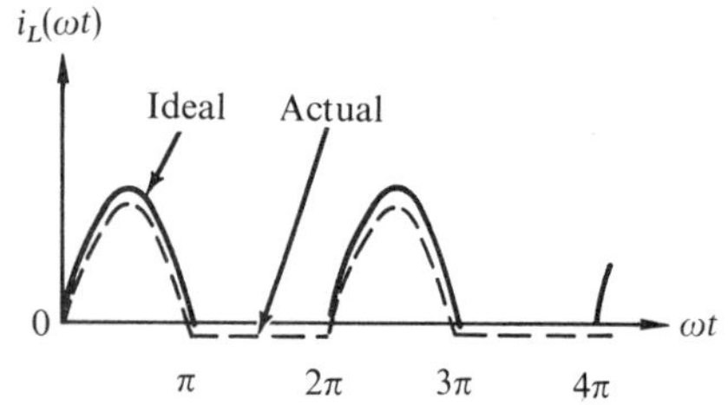

Fig. 15–7. *Ideal and actual current flow in a half-wave rectifier.*

We have examined the effect of the diode forward-voltage drop on output voltage. When the diode is reverse biased, it exhibits a high finite resistance and a small leakage current. This results in a slight negative potential at the output. The ideal and actual current flow in a half-wave rectifier are compared in Fig. 15–7. For most rectifier applications, the diode can be assumed to be ideal.

Rectifiers can be constructed from individual diodes or purchased in an integrated package. Some commercially available rectifiers are illustrated in Fig. 15–8.

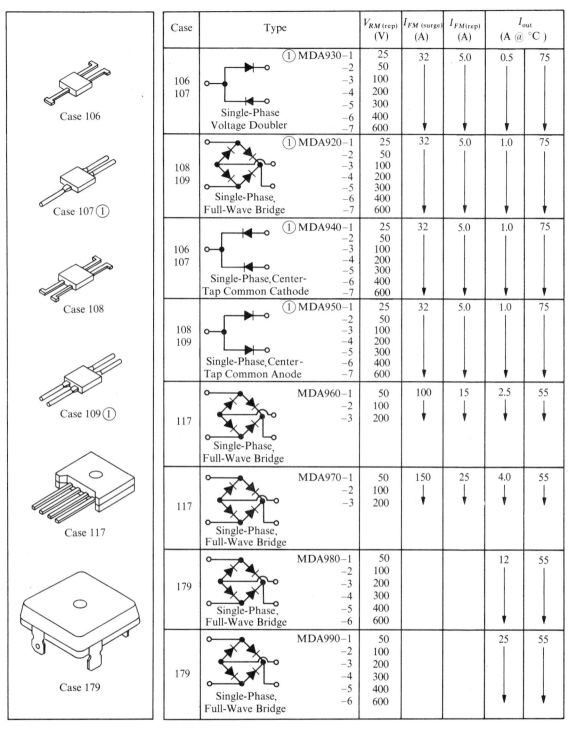

Case drawing	Case	Type	$V_{RM\,(rep)}$ (V)	$I_{FM\,(surge)}$ (A)	$I_{FM(rep)}$ (A)	I_{out} (A)	(@ °C)
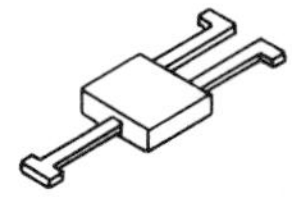 Case 106	106, 107	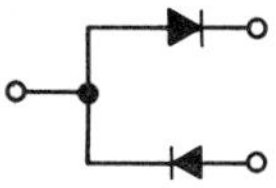 ① MDA930-1	25	32	5.0	0.5	75
		-2	50				
		-3	100				
		-4	200				
		-5	300				
		Single-Phase Voltage Doubler -6	400				
		-7	600				
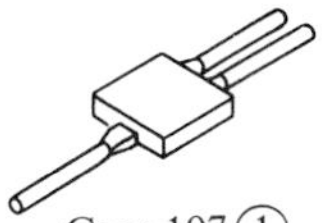 Case 107 ①	108, 109	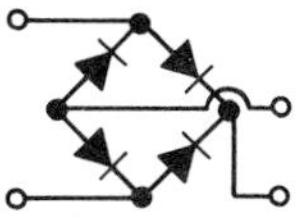 ① MDA920-1	25	32	5.0	1.0	75
		-2	50				
		-3	100				
		-4	200				
		-5	300				
		Single-Phase, Full-Wave Bridge -6	400				
		-7	600				
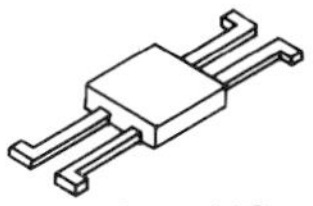 Case 108	106, 107	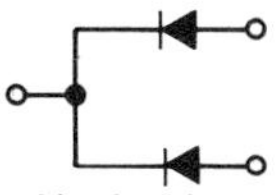 ① MDA940-1	25	32	5.0	1.0	75
		-2	50				
		-3	100				
		-4	200				
		-5	300				
		Single-Phase, Center-Tap Common Cathode -6	400				
		-7	600				
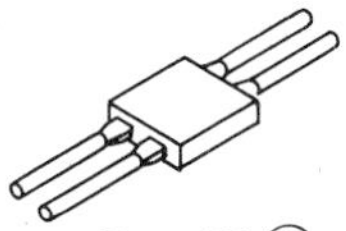 Case 109 ①	108, 109	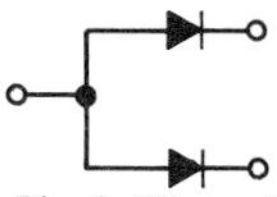 ① MDA950-1	25	32	5.0	1.0	75
		-2	50				
		-3	100				
		-4	200				
		-5	300				
		Single-Phase, Center-Tap Common Anode -6	400				
		-7	600				
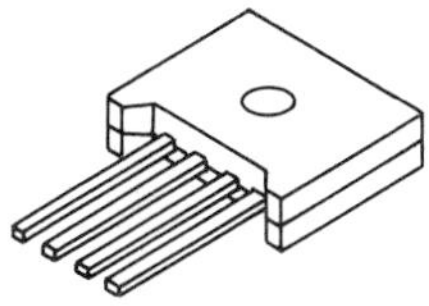 Case 117	117	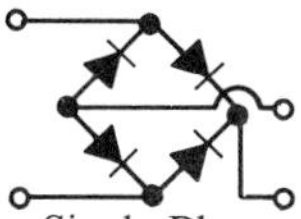 MDA960-1	50	100	15	2.5	55
		-2	100				
		-3 Single-Phase, Full-Wave Bridge	200				
	117	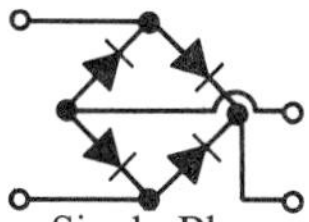 MDA970-1	50	150	25	4.0	55
		-2	100				
		-3 Single-Phase, Full-Wave Bridge	200				
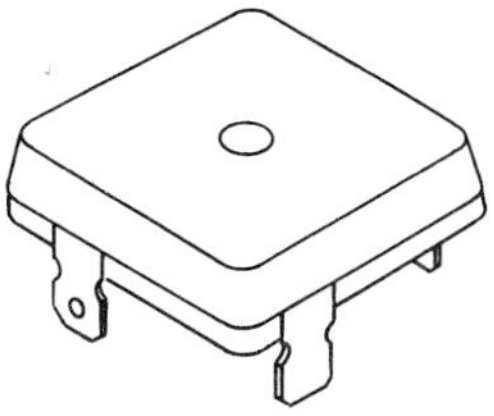 Case 179	179	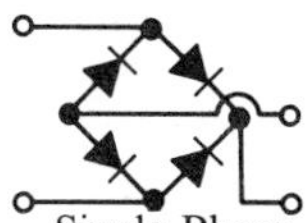 MDA980-1	50			12	55
		-2	100				
		-3	200				
		-4	300				
		Single-Phase, -5	400				
		Full-Wave Bridge -6	600				
	179	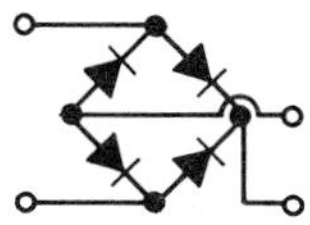 MDA990-1	50			25	55
		-2	100				
		-3	200				
		-4	300				
		-5	400				
		Single-Phase, Full-Wave Bridge -6	600				

Fig. 15–8. *Commercially available rectifiers. (Courtesy Motorola Semiconductor Products, Inc.)*

15.7 Shunt-Capacitance Filter

The outputs of the rectifiers discussed are not, in general, suitable as a dc source. The ripple in the output waveform must be reduced. A capacitor connected in parallel with the load, as in Fig. 15–9A, can be used for this purpose. Capacitor C acts as a filter and is called a *shunt-capacitance filter*.

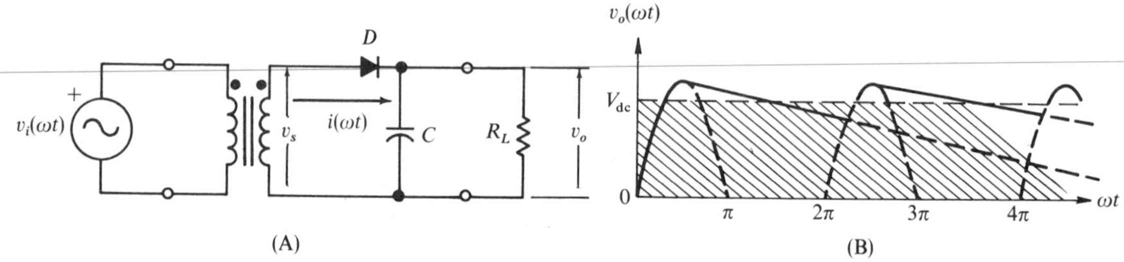

Fig. 15–9. *Half-wave rectifier with shunt-capacitance filter. (A) Circuit. (B) Output waveform.*

The capacitor charges during the time that the diode conducts and discharges through the load when the diode is not conducting (Fig. 15–9B). The time constant during the charging cycle is very short. It is equal to the product of r_d and C. Therefore, the capacitor voltage essentially follows the input voltage during the charging cycle. When the diode is nonconducting, the capacitor discharges through the load with a time constant of R_LC.

The discharge time constant is much greater than the charge time constant ($R_LC \gg r_dC$). In fact, R_LC is so long that the capacitor usually does not have an opportunity to discharge fully before the next charging cycle begins. As a result, the average value of the output waveform is much greater than that without a capacitor. This higher average value means a higher dc output and a lower ripple factor.

The effectiveness of the shunt-capacitance filter depends on the values of

1. Capacitor C.
2. Load R_L.
3. Frequency of the rectified output, f.

The larger the value of C, the longer is the time constant. Consequently, during the discharge cycle, the output does not reach a low voltage level before the capacitor begins charging again. The result is a higher dc output.

Loading conditions have a similar effect on a capacitance filter. The lighter the loading (R_L high), the less the capacitor discharges. Again, the result is a smoother output waveform with a higher dc voltage. Figure 15–10 illustrates the variation in the dc output voltage for different values of C and R_L.

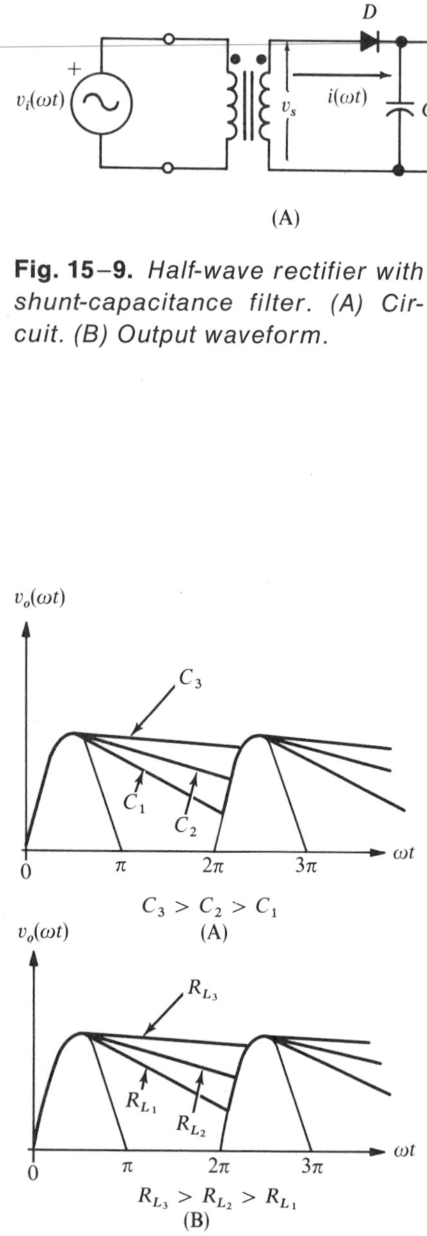

Fig. 15–10. *Output of half-wave rectifier with shunt-capacitance filters as (A) C and (B) R_L vary.*

The performance of a shunt-capacitance filter with frequency of the rectified signal can be seen in Fig. 15–11. The output of a full-wave or bridge rectifier is compared with that of a half-wave rectifier. Both circuits use a shunt-

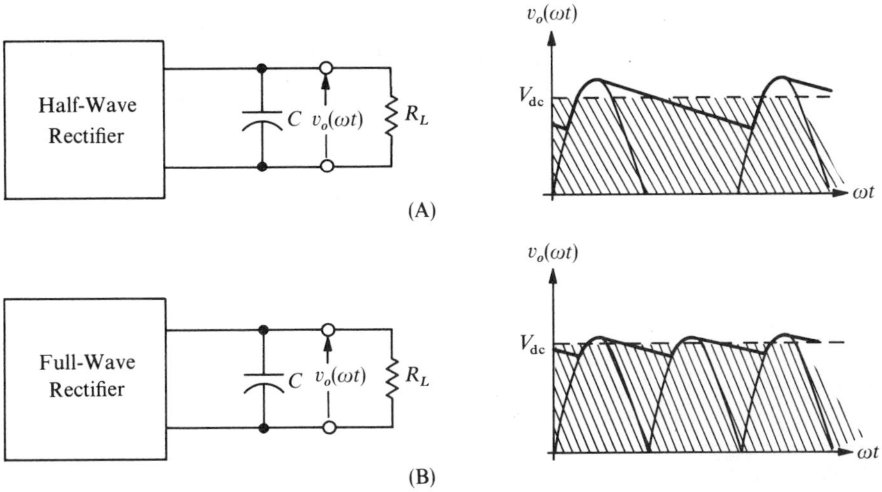

Fig. 15–11. *The same value of capacitance used with a full-wave rectifier in (B) produces a higher dc output than when used with a half-wave rectifier in (A).*

capacitance filter. With the same value of $R_L C$, the dc output of the full-wave rectifier is greater than for a half-wave rectifier. We conclude that the shunt-capacitance filter is more effective with a full-wave than with a half-wave rectifier.

The dc load voltage of a full-wave rectifier with a shunt-capacitance filter is given by

$$V_{dc} = V_{s(\max)} - \frac{I_{dc}}{4fC} \qquad \textbf{(15–23a)}$$

$$= \frac{V_{s(\max)}}{1 + \dfrac{1}{4fR_L C}} \qquad \textbf{(15–23b)}$$

line f

The ripple factor is calculated from

$$RF = \frac{1}{4\sqrt{3}fCR_L} \qquad \textbf{(15–24)}$$

By Eq. (15–24), the ripple factor is inversely proportional to C, R_L, and f. This means that for a low ripple factor, a large capacitor must be used, the loading should be light, and f should be high.

EXAMPLE 15–8.

The rectifier circuit of Fig. 15–12 is used to power an audio amplifier. Determine

(a) dc load voltage, V_{dc}.
(b) $\%RF$.

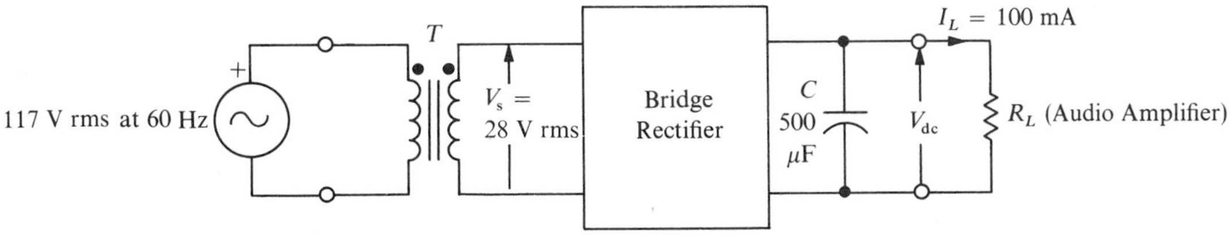

Fig. 15–12. *Rectifier circuit for Example 15–8.*

Solutions:

(a) First, the value of $V_{s(\max)}$ is determined:

$$V_{s(\max)} = \sqrt{2} \times V_s = \sqrt{2} \times 28 = 39.6\ \text{V}$$

By Eq. (15–23a),

$$V_{dc} = 39.5 - \frac{0.1}{4 \times 60 \times 500 \times 10^{-6}}$$
$$= 39.5 - 0.84 = 38.7\ \text{V}$$

TABLE 15–2. Comparison of filters.*

Filter	V_{dc}	*RF*
Shunt-Capacitance 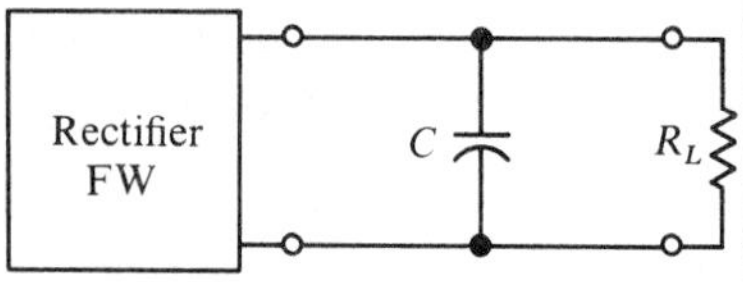	$\dfrac{V_{s(\max)}}{1 + 1/(4fR_LC)}$ For 60 Hz: $\dfrac{V_{s(\max)}}{0.00417/R_LC}$	$\dfrac{1}{4\sqrt{3}fR_LC}$ For 60 Hz: $\dfrac{2.41 \times 10^{-3}}{R_LC}$
Pi 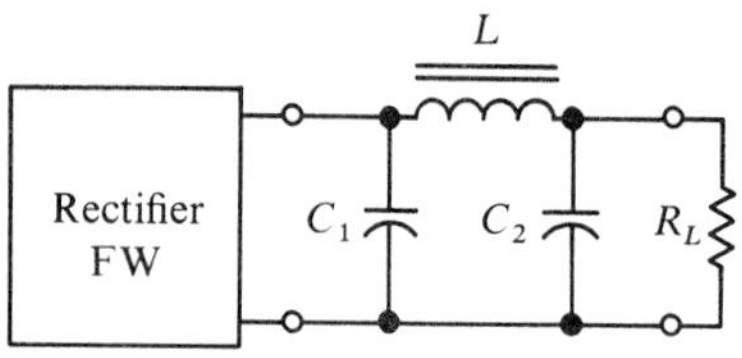	$\dfrac{V_{s(\max)}R_L/(R_L + r_L)}{1 + 1/(4fR_LC_1)}$ For 60 Hz: $\dfrac{V_{s(\max)}R_L/(R_L + r_L)}{1 + 0.00417/R_LC}$	$\dfrac{\sqrt{2}}{\omega^3C_1C_2LR_L}$ For 60 Hz: $\dfrac{0.026}{C_1C_2R_LL} \times 10^{-6}$
RC 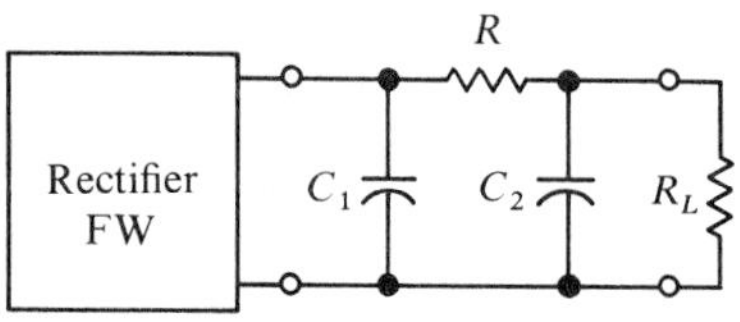	$\dfrac{V_{s(\max)}R_L/(R_L + R)}{1 + 1/(4fR_LC_1)}$ For 60 Hz: $\dfrac{V_{s(\max)}R_L/(R_L + R)}{1 + 0.00417/R_LC}$	$\dfrac{\sqrt{2}}{\omega^2C_1C_2R_LR}$ For 60 Hz: $\dfrac{9.95}{C_1C_2R_LR} \times 10^{-6}$
L-Section 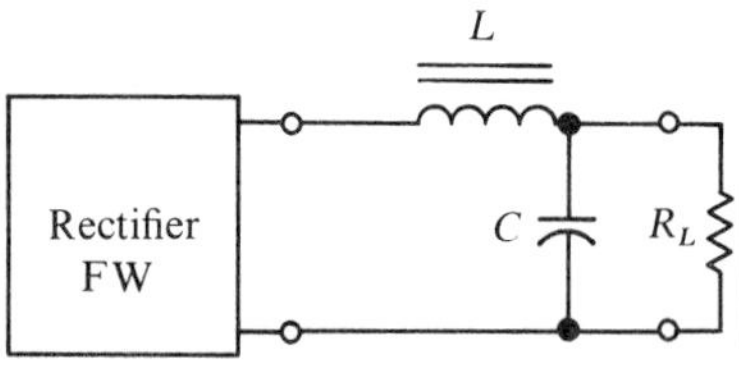	$0.636V_{s(\max)}$ For 60 Hz: $0.636V_{s(\max)}$	$\dfrac{0.118}{(\omega^2LC)}$ For 60 Hz: $\dfrac{0.83}{LC} \times 10^{-6}$

* Equations are given for any line frequency and for a 60-Hz frequency.

(b) By Eq. (15–24),

$$RF = \frac{1}{4\sqrt{3}fCR_L}$$

where $R_L = V_{dc}/I_{dc} = 38.7/0.1 = 387\,\Omega$. Hence,

$$RF = \frac{1}{4 \times \sqrt{3} \times 60 \times 500 \times 10^{-6} \times 387} = 0.0125$$

$$\%RF = 1.25\%$$

The results obtained indicate that an almost pure dc output is realized with the circuit. A $\%RF$ of 1.25% is generally considered to be low.

Equations summarizing the characteristics of the shunt-capacitance filter, as well as of other filters considered in this chapter, are provided in Table 15–2.

15.8 Graphical Analysis

Graphical techniques also may be used in the analysis and design of power supplies. We shall use the curves of Fig. 15–13 in this manner. Here, V_{dc}/V_{max} (normalized output) is plotted against the product $\omega R_L C$. All the significant variables are thereby considered. The use of the curves is illustrated in the next example.

EXAMPLE 15–9.

The half-wave rectifier of Fig. 15–9 has a secondary rms voltage of 12.6 V at a frequency of 60 Hz. Load $R_L = 100\,\Omega$.

(a) Find the value of C for a $\%RF = 3\%$.

(b) With the value of C found in part (a), determine the dc load voltage.

Use the curves of Fig. 15–13.

Solutions:

(a) In Fig. 15–13B, a horizontal (dashed) line is projected from $RF = 0.03$ to the half-wave rectifier curve. From the intersection of the horizontal line and curve, a line is projected vertically to the $\omega R_L C$-axis. The result obtained is $\omega R_L C = 60$, or

$$C = \frac{60}{\omega R_L}$$

The angular frequency, ω, is

$$\omega = 2\pi f = 2\pi \times 60 = 377 \text{ radians/s}$$

Hence,

$$C = \frac{60}{377 \times 100} \simeq 1600\,\mu\text{F}$$

(b) From the half-wave curve of Fig. 15–13A and the value of $\omega R_L C$ found in part (a),

$$\frac{V_{dc}}{V_{max}} = 0.96$$

The maximum voltage $V_{max} = V_{s(max)} = \sqrt{2} \times 12.6 = 17.81$ V. Hence,

$$V_{dc} = 0.96 \times 17.81 = 17.09 \text{ V}$$

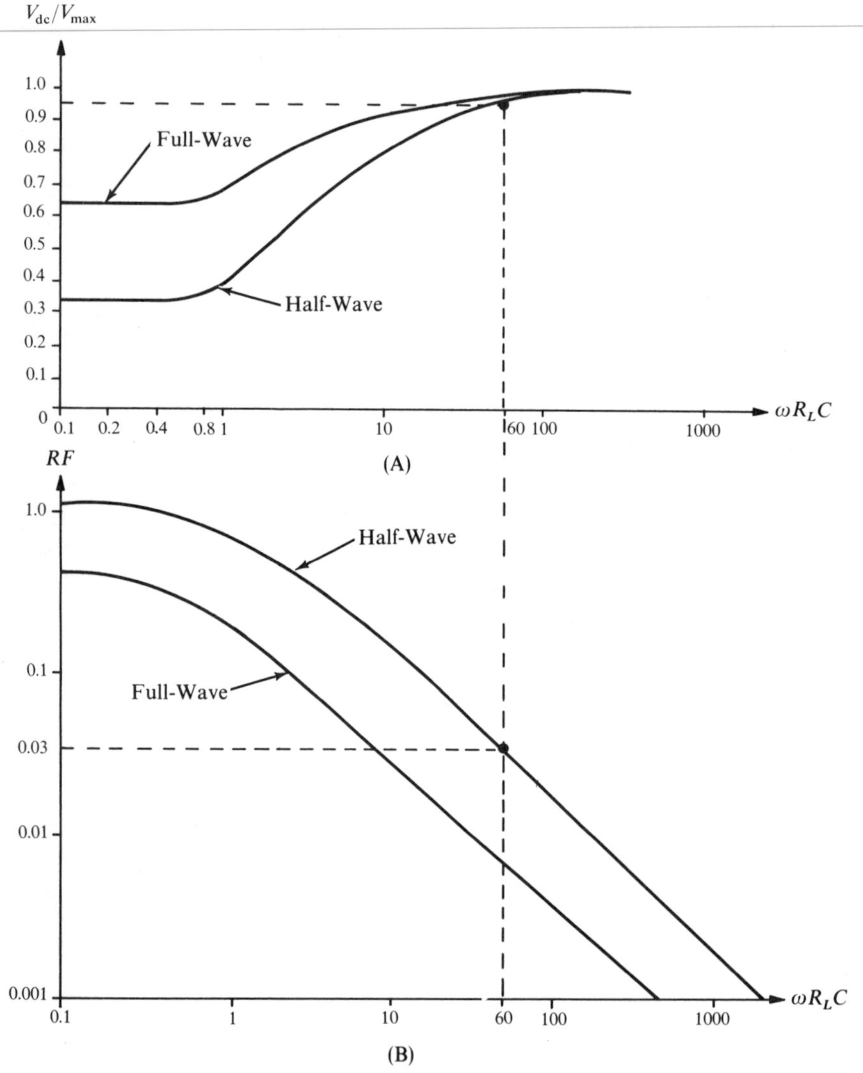

Fig. 15–13. *Design curves for rectifiers using a shunt-capacitance filter. (A) V_{dc}/V_{max} versus $\omega R_L C$. (B) RF versus $\omega R_L C$.*

15.9 Pi Filter

The most effective filter is the pi filter of Fig. 15–14. Capacitor C_1 provides initial filtering. The ac ripple is then further filtered by inductor (choke) L and capacitor C_2. Inductor L provides a high impedance compared with the impedance of C_2; hence, most of the ripple voltage is dropped across L, and the output is virtually free of ac.

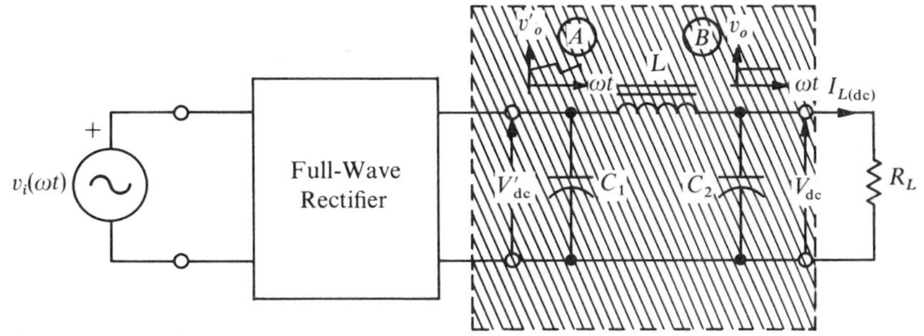

Fig. 15–14. *Full-wave rectifier and pi filter.*

Because of resistance r_L of the inductor winding, the output voltage V_{dc} is less than voltage V'_{dc} at the output of the rectifier. It is expressed by

$$V_{dc} = V'_{dc} - I_{dc}r_L \tag{15–25}$$

Based on Eq. (15–25), one may conclude that r_L should be less than R_L for a high value of V_{dc}. Applying the voltage divider rule to the dc circuit, the dc output voltage also may be expressed by

$$V_{dc} = \frac{V'_{dc}R_L}{R_L + r_L} \tag{15–26}$$

It was pointed out that the impedance of the inductor should be high compared with the impedance of C_2. This implies an inductor having a high value of inductance, since $X_L = \omega L$. The physical size of such an inductor also has to be considered. A sizable inductor with an iron core, called a choke, is usually employed. This makes the pi filter bulky and expensive.

For given values of R_L and ω, the ripple factor in a rectifier with a pi filter is inversely proportional to the product C_1C_2L. It is expressed by

$$RF = \frac{\sqrt{2}}{\omega^3 R_L C_1 C_2 L} \tag{15–27}$$

EXAMPLE 15–10.

For the full-wave rectifier with a pi filter of Fig. 15–14, the following component values are used: $L = 6.8\,\text{H}$, $r_L = 20\,\Omega$, $C_1 = 20\,\mu\text{F}$, $C_2 = 40\,\mu\text{F}$, and $R_L = 1000\,\Omega$.

Find

(a) The dc output if $V'_{dc} = 80\,\text{V}$.

(b) The ripple factor.

The line frequency is 60 Hz.

Solutions:

(a) By Eq. (15–26),

$$V_{dc} = \frac{80 \times 1000}{1000 + 20} = 78.5\,\text{V}$$

(b) Substitution of the component values in Eq. (15–27) yields

$$RF = \frac{\sqrt{2}}{377^3 \times 10^3 \times 20 \times 10^{-6} \times 40 \times 10^{-4} \times 6.8} = 0.0048$$

which corresponds to a $\%RF$ of 0.48%.

15.10 *RC* Filter

The *RC* filter illustrated in Fig. 15–15 is a modification of the pi filter. Inductor L has been replaced by resistor R. The function of resistor R is to oppose the flow of ac. Its value must be greater than the value of X_{C_2} to be effective. The dc output voltage suffers because of an appreciable voltage drop across R. It is given by

$$V_{dc} = \frac{V'_{dc} R_L}{R_L + R} \tag{15–28}$$

The *RC* filter cannot be used with heavy loading because R_L must be much greater than R. Otherwise, the dc output is reduced significantly.

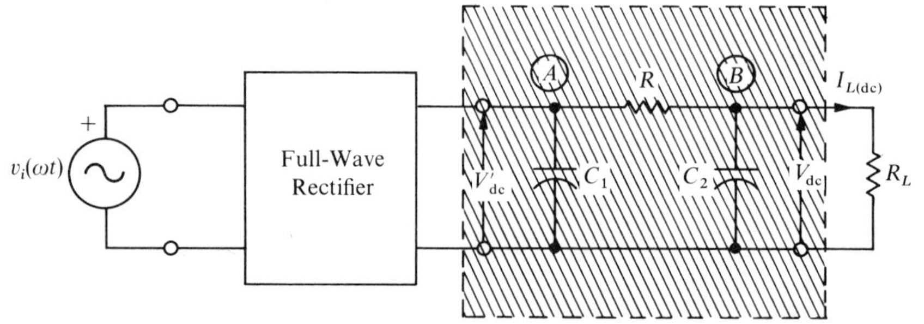

Fig. 15–15. *Full-wave rectifier and RC filter.*

15.11 Peak Diode Currents

The filters considered thus far rely on a shunt capacitor for primary filtering. The diodes in the rectifier for this type of filter conduct only during the time the capacitor is charging. A plot of current in the diode for a half-wave rectifier is shown in Fig. 15–16. Angle α is called the *conduction angle,* indicating the interval over which the diode conducts.

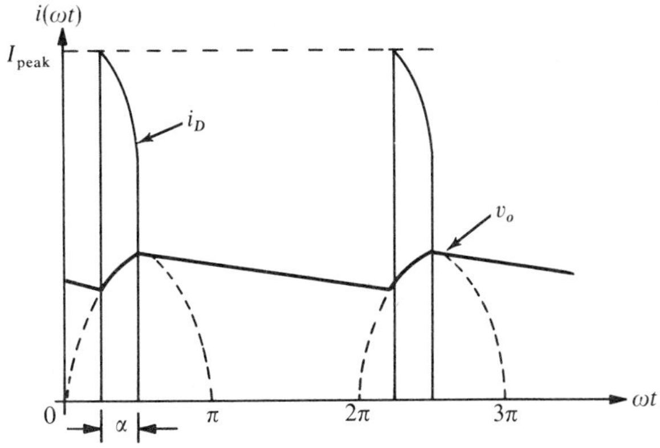

Fig. 15–16. *Diode conduction with a shunt-capacitance filter.*

When the diode is nonconducting, the capacitor becomes the sole supplier of current to the load. The shorter the conduction angle, the higher is the current in the diode. This is true because the average current flowing in the diode remains the same, regardless of the conduction angle.

The higher the value of C, the shorter is the conduction angle. This results in *high peak currents* in the diode. Essentially, the lower the ripple factor, the higher is the peak current. When selecting a rectifier, therefore, we must make sure that the peak, as well as the average current rating, is not exceeded.

15.12 *L*-Section Filter

The filter circuit known as the *L-section filter* is illustrated in Fig. 15–17. It overcomes the problems of high peak current in the diode associated with a shunt-capacitance filter. The diodes conduct continuously when the value of L is properly selected for an L-section (*choke-input*) filter.

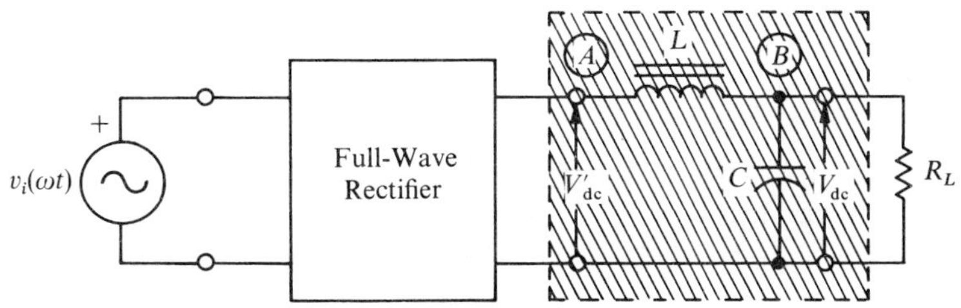

Fig. 15–17. *Full-wave rectifier and L-section (choke-input) filter.*

Continuous conduction is ensured if the following relationship is satisfied:

$$L \geqslant \frac{R_L}{3\omega} \qquad \textbf{(15–29a)}$$

For a line frequency of 60 Hz,

$$L \geqslant \frac{R_L}{1130} \qquad \textbf{(15–29b)}$$

The L-section filter is frequently used with high-load current circuits. It is, however, not convenient to use with a half-wave rectifier.

15.13 Voltage Multiplier

Some applications require a high dc voltage with extremely light loading. A *voltage multiplier* may be used in such applications. The circuit is capable of delivering a dc output that is equal to several times the peak transformer voltage. For example, the *voltage doubler* of Fig. 15–18A provides a dc output equal to $2V_{s(\max)}$.

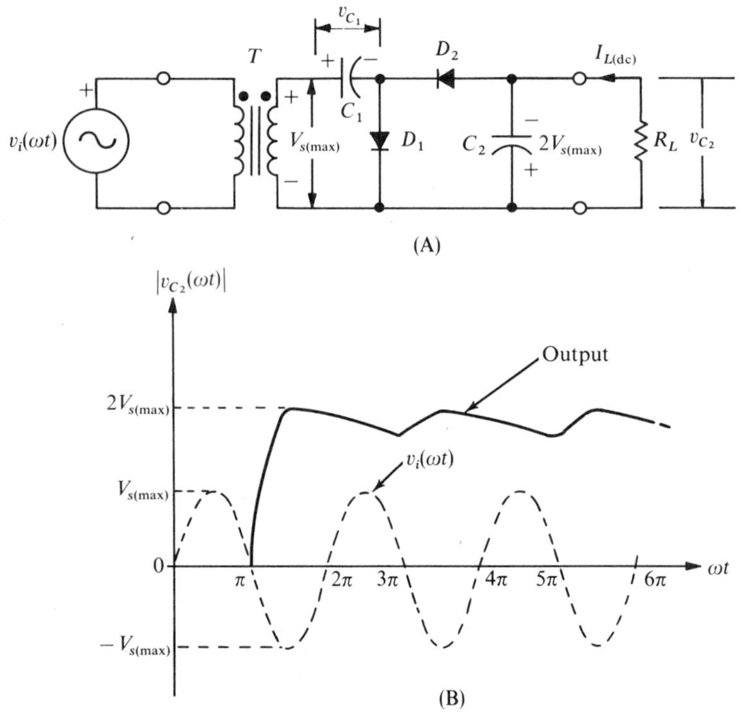

Fig. 15–18. *Voltage doubler. (A) Basic circuit. (B) Output and input waveforms.*

In Fig. 15–18B, during the positive half-cycle ($0 \leqslant \omega t \leqslant \pi$), D_1 is ON, and D_2 is OFF. Current flows through C_1 and charges rapidly to $V_{s(\max)}$ volts, with the indicated polarity. During the negative half-cycle ($\pi \leqslant \omega t \leqslant 2\pi$), D_1 is OFF, and D_2 is ON. Capacitor C_2 is now charged to V_{C_2} volts:

$$V_{C_2} = V_{C_1} + V_{s(\max)} \qquad \textbf{(15–30a)}$$

Because $V_{C_1} = V_{s(\max)}$,

$$V_{C_2} = V_{s(\max)} + V_{s(\max)} = 2V_{s(\max)} \qquad \textbf{(15–30b)}$$

During the next positive half-cycle ($2\pi \leqslant \omega t \leqslant 3\pi$), C_2 discharges through R_L; C_1, however, remains charged. In the following negative half-cycle ($3\pi \leqslant \omega t \leqslant 4\pi$), C_2 recharges to the value of $2V_{s(\max)}$. The lighter the load, the smoother is the output waveform.

The addition of diode-capacitor sections in Fig. 15–18A results in a voltage multiplier which is greater than two. In this circuit, the output is equal to the number of sections multiplied by $V_{s(\max)}$ (see Fig. 15–19). The output is equal to $6V_{s(\max)}$, and the multiplier is a *sextupler*.

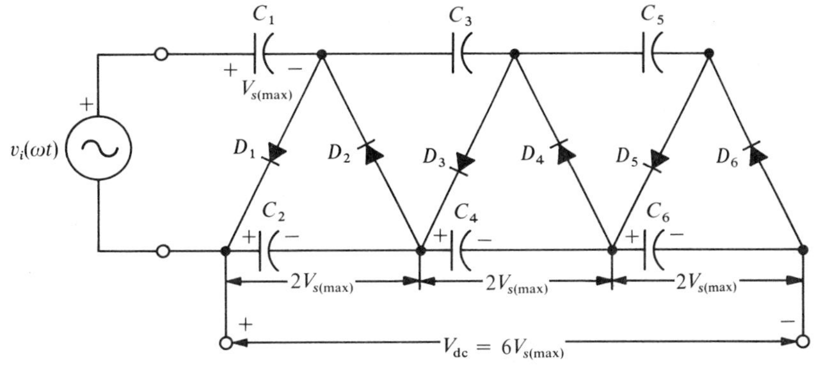

Fig. 15–19. *Voltage sextupler.*

SUMMARY

Three important rectifier circuits for converting ac to a unidirectional dc are the half-wave, full-wave, and bridge rectifiers. The full-wave and bridge rectifiers yield twice the dc output of a half-wave circuit. Whereas a bridge rectifier has no center-tapped transformer, it requires four, instead of two, diodes used in a center-tapped transformer full-wave rectifier.

Filters are necessary to "smooth out" the unidirectional dc. Commonly used filters include the shunt-capacitance, pi, *RC*, and *L*-section types. The capacitor-type filter may be used where the load current is low. In other applications, the pi, *L*-section, and occasionally the *RC*, filters are used.

By employing a voltage multiplier circuit, we can obtain a dc voltage that is a multiple of the maximum secondary winding voltage. Examples of voltage multipliers are the doubler and sextupler. These circuits, however, are generally effective for extremely low values of load current.

Further Reading

Boylestad, R. L., and L. Nashelsky. *Electronic Devices and Circuit Theory*. Englewood Cliffs, N.J.: Prentice-Hall, 1972, Chapter 2.

Cirovic, Michael. *Basic Electronics: Devices, Circuits, and Systems.* Reston, Va.: Reston Publishing Company, 1974, Chapter 8.

Cooper, William D. *Solid State Devices: Analysis and Applications.* Reston, Va.: Reston Publishing Company, 1974, Chapter 7.

Kaufman, M., and A. H. Seidman, eds. *Handbook for Electronics Engineering Technicians.* New York: McGraw-Hill Book Company, 1976, Chapter 16.

Manera, Anthony S. *Solid State Electronic Circuits for Engineering Technology.* New York: McGraw-Hill Book Company, 1973, Chapter 3.

Pierce, J. F., and T. J. Paulus. *Applied Electronics.* Columbus, Ohio: Charles E. Merrill Publishing Company, 1972, Chapter 2.

REVIEW QUESTIONS

15.1 What is the principal circuit element used in rectifiers?

15.2 What type of output waveform is obtained when rectifying an ac signal?

15.3 What is the purpose of a transformer at the input of a rectifier?

15.4 Which type of rectifier, half-wave or full-wave, delivers a higher dc output for the same ac input voltage?

15.5 Identify the major characteristics of rectifier diodes.

15.6 Define ripple factor.

15.7 Which type of rectifier has the highest efficiency?

15.8 Which is more desirable, a low- or a high-percent load regulation? Why?

15.9 When a shunt-capacitance filter is used, which will result in a lower ripple factor, light or heavy loading? Why?

15.10 What limits the maximum value of C in a shunt-capacitor filter?

15.11 How does the resistance of a diode in a pi filter affect the dc output of a power supply?

15.12 Describe under what conditions an L-section filter is used.

15.13 Why is an RC filter inferior to a pi filter?

15.14 What is the chief drawback of a voltage multiplier?

15.15 What will be the effect of shorting out diode D_2 in the circuit of Fig. 15–5A? Why?

15.16 What will be the effect of reversing diode D_2 in the circuit of Fig. 15–5A. Why?

15.17 What is the output voltage of the voltage doubler of Fig. 15–18A with diode D_1 open?

15.18 Why is there no need for a center-tapped transformer in a full-wave bridge rectifier?

PROBLEMS

P15–1 For the circuit of Fig. 15–1A, calculate the dc output voltage if the input is 117 V rms. Assume that the diode is ideal.

P15–2 Repeat prob. P15–1 for an input voltage of 220 V rms.

P15–3 Calculate the average load current for the half-wave rectifier in prob. P15–1 for an $R_L = 100\,\Omega$.

P15–4 The output of the half-wave rectifier of Fig. 15–3 is measured to be 50 V dc.
(a) What is the secondary rms voltage?
(b) Calculate the transformer ratio for a 28-V-rms input.

P15–5 Repeat prob. P15–4 if the measured dc voltage is 30 V.

P15–6 Determine the PIV rating for the diode in prob. P15–4.

P15–7 The input voltage to the full-wave rectifier of Fig. 15–4A is 117 V rms. The transformer turns ratio is 1:2. Calculate
(a) The maximum value of the secondary voltage with respect to the center tap.
(b) The dc output voltage.

P15–8 Repeat prob. P15–7 for a transformer turns ratio of 2:1.

P15–9 (a) Design a center-tapped full-wave rectifier to deliver 100 V and 1 A dc to a load. The line voltage is 117 V rms.
(b) What is the PIV of the diodes?

P15–10 Repeat prob. P15–9 for a 12-V, 5-A dc supply.

P15–11 Design a full-wave bridge rectifier to meet the specifications given in prob. P15–9.

P15–12 Calculate the input power to the rectifier in prob. P15–9.

P15–13 A power supply employing a bridge rectifier and a shunt-capacitance filter has a transformer secondary voltage of 50 V rms. The line frequency is 60 Hz. Capacitance $C = 100\,\mu F$, and $R_L = 500\,\Omega$. Calculate
(a) V_{dc}.
(b) I_{dc}.
(c) $\%RF$.

P15–14 Repeat prob. P15–13 for a line frequency of 400 Hz.

P15–15 Calculate the $\%LR$ in prob. P15–13.

P15–16 To what should the capacitor value be changed for a $\%RF = 1$ percent in prob. P15–13?

P15–17 Employing the curves of Fig. 15–13, design a half-wave rectifier, shunt-capacitance filter power supply to deliver 10 V, 1 A dc. The $\%RF$ should be less than 5 percent. The line voltage is 117 V rms at 60 Hz.

P15–18 Repeat prob. P15–17 for a $\%RF$ less than 3 percent.

P15–19 Using the curves of Fig. 15–13, design a power supply employing a bridge rectifier to power a 12-V car tape deck from household current. The maximum load current is 3 A, and $\%RF$ should not exceed 3 percent.

P15–20 Repeat prob. P15–19 for a maximum load current of 5 A.

P15–21 In the pi filter of Fig. 15–14, $C_1 = 10\,\mu F$, $C_2 = 20\,\mu F$, $R_L = 1\,k\Omega$, and the line frequency is 60 Hz. Determine the value of L for $\%RF = 1$ percent.

P15–22 Repeat prob. P15–21 for a 400-Hz line frequency.

P15–23 If in prob. P15–21, $V'_{dc} = 100\,\text{V}$ and $r_L = 50\,\Omega$, what is the value of V_{dc}?

P15–24 In Fig. 15–15, $C_1 = 20\,\mu\text{F}$, $C_2 = 40\,\mu\text{F}$, $R = 100\,\Omega$, and $R_L = 1\,\text{k}\Omega$. The line frequency is 60 Hz. Calculate $\%RF$.

P15–25 Repeat prob. P15–24 for a line frequency of 400 Hz.

P15–26 For the circuit in prob. P15–24, solve for the $\%RF$ assuming that resistor R is shorted out.

P15–27 Calculate the minimum value of L in the L-section filter of Fig. 15–17 for a dc output of 1000 V at 10 A. The line frequency is 60 Hz.

P15–28 Repeat prob. P15–27 for a line frequency of 400 Hz.

P15–29 Draw a schematic diagram of a voltage quadrupler. Indicate the voltage drop across each capacitor.

16

Regulated Power Supplies

To improve the performance of dc power supplies, a *regulator circuit* is inserted between the output terminals of the filtered rectifier and the load. The task of the regulator is to maintain a constant dc output which is unaffected by variations in load current or in line voltage.

Different types of regulators and their applications will be considered in this chapter. They include the simple zener diode, and feedback regulators in discrete and integrated form. We shall also consider regulators featuring short-circuit and overload protection.

16.1 Zener Diode Regulator

The zener diode (see Chapter 4) operates on the principle of reverse breakdown. When a zener diode breaks down in the reverse direction, the voltage across it remains nearly constant for a wide range of zener current. This property of nearly constant voltage makes the zener diode a key element in voltage regulators.

Zener diodes are commercially available in a large variety of zener voltage and power ratings. The voltage-current characteristic of a typical zener diode is shown in Fig. 16–1. This particular device has a zener voltage, V_Z, of 5.6 V. The zener voltage is usually specified at a given

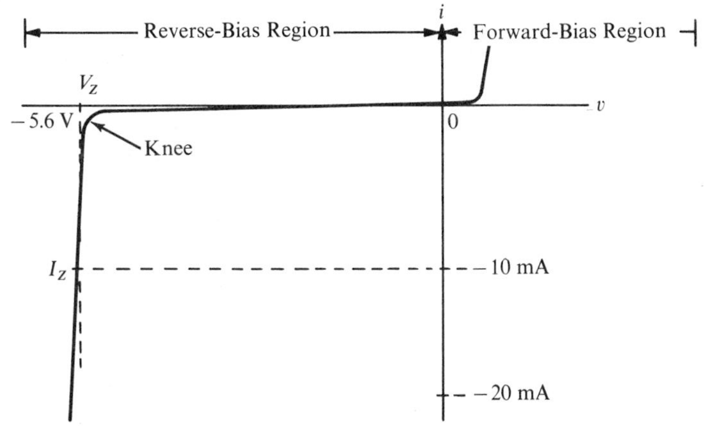

Fig. 16–1. *Voltage-current characteristic of a typical zener diode.*

value of zener current, I_Z. In Fig. 16–1, $V_Z = 5.6\,V$ at $I_Z = 10\,mA$. The characteristic indicates that the diode voltage changes slightly with variations in I_Z. For stable operation, the operating point is kept below the knee of the curve.

A zener diode rated at approximately $V_Z = 6\,V$ has a near-zero temperature coefficient. It has a positive temperature coefficient for $V_Z > 6\,V$, and a negative temperature coefficient for $V_Z < 6\,V$. Temperature compensation may be incorporated in a zener circuit by connecting a zener and junction diode back to back (opposing). Assume both diodes have the same temperature coefficient. When the voltage across the zener diode changes because of temperature, a similar change in voltage occurs across the junction diode. Because they are connected back to back, the voltage changes cancel each other.

The circuit of Fig. 16–2 is a simple regulator that maintains a nearly constant output for a range of variations in R_L and V_i. Resistance R is connected in series with, and the zener diode across, load resistance R_L. Load voltage, V_o, is

$$V_o = V_i - IR \tag{16–1}$$

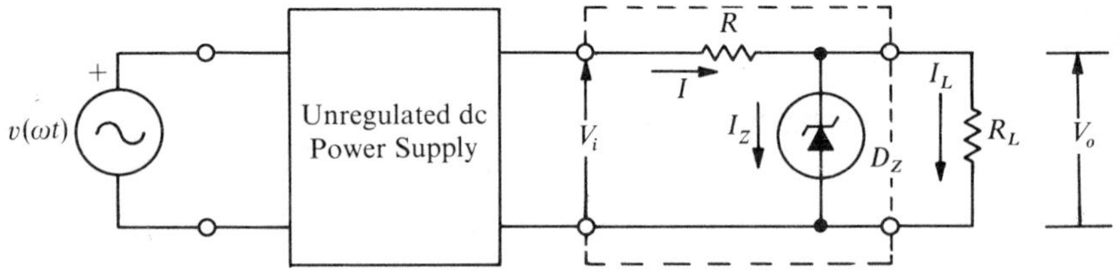

Fig. 16–2. *dc power supply with zener diode regulator.*

where I is the current in R and V_i is the output voltage of the unregulated supply. At breakdown, zener current I_Z flows, and the output is maintained at approximately V_Z volts:

$$V_o \simeq V_Z \tag{16–2}$$

The circuit is analyzed for two cases: (1) Input V_i to the regulator varies and (2) load R_L changes in value.

(1) V_i Varies

Rearranging Eq. (16–1), we see that

$$IR = V_i - V_o$$

Substitution of $V_o = V_Z$ in the expression yields

$$IR = V_i - V_Z \tag{16–3}$$

Equation (16–3) shows that if input voltage, V_i, varies within limits where V_Z remains constant, the voltage across R (IR) varies to compensate for the change. The output is taken across the zener diode and is approximately equal to V_Z volts.

From the aspect of current flow, for I_L to remain constant, the zener current must vary if I varies:

$$I = I_Z + I_L \qquad \textbf{(16–4)}$$

This is precisely the zener diode action occurring in a regulator circuit. The output voltage stays constant because of a constant V_Z, while I_Z varies. The voltage across R varies with changes in the input.

If V_i is not sufficiently high to break down the zener diode, regulation is not obtained. The output voltage, then, is, by voltage division,

$$V_o = \frac{V_i R_L}{R_L + R} \qquad \textbf{(16–5)}$$

The diode has no effect in the circuit.

(2) R_L Varies

Assume that V_i is constant and that the value of R_L is changing. Load current, I_L, must change for a constant voltage to be present; that is,

$$I_L = \frac{V_Z}{R_L} \qquad \textbf{(16–6)}$$

The output remains essentially constant as long as the relationship $I > I_L$ holds. If the load current demands are such that $I_L \geqslant I$, then no current flows in the zener diode. Regulation ceases, and the output voltage becomes a function of the voltage divider network of R and R_L, as expressed by Eq. (16–5). The following examples illustrate the two cases discussed.

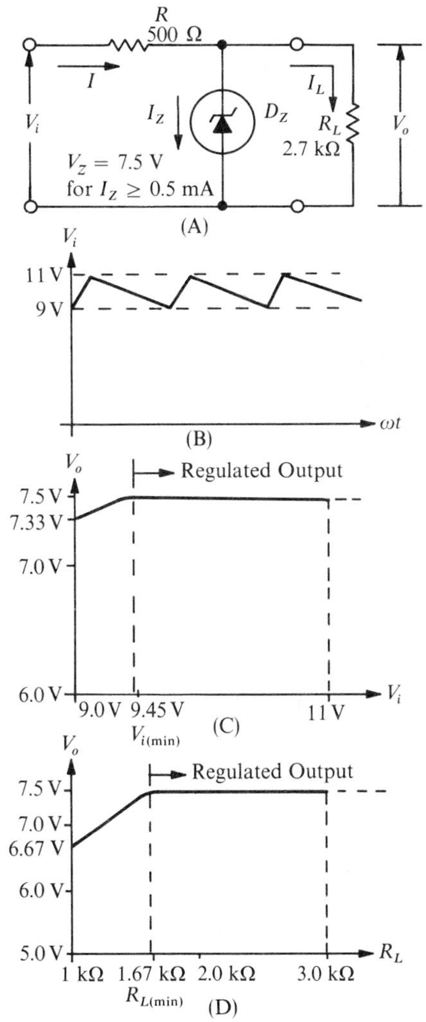

Fig. 16–3. *(A) Circuit for Examples 16–1 and 16–2. (B) Regulator input waveform. (C) Output voltage versus changes in input voltage for Example 16–1. (D) Output voltage versus load resistance for Example 16–2.*

EXAMPLE 16–1.

The input to the zener regulator of Fig. 16–3A fluctuates from 9 V to 11 V as indicated in Fig. 16–3B. Plot a graph of V_o as a function of V_i.

Solution:

The circuit is analyzed for the two extremes of V_i: 9 V and 11 V, respectively. Assume that the zener diode is conducting for $V_i = 11$ V. Then, $V_o \simeq V_Z = 7.5$ V, and by Eq. (16–3),

$$IR = 11 - 7.5 = 3.5\,\text{V}$$

and

$$I = \frac{3.5}{500} = 7\,\text{mA}$$

Load current, I_L, is

$$I_L = \frac{V_Z}{R_L}$$

$$= \frac{7.5}{2.2} = 3.41\,\text{mA}$$

Substituting the preceding results in Eq. (16–4),

$$I_Z = 7 - 3.41 = 3.59\,\text{mA}$$

A zener current of 3.59 mA ensures a zener voltage, $V_Z = 7.5\,\text{V}$. The assumption that the zener diode conducts for $V_i = 11\,\text{V}$ is therefore verified.

For $V_i = 9\,\text{V}$, the assumption again is made that $V_o \simeq V_Z = 7.5\,\text{V}$. Hence,

$$I = \frac{9 - 7.5}{500} = 3\,\text{mA}$$

Load current, I_L, is still 3.41 mA because R_L and V_o have not changed. Hence,

$$I_Z = 3 - 3.41 = -0.41\,\text{mA}$$

The zener current is negative, which is impossible. Physically, no current flows in the zener diode. The diode is nonconducting and therefore not contributing to the circuit. In this case, the assumption that the output voltage is also 7.5 V for $V_i = 9\,\text{V}$ is incorrect. By Eq. (16–5),

$$V_o = \frac{9 \times 2.2}{2.2 + 0.5} = 7.33\,\text{V}$$

The circuit with the given component values is incapable of regulating fully as the input varies from 9 V to 11 V.

The point at which full regulation begins is now calculated. To avoid operation at the knee, for the diode in this example, $I_Z \geqslant 0.5\,\text{mA}$. Hence, for proper regulation,

$$I \geqslant I_L + 0.5\,\text{mA}$$

and

$$I \geqslant 3.41 + 0.5 = 3.91\,\text{mA}$$

The voltage across R, V_R, is

$$V_R = 3.91 \times 0.5 = 1.95\,\text{V}$$

The minimum input voltage at which regulation occurs, $V_{i(\text{min})}$, is

$$\begin{aligned} V_{i(\text{min})} &= V_o + V_R \\ &= 7.5 + 1.95 = 9.45\,\text{V} \end{aligned}$$

For values of $V_i \geqslant 9.45\,\text{V}$, there is sufficient voltage for zener breakdown, and the output equals 7.5 V. (The upper limit on V_i is imposed by the maximum power dissipation rating of the zener diode.)

A plot of V_o versus V_i is given in Fig. 16–3C. Regulation is obtained for $9.45\,\text{V} \leqslant V_i \leqslant 11\,\text{V}$.

EXAMPLE 16–2.

For the circuit in Fig. 16–3A, assume a constant input voltage of 10 V and a varying load of $1\,\text{k}\Omega \leqslant R_L \leqslant 3\,\text{k}\Omega$. Plot a graph of V_o versus R_L.

Solution:

We shall use the same approach as in Example 16–1. In this example, however, the circuit is analyzed at both extremes of R_L, instead of V_i.

For $R_L = 3\,\text{k}\Omega$, assume $V_o \simeq V_Z = 7.5\,\text{V}$; hence,

$$I_L = \frac{7.5}{3} = 2.5\,\text{mA}$$

and

$$V_R = IR = V_i - V_o$$
$$= 10 - 7.5 = 2.5\,\text{V}$$

Hence,

$$I = \frac{2.5}{500} = 5\,\text{mA}$$

and

$$I_Z = 5 - 2.5 = 2.5\,\text{mA}$$

Clearly, the zener diode conducts, and $V_o \simeq V_Z = 7.5\,\text{V}$, confirming our assumption.

For $R_L = 1\,\text{k}\Omega$, assume again that $V_o \simeq V_Z$. The load current is now equal to

$$I_L = \frac{7.5}{1} = 7.5\,\text{mA}$$

Because I does not change (V_i is constant),

$$I_Z = I - I_L$$
$$= 5 - 7.5 = -2.5\,\text{mA}$$

The preceding calculation shows that I_Z is negative. Since this is physically impossible, the zener diode is cut off, and V_o, by Eq. (16–5), is

$$V_o = \frac{10 \times 1}{1 + 0.5} = 6.67\,\text{V}$$

We now find the minimum value of R_L, $R_{L(\text{min})}$, for which the zener diode regulates the output. Current I remains constant at 5 mA as long as the zener diode is conducting. With a minimum zener current of 0.5 mA,

$$I_{L(\text{max})} = I - I_{Z(\text{min})}$$
$$= 5 - 0.5 = 4.5\,\text{mA}$$

The load current cannot exceed 4.5 mA. For an output of 7.5 V,

$$R_{L(\text{min})} = \frac{V_Z}{I_{L(\text{max})}}$$
$$= \frac{7.5}{4.5} = 1.67\,\text{k}\Omega$$

In conclusion, the minimum value of R_L is 1.67 kΩ. A plot of V_o versus R_L is given in Fig. 16–3D.

Several disadvantages inherent in the simple zener diode regulator became apparent in the preceding examples. When loading was increased (R_L decreased to a minimum value), regulation ceased. The output voltage also is always less than the input. This results in a voltage drop across R and wasted power.

To overcome the first disadvantage, an op amp connected as a voltage follower is used to isolate the load from the remaining circuit (Fig. 16–4). Owing to the high input and low output impedance of the voltage follower, the zener regulator is virtually independent of R_L. The output voltage is still equal to approximately V_Z volts because a voltage follower has unity gain.

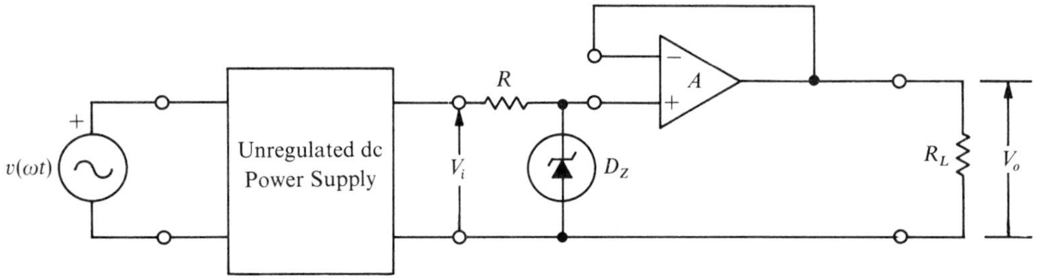

Fig. 16–4. *Zener voltage regulator with an op-amp voltage follower.*

16.2 Feedback Regulators

Voltage regulation can be improved significantly over the simple zener regulator by using feedback. A block diagram of a feedback voltage regulator is given in Fig. 16–5. The controlling element is generally a transistor, called the *pass element*. In a feedback regulator, the dc output is compared continuously by the *comparator* with respect to a *reference*

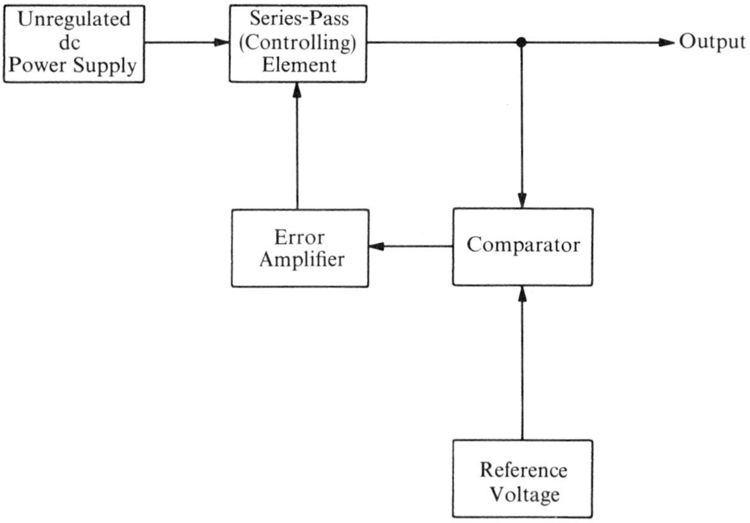

Fig. 16–5. *Block diagram of a series-type voltage regulator.*

voltage. Any difference is amplified by the *error amplifier* and returned to the pass element.

Feedback regulators are classified by the location of the pass element in the circuit with respect to the load. They are either *series*-, or *shunt-type regulators*. In the series regulator, the pass element, which is a transistor, is connected in series with the load. In a shunt regulator, the pass element is connected in parallel (shunt) with the load. Because it is less efficient in most applications, the shunt regulator is less used than the series type.

When the pass transistor operates in the linear mode (*between* cutoff and saturation), the regulator is called a *linear voltage regulator*. If the transistor operates in its switching mode (*at* cutoff and saturation), the circuit is called a *switching voltage regulator*. Some switching regulators employ an SCR as the control element.

16.3 Series Voltage Regulator

A series voltage regulator is illustrated in Fig. 16–6. In the circuit, transistor Q_1 is the control (pass) element, and Q_2 serves as the comparator and error amplifier. Zener diode D_Z provides the reference voltage. The voltage monitoring network, composed of resistors R_3 and R_4, is adjusted by the potentiometer for the desired output voltage over the operating range of the regulator.

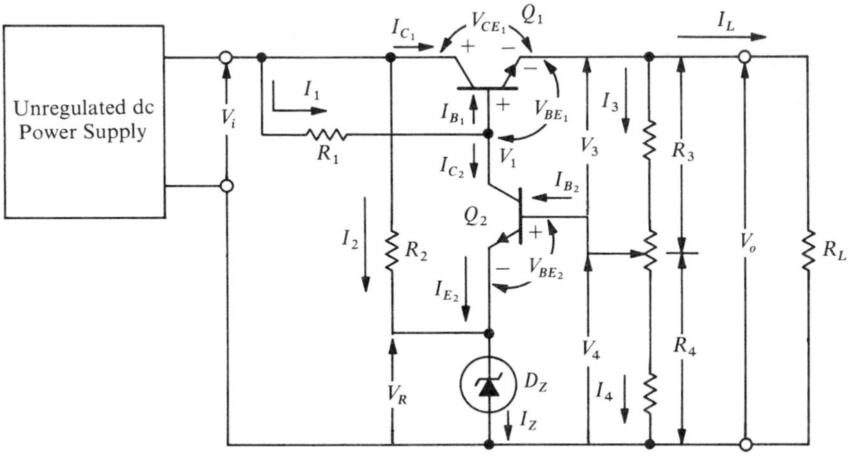

Fig. 16–6. *Series-type voltage regulator.*

The voltage of the monitoring network, V_4, is adjusted to

$$V_4 = \frac{V_o R_4}{R_3 + R_4} \tag{16–7a}$$

Another expression for V_4 is

$$V_4 = V_{BE_2} + V_R \tag{16–7b}$$

where V_R is the voltage across the zener diode.

The output voltage of the regulator is given by

$$V_o = V_R + V_{BE_2} + V_3$$

Because $V_3 = V_oR_3/(R_3 + R_4)$,

$$V_o = V_R + V_{BE_2} + \frac{V_oR_3}{R_3 + R_4} \qquad \textbf{(16–8)}$$

Solving Eq. (16–8) for V_o,

$$V_o = (V_R + V_{BE_2})\left(1 + \frac{R_3}{R_4}\right) \qquad \textbf{(16–9)}$$

Equation (16–9) shows that the output voltage is essentially a function of the reference voltage and the monitoring network. A variation in the potentiometer setting changes the output level. Similarly, by Eq. (16–7b), a change in the output voltage affects the value of V_4 and V_{BE_2}, since V_R is constant.

Examining the effect of the control element on the output, from Fig. 16–6,

$$V_o = V_i - V_{CE_1} \qquad \textbf{(16–10)}$$

where V_{CE_1} is the collector-emitter voltage of Q_1. The output varies with changes in V_{CE_1}. The value of V_{CE_1}, however, depends on I_{B_1}. Base current I_{B_1} is equal to the difference in I_1 and I_{C_2}:

$$I_{B_1} = I_1 - I_{C_2} \qquad \textbf{(16–11)}$$

Because I_{B_1} is a function of I_{C_2}, V_{CE_1} and V_o vary with changes in the collector current of Q_2. Continuing with the same line of reasoning, we see that I_{C_2} is controlled by I_{B_2}. Changes in I_{B_2} stem from changes in V_o, which is sensed across R_4. We can therefore state that a change in the output voltage is transferred to, and amplified by, Q_2. The resulting change in V_{CE_1} acts to return V_o to its original level.

We consider two cases: (1) an increase and (2) a decrease in output voltage.

(1) V_o Increases

The output voltage may tend to rise because of an increase in V_i and/or an increase in R_L. Voltage V_4 will also rise, causing an increase in V_{BE_2}. Collector current I_{C_2} and collector-emitter voltage V_{CE_1} increase. The output voltage is reduced to its nominal value.

(2) V_o Decreases

In this case, V_{BE_2} drops, reducing I_{C_2}. Base current I_{B_1} increases, forcing I_{C_1} to rise and V_{CE_1} to decrease. The effect is again to stabilize the output voltage.

For the output to return to its original level, the control circuit must be carefully designed. Transistor Q_1 must operate in its active region to provide linear operation.

Because the load current passes through Q_1, the power dissipated in the series pass transistor can reach high levels. A power transistor is therefore used for Q_1 and is mounted on a heat sink.

EXAMPLE 16–3.

For the regulator of Fig. 16–6,

$$R_1 = 220\,\Omega$$
$$R_2 = 1000\,\Omega$$
$$R_3 = 1050\,\Omega$$
$$R_4 = 2.2\,\text{k}\Omega$$

For Q_1,

$$h_{FE_1} = 30$$
$$I_{C_1(\max)} = 1\,\text{A}$$
$$P_{D_1(\max)} = 5\,\text{W}$$

For Q_2,

$$h_{FE_2} = 100$$
$$I_{C_2(\max)} = 100\,\text{mA}$$
$$P_{D_2(\max)} = 360\,\text{mW}$$

For the zener diode,

$$V_Z = 7.5\,\text{V} \quad \text{at } I_Z = 10\,\text{mA}$$
$$P_{Z(\max)} = 400\,\text{mW}$$

Show that a constant output is maintained for $15\,\text{V} \leqslant V_i \leqslant 20\,\text{V}$ and a 50-Ω load.

Solution:

We begin by considering the lower voltage limit, $V_i = 15\,\text{V}$. Current I_2 flowing in R_2 is

$$I_2 = \frac{V_i - V_R}{R_2}$$
$$= \frac{15 - 7.5}{1} = 7.5\,\text{mA}$$

Because $I_Z = I_2 + I_{E_2}$, we may assume that the zener voltage is maintained at 7.5 V.

Solving for V_4,

$$V_4 = V_R + V_{BE_2}$$
$$= 7.5 + 0.7 = 8.2\,\text{V}$$

and current I_4 is

$$I_4 = I_3 - I_{B_2}$$

If $I_{B_2} \ll I_4$, then

$$I_3 \simeq I_4 = \frac{V_4}{R_4}$$
$$= \frac{8.2}{2.2} = 3.72\,\text{mA}$$

Therefore,

$$\begin{aligned} V_o &= I_4(R_3 + R_4) \\ &= 3.72(1.05 + 2.2) = 12\,\text{V} \end{aligned}$$

and

$$\begin{aligned} I_L &= \frac{V_o}{R_L} \\ &= \frac{12}{50} = 240\,\text{mA} \end{aligned}$$

Collector current I_{C_1} is

$$\begin{aligned} I_{C_1} &= I_3 + I_L \\ &= 3.72 + 240 \simeq 243.7\,\text{mA} \end{aligned}$$

and

$$\begin{aligned} V_{CE_1} &= V_i - V_o \\ &= 15 - 12 = 3\,\text{V} \end{aligned}$$

The dissipation in Q_1 is

$$P_{D(Q_1)} = 3 \times 243.7 = 0.73\,\text{W}$$

The maximum ratings of Q_1 have not been exceeded: 243.7 mA is less than 1 A, and 0.73 W is less than 5 W.

Base current I_{B_1} is

$$\begin{aligned} I_{B_1} &= \frac{I_{C_1}}{h_{FE_1}} \\ &= \frac{243.7}{30} = 8.1\,\text{mA} \end{aligned}$$

The voltage at the base of Q_1 with respect to ground is

$$\begin{aligned} V_{B_1} &= V_{BE_1} + V_o \\ &= 0.7 + 12 = 12.7\,\text{V} \end{aligned}$$

Then,

$$\begin{aligned} I_1 &= \frac{V_i - V_{B_1}}{R_1} \\ &= \frac{15 - 12.7}{220} = 10.4\,\text{mA} \end{aligned}$$

By Eq. (16–11),

$$\begin{aligned} I_{C_2} &= I_1 - I_{B_1} \\ &= 10.4 - 8.1 = 2.3\,\text{mA} \end{aligned}$$

The zener current can now be calculated:

$$I_Z = I_2 + I_{E_2}$$

Because $I_{E_2} \simeq I_{C_2}$,

$$I_Z = 7.5 + 2.3 = 9.8\,\text{mA}$$

The power dissipated in the zener diode is

$$P_Z = 9.8 \times 7.5 = 73.5\,\text{mW}$$

which is well within its maximum rating.

Solving for I_{B_2},

$$I_{B_2} = \frac{I_{C_2}}{h_{FE_2}}$$
$$= \frac{2.3}{100} = 23\,\mu\text{A}$$

The initial assumption of $I_{B_2} \ll I_4$ is valid.

If the output is to remain constant at 12 V when $V_i =$ 20 V, then the following must be true:

$$V_{CE_1} = 20 - 12 = 8\text{ V}$$

and

$$I_1 = \frac{20 - 12.7}{220} = 33.1\text{ mA}$$

Because the load is still the same, I_{C_1} remains almost constant at 243.7 mA.

The maximum dissipated power in Q_1 is

$$P_{D(\text{max})} = 8 \times 243.7 = 1.95\text{ W}$$

which is within its maximum rating of 5 W. Current I_2 is

$$I_2 = \frac{20 - 7.5}{1} = 12.5\text{ mA}$$

The zener current is now

$$I_Z = 12.5 + I_{C_2}$$

Collector current I_{C_2} is equal to the difference in I_1 and I_{B_1}:

$$I_{C_2} = 33.1 - 8.1 = 25\text{ mA}$$

and

$$I_Z = 12.5 + 25 = 37.5\text{ mA}$$

Also,

$$P_Z = 7.5 \times 37.5 = 282\text{ mW}$$

which is within its maximum rating. Base current I_{B_2} is

$$I_{B_2} = \frac{25}{100} = 250\,\mu\text{A}$$

Note that I_{B_2} has changed, forcing an increase in I_{C_2}. The change in I_{B_2} stems from a slight change in the output sensed by the monitoring network, R_3 and R_4.

EXAMPLE 16–4.

For what value of V_i does the regulator of Example 16–3 becomes ineffective?

Solution:

A few factors which are critical in the operation of the regulator became apparent in Example 16–3. The power dissipated in Q_1 rose as V_i increased. Hence, a critical value of V_i forces the power dissipated in Q_1 to exceed its maximum rating.

The maximum value of V_{CE1}, $V_{CE1(max)}$, is

$$V_{CE1(max)} = \frac{P_{D1(max)}}{I_L} = \frac{5}{0.24} = 20.8\text{ V}$$

and the corresponding critical input voltage, $V_{i(CR)}$, is

$$V_{i(CR)} = V_o + V_{CE1(max)} = 12 + 20.8 = 32.8\text{ V}$$

Zener current, I_Z, also changes with V_i. As a result, P_Z and V_Z vary with the zener current. The maximum zener current is

$$I_{Z(max)} = \frac{P_{Z(max)}}{V_Z} = \frac{400}{7.5} = 53.2\text{ mA}$$

Also,

$$I_{C_2} = I_1 - I_{B_1}$$

and

$$I_1 = \frac{V_i - (V_o + V_{BE_1})}{R_1}$$

$$I_2 = \frac{V_i - V_R}{R_2}$$

The maximum zener current is equal to the sum of I_{C_2} and I_2:

$$I_{Z(max)} = I_{C_2} + I_2$$

Letting the input assume the critical value, $V_{i(CR)}$,

$$I_{Z(max)} = \frac{V_{i(CR)} - (V_o + V_{BE_1})}{R_1} - I_{B_1} + \frac{V_{i(CR)} - V_R}{R_2}$$

Substitution of the values in the preceding equation yields

$$V_{i(CR)} = 22.7\text{ V}$$

An input of 22.7 V or greater causes the zener diode to exceed its dissipation rating of 400 mW.

At the other extreme, when V_i decreases, a point is reached where regulation ceases. This occurs when I_1 is less than $I_{B_1} = 8.1$ mA. For this condition, $I_{1(CR)} = 8.1$ mA. Hence,

$$V_{i(CR)} = I_{1(CR)}R_1 + V_{BE_1} + V_o = 8.1 \times 0.220 + 12.7 = 12.68\text{ V}$$

The regulator in this example is effective only within the range of $12.68 \leqslant V_i \leqslant 22.7\,\text{V}$.

In the next set of examples, the load varies and the input remains constant.

EXAMPLE 16–5.

For the regulator in Example 16–3, assume that the input remains constant at 15 V and the load varies from 40 Ω to 60 Ω. Show that the output is at a constant 12 V.

Solution:

For $R_L = 60\,\Omega$,

$$I_L = \frac{12}{60} = 200\,\text{mA}$$

$$I_{C_1} = I_3 + I_1$$
$$= 3.7 + 200 = 203.7\,\text{mA}$$

$$I_{B_1} = \frac{203}{30} = 6.77\,\text{mA}$$

$$I_1 = \frac{V_i - V_{B_1}}{R_1}$$

$$= \frac{15 - 12.7}{220} = 10.4\,\text{mA}$$

and

$$I_{C_2} = 10.4 - 6.77 = 3.6\,\text{mA}$$

Then,

$$I_{B_2} = \frac{3.6}{100} = 36\,\mu\text{A}$$

$$I_2 = 7.5\,\text{mA}$$

and

$$I_Z = 3.6 + 7.5 = 11.1\,\text{mA}$$

Also,

$$V_{CE_1} = 15 - 12 = 3\,\text{V}$$

For $R_L = 40\,\Omega$,

$$I_L = \frac{12}{40} = 300\,\text{mA}$$

$$I_{C_1} = 300 + 3.7 = 303.7\,\text{mA}$$

and

$$I_{B_1} = \frac{303.7}{30} = 10.1\,\text{mA}$$

Because I_1 is constant at 10.4 mA, we have

$$I_{C_2} = 10.4 - 10.1 = 0.3\,\text{mA}$$

Hence,

$$I_{B_2} = \frac{0.3}{100} = 3\,\mu\text{A}$$

and

$$I_Z = 7.5 + 0.3 = 7.8\,\text{mA}$$

In this example, I_1 is constant. Current I_{C_2} changes because of variations in the output. Base current I_{B_1} is affected by the controlling action of Q_2, which changes I_{C_1}. A change in I_{C_1} affects the load current to restore the nominal value of V_o.

EXAMPLE 16–6.

For what range of values of R_L will the regulator in Example 16–5 be effective?

Solution:

To find the limits of R_L, let us consider the factors that influence the output as R_L changes. As the load current increases, I_{C_1} rises, increasing the power dissipation in Q_1. To accommodate the demands on I_{C_1}, base current I_{B_1} must rise. With I_1 constant, a point is reached at which $I_{B_1} > I_1$. This condition is impossible, and the output is no longer regulated.

For the condition $I_{B_1} = I_1$,

$$I_1 = I_{B_1} \simeq \frac{I_L}{h_{FE_1}}$$

Solving for I_L,

$$I_L = 30 \times 10.4 = 312\,\text{mA}$$

The critical value for R_L, $R_{L(CR)}$, is

$$R_{L(CR)} = \frac{12}{0.312} = 38.3\,\Omega$$

For values of R_L less than $38.3\,\Omega$, V_o is less than 12 V. For higher values of R_L, the output is constant at 12 V.

16.4 An Improved Regulator

The preceding examples demonstrated how a feedback regulator maintains a constant output as V_i and R_L vary. For a correction to occur, a change from the nominal voltage must be sensed at the output. Therefore, the sensitivity and frequency response of the error amplifier are of great importance. Substituting an op amp for the circuit of Q_2 results in a significantly improved regulator (Fig. 16–7).

In the circuit of Fig. 16–6, the collector current of Q_2 had to change significantly with changes in V_i and R_L. To reduce the demands on the op amp output current, and to make the pass transistor more sensitive, a Darlington pair (Q_3, Q_4) is substituted for Q_1 in Fig. 16–7.

To achieve even greater regulation, a true constant current, I_1, in Fig. 16–6 is desirable. To accomplish this, R_1 is replaced by a constant current source called a *preregulator*.

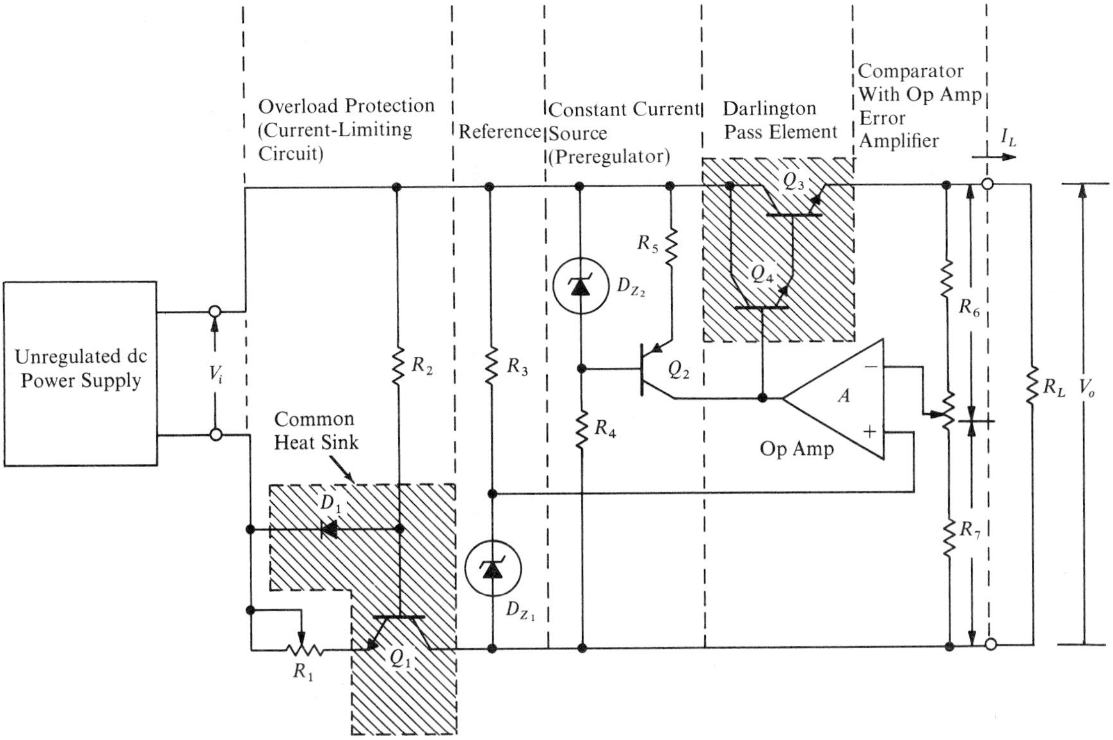

Fig. 16–7. *Improved regulated power supply using an op amp and featuring current-limiting overload protection.*

16.5 Circuit Protection

Protection is included in a regulator to ensure that, when excessive load currents are demanded, the circuit components are not damaged. The series-pass transistor is most vulnerable. In the extreme case, when the output terminals are shorted, $V_{CE_1} = V_i$ and I_{C_1} is at its maximum value. The power dissipated in the transistor becomes much higher than its rated maximum, resulting in damage to the device. A circuit that provides *short-circuit* and *overload protection* is generally included in a regulated power supply.

The simplest type of protection is a fuse in series with the load. Unfortunately, the fuse does not always provide the necessary protection. The thermal time constant of a fuse is, in most cases, longer than that of a transistor. Consequently, the pass transistor is damaged before the fuse disconnects.

An effective overload protection circuit is included in the regulator of Fig. 16–7. The current-limiting circuit operates as follows: During normal operation, transistor Q_1 is saturated and has little effect on the regulator circuit. The value of R_2 is chosen to ensure transistor saturation. Resistor R_1 is preadjusted so that when the regulator is overloaded, the maximum allowable overload current produces sufficient voltage across R_1 to allow D_1 to conduct.

A current in D_1 acts to reduce the base current of Q_1. Transistor Q_1 is brought out of saturation, resulting in a voltage across its collector and emitter greater than the saturation voltage. A reduction in voltage across the series-pass transistor, Q_3, occurs. The power burden is now shared between Q_1 and Q_3. Therefore, Q_1 is also a power transistor. Transistor Q_1 and diode D_1 are mounted on a common heat sink. This ensures that current limiting is not affected by changes in temperature.

The need for an additional power transistor may be avoided in the limiting circuit of Fig. 16–8. Current limiting is realized by adjusting resistor R so when the maximum load current is reached, diode D turns ON. This reduces the current in the series-pass transistor.

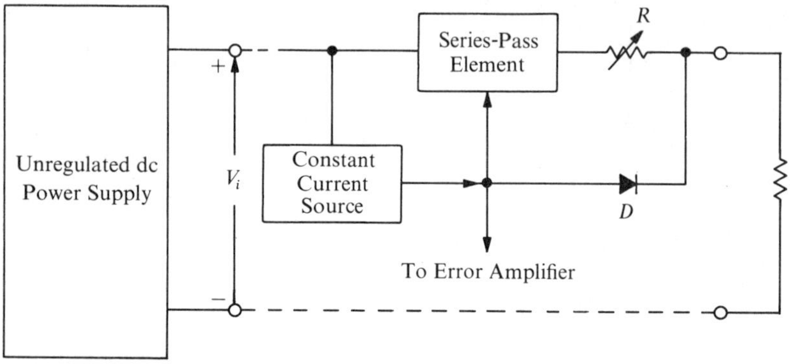

Fig. 16–8. *Another example of a current-limiting protection circuit.*

Foldback current limiting is another method of overload protection. This method is popular with IC voltage regulators and is discussed in the next section.

16.6 IC Voltage Regulators

Voltage regulators are available as monolithic integrated circuits. Monolithic regulators are designed to operate over a wide range of input voltages and tens of amperes of load current (using an external pass transistor). An IC regulator, in addition to the features of the regulator of Fig. 16–7, is of small size and low cost.

An IC regulator is shown in Fig. 16–9A, with its data sheet, supplied by the manufacturer, in Fig. 16–10. The output voltage is adjustable from 2 V to 30 V. The circuit exhibits a 1 percent temperature stability and a better than 1 percent load and line regulation.

Typical applications for the regulator are illustrated in Fig. 16–9B. In the basic regulator circuit (1), the desired output voltage is set by potentiometer R_3. In the other circuits, the output is fixed by the ratio of resistors R_1 and R_2. The basic regulator cannot deliver high load currents. The maximum load current, $I_{L(\max)}$, is

$$I_{L(\max)} = \frac{P_{D(\max)}}{V_o} \qquad \textbf{(16–12)}$$

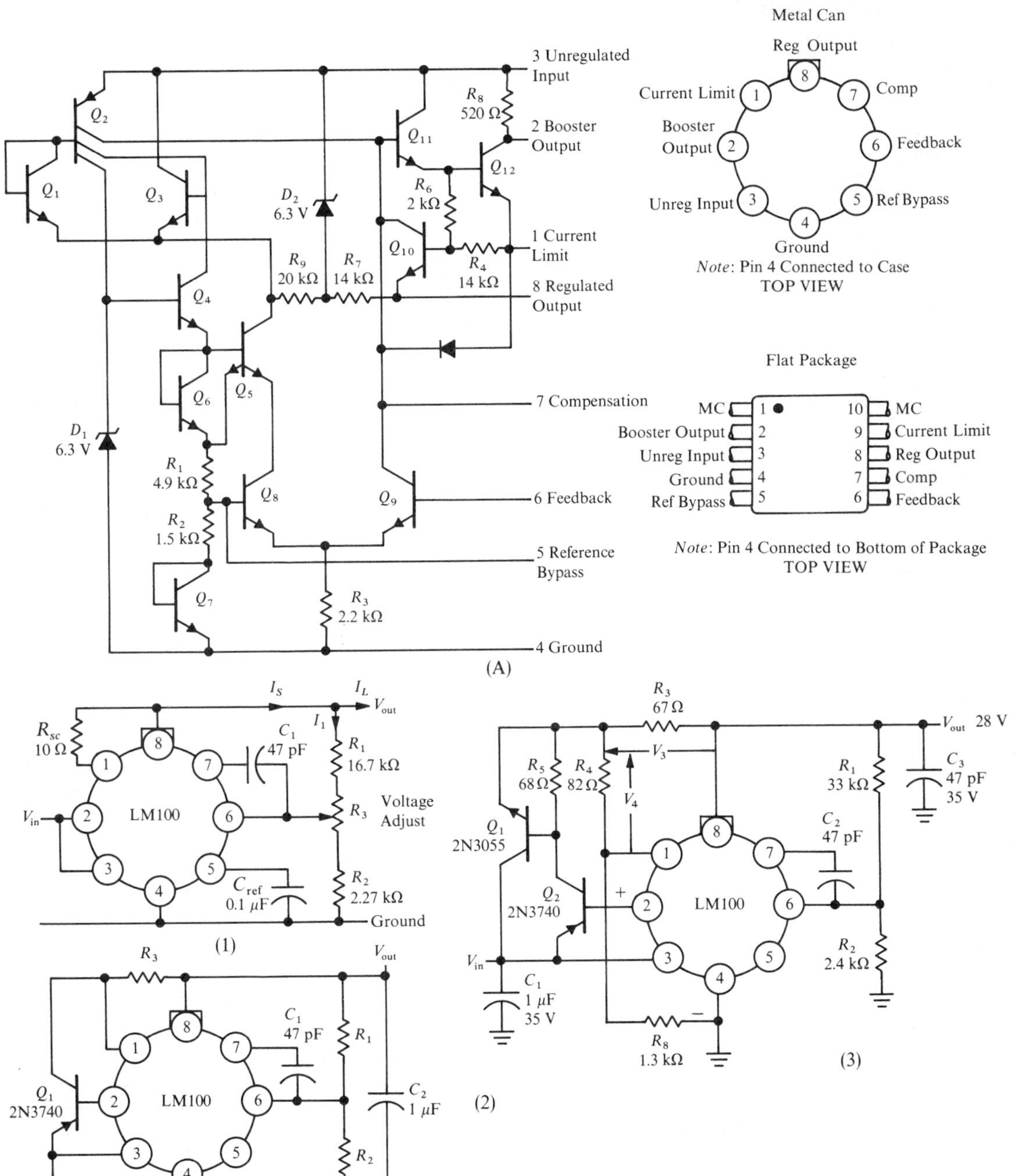

Fig. 16–9. *Example of an integrated circuit voltage regulator. (A) Circuit. (B) Typical applications. (Courtesy National Semiconductor Corp.)*

Because $P_{D(\max)}$ is 800 mW $= 0.8$ W (specified by the manufacturer) for the LM100 and LM200 devices (Fig. 16–10), for $V_o = 12$ V, for example,

$$I_{L(\max)} = \frac{0.8}{12} = 66.5\,\text{mA}$$

External series-pass transistors are added in circuits 2 and 3 for greater load current.

absolute maximum ratings

Input Voltage	
LM100, LM200	40V
LM300	35V
Input-Output Voltage Differential	
LM100, LM200	40V
LM300	30V
Power Dissipation (Note 1)	
LM100, LM200	800 mW
LM300	500 mW
Operating Temperature Range	
LM100, LM200	−55°C to +150°C
LM300	0°C to 70°C
Storage Temperature Range	−65°C to 150°C
Lead Temperature (soldering, 10 sec)	300°C

electrical characteristics (Note 2)

PARAMETER	CONDITIONS	MIN	TYP	MAX	UNITS
Input Voltage Range					
LM100/LM200		8.5		40	V
LM300		8.5		30	
Output Voltage Range					
LM100/LM200		2.0		30	V
LM300				20	
Output-Input Voltage Differential					
LM100/LM200		3.0		30	V
LM300				20	
Load Regulation (Note 3)	$R_{SC} = 0$, $I_O < 12$ mA		0.1	0.5	%
Line Regulation	$V_{IN} - V_{OUT} \leq 5V$		0.1	0.2	%/V
	$V_{IN} - V_{OUT} \leq 5V$		0.05	0.1	%/V
Temperature Stability					
LM100	$-55°C \leq T_A \leq +125°C$		0.3	1.0	
LM200	$-25°C \leq T_A \leq 85°C$		0.3	1.0	%
LM300	$0°C \leq T_A \leq 70°C$		0.3	2.0	
Feedback Sense Voltage		1.63	1.7	1.81	V
Output Noise Voltage	10 Hz $\leq f \leq$ 10 kHz				
	$C_{REF} = 0$		0.005		%
	$C_{REF} = 0.1\ \mu F$		0.002		%
Long Term Stability			0.1	1.0	%
Standby Current Drain					
LM100/LM200	$V_{IN} = 40V$		1.0	3.0	mA
LM300	$V_{IN} = 30V$				
Minimum Load Current					
LM100/LM200	$V_{IN} - V_{OUT} = 30V$		1.5	3.0	mA
LM300	$V_{IN} - V_{OUT} = 20V$				

Fig. 16–10. *Data sheet for an integrated circuit voltage regulator. (Courtesy National Semiconductor Corp.)*

Acting as a current limiter, external resistor R_3 provides short-circuit protection in circuits 2 and 3. Resistor R_3 is connected in series with the load and the pass transistor. An increase in load current causes the voltage across R_3 to rise. When this voltage is sufficient to turn ON transistor Q_{10} (Fig. 16–9A), the base drive for Q_{11} is reduced. The current in Q_{12} and the load are thereby limited to safe values.

Circuit 3 is a 2-A regulator which employs foldback current limiting. The difference between regulator circuits 2 and 3 is that an additional transistor, Q_1, is used to boost the load current to 2 A. Resistors R_4 and R_6 are added for foldback current limiting.

The voltage developed across R_4 is influenced by the voltage divider network of R_4 and R_6. The base-emitter voltage of limiting transistor Q_{10} depends on the difference between voltages V_3 and V_4. The values of these two voltages are such that under normal operation, V_4 cancels V_3, and Q_{10} is OFF.

When the impedance of the load decreases, and the load current increases above the rated maximum values, the voltage across R_3 increases, and Q_{10} turns ON. The load current is reduced because of the reduction in current through Q_{12} and Q_1. A smaller current in Q_1 also means an increase in V_{CE_1}, resulting in a lower output voltage and current. Voltage V_3 is reduced, as is the voltage across R_4. The circuit is designed for the two voltages to compensate for each other while Q_{10} continues to conduct.

A further reduction in load impedance increases the voltage across R_3 and the current in Q_{10}. This reduces further the output voltage and current. Figure 16–11 illustrates the basic current-limiting action of circuits 1 and 2, and the foldback limiting of circuit 3. With basic current limiting, as current demands increase beyond the maximum level, the load current is limited to a constant limiting value,

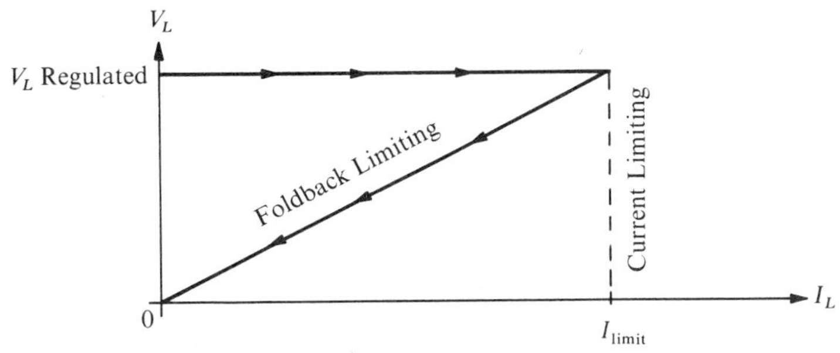

Fig. 16–11. *Plot of load voltage versus load current depicting foldback current limiting. With foldback limiting, the load current and voltage decrease together.*

I_{limit}. With foldback current limiting, as the load impedance drops, *the load voltage*, in addition to the load current, decreases.

EXAMPLE 16–7.

The LM100 regulator is connected as circuit 1 in Fig. 16–9B. It supplies a constant load voltage of 15 V operating at an ambient temperature of 75°C. The input to the regulator is 30 V. The LM100 has a maximum rated chip temperature, $T_{j(\max)}$, of 150°C and a junction-to-ambient thermal resistance, θ_{ja}, of 150°C/W. Find the maximum load current that the regulator can supply.

Solution:

From the thermal data, the maximum allowable power dissipated by the device at 75°C is

$$\frac{150 - 75}{150} = 0.5\text{ W} = 500\text{ mW}$$

On the data sheet of Fig. 16–10, the worst-case standby current drain listed is 3 mA. Therefore, the internal dissipation with no load is

$$30 \times 0.003 = 0.09\text{ W} = 90\text{ mW}$$

The power dissipated in the integrated circuit to supply load current is

$$P_D = 500\text{ mW} - 90\text{ mW} = 410\text{ mW}$$

The voltage across the internal series-pass circuit, V, is

$$\begin{aligned} V &= V_i - V_o \\ &= 30 - 15 = 15\text{ V} \end{aligned}$$

and the current in the series-pass transistor, I_s, is

$$I_s = \frac{0.410}{15} = 27.3\text{ mA}$$

Because I_1 is negligible, the maximum load current is approximately equal to $I_s = 27.3$ mA

Another example of an IC regulator is the LM340 type of Fig. 16–12. The device is self-contained and preadjusted for a specific output voltage. It comes in a standard package with three terminals: input, output, and ground. The maximum load current the unit delivers is 500 mA. By adding external circuitry, the regulator can be expanded to provide higher load currents and adjustable output voltages.

The output voltage for the adjustable version of Fig. 16–13 is given by

$$V_o = 5 + (16.7\text{ mA} + I_Q)R_2 \qquad \textbf{(16–13)}$$

where I_Q is the quiescent current equal to 6 mA and R_2 is a potentiometer.

Voltage Regulators

LM340 series voltage regulators

general description

The LM340-XX series of three terminal regulators is available with several fixed output voltages making them useful in a wide range of applications. One of these is local on card regulation, eliminating the distribution problems associated with single point regulation. The voltages available allow these regulators to be used in logic systems, instrumentation, HiFi, and other solid state electronic equipment. Although designed primarily as fixed voltage regulators these devices can be used with external components to obtain adjustable voltages and currents.

The LM340-XX series is available in two power packages. Both the plastic TO-220 and metal TO-3 packages allow these regulators to deliver over 1.0A if adequate heat sinking is provided. Even with over 1.0A of output current available the regulators are essentially blow-out proof. Current limiting is included to limit the peak output current to a safe value. Safe area protection for the output transistor is provided to limit internal power dissipation. If internal power dissipation becomes too high for the heat sinking provided, the thermal shutdown circuit takes over preventing the IC from overheating.

Considerable effort was expended to make the LM340-XX series of regulators easy to use and minimize the number of external components. It is not necessary to bypass the output, although this does improve transient response. Input bypassing is needed only if the regulator is located far from the filter capacitor of the power supply.

features

- Output current in excess of 1A
- Internal thermal overload protection
- No external components required
- Output transistor safe area protection
- Internal short circuit current limit
- Available in plastic TO-220 and metal TO-3 packages

voltage range

LM340-05	5V	LM340-15	15V
LM340-06	6V	LM340-18	18V
LM340-08	8V	LM340-24	24V
LM340-12	12V		

schematic and connection diagrams

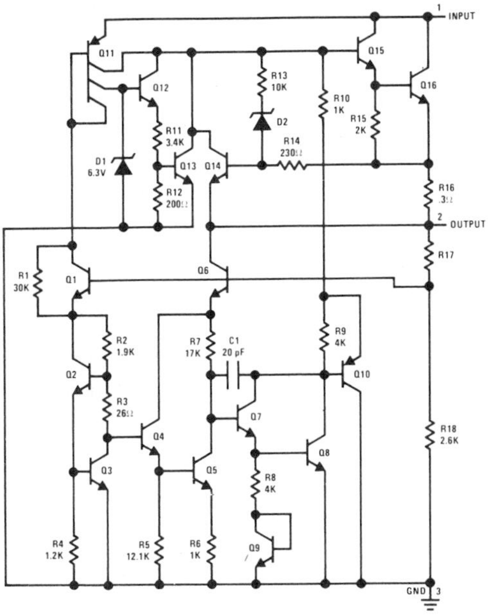

TO-220 (T)

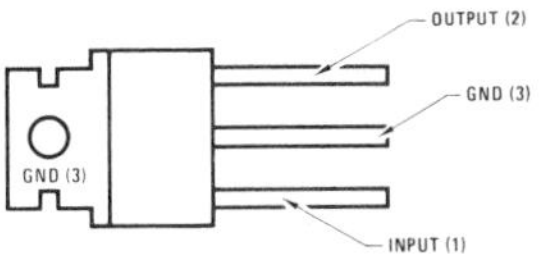

TOP VIEW

Order Numbers:

LM340-05T LM340-15T
LM340-06T LM340-18T
LM340-08T LM340-24T
LM340-12T
See Package 26

TO-3 (K)

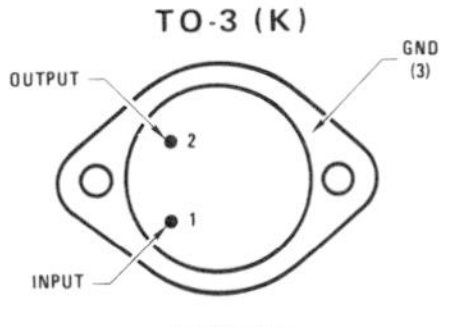

BOTTOM VIEW

Order Numbers:

LM340-05K LM340-15K
LM340-06K LM340-18K
LM340-08K LM340-24K
LM340-12K
See Package 18

Fig. 16–12. *LM340 series-type voltage regulator. (Courtesy National Semiconductor Corp.)*

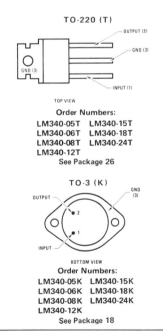

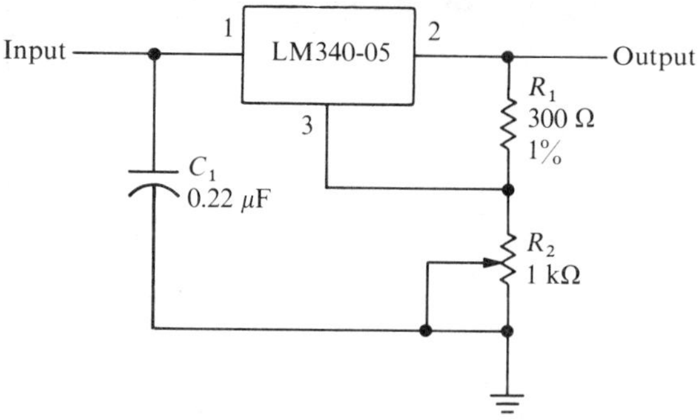

Fig. 16–13. *Example of an adjustable voltage regulator. (Courtesy National Semiconductor Corp.)*

EXAMPLE 16–8.

For the circuit of Fig. 16–13, at what should R_2 be set for an output of 10 V?

Solution:

Solving Eq. (16–13) for R_2,

$$R_2 = \frac{V_o - 5}{16.7 + I_Q}$$

$$= \frac{10 - 5}{16.7 + 6} = 220\,\Omega$$

16.7 Shunt Voltage Regulator

A shunt regulator is not as efficient as a series regulator. Nevertheless, it is used in some applications because of its positive features. Shunt regulators are not as sensitive to input voltage transients as series-type regulators. Also, they do not feed load current transients back to the supply. The shunt regulator is short-circuit proof because the load is in shunt with the pass transistor.

The shunt regulator of Fig. 16–14 contains a parallel controlling element, a reference element, and a series-dropping resistor. The controlling element is a Darlington pair, Q_1 and Q_2. The current in the shunt element changes as the load current or the input voltage varies. The voltage

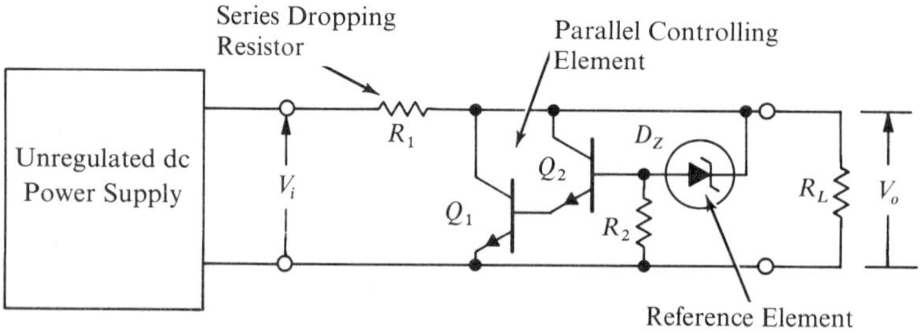

Fig. 16–14. *Circuit of a basic shunt voltage regulator.*

across series-dropping resistor R_1 varies to keep the output constant. Because power is dissipated in R_1, the circuit is not as efficient as the series-type regulator.

An LM305A device can be used as the basic element in an IC shunt regulator. The circuit of a 10-V, 200-mA regulator is illustrated in Fig. 16–15. The output voltage is sensed across resistors R_1 and R_2. A constant output voltage is maintained between pin 8 and ground. Transistor Q_1 is used as a shunt element which conducts excess current not absorbed by the load. Zener diode D_1 provides level shifting for the proper operation of the output transistors contained in the LM305A. Resistor R_4 is a series-dropping element, and R_3 provides base drive for Q_1.

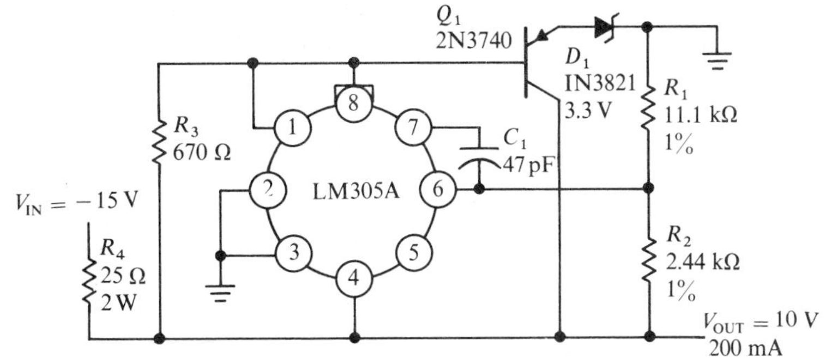

Fig. 16–15. *An LM305A used as the basic element in an IC shunt voltage regulator. (Courtesy National Semiconductor Corp.)*

16.8 Current Regulator

A current regulator supplies a constant load current regardless of variations in the input or output voltage. A voltage regulator can be modified to provide current regulation. In Fig. 16–16, an LM305A is used in conjunction with external elements to provide a constant output current of 1 A.

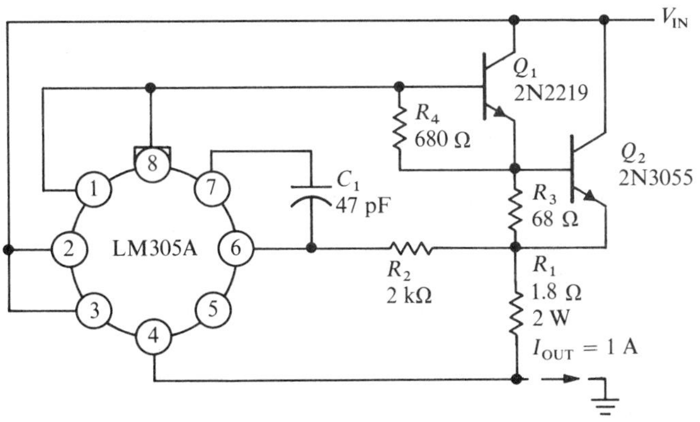

Fig. 16–16. *An LM305A used in a current regulator circuit. (Courtesy National Semiconductor Corp.)*

Transistors Q_1 and Q_2 form a Darlington pair. By maintaining a constant voltage at pin 8, the LM305A regulates the emitter current of the Darlington pair. The output current is preset by resistor R_1. When a need for a variable output current arises, resistor R_1 is replaced by a potentiometer.

Resistor R_2 is inserted in series with the terminal for impedance matching. For minimum thermal drift and good frequency compensation of the LM305A, feedback terminal 6 is operated from approximately a 2-kΩ source.

SUMMARY

Regardless of variations in load current or input voltage, a constant dc load voltage is maintained by a voltage regulator. The simplest type is the zener diode regulator. The most efficient is the IC series voltage regulator. Shunt regulators are not as efficient as the series type. Protection circuits are provided to ensure that a regulator is not damaged because of overloading or a short circuit.

A current regulator supplies a constant load current regardless of variations in the input or output voltage. A current regulator may be realized by employing a voltage regulator which is suitably modified for the purpose.

Further Reading

Cowles, L. G. *Transistor Circuits and Applications.* 2nd ed. Englewood Cliffs, N.J.: Prentice-Hall, 1974, Chapter 7.

Driscoll, F. F., and R. F. Coughlin. *Solid State Devices and Applications.* Englewood Cliffs, N.J.: Prentice-Hall, 1975, Chapter 6.

Hewlett-Packard. *DC Power Supply Handbook.* Palo Alto, Calif.: Hewlett-Packard Company, 1970.

Kaufman, M., and A. H. Seidman, eds. *Handbook for Electronics Engineering Technicians.* New York: McGraw-Hill Book Company, 1976, Chapter 16.

Manera, A. S. *Solid State Electronic Circuits for Engineering Technology.* New York: McGraw-Hill Book Company, 1973, Chapter 11.

Millman, J., and C. C. Halkias. *Integrated Electronics: Analog and Digital Circuits and Systems.* New York: McGraw-Hill Book Company, 1972, Chapter 18.

Pierce, J. F., and T. J. Paulus. *Applied Electronics.* Columbus, Ohio: Charles E. Merrill Publishing Company, 1972, Chapter 12.

REVIEW QUESTIONS

16.1 Explain the purpose of a regulator.

16.2 What is the key element in a voltage regulator?

16.3 Why is it important to know the temperature coefficient of a zener diode?

16.4 Can the output voltage of a zener regulator be greater than or equal to the input voltage? Why?

16.5 Is there any power consumed by the regulator circuit? Why?

16.6 Describe the function of the op amp in Fig. 16–4.

16.7 What is meant by the *pass element* in a feedback-type voltage regulator?

16.8 Describe the function of the error amplifier in Fig. 16–5.

16.9 What is the main difference between a series and a shunt regulator?

16.10 How is the output voltage level adjusted in the regulator of Fig. 16–6?

16.11 What is the effect of resistor R_2 opening in Fig. 16–6?

16.12 What is the function of the preregulator in Fig. 16–7?

16.13 Discuss the purpose of a current-limiting circuit.

16.14 Explain foldback limiting.

16.15 What are the advantages of a shunt regulator over a series regulator?

16.16 Describe the function of a current regulator.

16.17 What is the simplest type of overcurrent protection?

16.18 What is the adjustment criterion for resistor R in Fig. 16–8?

16.19 What is the effect of reversing the zener diode in Fig. 16–2?

16.20 Which transistor in the circuit of Fig. 16–6 dissipates the greatest amount of power? Why?

PROBLEMS

P16–1 For the zener regulator of Fig. 16–2, V_i varies from 15 to 20 V. Series resistor $R = 100\,\Omega$, $V_Z = 10\,\text{V}$ for $I_Z \geqslant 5\,\text{mA}$, and $R_L = 500\,\Omega$. Determine if the output will be regulated for the given variations in input voltage.

P16–2 Repeat prob. P16–1 for V_i varying from 12 to 16 V.

P16–3 The zener diode in prob. P16–1 is rated at $P_{D(\max)} = 500\,\text{mW}$. Will the diode operate safely under the given input conditions?

P16–4 Repeat prob. P16–3 for prob. P16–2.

P16–5 The regulator of Fig. 16–2 has a constant input of $V_i = 15\,\text{V}$; load resistance, R_L, however, varies from 50 to 500 Ω. The zener diode is the same as the one used in prob. P16–1, and $R = 50\,\Omega$. For what range of R_L is the output regulated?

P16–6 Repeat prob. P16–5 for $R = 60\,\Omega$.

P16–7 In Fig. 16–2, V_i varies from 15 to 20 V, and R_L varies from 100 to 500 Ω. The zener diode is the same as specified in probs. P16–1 and P16–3 with $R = 50\,\Omega$. Determine if the output remains at 10 V for the given variations in V_i and R_L. (*Hint*: Examine the circuit under worst-case conditions.)

P16–8 Calculate the value of R in Fig. 16–2 for $8\text{ V} \leqslant V_i \leqslant 12\text{ V}$, $R_L = 1\text{ k}\Omega$, $V_Z = 5\text{ V}$ for $I_Z \geqslant 1\text{ mA}$, and $P_{D(\max)} = 1\text{ W}$. The output is to be constant at 5 V for the variations in V_i.

P16–9 Repeat prob. P16–8 for V_i constant at 10 V and $200\,\Omega \leqslant R_L \leqslant 2\text{ k}\Omega$.

P16–10 For the regulator of Fig. 16–6, $V_Z = 10\text{ V}$ at $I_Z = 10\text{ mA}$, $P_{D(\max)} = 500\text{ mW}$, $R_1 = 330\,\Omega$, $R_2 = 1\text{ k}\Omega$, $R_3 = 1.5\text{ k}\Omega$, and $R_4 = 3.3\text{ k}\Omega$. What is the output voltage for $V_i = 20\text{ V}$?

P16–11 Repeat prob. P16–10 for $V_i = 30\text{ V}$.

P16–12 Show that the output voltage calculated in prob. P16–10 remains constant as the input V_i varies from 18 to 22 V; $R_L = 500\,\Omega$. For the transistors, $h_{FE_1} = 50$, $I_{C1(\max)} = 800\text{ mA}$, $P_{D1(\max)} = 5\text{ W}$, $h_{FE_2} = 100$, $I_{C_2(\max)} = 200\text{ mA}$, and $P_{D_2(\max)} = 360\text{ mW}$.

P16–13 Over what input voltage range is regulation maintained in prob. P16–12?

P16–14 The regulator in prob. P16–10 has a constant input $V_i = 20\text{ V}$; load R_L varies from 100 Ω to 1 kΩ. For the transistors, $h_{FE_1} = h_{FE_2} = 60$, $I_{C1(\max)} = 1\text{ A}$, $I_{C_2(\max)} = 100\text{ mA}$, $P_{D1(\max)} = 4\text{ W}$, and $P_{D_2(\max)} = 500\text{ mW}$. Is regulation still maintained as the load varies?

P16–15 Determine the minimum value of R_L for which regulation is maintained in prob. P16–14.

P16–16 The LM100 regulator of Fig. 16–9B(1) delivers a regulated 10 V when the input is 25 V. The circuit operates in an ambient temperature of 50°C; $T_{j(\max)} = 150°\text{C}$, $\theta_{ja} = 150°\text{C/W}$, and $P_D = 800\text{ mW}$ at 25°C. Calculate the maximum load current the regulator can deliver.

P16–17 Repeat prob. P16–16 for an ambient temperature of 75°C.

P16–18 The LM100 regulator of Fig. 16–9B(1) delivers a load current of 50 mA at 20 V. The input voltage is 30 V. What is the maximum ambient temperature in which the circuit can operate safely?

P16–19 Repeat prob. P16–18 for a load current of 20 mA.

P16–20 Calculate the output voltage in the regulator of Fig. 16–13 if R_2 is set to 500 Ω.

17

Power Control Circuits

The thyristor is a basic element in power control circuits. In Chapter 4, we saw that the popularity of thyristors, such as the SCR, stems from their ability to control large amounts of power efficiently. Thyristors are commercially available in a wide range of current and voltage ratings. They are used in applications where currents range from a few milliamperes to more than 1000 A for some devices and voltages exceed 1000 V.

The SCR, because of its rectification properties, is generally used in dc switching, rectification, and dc control applications. Because of its bidirectional current conduction properties, the TRIAC is used in controlling ac power. The TRIAC controls current during the positive and negative half-cycles of a sine wave.

The *silicon-controlled switch*, SCS, is utilized primarily in the same applications as the SCR. They differ in that the SCS provides greater controlling flexibility than the SCR.

We shall also consider circuits that employ the DIAC. Similar to the TRIAC, this device is capable of bidirectional conduction, but without an external control signal. The operation of the DIAC is based on exceeding the *breakover voltage* of the device in both directions. The breakover voltage is the minimum voltage across the anode and cathode needed to trigger the device.

Applications of thyristors are numerous. They include the following:

1. Replacement of electromechanical devices, such as relays, automobile ignition and flasher systems, and overload protectors.
2. Motor-speed control of small appliances and large industrial rotating systems.
3. Power conversion systems such as dc-to-ac inversion, welding, battery charging, and pulse modulation.
4. Logic, alarm, and other emergency circuits.

17.1 The Thyristor as a Control Element

Thyristors are switching devices that remain in the nonconducting (OFF) state until triggered to the conducting (ON) state. They remain in the ON state until the current

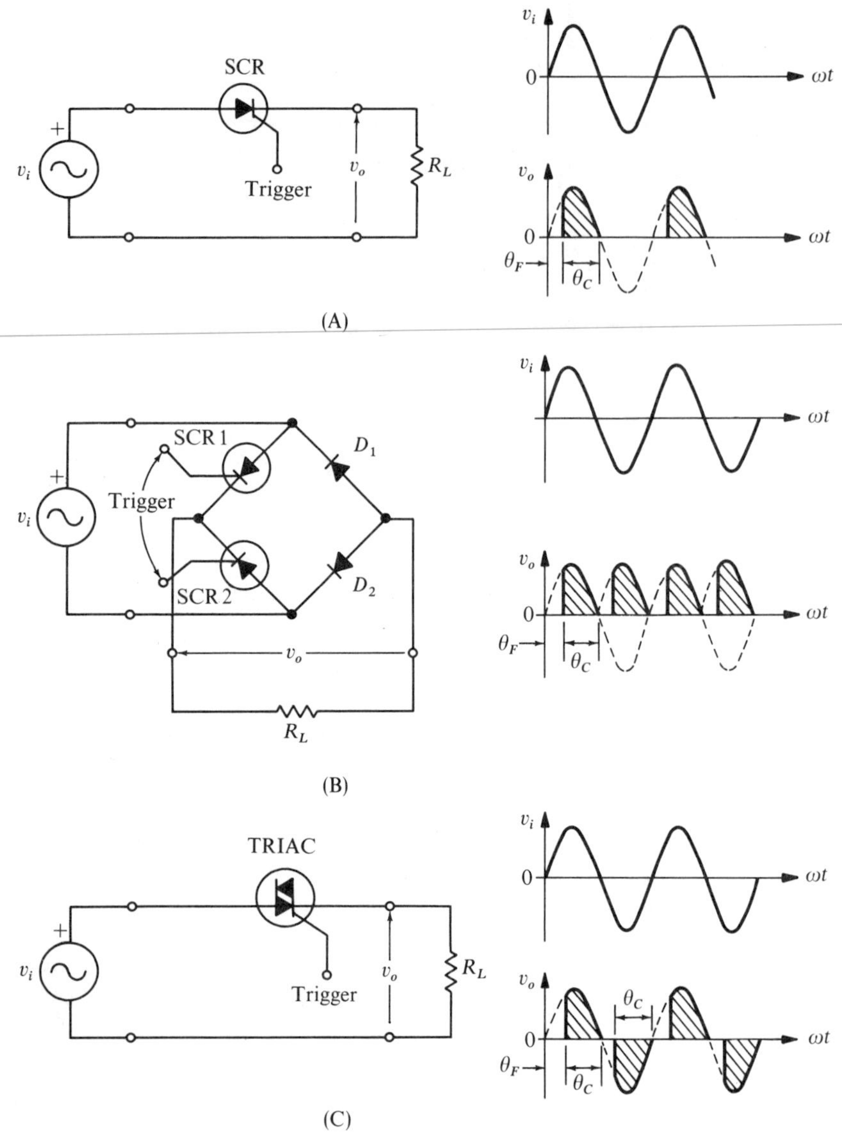

Fig. 17–1. *Basic thyristor power control circuits and their input and output waveforms. (A) SCR half-wave operation. (B) SCR full-wave operation. (C) TRIAC full-wave operation.*

in the device is reduced to below the holding current.* Switching from the OFF to the ON state occurs when the voltage across the anode and cathode reaches the forward breakover voltage, with the gate open.

The thyristor also can be turned ON by supplying a minimum current to the gate. With gate triggering, less anode-cathode voltage is required to turn ON the device. Controlling the time at which the trigger is applied to the gate results in conduction during a portion of the ac cycle. This is called *phase control* operation. Basic SCR and TRIAC power control circuits, and their respective waveforms, are illustrated in Fig. 17–1.

* See Chapter 4 for a description of thyristor operation.

The *firing angle*, θ_F, is the angle of the ac input signal at which the thyristor triggers. The *conduction angle*, θ_C, is the total angle for which the thyristor remains in the ON state. For the half-wave SCR circuit of Fig. 17–1A,

$$\theta_C = 180^\circ - \theta_F \qquad \textbf{(17–1a)}$$

For a full-wave SCR or TRIAC circuit of Figs. 17–1B and C,

$$\theta_C = 2(180^\circ - \theta_F) \qquad \textbf{(17–1b)}$$

Ratings of thyristors are given as a function of the conduction or firing angle. Curves plotted in Fig. 17–2 show how current and power in an SCR and a TRIAC are dependent on the conduction and firing angles.

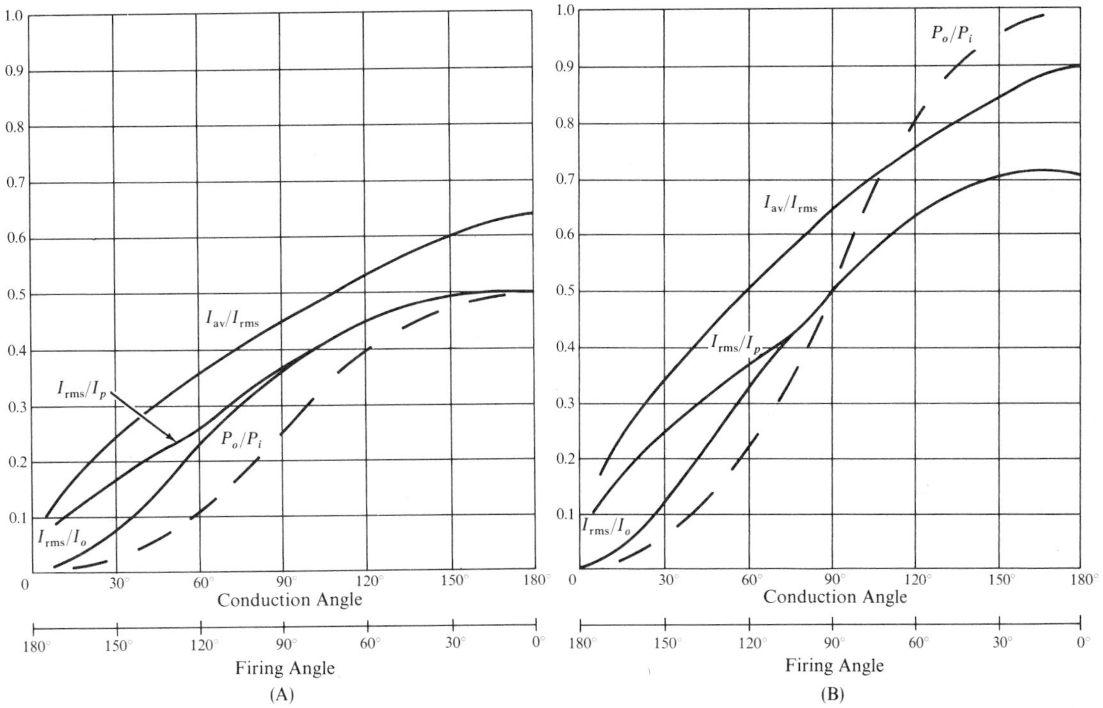

Fig. 17–2. *Current and power ratios for thyristors as a function of conduction and firing angles. (A) For half-wave conduction (SCR). (B) For full-wave conduction (TRIAC).*

Term I_{av} is the average current, I_{rms} is the rms current, I_p is the peak current, and I_o is a *reference current*. Reference current is defined by

$$I_o = \frac{V_{i(\max)}}{R_L} \qquad \textbf{(17–2)}$$

where $V_{i(\max)}$ is the maximum value of the input voltage, v_i, and R_L is the load resistance. Current I_o is a circuit constant and independent of the thyristor.

The dashed curves in Figs. 17–2A and B represent the ratio of the power delivered to the load to the input power as a function of the firing and conduction angles. From these curves, we see that the maximum efficiency $[(P_o/P_i)_{\max}]$ obtained from an SCR is 50 percent at a conduction angle of 180°. When the conduction angle is reduced, the efficiency is lowered. A similar effect, with higher efficiencies, is observed for a TRIAC. The following examples illustrate the use of the ratio curves in the analysis and design of thyristor circuits.

EXAMPLE 17–1.

The circuit of Fig. 17–3 controls power from a 120-V rms source to a 4-Ω load. If the trigger controls the conduction angle from 20° to 90°, what is the variation in I_{rms} flowing in the load?

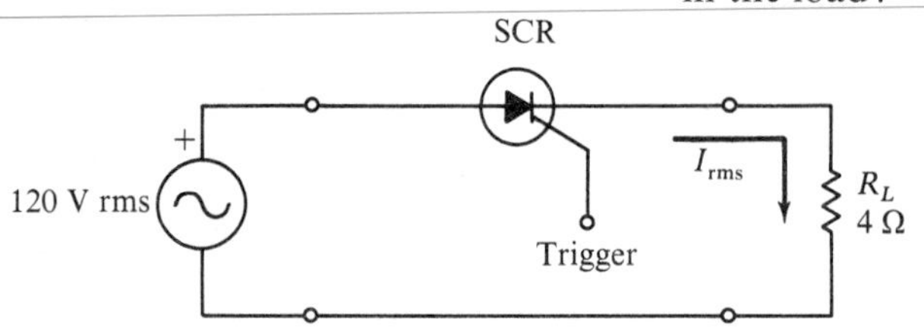

Fig. 17–3. *Half-wave SCR circuit for Example 17–1.*

Solution:

The maximum input voltage, $V_{i(\max)}$, is

$$V_{i(\max)} = \sqrt{2} \times 120 \simeq 170\,\text{V}$$

The reference current, by Eq. (17–2), is

$$I_o = \frac{170}{4} = 42.5\,\text{A}$$

From the I_{rms}/I_o curve of Fig. 17–2A,

For $\theta_C = 20°$:

$$\frac{I_{rms}}{I_o} = 0.04$$

and

$$I_{rms} = 0.04 \times 42.5 = 1.7\,\text{A}.$$

For $\theta_C = 90°$:

$$\frac{I_{rms}}{I_o} = 0.35$$

and

$$I_{rms} = 0.35 \times 42.5 = 14.87\,\text{A}$$

Therefore, for $20° \leqslant \theta_C \leqslant 90°$, $1.7\,\text{A} \leqslant I_{rms} \leqslant 14.87\,\text{A}$.

EXAMPLE 17–2.

The TRIAC circuit of Fig. 17–4 supplies a constant load current of 10 A rms as the load varies from 1 Ω to 2.5 Ω.

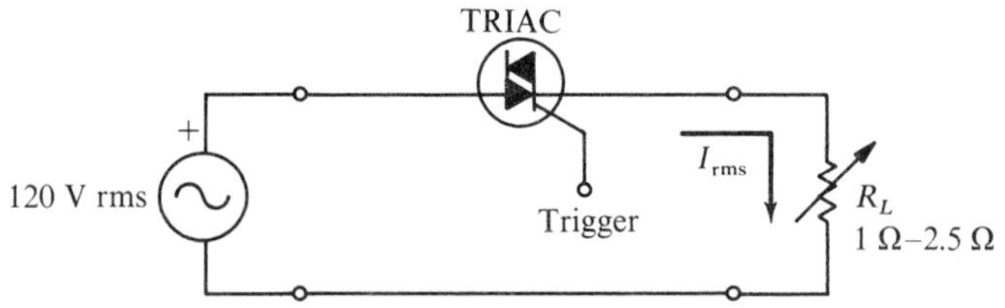

Fig. 17–4. *Full-wave TRIAC circuit for Example 17–2.*

(a) Calculate the range of the conduction angle necessary for a constant load current of 10 A.
(b) What is the peak current, I_p, flowing in the TRIAC?

Solutions:

(a) Two values of I_o must be found, one for each extreme of R_L.

For $R_L = 1\,\Omega$:

$$I_o = \frac{170}{1} = 170\text{ A}$$

$$\frac{I_{\text{rms}}}{I_o} = \frac{10}{170} \simeq 0.059$$

From the I_{rms}/I_o curve of Fig. 17–2B, $\theta_C = 18°$.

For $R_L = 2.5\,\Omega$:

$$I_o = \frac{170}{2.5} = 68\text{ A}$$

$$\frac{I_{\text{rms}}}{I_o} = \frac{10}{68} \simeq 0.15$$

$$\theta_C = 36°$$

For a constant load current of 10 A rms, $18° \leqslant \theta_C \leqslant 36°$.

(b) From the I_{rms}/I_p curve of Fig. 17–2B for the two values of θ_C,

$\theta_C = 18°$:

$$\frac{I_{\text{rms}}}{I_p} = 0.18$$

$$I_p = \frac{I_{\text{rms}}}{0.18} = \frac{10}{0.18} = 55.5\text{ A}$$

$\theta_C = 36°$:

$$\frac{I_{\text{rms}}}{I_p} = 0.27$$

$$I_p = \frac{10}{0.27} = 37\text{ A}$$

The TRIAC must be capable of handling a peak current of 55.5 A. The value of peak current is almost six times the continuous rms current of 10 A.

EXAMPLE 17–3.

For the half-wave SCR circuit of Fig. 17–1A, the power delivered to the load is 120 W. If the firing angle is constant at 60°, what is the input power, P_i, required to supply the load?

Solution:

From Fig. 17–2A, for $\theta_F = 60°$,

$$\frac{P_L}{P_i} = 0.4$$

Hence,

$$P_i = \frac{P_L}{0.4} = \frac{120}{0.4} = 300\text{ W}$$

17.2 Thyristor Trigger Circuits

The type of trigger circuit used for a thyristor depends on the application. A few of the more commonly used trigger circuits are discussed in this section.

The simplest trigger circuit, employing a switch for control, is shown in Fig. 17–5A. Once the SCR is turned ON, it remains conducting until the power source is disconnected from the circuit by the switch. The value of R_G, connected across the gate and anode, is chosen to ensure that sufficient gate current flows to turn ON the SCR. Once conduction starts, the voltage across the anode and cathode drops to a low value, in the order of 1 V.

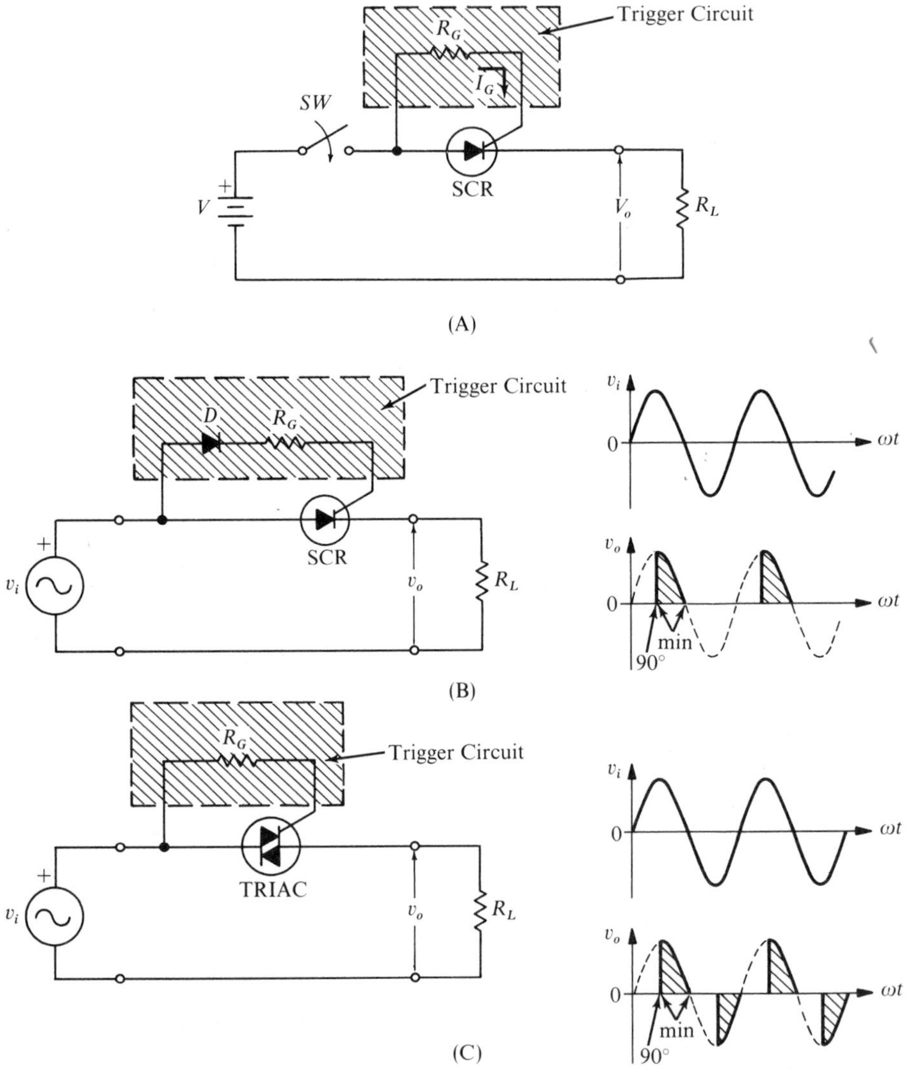

Fig. 17–5. *Thyristor trigger circuits for (A) SCR dc operation, (B) SCR ac operation, and (C) TRIAC ac operation.*

The SCR of Fig. 17–5B is used in ac applications. Assume that the input voltage reaches a sufficient level to turn ON the SCR. The device remains ON as long as the anode current exceeds the rated minimum holding current. The conduction angle shown in the output graph of Fig. 17–5B varies from 90° to 180°. The value of the angle depends on v_i and R_G. Diode *D* ensures that a reverse voltage does not appear across the gate and cathode of the device.

The TRIAC of Fig. 17–5C is used in ac applications in a manner similar to the SCR of Fig. 17–5B. The minimum conduction angle for one cycle is 180° (90°–180° and 270°–360°).

To increase the controlling ranges of an SCR, the trigger circuit must be capable of causing an SCR to conduct for less than 90°. Such a circuit is shown in Fig. 17–6. Capacitor *C* charges through resistor *R* as the sine wave rises. When the voltage across the capacitor reaches the proper triggering level, the SCR begins to conduct. The capacitor discharges through the gate after the SCR fires. The SCR turns OFF when the input reaches zero. Diode *D*, as in Fig. 17–5B, prevents a reverse voltage from appearing across the gate and cathode.

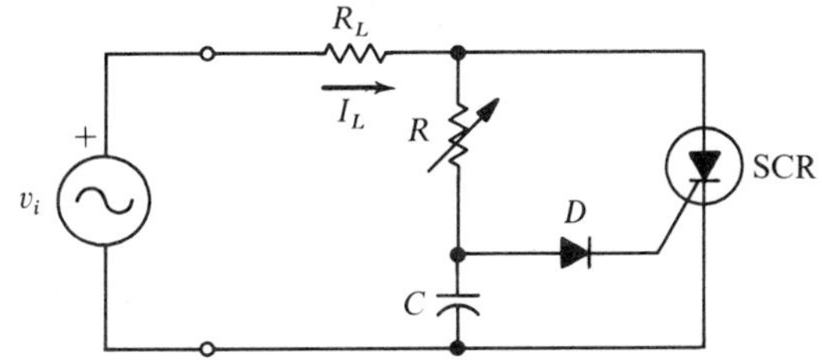

Fig. 17–6. *RC trigger network used to control the conduction angle of an SCR.*

The conduction angle in the circuit can be changed by varying *R* or *C*, or both. Because it is easier to change the value of *R* than *C*, a potentiometer (*R*) is used to vary the conduction angle. This configuration provides for conduction angles from approximately 90° to 180°.

Gate characteristics of thyristors vary from unit to unit for the same type number. Temperature characteristics also change for devices. To make the trigger less dependent on variations in device parameters, a *double-time constant trigger* may be used. The circuit is illustrated in Fig. 17–7.

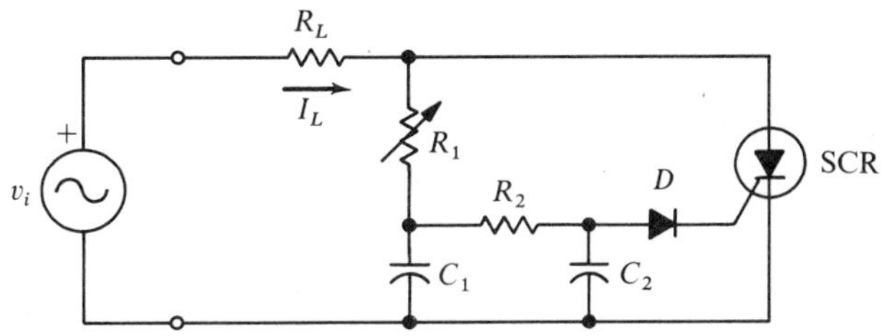

Fig. 17–7. *Double-time constant RC trigger circuit.*

Capacitor C_1 charges through R_1, causing C_2 to charge through R_2. The SCR turns ON when the voltage across C_2 reaches the gate-firing potential. The effect is to increase the rate of change in the trigger voltage. This results in a fast-rising trigger which fires the device at the desired time.

To improve further the operation of trigger networks, another thyristor may be used to trigger an SCR or a

TRIAC. In Fig. 17–8A, a DIAC (bilateral switch) is used in a light dimmer to trigger a TRIAC.

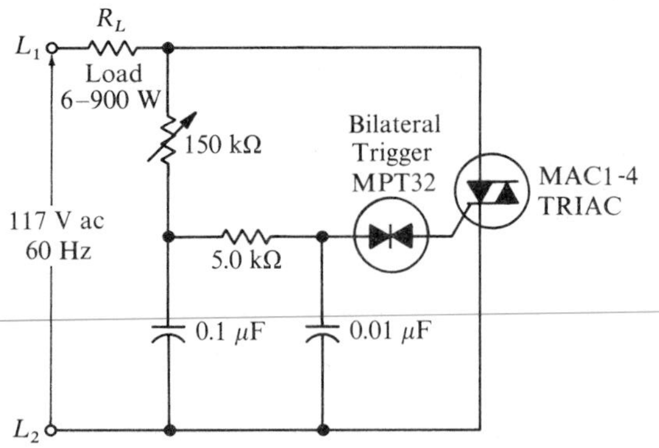

Fig. 17–8. *DIAC used in a light dimmer. (Courtesy Motorola Semiconductor Products, Inc.)*

When the breakover potential across a DIAC is reached in either direction (positive or negative), the device conducts. The firing angle is controlled by the 150-kΩ potentiometer. When the input voltage reaches zero, the TRIAC turns OFF. The breakover voltage for the Motorola MPT 32 DIAC is nominally 32 V. The circuit is capable of controlling 6 W–900 W of power from a 117-V rms source.

The UJT is a perfect companion for thyristors as trigger elements. It was shown in Chapter 4 that a UJT conducts current in only one direction and, therefore, supplies positive trigger pulses. The circuit delivers a current trigger for a short duration at desired time intervals. A simple UJT trigger is shown in Fig. 17–9. Capacitor C charges through resistor R. When the voltage across C reaches voltage V_p (the peak emitter voltage), the capacitor discharges through the emitter and base 1 of the UJT. A trigger voltage is thereby developed across R_1 to fire the SCR.

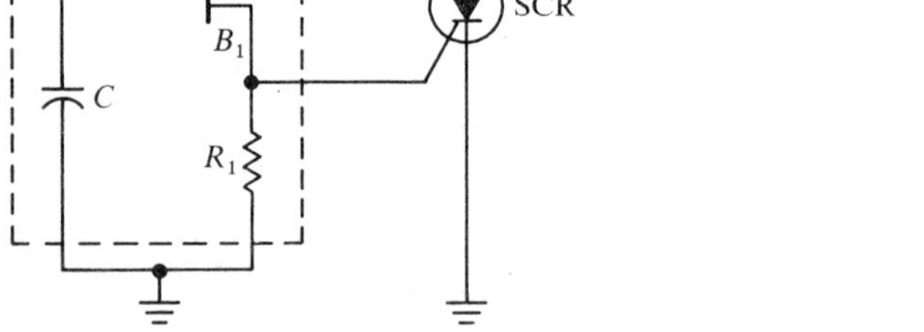

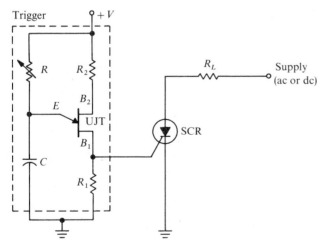

Fig. 17–9. *Simple UJT trigger circuit.*

Time constant RC influences the timing for the triggering of an SCR. The total period T, which includes charge and discharge times, is

$$T = RC \ln \frac{1}{1 - \eta} \tag{17-3}$$

where η is the intrinsic standoff ratio of the UJT.

The circuit of Fig. 17–9 is shown powered from separate sources. In practice, the complete circuit is operated from a single source. In the case of dc power control, the trigger circuit may be connected to the common source through a series-dropping resistor. The dropping resistor is required to reduce the voltage across the UJT.

In an ac power control circuit, the UJT may be powered by a full-wave rectifier, as shown in Fig. 17–10. The zener diode clips the peaks of the rectified waveform and yields a regulated output. Resistor R_3 is a dropping resistor which ensures that the maximum voltage across the UJT does not exceed its rated value.

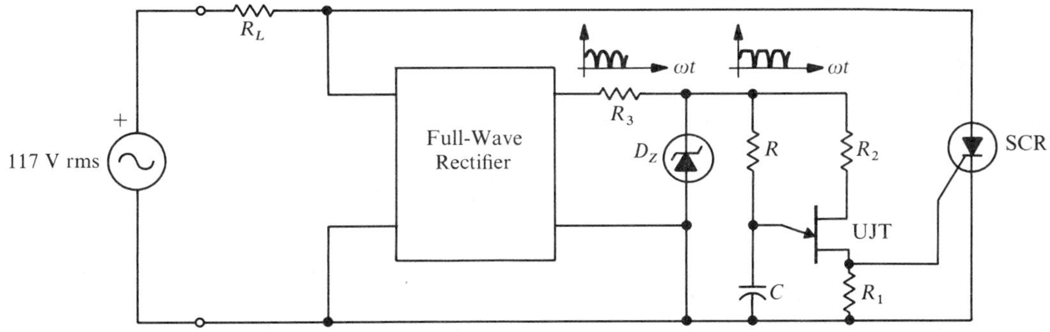

Fig. 17–10. *Line-synchronized UJT trigger circuit.*

The circuit of Fig. 17–10 has the advantage of being synchronized with the line frequency. At the end of each half-cycle, the voltage at the bases of the UJT drops to zero, forcing the capacitor to discharge. The capacitor is therefore fully discharged at the beginning of each half-cycle.

A *two-transistor regenerative feedback circuit* (Fig. 17–11) also may be used to trigger thyristors. Such a circuit may

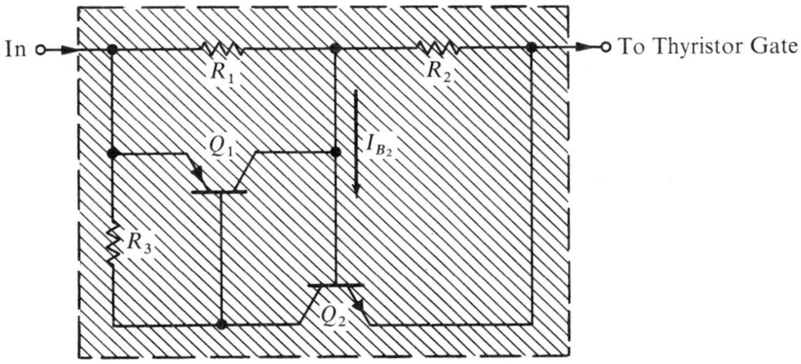

Fig. 17–11. *Two-transistor, regenerative-feedback trigger circuit.*

be substituted for the bilateral switch in Fig. 17–8. In Fig. 17–11, Q_2 turns ON when the positive-going input is sufficient to supply the necessary base current, I_{B_2}. Transistor Q_2 then supplies current to turn ON transistor Q_1. In turn, Q_1 starts supplying base current to Q_2, further increasing the current in Q_1. In this manner, both transistors reach saturation in a short time because of the regenerative action.

An interesting approach to ac power control is now described. In this method, the thyristor is turned ON for an integral number of cycles and then OFF for another preset number of cycles. The method is called *zero-voltage switching*, or *integral cycle switching* control. The waveforms of load voltage for an SCR and a TRIAC are illustrated in Fig. 17–12.

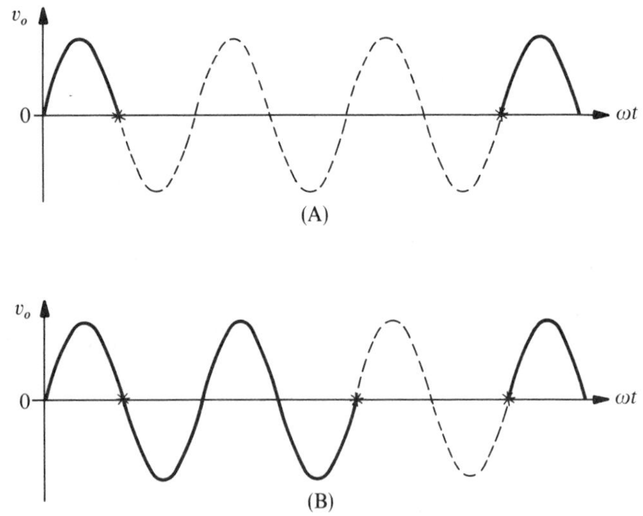

Fig. 17–12. *Zero-voltage, switching-control output waveforms for (A) an SCR and (B) a TRIAC.*

Switching occurs at either 0° or 180°. The noise that is generally associated with power switching is therefore eliminated. This noise is called *radio-frequency interference* (RFI). The average power delivered to the load in a circuit using integral cycle switching is proportional to the ratio of cycles during the ON interval to the OFF interval.

17.3 Power Control Applications

The first application we shall consider is the time-delay power circuit of Fig. 17–13. It may be viewed as an extension of the circuit in Fig. 17–9, and it operates in a similar manner. The circuit is powered from a single source. Zener diode D_Z regulates the voltage across the UJT timing circuit. Delay is provided by the *charging cycle* of R_T and C_T and the *discharge* of C_T through the UJT.

The SCR is triggered as in the circuit of Fig. 17–9. Delay time, t_d, is approximately equal to the charging time of

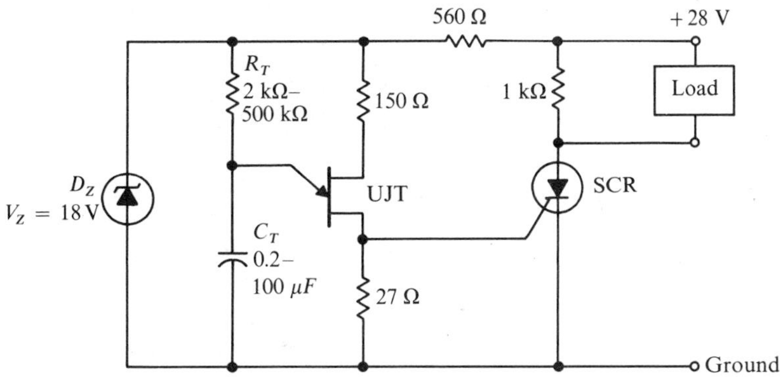

Fig. 17–13. *Time-delay circuit. (Coutesy General Electric Semiconductor Products Department, Syracuse, N.Y.)*

capacitor C_T. Because the discharge cycle is much shorter than the charge cycle, $t_d \simeq T$, expressed by Eq. (17–3). By varying the values of R_T and C_T, delays from 0.4 ms to 1 min are realized.

EXAMPLE 17–4.

An alarm system in a bank is set to go ON 20 s after a break-in occurs. If the circuit of Fig. 17–13 is used, determine the value of R_T if $C_T = 100\,\mu\text{F}$. For a 2N1671B, $\eta = 0.62$.

Solution:

By Eq. (17–3),

$$t_d \simeq T = R_T C_T \ln\left(\frac{1}{1-\eta}\right)$$

Solving for R_T,

$$R_T = \frac{t_d}{C_T \ln\left(\dfrac{1}{1-\eta}\right)}$$

$$= \frac{20}{100 \times 10^{-6} \ln\left(\dfrac{1}{1-0.62}\right)} = 208\,\text{k}\Omega$$

A power circuit activated by the *absence* of light is illustrated in Fig. 17–14. This type of circuit is popular as

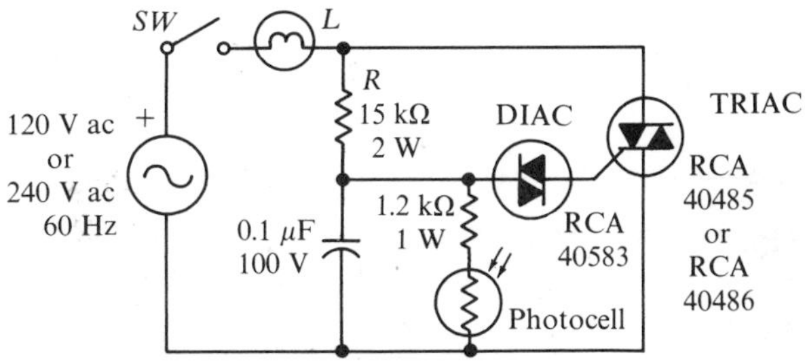

Fig. 17–14. *Light-controlled power circuit. (Courtesy RCA Solid State Division.)*

an automatic light turn-ON for highways and as a warning alarm for lighting failures. When light strikes the surface of the photocell, its resistance is reduced. The capacitor is thereby prevented from charging to a level necessary to break down the DIAC.

In absence of light (when it gets dark on a road or when lights go out indoors), the resistance of the photocell increases to a higher value. The capacitor is allowed to charge, and the TRIAC is activated. Lights on the highway go ON. In a lighting failure, an alarm is sounded.

Switching large amounts of power, such as in heating control applications, presents the problem of RFI generation discussed previously. Although it is possible to use phase control, filters must be added to suppress RFI. This makes the circuit bulkier and more expensive.

Zero-voltage switching circuits are used often in heating control applications. The circuit of Fig. 17–15 is an example of an ON-OFF temperature controller. It uses a special IC, the RCA CA3059. This device is a *zero-crossing voltage switch.* It generates pulses at its output at zero crossings of input voltage. The thermistor (NTC sensor) senses the temperature.

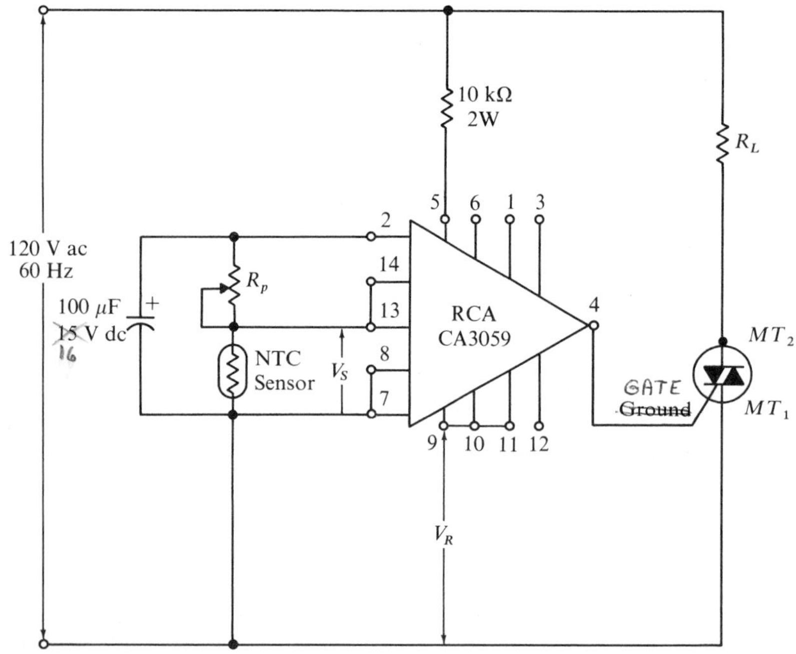

Fig. 17–15. *ON–OFF temperature controller using a zero-crossing switch. (Courtesy RCA Solid State Division.)*

The circuit is capable of controlling up to 80 A of current at 600 V. The thermistor has a negative-temperature coefficient (NTC). As the temperature increases, the resistance of the thermistor decreases.

One of the most important applications for thyristors is in *motor-speed control.* Thyristor motor control circuits are widely used because of their excellent reliability and efficiency.

A typical motor used in small appliances and tools is the *universal* motor. It may be powered from an ac or a dc source. The main characteristic of this motor is that it is series wound, that is, the field winding is in series with the armature. Its speed is controlled by varying the voltage across the armature. The voltage is varied by changing the conduction angle of a thyristor. Universal motors operate efficiently with half-wave, as well as with full-wave, voltage applied across them.

An example of a speed-control circuit for a universal motor is given in Fig. 17–16. Assume that the load on the motor increases. For this condition, the speed tends to decrease, and the current in the motor increases. The voltage across R_7, which serves as a feedback element, rises. This causes the voltage across C_2 to increase. The two-transistor switch (Q_1 and Q_2) is forced to turn ON earlier in the cycle, thereby increasing the conduction angle of the SCR. More power is therefore supplied to the motor to "bring up" the speed to its nominal value.

Analog for SCR Polarized.

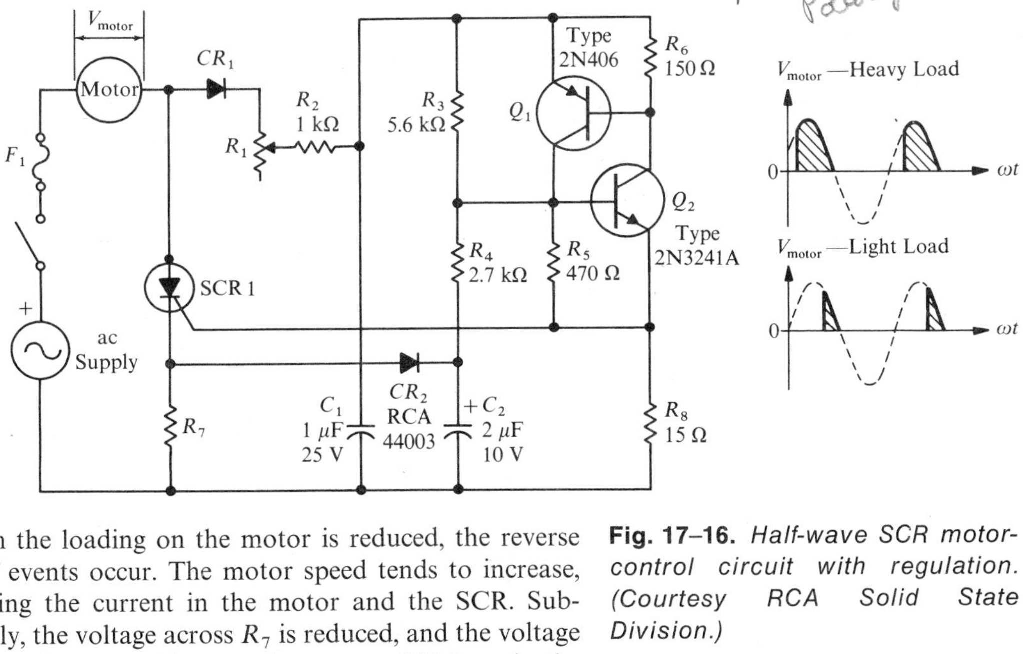

Fig. 17–16. *Half-wave SCR motor-control circuit with regulation. (Courtesy RCA Solid State Division.)*

When the loading on the motor is reduced, the reverse state of events occur. The motor speed tends to increase, decreasing the current in the motor and the SCR. Subsequently, the voltage across R_7 is reduced, and the voltage across C_2 decreases. The transistors turn ON later in the cycle, thereby decreasing the conduction angle. The speed of the motor returns to its nominal value.

Full-wave thyristor motor controls are possible using a TRIAC as the power-controlling element. Another possibility is the control circuit of Fig. 17–16 supplied by a full-wave rectifier. TRIACs are also used in the speed control of split-phase induction motors.

The TRIAC has proven to be ideally suited for use in *motor reversing* for such applications as automatic safe openers and garage door openers. The circuit of Fig. 17–17 is an example of a power-control circuit for a motor reversing system. Illustrated is a split-phase induction, capacitor-run motor. Such a motor rotates in either direction by selectively energizing the forward or reverse winding. The control circuit is composed of two TRIACs. TRIAC 1 controls forward motion, and TRIAC 2 controls motion in the reverse direction.

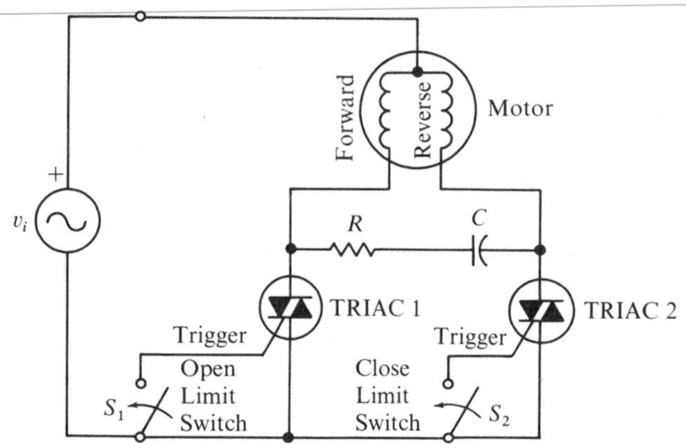

Fig. 17–17. *Motor reversing circuit.*

Resistor R and capacitor C protect the TRIACs from a large loop current in case they are turned ON simultaneously. Limit switches between the gate and cathode of a TRIAC are used for making an emergency stop of the motor.

Motor reversing controls are used in opening and closing doors. For example, they are employed as automatic garage openers. Triggering is generally initiated by a transmitted radio signal. Another example is the automatic opening or closing of a safe.

Assume that a safe can be opened when the correct switch combination is depressed on a control panel. Similarly, the safe can be closed by depressing another combination on the panel. Each of the combinations triggers only one of the TRIACs, energizing either the forward or the reverse winding.

Suppose the correct combination for the "open" command is depressed. TRIAC 1 is triggered. Current flows in the forward winding, and the safe door is opened. When fully opened, limit switch S_1 is closed. This prevents the retriggering of TRIAC 1, and the motor is also stopped. To close the safe door, TRIAC 2 is triggered. The reverse winding is energized, and the motor stops when limit switch S_2 closes.

Another example of an SCR triggered by a UJT is illustrated in Fig. 17–18. The circuit provides *sequential turn signals* in an automobile. Lights flash in sequence to indicate a right or a left turn. There are two identical circuits, one for each side. When the turn signal switch is pressed, bulb 1 goes ON, then center bulb 2, and finally bulb 3. At this point, all three bulbs are ON.

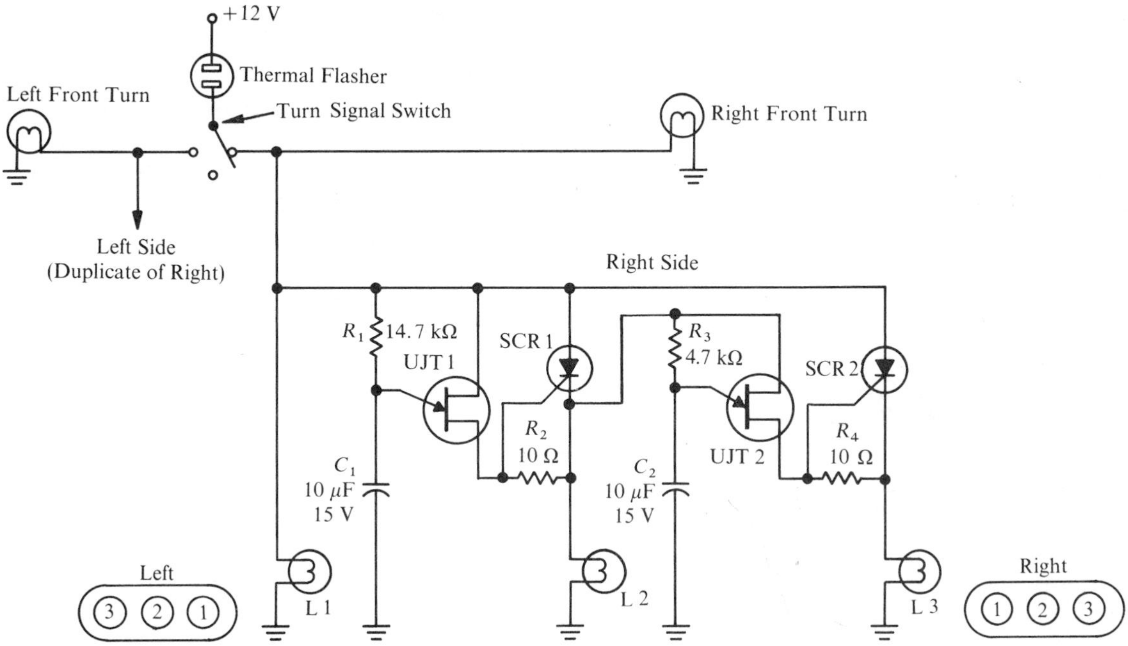

Fig. 17–18. *Automobile sequential-turn signal circuit.*

The circuit is powered through a *thermal flasher*. A flasher conducts current for a longer interval than required for all three bulbs to turn ON. At the end of the interval, the flasher turns OFF. A new cycle begins when the flasher cools off and power is supplied again to the circuit.

The turn-on time of SCR 1 is controlled by time constant R_1C_1. When SCR 1 turns ON, bulb 2 lights, and the timing for UJT 2 and SCR 2 starts. Similar circuits are used as flashers for airplanes and road barricades. These circuits are generally operated from a battery.

17.4 dc-to-ac Inverters and dc-to-dc Converters

A discussion of power control circuits is not complete without showing how dc is converted to ac or how to increase the dc level of a dc source. The transformer is an ideal device for stepping up ac voltages. With dc, there is no device equivalent to a transformer.

An *inverter* is used to change dc to ac. If the ac output is stepped up by a transformer and rectified, a dc voltage is obtained. The overall circuit for changing dc to dc is called a *converter*. Applications for these circuits are numerous. Inverters are used with many types of recreational vehicles where the only power source is an automobile battery. Their uses include the powering of mobile radio transmitters, high-frequency lighting supplies, telephone equipment, and battery chargers.

The basic circuit of an inverter, or converter, consists of a switching circuit, called a *chopper*, and a transformer. Switching is obtained from a transistor or an SCR. The most commonly used inverter is the *push-pull switching inverter* of Fig. 17–19. This circuit generates a square wave output at an operating frequency in the kilohertz range.

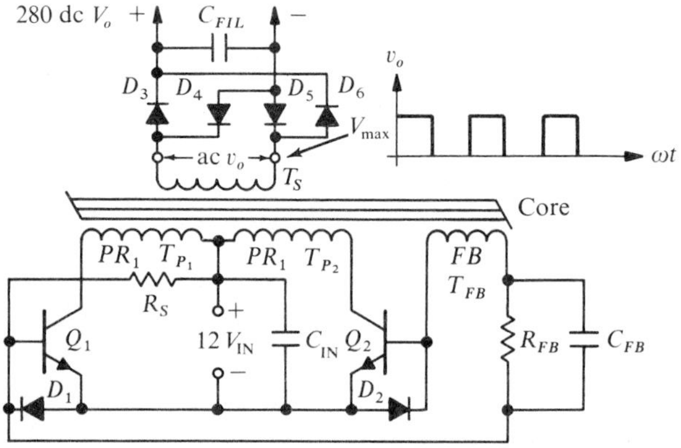

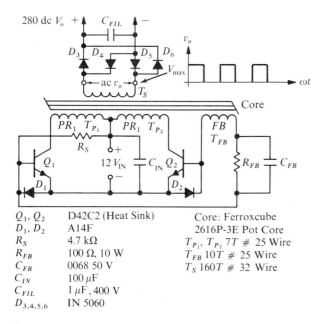

Q_1, Q_2	D42C2 (Heat Sink)
D_1, D_2	A14F
R_S	4.7 kΩ
R_{FB}	100 Ω, 10 W
C_{FB}	0068 50 V
C_{IN}	100 μF
C_{FIL}	1 μF, 400 V
$D_{3,4,5,6}$	IN 5060

Core: Ferroxcube
2616P-3E Pot Core
T_{P_1}, T_{P_2} 7T # 25 Wire
T_{FB} 10T # 25 Wire
T_S 160T # 32 Wire

Fig. 17–19. *Example of a dc-dc converter. (Courtesy General Electric Semiconductor Products Department, Syracuse, N.Y.)*

The circuit of Fig. 17–19 may be used as an inverter or converter. It delivers 280 V dc output from a 12-V dc input. The square wave is delivered to the bridge rectifier. Output voltage V_o is a function of the transformer turns ratio.

The circuit operates as follows: Transistor Q_1 starts conducting first because of the base current supplied to it through resistor R_S. A change in current in primary winding T_{P_1} induces a voltage in the feedback winding, *FB*. The current in Q_1 is increased, and Q_2 remains OFF. The increase in current in Q_1 causes the core to saturate. Because its core is saturated, the inductance of primary winding

T_{P_1} has no restricting effect on the rise in collector current in Q_1. Transistor Q_1, therefore, is saturated.

With a constant current in the primary winding, no voltage is induced in the feedback winding. This causes Q_2 to turn ON. A change in current of Q_2 and primary winding T_{P_2} induces a voltage in the feedback winding. The polarity of the induced voltage is such that Q_2 is driven further into conduction. Eventually, Q_1 is turned OFF. Because of the saturation of primary winding T_{P_2}, Q_2 saturates. A new cycle starts with Q_1 beginning to conduct.

Resistor R_{FB} limits the base current during switching when the core is saturated. The output across the secondary winding is a square wave. It may be rectified and filtered to obtain a dc output.

The SCR inverter operates in a manner similar to that of the push-pull type. Additional circuitry, however, is required for triggering the SCRs. Both inductive and capacitive loads can be operated safely from an SCR inverter.

17.5 Electronic Ignition Systems

The use of the SCR in automotive ignition systems has made possible more reliable engines, a reduction in emissions, and increased performance. Two types of ignition systems are popular: the *inductive-discharge* and the *capacitive-discharge* systems.

The basic requirements for a reliable ignition system are:

1. A voltage spike of approximately 22,000 V with a minimum of 20 mJ of energy to ignite the fuel mixture and ensure a stable flame.
2. The rise time of the voltage spike must be approximately 10 μs. A rise time which is too long results in a waste of energy. A short rise time results in high-frequency radiation through the ignition wires.

In an electronic ignition system, the circuit stores energy either in an inductor or in a capacitor. The stored energy then is delivered to the spark plugs. The capacitive-discharge system is superior to the inductive type, but it is also more complex and expensive. In the capacitive-discharge system, higher rise times can be obtained. In addition, input power increases with increased demands on output power at higher speeds.

The input power does not increase with increased demands or output power for the inductive-discharge system or with conventional ignition. In these systems, the output voltage drops at higher speeds, resulting in incomplete ignition and wasted fuel.

A block diagram of an inverter-charged ignition system is illustrated in Fig. 17–20. The dc-to-ac inverter generates a square wave at a voltage level greater than the battery voltage. Capacitor *C* is charged to the higher voltage level. When the SCR is triggered, the capacitor discharges through the SCR and transformer.

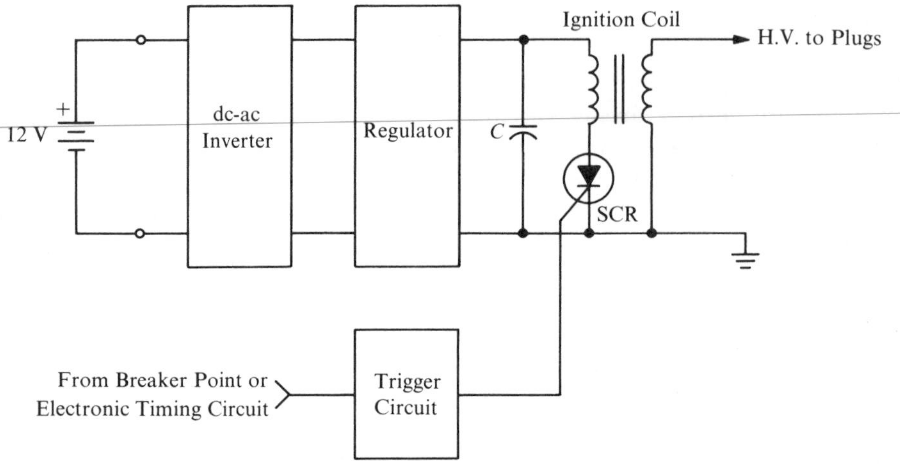

Fig. 17–20. *Block diagram of an inverter-charged, capacitive discharge ignition system.*

The regulator connected between the inverter and capacitor isolates the output from the inverter. When the output changes, as with an increase in engine rpm, the output power demands increase. As a result, the inverter is loaded. A regulator ensures the same charging current in the capacitor, regardless of load variations.

The breaker point in the distributor initiates the trigger circuit which supplies the gate signal to the SCR. Much lower currents flow through the points than in a conventional ignition system, thus increasing their life. Since the points are used to provide timing for the SCR, in some systems they are replaced by an electronic timing circuit.

The transformer is a standard ignition coil. In this circuit, the coil is used as a pulse transformer to step up the voltage. It is not used as an energy storage element.

SUMMARY

Thyristors are key elements in power-control circuits. The SCR and TRIAC control the output power to a load by controlling the conduction angle of the current flowing in the load. Ac power control is required in many industrial applications, including motor speed, time delay, light, and heating control.

Various circuits are used to trigger thyristors. One commonly used circuit employs the unijunction transistor (UJT).

The dc-to-ac inverter provides a square wave output from a dc source. If the square wave is rectified, a dc output, which may be greater than the dc input voltage, is obtained. In this case, the circuit is called a dc-to-dc converter.

Further Reading

Deboo, G. J., and C. N. Burrous. *Integrated Circuits and Semiconductor Devices: Theory and Application.* New York: McGraw-Hill Book Company, 1971, Chapters 8 and 9.

Driscoll, F. F., and R. F. Coughlin. *Solid State Devices and Applications.* Englewood Cliffs, N.J.: Prentice-Hall, 1975, Chapters 7–9.

RCA. *Solid State Power Circuits.* (Technical Series SP-52.) Somerville, N.J.: RCA Corporation, 1971.

Thomas, Harry E. *Handbook of Transistors, Semiconductors, Instruments, and Microelectronics.* Englewood Cliffs, N.J.: Prentice-Hall, 1968, Chapter 6.

REVIEW QUESTIONS

17.1 What is the difference between an SCR and a TRIAC?

17.2 Describe the methods for turning ON a thyristor.

17.3 At what conduction angle is an SCR most efficient?

17.4 Explain the purpose of diode *D* in the trigger circuit of Fig. 17–5B.

17.5 What is the advantage of a double-time constant over a single-time constant trigger?

17.6 What is the function of the UJT in the circuit of Fig. 17–9?

17.7 Is the SCR in Fig. 17–9 fired during the charging or discharging of capacitor *C*?

17.8 Which components determine the firing angle of the SCR in Fig. 17–10?

17.9 How is the operation of the circuit different when a half-wave rectifier is used instead of a full-wave rectifier in Fig. 17–10?

17.10 Explain how the circuit of Fig. 17–11 is used as a trigger.

17.11 Describe what is meant by integral switching control.

17.12 Describe how the speed of a universal motor can be controlled.

17.13 How is a TRIAC utilized in motor reversing applications?

17.14 What is the effect of opening resistor *R* in the circuit of Fig. 17–17?

17.15 In Fig. 17–18, what is the effect on the circuit if
(a) A permanent short occurs across the thermal flasher?

(b) A UJT burns out (opens)?
(c) Capacitor C_2 shorts out?

17.16 How can the output voltage of the converter of Fig. 17–19 be altered?

17.17 Discuss the purpose of the dc-to-ac inverter in the ignition system of Fig. 17–20.

PROBLEMS

P17–1 For the control circuit of Fig. 17–1A, the input voltage is 440 V rms, and $R_L = 20\,\Omega$. Employing the curves of Fig. 17–2, determine the conduction angle range if the variation in I_{rms} in the load is from 5 A to 10 A.

P17–2 Repeat prob. P17–1 for a voltage source of 220 V rms and a 6-Ω load.

P17–3 The circuit of Fig. 17–1A supplies a constant load current of 10 A rms when the input is 120 V rms and the load varies from 2 Ω to 5 Ω. Calculate the conduction angle range of the SCR.

P17–4 At what value of R_L will the circuit in prob. P17–3 be most efficient?

P17–5 What is the maximum current, I_p, that the SCR must be capable of handling in the circuit of prob. P17–3?

P17–6 Determine the input power to the circuit of Fig. 17–3 for a conduction angle of 60°.

P17–7 Repeat prob. P17–6 for a conduction angle of 45°.

P17–8 The TRIAC circuit of Fig. 17–1C delivers 100 W of power to a load.

(a) What is the efficiency of the circuit if the firing angle is 90°?
(b) How much input power is consumed at a firing angle of 90°?

P17–9 Repeat prob. P17–8 for a 60-W load.

P17–10 For the circuit of prob. P17–8, find the average current in a 10-Ω load if the conduction angle is 120°.

P17–11 For the SCR circuit of Fig. 17–6, $C = 1\,\mu F$, $R_L = 100\,\Omega$, and $V_i = 50$ V dc. If the SCR fires when the voltage across the capacitor is 1.5 V, to what should R be set for the SCR to fire 10 μs after V_i is applied to the circuit?

P17–12 For the circuit of Fig. 17–9, $C = 10\,\mu F$, $R = 50\,k\Omega$, and $\eta = 0.56$. Calculate the operating frequency of the UJT circuit.

P17–13 Repeat prob. P17–12 for $C = 50\,\mu F$.

P17–14 Determine the values of R_T and C_T in the circuit of Fig. 17–13 for a 2-s delay. Assume that $\eta = 0.60$.

P17–15 Repeat prob. P17–14 for a 5-s delay.

P17–16 Redesign the circuit of Fig. 17–14 to be activated by the *presence* of light. (*Hint*: The photocell is located in a different part of the circuit.)

P17–17 For the sequential turn signal of Fig. 17–18, determine the time required for all bulbs on one side to be lit during one cycle of operation ($\eta = 0.55$)

part v

SWITCHING OPERATION

Digital operations play an important role in the study of electronic circuits. This section of the text is concerned with the analysis and application of digital circuits and systems. Digital, or logic, circuits are designed to operate as switches. The switching device, such as a diode or transistor, is either conducting current (ON) or is nonconducting (OFF).

The digital computer, as well as other digital systems, is largely composed of logic circuits. The objective of Chapter 18 is to provide the background for the understanding of these circuits. Some topics covered in the chapter include binary arithmetic, Boolean algebra, basic logic gates, truth tables, and Karnaugh maps. Chapter 19 deals with the analysis and application of diode and transistor logic gates.

Integrated circuit (IC) logic is classified on the basis of a particular circuit design philosophy. Such a classification divides the various logic circuits into logic families. The different logic families are studied and compared in Chapter 20.

Multivibrators are essential elements of computers and are discussed in Chapter 21. The use of multivibrators in shift registers, counters, and memory elements is examined in Chapter 22. Special attention is devoted to semiconductor memories, such as the read-only memory (ROM) and the random-access memory (RAM).

The concluding chapter of the text, Chapter 23, completes the study of electronic circuits by examining analog-to-digital (A/D) converters, digital-to-analog (D/A) converters, visual displays, and the microprocessor.

18

Introduction to Computers

Ever since people learned how to count and recognized the importance of numbers in everyday life, they have sought ways for reducing calculating time. The modern computer bears little resemblance to the first computing aids, such as the counting board and its big brother, the abacus. The only similarity between the ancient and modern computers is that today's computer is still designed, built, given instructions, and operated by human beings.

Two basic types of electronic computers are in use today. The *analog* computer, which solves differential equations, finds many applications in engineering and in the simulation of physical systems. This section is concerned with the *digital* computer and its electronic circuits. Digital computers are used in virtually every field of human endeavor. The wide use of digital computers stems from the speed and accuracy with which they perform calculations and store and process numerical data.

18.1 Computer Organization

A block diagram showing the major sections of a digital computer is given in Fig. 18–1. Information in the form of numbers and instructions is fed into the computer through the *input* section. The information may be on punched cards, teletypewriters, paper tape, magnetic tape, etc. The

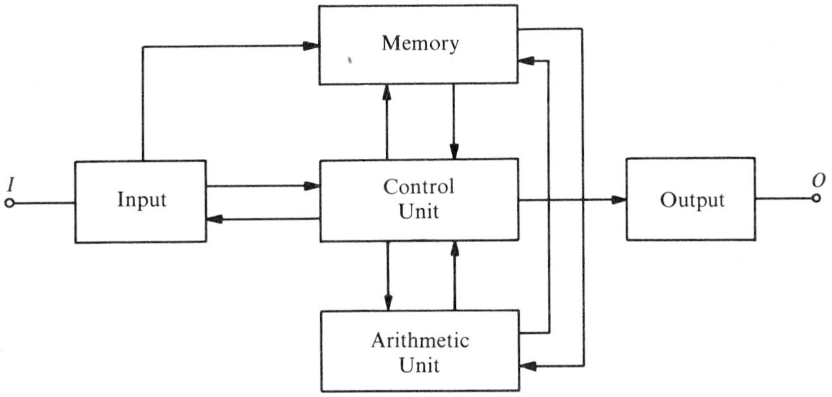

Fig. 18–1. *Block diagram of a digital computer.*

memory section stores numbers fed into the computer. It also stores the results of intermediate calculations and instructions the computer is to follow.

The *control* section initiates and directs the computer operations. It supplies the required electric signals to the appropriate sections in accordance with the instructions stored in the memory. Mathematical operations are performed in the *arithmetic* section. It contains circuits that perform the basic operations of addition, subtraction, multiplication, and division.

Results obtained in the computer are directed to the *output* section. In addition to tape, etc., used at the input, results may be displayed on a cathode-ray tube or an X-Y plotter. As in any electronic system, a power supply is needed to furnish power to each section of the computer.

One important concern with digital computers is the formulation of mathematical problems in a manner that is acceptable to a computer. This is called *programming* the computer. A program is a set of instructions, written by a person, which instructs the computer which numbers to use and the type and sequence of operations. In other words, a program is a set of instructions that a computer must follow to solve a problem. The modern digital computer accepts instructions written in a number of programming languages, such as FORTRAN, BASIC, and COBOL. Programs and other computer operating information are called *software.*

Computer *hardware* refers to the electronic and mechanical components of which the computer is constructed. To understand the circuits, known as *digital* or *switching* circuits, one must learn how electric signals can be related to numbers. One obvious method is to relate electric signal levels to correspond to a number. For example, 5 V may correspond to number 5, 10 V to number 10, and so on. This procedure is employed in analog computers where calibration of the unit is necessary before a new problem is solved on the computer.

A digital computer, which performs a multitude of mathematical computations in a fraction of a second, cannot be based on a number system where ten levels (0–9) of signals must be sensed accurately. Consider, for example, the problems caused by changes due to temperature or the aging of components. A number system that can be represented by two voltage levels and which is independent of variations in components is needed.

A device suitable for the representation of two levels is a switch. A switch is either open (OFF) or closed (ON). The simple circuit of Fig. 18–2A employing a mechanical switch produces two levels: 0 V when the switch is open and 6 V when it is closed. The circuit of Fig. 18–2B shows a transistor operating as a switch. It is either in the cutoff or in the

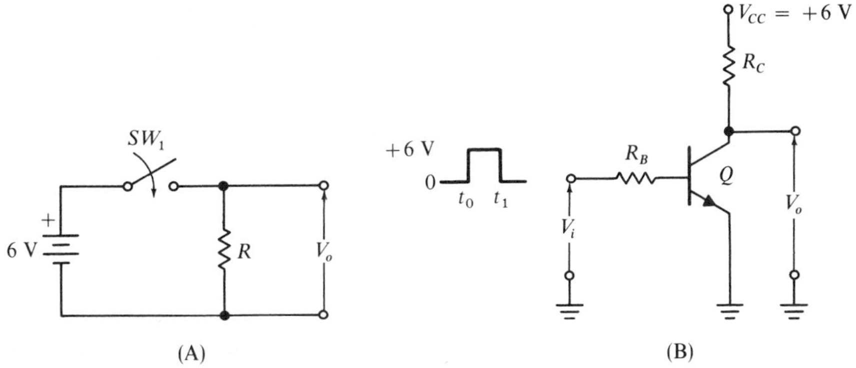

Fig. 18–2. *Basic switching circuits. (A) Using a mechanical switch. (B) Transistor replaces the mechanical switch.*

saturation region of operation. When the input is zero, the transistor is cut off, and the output is approximately equal to V_{CC}, or 6 V. When the input voltage is 6 V, the transistor is saturated, and the output is equal to V_{sat}, or approximately 0 V.

Now that we see how it is possible to build circuits which provide two distinct voltage levels, let us examine a number system which contains only two numerals: 0 and 1. Such a system is known as the *binary number system.*

18.2 Binary Numbers

The number system we use daily and know so well is the *decimal system.* It contains ten numerals, 0–9; therefore, the *base*, or *radix*, of the system is 10. Consider the number 39. In decimal notation, it has an equivalent weight of

$$39 = 3 \times 10^1 + 9 \times 10^0 = 30 + 9$$

The relative *position* of each digit is significant. The 9 occupies the units location and the 3 the tens slot. A number is written as a sum of digits, represented by the product of the coefficients and powers of 10 (10 being the base of the number system). Changing the base to 2, the number 39 is represented in the binary system as

$$\begin{array}{ccccccccccccc} 32 & + & 0 & + & 0 & + & 4 & + & 2 & + & 1 & = & 39 \text{ (decimal)} \\ \updownarrow & & \updownarrow & & \updownarrow & & \updownarrow & & \updownarrow & & \updownarrow & & \\ 1 \times 2^5 & + & 0 \times 2^4 & + & 0 \times 2^3 & + & 1 \times 2^2 & + & 1 \times 2^1 & + & 1 \times 2^0 & = & 100111 \text{ (binary)} \end{array}$$

All basic operations that apply to decimal numbers also apply to binary numbers. It takes six binary digits, or *bits*, to express the number 39, which can be represented by two decimal digits. The usefulness of the binary representation of numbers lies in its implementation by reliable electronic circuits.

A computer performs arithmetic with binary numbers but accepts information and displays answers in decimal form. The computer's ability to make this conversion requires coding techniques, such as the *binary coded decimal* (BCD).

In this code, each decimal digit is represented by its binary equivalent. For example, a four-digit decimal number requires 16 bits for its representation:

The decimal number:	2	3	4	5
In BCD:	0010	0011	0100	0101

The conversion of a binary to a decimal number requires the multiplication of each bit by 2 raised to an appropriate power, depending on the position of the bit. The right-most bit, or *least significant bit* (LSB) has a weight of 1 ($2^0 = 1$). Progressing to the left, the next bit has a weight of 2 ($2^1 = 2$), and so on. The decimal equivalent is computed by finding the sum of the values in each position.

EXAMPLE 18–1.

Convert the binary number 11011 to its decimal equivalent.

Solution:

Each bit is multiplied by 2 raised to the appropriate power, and the values of the bits are added:

$$1 \times 2^4 + 1 \times 2^3 + 0 \times 2^2 + 1 \times 2^1 + 1 \times 2^0$$
$$= 16 + 8 + 0 + 2 + 1 = 27$$

Therefore, $11011_B = 27_D$ where the subscript B denotes a binary number and D denotes a decimal number.

Conversion of a decimal to a binary number requires the successive division by 2 of the decimal number. A binary bit (0 or 1) results as a remainder of each division. The first remainder becomes the least significant bit, and the last remainder the most significant bit (MSB).

EXAMPLE 18–2.

Convert the decimal number 47 to its binary equivalent.

Solution:

Successive division by 2 yields

	Remainder
$47/2 = 23$	1 (LSB)
$23/2 = 11$	1
$11/2 = 5$	1
$5/2 = 2$	1
$2/2 = 1$	0
$1/2 = 0$	1 (MSB)

Therefore, $47_D = 101111_B$. The result may be verified by performing a binary-to-decimal conversion, as in Example 18–1.

18.3 Logic Gates

A digital computer performs mathematical calculations by repeated execution of a few simple operations. That is why a computer is constructed of only a few different types of switching circuits. Thousands of these basic circuits are used in the computer. They are of two general types: the multivibrator and the logic gate. The multivibrator, to be considered in Chapter 21, is used in counters and storage elements. Logic gates are used to control the flow of data and in the arithmetic section of the computer.

Logic gating functions are performed in accordance with the rules of *Boolean algebra.* George Boole invented the algebra in the middle of the nineteenth century. Almost a hundred years later (1938), Claude E. Shannon utilized Boolean algebra in the design of switching systems. This marked the beginning of logic circuit design, which led to the digital computer.

OR Gate

Letters of the alphabet and other symbols are used to write Boolean equations, in the same manner as one writes ordinary algebraic equations. The numbers that are substituted for the variables in these equations, however, are either 0 or 1. The operations performed on these numbers are different from basic arithmetic operations.

Consider the following Boolean expression:

$$A + B = C \qquad \textbf{(18–1)}$$

This is read "*A or B* is equal to *C*." (It is *not* the same as "*A plus B* is equal to *C*.") The symbol of the logic gate which performs the OR operation, called an *OR gate,* is shown in Fig. 18–3A.

The gate has two inputs, *A* and *B*, and one output, *C*. Keeping in mind that *A*, *B*, and *C* can assume values of only 0 and 1, we can construct a table which lists all their possible values. Such a tabulation is known as a *truth table.* Table 18–1 is the truth table for the OR operation. From the truth table, *the output of an OR gate is a logic 1 if at least one of its inputs is a 1.* This definition is also true for OR gates with more than two inputs.

TABLE 18–1. Truth table for a two-input OR gate.

A	B	C
0	0	0
0	1	1
1	0	1
1	1	1

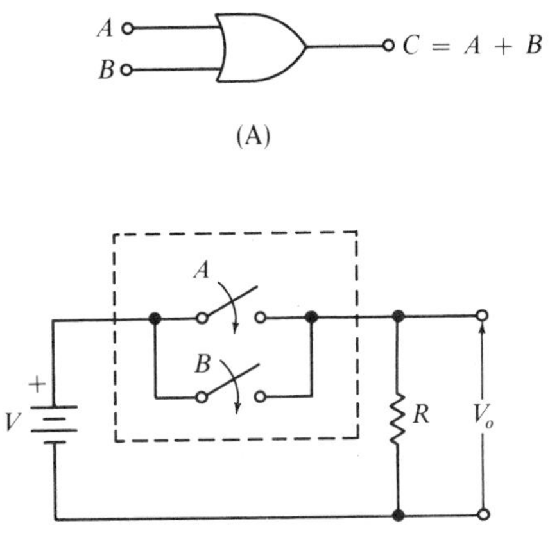

Fig. 18–3. *The OR gate. (A) Logic symbol. (B) OR gate implemented with two mechanical switches in parallel.*

In Fig. 18–3B, the OR operation is illustrated by switches connected in parallel. Output voltage $V_o = 0$ when both switches are open; this corresponds to $A = B = 0$. For all other conditions—switch A open and switch B closed, switch B closed and switch A open, or both switches closed—the output is equal to V volts.

To this point, we have assumed that 0 V corresponds to a logic 0, and a higher voltage corresponds to a logic 1. Such a system is called *positive logic*. A system where the more negative voltage corresponds to a logic 1 is known as *negative logic*.

A *dynamic* logic system accepts time-varying signals in the form of pulses. The presence of a pulse denotes a logic 1; the absence of a pulse, a logic 0. For example, two pulse trains are applied to the two-input OR gate of Fig. 18–4. The corresponding output is also shown. It was determined by carefully examining the response of the OR gate from the truth table to the inputs at each time interval T.

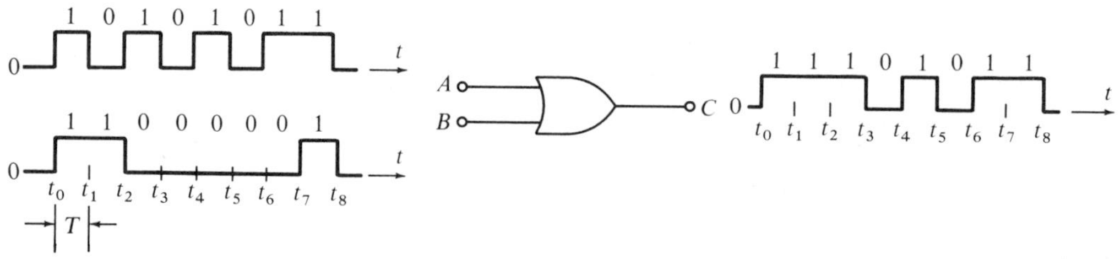

Fig. 18–4. *Response of a two-input OR gate to trains of pulses.*

The presence or absence of a pulse within time interval T represents a bit, 1 or 0, respectively. Applied to input A is the sequence 10101011; to B, 11000001. The resulting output is 11101011. Pulse trains representing groups of bits are called *bytes* and *words*.

EXAMPLE 18–3.

The following pulse trains are applied to a three-input OR gate:

$$A = 1010 \qquad B = 1001 \qquad C = 1000$$

Determine the train of pulses at the output terminal, D.

Solution:

The Boolean equation for a three-input OR gate is $A + B + C = D$. The truth table is

A	B	C	D
0	0	0	0
0	0	1	1
0	1	0	1
0	1	1	1
1	0	0	1
1	0	1	1
1	1	0	1
1	1	1	1

Eight possible input combinations exist for a three-input OR gate. The total number of possible input combinations, n, for any gate is

$$n = 2^z \qquad \textbf{(18–2)}$$

where z is the number of inputs. For example, if $z = 3$, $n = 2^3 = 8$.

Examining the corresponding bits in each input word with the truth table, we obtain 1 for the MSB. The next corresponding bits in A, B, and C are 0, 0, and 0, respectively. This results in an output bit of 0. Similarly, 1, 0, 0 yields a 1; and 0, 1, 0 results in a 1 for the LSB. The output at $D = 1011$.

AND Gate

The symbol for a two-input AND gate is shown in Fig. 18–5A. The Boolean expression for an AND gate is

$$A \cdot B = C \qquad \textbf{(18–3)}$$

Expression (18–3) is read "*A and B* is equal to *C*." The dot indicates the AND operation; it does not represent multiplication. The dot is usually omitted, and Eq. (18–3) is written as $AB = C$.

From the truth table for a two-input AND gate (Table 18–2), the output is a logic 1 only when *both inputs* are a logic 1. This result can be extended to include gates with more than two inputs by stating that the output of an AND gate is a logic 1 if and only if *all* inputs are a logic 1.

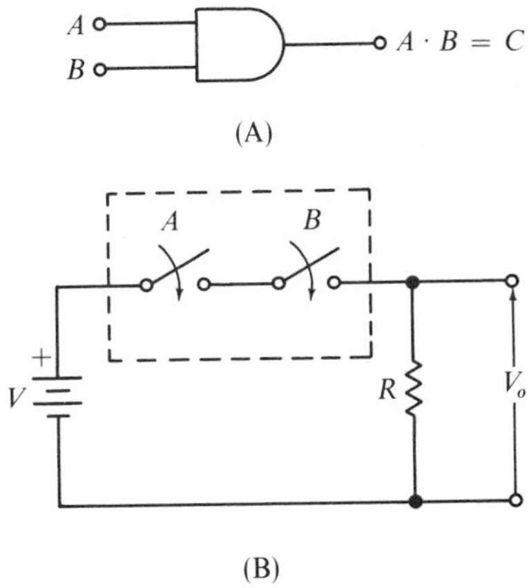

Fig. 18–5. *The AND gate. (A) Logic symbol. (B) AND gate implemented with two mechanical switches in series.*

TABLE 18–2. Truth table for a two-input AND gate.

A	B	C
0	0	0
0	1	0
1	0	0
1	1	1

Figure 18–5B illustrates the AND operation by two mechanical switches, A and B, in series. If either or both switches are open, $V_o = 0$. Output $V_o = V$ volts only if *both* switches are closed.

INVERTER

The INVERTER, or NOT circuit, has one input. Its function is to change a logic 1 to a 0 or a 0 to a 1. This process is known as *logic negation*. The INVERTER is represented symbolically by an amplifier with a small circle indicating

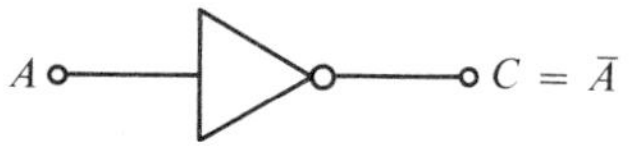

Fig. 18–6. *Logic symbol for an INVERTER (NOT circuit).*

inversion (Fig. 18–6). The Boolean, or logic equation, for the INVERTER is

$$C = \overline{A} \qquad \textbf{(18–4)}$$

The horizontal bar above A indicates inversion. Equation (18–4) is read "C is equal to A NOT." Term $\overline{A}$ also is called the *complement of A*.

The truth table for the INVERTER (Table 18–3) is exceedingly simple because of its single input, A. By connecting the output of one INVERTER to the input of another INVERTER, the output obtained is equal to A. This process is called *double inversion*, or *double negation*, and is indicated by two horizontal bars above the A:

$$\overline{\overline{A}} = A \qquad \textbf{(18–5)}$$

TABLE 18–3. Truth table for an INVERTER.

A	$C = \overline{A}$
0	1
1	0

NOR and NAND

An INVERTER connected to the output of an OR gate performs the NOT-OR, or NOR, operation. For a two-input (A and B) NOR gate, its output, C, is

$$C = \overline{A + B} \qquad \textbf{(18–6)}$$

which is read "C is equal to the NOT of A *or* B."

For a two-input NAND gate, inputs A and B are related to output C by

$$C = \overline{AB} \qquad \textbf{(18–7)}$$

which is read "C is equal to the NOT of A *and* B." Truth tables and logic symbols for two-input NOR and NAND gates are given in Table 18–4 and Fig. 18–7, respectively.

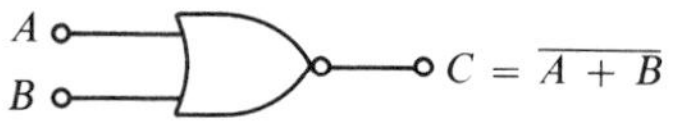

(A)

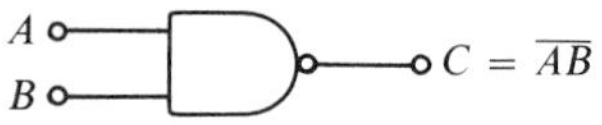

(B)

Fig. 18–7. *Logic symbols for (A) NOR gate and (B) NAND gate.*

TABLE 18–4. Truth tables for a two-input (A) NOR and (B) NAND gate.

(A)

A	B	C
0	0	1
0	1	0
1	0	0
1	1	0

(B)

A	B	C
0	0	1
0	1	1
1	0	1
1	1	0

An examination of the truth tables reveals that the inversion of a NOR results in an OR operation. Similarly, an inversion of a NAND yields an AND. Therefore, a NOR gate followed by an INVERTER may be substituted for an

OR gate. Similarly, a NAND gate followed by an INVERTER is equivalent to an AND gate.

If, for example, terminal A of a NOR is allowed to assume a 0 level (accomplished by connecting the A input to ground or to a low potential in a positive logic system), output C is a 1 when $B = 0$, and $C = 0$ when $B = 1$. In other words, the gate acts as an INVERTER for the signal at terminal B. Another method for converting a NOR gate to an INVERTER is to connect all the inputs of the NOR gate, which become the common input terminal.

In a similar manner, the two-input NAND gate can be used as an INVERTER by forming a single input terminal. The single input terminal is formed by connecting input A to a high voltage level for a logic 1 and using B as the input terminal. Also, the input terminals may be connected, as described for the NOR gate. The implementation of the OR function with NOR gates, and the AND function with NAND gates, is shown in Figs. 18–8 and 18–9, respectively.

The previous discussion may be summarized as follows: OR, AND, NOT, NOR, and NAND operations can be implemented with only NAND and NOR gates. This simple fact enables the designer of a logic system, such as a computer, to work with large numbers of a few basic gates. It eliminates layout and wiring errors and simplifies troubleshooting.

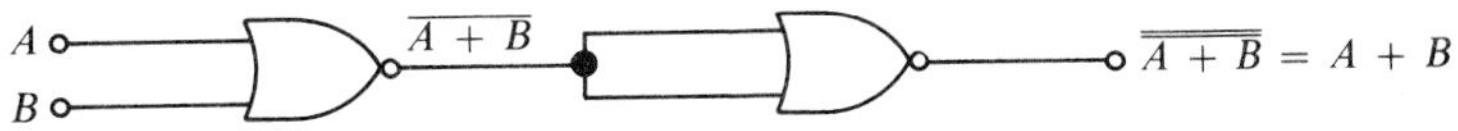

Fig. 18–8. *Using two NOR gates to implement the OR function.*

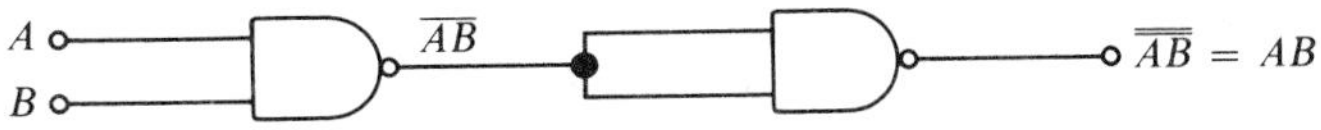

Fig. 18–9. *Two NAND gates used to implement the AND function.*

Another type of logic circuit is the EXCLUSIVE-OR gate of Fig. 18–10. Its truth table (Table 18–5) shows that

TABLE 18–5. Truth table for a two-input EXCLUSIVE-OR gate.

A	B	C
0	0	0
0	1	1
1	0	1
1	1	0

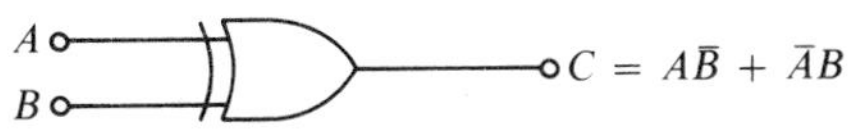

Fig. 18–10. *Logic symbol for an EXCLUSIVE-OR gate.*

the output for a two-input EXCLUSIVE-OR gate is 1 only if *one, but not both,* of the inputs is logic 1. The only difference between this gate and the OR gate is that its output is a 0 when both inputs are 1.

18.4 Elementary Boolean Algebra

At this point, it should be clear that it is possible to build electronic circuits to perform logic operations. We now must familiarize ourselves with the laws of Boolean algebra. Knowledge of Boolean algebra will permit us to develop and manipulate expressions in order to arrive at the simplest relationships for circuit implementation.

The basic properties of Boolean algebra are summarized in Table 18–6. Numerical examples are also provided to illustrate each property. Although one example is not sufficient, a truth table which examines all possibilities can be constructed to prove each property.

TABLE 18–6. Properties of Boolean algebra.

Property	Relation	Numerical Example for $A = 1, B = C = 0$
	$A + 0 = A$ $A \cdot 0 = 0$ $A + 1 = 1$ $A \cdot 1 = A$	$1 + 0 = 1$ $1 \cdot 0 = 0$ $1 + 1 = 1$ $1 \cdot 1 = 1$
Commutative	$A + B = B + A$ $A \cdot B = B \cdot A$	$1 + 0 = 0 + 1$ $1 \cdot 0 = 0 \cdot 1$
Associative	$(A + B) + C = A + (B + C)$ $(A \cdot B) \cdot C = A \cdot (B \cdot C)$	$(1 + 0) + 0 = 1 + (0 + 0)$ $(1 \cdot 0) \cdot 0 = 1 \cdot (0 \cdot 0)$
Distributive	$A + (B \cdot C) = (A + B)(A + C)$ $A \cdot (B + C) = (A \cdot B) + (A \cdot C)$	$1 + (0 \cdot 0) = (1 + 0)(1 + 0)$ $1 \cdot (0 + 0) = (1 \cdot 0) + (1 \cdot 0)$
Negation	$\overline{\overline{A}} = A$	$\overline{\overline{1}} = 1$
Redundancy	$A + A \cdot B = A$ $A \cdot (A + B) = A$ $A + \overline{A} \cdot B = A + B$ $A \cdot (\overline{A} + B) = A \cdot B$	$1 + 1 \cdot 0 = 1$ $1 \cdot (1 + 0) = 1$ $1 + (0 \cdot 0) = 1 + 0$ $1 \cdot (0 + 0) = 1 \cdot 0$
Identity	$A + A = A$ $A \cdot A = A$ $\overline{A} + A = A$ $\overline{A} \cdot A = 0$	$1 + 1 = 1$ $1 \cdot 1 = 1$ $0 + 1 = 1$ $0 \cdot 1 = 0$
DeMorgan's Theorems	$(\overline{A + B}) = \overline{A} \cdot \overline{B}$ $(\overline{A \cdot B}) = \overline{A} + \overline{B}$	$(\overline{1 + 0}) = 0 \cdot 1$ $(\overline{1 \cdot 0}) = 0 + 1$

EXAMPLE 18–4.

Prove that
(a) $A + BC = (A + B)(A + C)$.
(b) $A(B + C) = AB + AC$ (the distributive laws).

Solutions:

(a) From the following truth table, $A + BC = (A + B)(A + C)$:

Inputs			Outputs	
A	B	C	$A + BC$	$(A + B)(A + C)$
0	0	0	0	0
0	0	1	0	0
0	1	0	0	0
0	1	1	1	1
1	0	0	1	1
1	0	1	1	1
1	1	0	1	1
1	1	1	1	1

(b) Similarly, the following truth table verifies that $A(B + C) = AB + AC$:

Inputs			Outputs	
A	B	C	$A(B + C)$	$AB + AC$
0	0	0	0	0
0	0	1	0	0
0	1	0	0	0
0	1	1	0	0
1	0	0	0	0
1	0	1	1	1
1	1	0	1	1
1	1	1	1	1

In the next two examples, we shall see how the properties listed in Table 18–6 may be used to simplify logic expressions. Logic diagrams will be drawn showing their implementation.

EXAMPLE 18–5.

Simplify $B(A + \overline{B})$.

Solution:

Simplification in this example means to arrive at a new expression which contains fewer terms. Fewer gates are therefore required to implement the expression.

By the distributive property,

$$B(A + \overline{B}) = BA + B\overline{B}$$

By the identity property, $B\overline{B} = 0$. Hence,

$$B(A + \overline{B}) = BA = AB \qquad \text{(by the commutative property)}$$

Using the truth table for verification, we see

Inputs		Outputs	
A	B	$B(A + \overline{B})$	AB
0	0	0	0
0	1	0	0
1	0	0	0
1	1	1	1

EXAMPLE 18–6.

Draw logic diagrams for

(a) $B(A + \overline{B})$.

(b) AB.

Recall from Example 18–5 that $B(A + \overline{B}) = AB$.

Solutions:

(a) From the equation, it is apparent that at least two logic operations are to be performed: A *or* $\overline{B}$ and B *and* $(A + \overline{B})$. If $\overline{B}$ is not available, B also must be inverted. The logic diagram is shown in Fig. 18–11. An INVERTER, an OR, and an AND gate are required to implement $B(A + \overline{B})$.

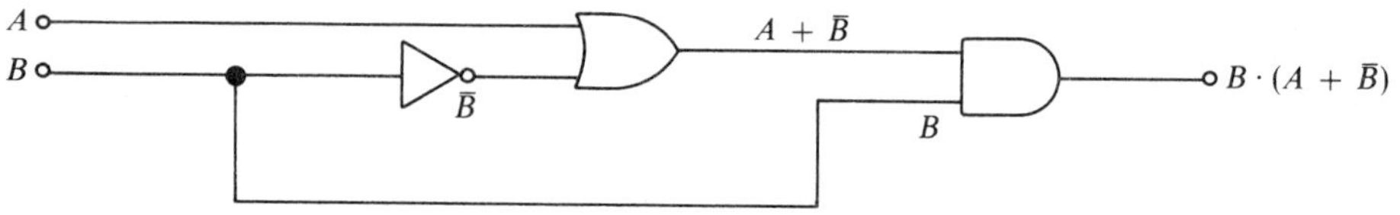

Fig. 18–11. *Logic diagram for Example 18–6(a).*

(b) For AB, only one operation is required: A *and* B. The logic diagram is given in Fig. 18–12, showing that only one AND gate is required. This example demonstrates why it pays, if possible, to simplify logic expressions.

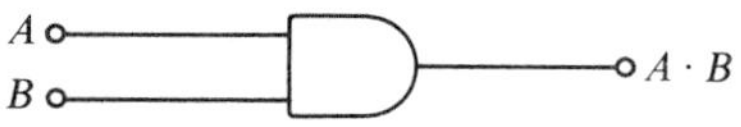

Fig. 18–12. *Logic diagram for Example 18–6(b).*

Occasionally, a logic circuit is given, and the logic expression for the circuit is to be obtained. The procedure to follow in this type of problem is illustrated in the next example.

EXAMPLE 18–7.

Write the logic equation for the logic circuit of Fig. 18–13A.

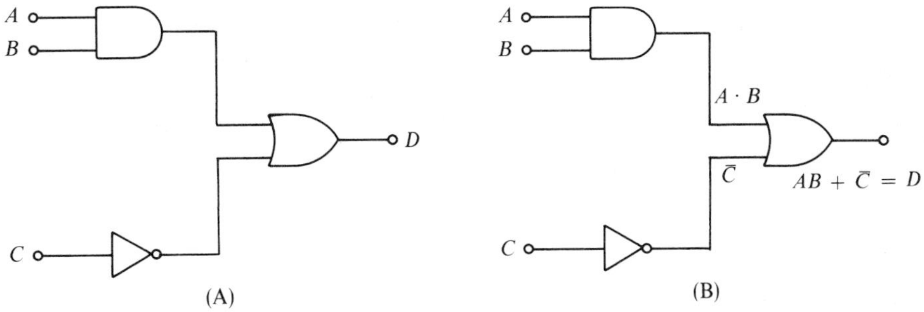

Fig. 18–13. *Logic diagrams for Example 18–7. (A) Original circuit. (B) Logic expressions added for each logic circuit.*

Solution:

The logic diagram is redrawn in Fig. 18–13B, and output expressions for each gate are listed. Hence, $D = AB + \bar{C}$.

DeMorgan's theorem (Table 18–6) implies that through inversion, a NOR operation is realized by using an AND gate with inverted inputs. Similarly, a NAND operation is obtained through the use of an OR gate with inverted inputs. DeMorgan's theorem is useful in manipulating an expression for NAND or NOR gate implementation.

EXAMPLE 18–8.

Arrange $D = (A + B)\bar{C}$ for NAND gate implementation. Draw a logic diagram for the obtained expression.

Solution:

Applying the distributive property,

$$(A + B)\bar{C} = A\bar{C} + B\bar{C}$$

Negating the obtained expression and applying DeMorgan's Theorem,

$$(A\bar{C} + B\bar{C})' = (A\bar{C})'(B\bar{C})'$$

where the prime ('), as the horizontal bar, is used for inversion (negation). Negating the expression a second time yields the original expression. Hence,

$$\overline{(A\bar{C})'(B\bar{C})'} = D$$

The logic diagram is drawn in Fig. 18–14.

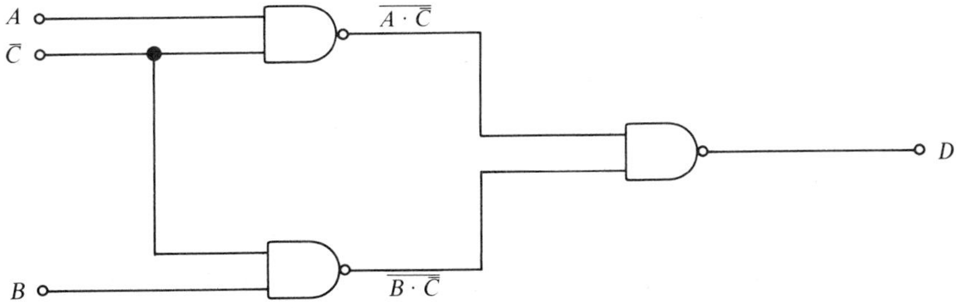

Fig. 18–14. *Logic diagram for Example 18–8.*

If input $\bar{C}$ *is not available*, an additional NAND gate is used as an INVERTER. The new logic diagram appears in Fig. 18–15.

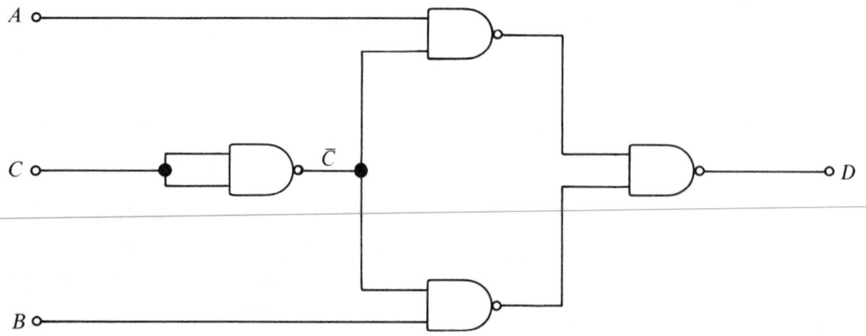

Fig. 18–15. *Alternate logic diagram for Example 18–8.*

We also can implement logic expressions with only NOR gates. A procedure similar to that used in the preceding example is illustrated by Example 18–9.

EXAMPLE 18–9.

Implement $D = (A + \bar{B})(A + C)$ using only NOR gates. Draw the resulting logic diagram.

Solution:

If the terms are not already ANDed, they must be manipulated into this form. In this example, both expressions are ANDed. Negating the equation and applying DeMorgan's theorem, we have

$$\bar{D} = \overline{(A + \bar{B})(A + C)} = \overline{(A + \bar{B})} + \overline{(A + C)}$$

Negating the expression a second time,

$$\bar{\bar{D}} = D = \overline{\overline{(A + \bar{B})} + \overline{(A + C)}}$$

The logic diagram is drawn in Fig. 18–16. A NOR gate is used as an INVERTER to obtain $\bar{B}$.

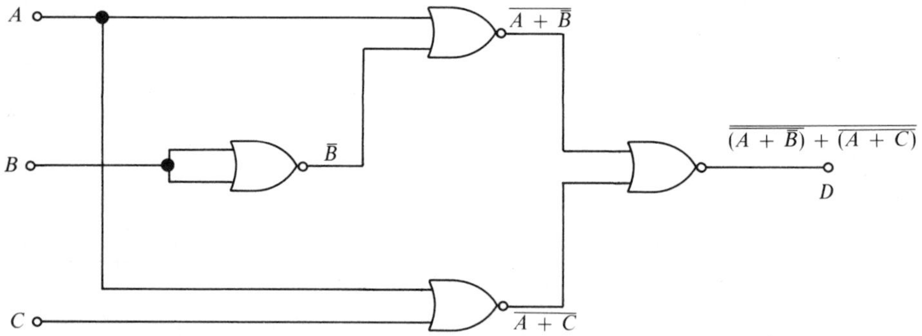

Fig. 18–16. *Logic diagram for Example 18–9.*

Conversions from an OR and AND gate to either a NOR or NAND gate are provided in Table 18–7. The application of the table is illustrated in the next example.

TABLE 18–7. Basic operations realized with NOR and NAND gates.

Basic Operation	NOR	NAND
INVERTER	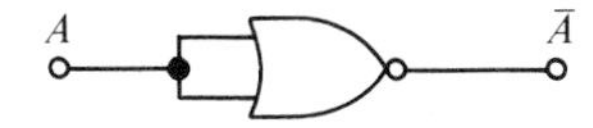	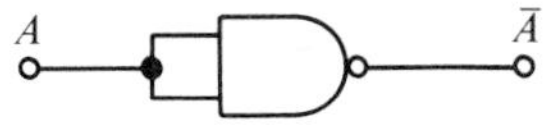
OR	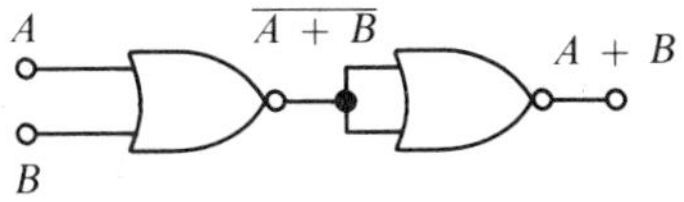	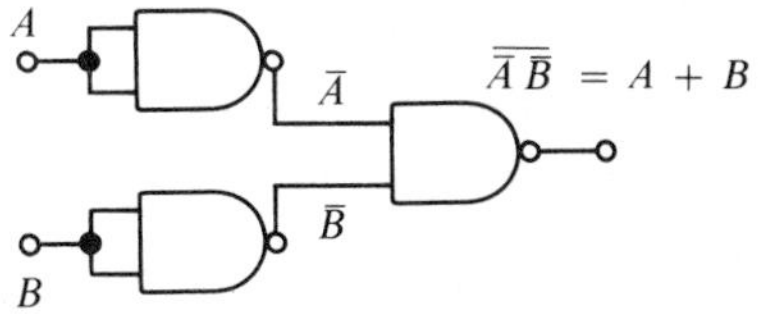
AND	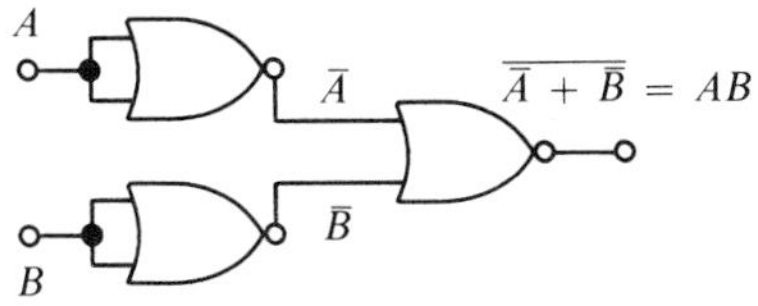	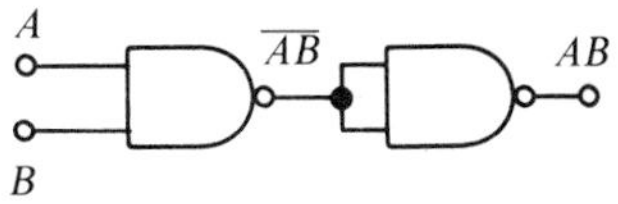

EXAMPLE 18–10.

With the aid of Table 18–7, implement $D = (A + \overline{B})(A + C)$ using only

(a) NOR gates.

(b) NAND gates.

Solutions:

(a) Based on the NOR operations listed in Table 18–7, the logic diagram for the function is drawn in Fig. 18–17. Note that two cases of double negation exist. The simplified logic circuit, which is the same as

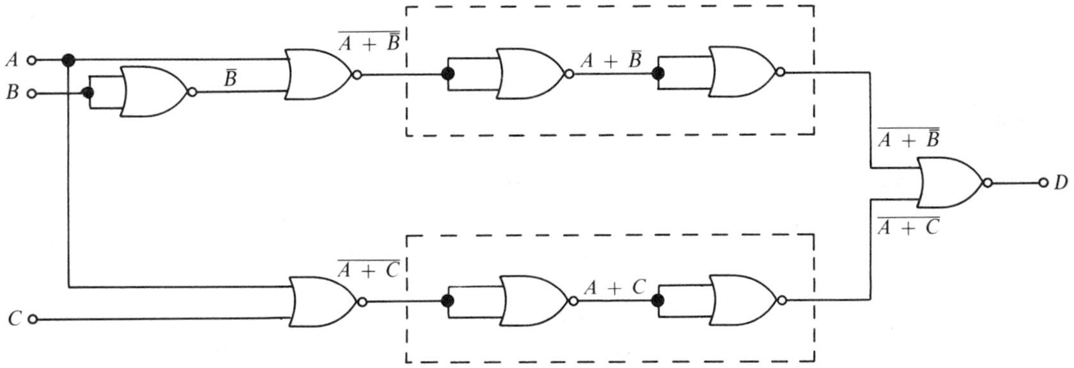

Fig. 18–17. *Logic diagram for Example 18–10 using NOR gates.*

that obtained in Example 18–9, is shown in Fig. 18–18.

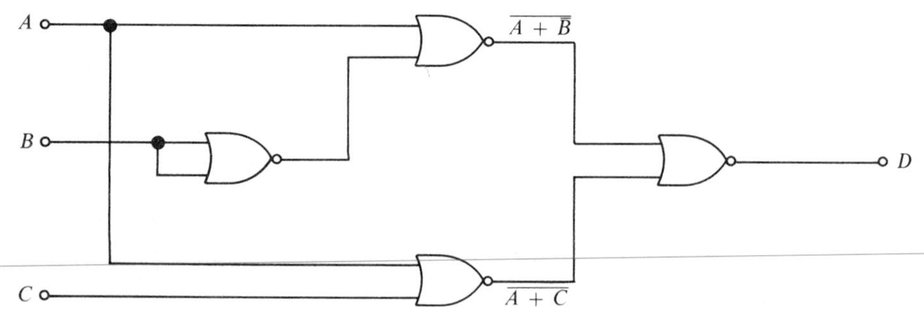

Fig. 18–18. *Simplified version of Fig. 18–17.*

(b) With the aid of Table 18–7, the logic circuit using only NAND gates appears in Fig. 18–19. With the double negation eliminated, the simplified circuit is provided in Fig. 18–20.

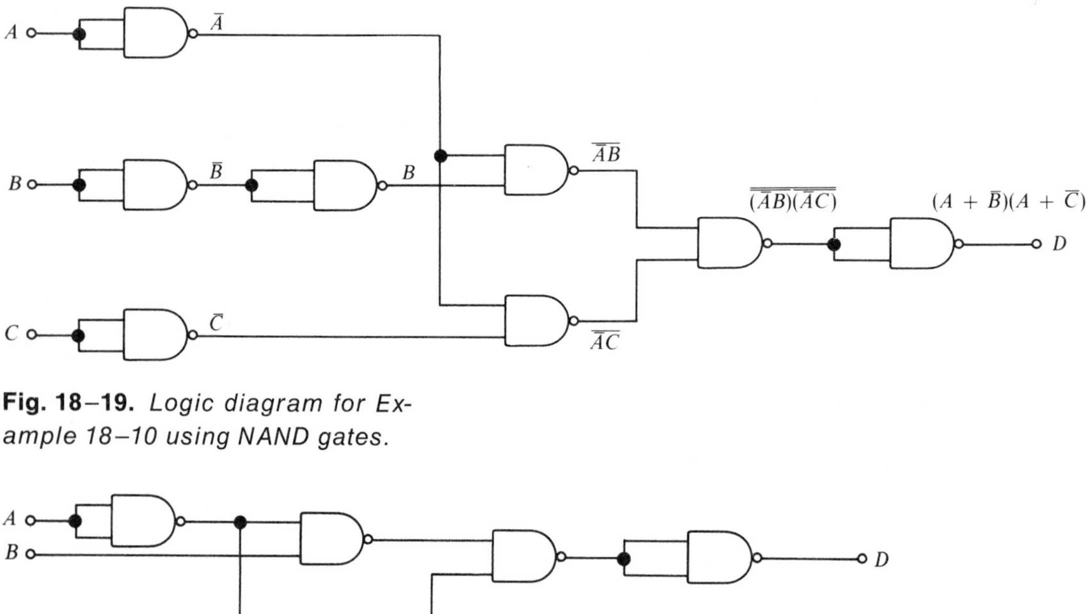

Fig. 18–19. *Logic diagram for Example 18–10 using NAND gates.*

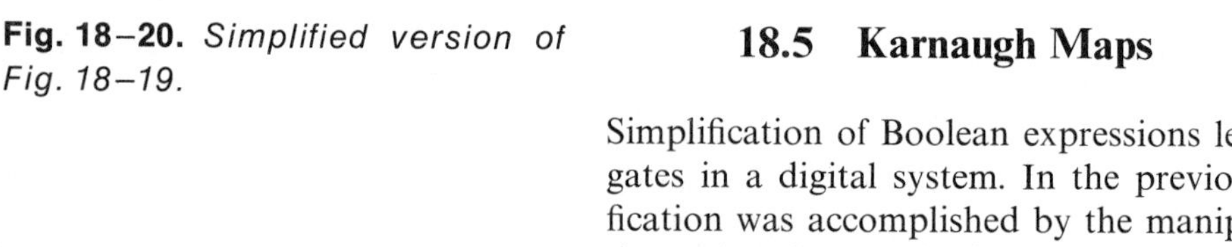

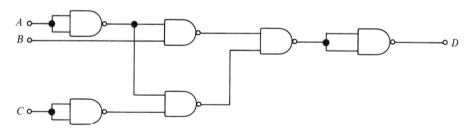

Fig. 18–20. *Simplified version of Fig. 18–19.*

18.5 Karnaugh Maps

Simplification of Boolean expressions leads to fewer logic gates in a digital system. In the previous section, simplification was accomplished by the manipulation of expressions. Another method of simplification is the use of a *Karnaugh map.* This technique provides a systematic graphical reduction of logic expressions. The procedure is as follows:

1. Determine the number of variables n in the expression.
2. Draw an n variable map (Fig. 18–21).

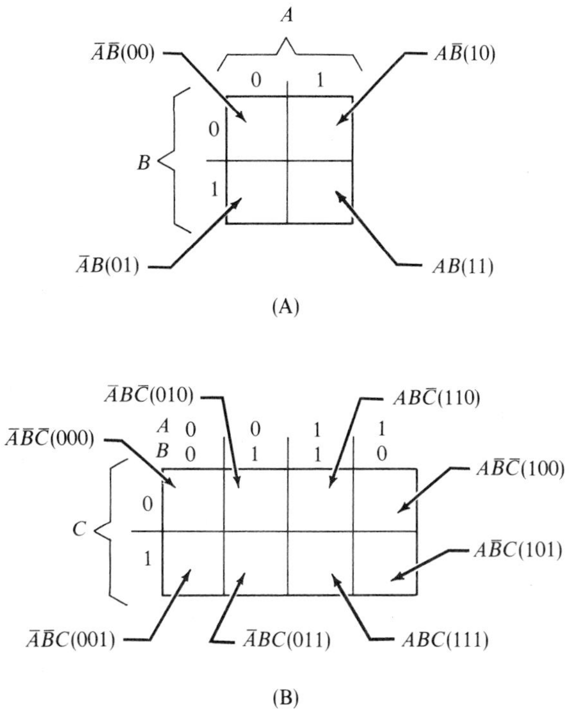

Fig. 18–21. *Karnaugh maps for (A) two variables and (B) three variables.*

3. Fill in the appropriate boxes with logic 1's.
4. Obtain the simplified expression by grouping *even* (2, 4, 8, 16, . . .) numbers of adjacent 1's.

Figure 18–21 illustrates a two- and a three-variable map. Although Karnaugh maps are used to simplify expressions containing more than three variables, they are seldom used for more than six variables. The number of boxes represents the possible combinations of n variables.

EXAMPLE 18–11.

Using a Karnaugh map, simplify the expression $\bar{A}B + \bar{A}\bar{B}$.

Solution:

Two variables, A and B, are present; hence, a two-variable map is drawn in Fig. 18–22. A logic 1 is inserted in each appropriate box to indicate that a combination of variables exists in the expressions $\bar{A}B$ and $\bar{A}\bar{B}$. The empty boxes correspond to terms not present in the original expression.

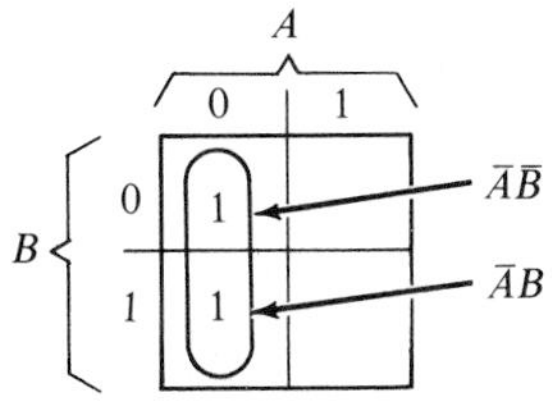

Fig. 18–22. *Two-variable Karnaugh map for Example 18–11.*

We seek even numbers of adjacent 1's which may be grouped horizontally or vertically. In this example, two 1's are grouped vertically. The group spans locations 0 and 1 for B, denoting a *change* in B. The group, however, remains within the $\bar{A}$ (0) location for A. Therefore, the simplified expression is $\bar{A}$ ($\bar{A}B + \bar{A}\bar{B} = \bar{A}$).

One term resulted from the simplification process of Example 18–11 which corresponds to a group of two 1's.

EXAMPLE 18–12.

Simplify $\bar{A}\bar{B}\bar{C} + AB\bar{C} + ABC + A\bar{B}\bar{C} + A\bar{B}C$ using a Karnaugh map.

Solution:

The simplification of this expression requires a three-variable map. Plotting the terms on the map results in Fig. 18–23. A group of four adjacent 1's and a group of two adjacent 1's are found. Two end boxes are considered to be adjacent if they are in the same row or column. This may be visualized by viewing the map as a *cylinder*, with the left and right borders touching.

For group x, the only unchanged variable is A; for group y, $\bar{B}\bar{C}$ remains unchanged. The simplified expression, therefore, is $A + \bar{B}\bar{C}$.

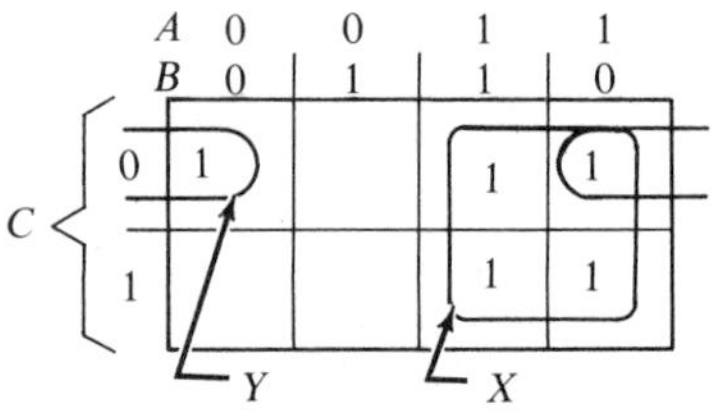

Fig. 18–23. *Three-variable Karnaugh map for Example 18–12.*

From Example 18–12, a group of four adjacent 1's yielded a single term; two adjacent 1's resulted in a two-term expression. For a four-variable map, eight adjacent 1's would yield a single term; four adjacent 1's, a two-term expression; and so on.

Plotting the terms of a Boolean expression on a Karnaugh map shows immediately if the expression can be simplified. This fact is important in determining if simplification should be attempted. To make this decision without mapping the expression can be difficult.

SUMMARY

A digital computer is composed of five major sections: input, output, control, arithmetic, and memory sections. All arithmetic and logic operations are performed using the binary number system. The binary number system has only two numerals: 0 and 1.

Logic operations are performed in accordance with the rules of Boolean algebra. They are implemented by OR, AND, NOT, NOR, and NAND gates. The truth table is an effective method for displaying the output for all possible inputs to a logic gate.

Simplification of Boolean expressions may yield an expression containing fewer terms. This means a saving in logic gates. The Karnaugh map provides a graphical method for the simplification of logic expressions.

Further Reading

Bartee, T. C. *Digital Computer Fundamentals.* 2nd ed. New York: McGraw-Hill Book Company, 1966, Chapters 1, 3, and 4.

Kaufman, M., and A. H. Seidman, eds. *Handbook for Electronics Engineering Technicians.* New York: McGraw-Hill Book Company, 1976, Chapter 14.

Kohavi, Zvi. *Switching and Finite Automata Theory.* New York: McGraw-Hill Book Company, 1970.

Malvino, A. F., and D. P. Leach. *Digital Principles and Applications.* New York: McGraw-Hill Book Company, 1969, Chapters 1, 2, and 4.

Millman, J., and C. C. Halkias. *Integrated Electronics: Analog and Digital Circuits and Systems.* New York: McGraw-Hill Book Company, 1972, Chapter 6.

Millman, J., and H. Taub. *Pulse, Digital, and Switching Waveforms.* New York: McGraw-Hill Book Company, 1965, Chapter 9.

Nashelsky, L. *Introduction to Digital Computer Technology.* New York: John Wiley and Sons, 1972, Chapters 1, 2, and 3.

Siegel, P. *Understanding Digital Computers.* New York: John Wiley and Sons, 1971, Chapters 1, 3, and 4.

REVIEW QUESTIONS

18.1 Discuss the differences between an analog and a digital computer.

18.2 Describe the function of a computer memory.

18.3 What is the function of the control unit in a digital computer?

18.4 What is the difference between computer software and hardware?

18.5 What types of problems are solved on an analog computer?

18.6 Describe the function of a computer programmer.

18.7 Why does a computer perform arithmetic with binary numbers?

18.8 Identify three basic logic operations.

18.9 What is a truth table?

18.10 Define logic gate.

18.11 What is the difference between an OR and a NOR gate?

18.12 Distinguish between a static and a dynamic logic system.

18.13 What is the difference between an AND and a NAND gate?

18.14 What is the difference between a positive logic system and a negative logic system?

18.15 How many possible input combinations are there for a five-input gate?

18.16 Define an INVERTER.

18.17 In what operating mode does a transistor switch exhibit a "high" output?

18.18 What is another term for complementing an expression?

18.19 What is meant by simplification of a Boolean expression?

18.20 Explain the purpose of Karnaugh mapping.

18.21 Is it possible to implement any Boolean expression with NAND or NOR gates only? Why?

18.22 State DeMorgan's theorem in your own words.

18.23 What is the difference between an OR and an EXCLUSIVE-OR gate?

18.24 Draw logic symbols for the following gates:
(a) OR.
(b) AND.
(c) NOT.
(d) NOR.
(e) NAND.
(f) EXCLUSIVE-OR.

PROBLEMS

P18–1 Convert each of the following *binary* numbers to its decimal equivalent:
(a) 1011.
(b) 110101.
(c) 100010.

P18–2 Express each of the following *decimal* numbers in BCD:
(a) 170.
(b) 345.
(c) 1001.

P18–3 Convert 1101100001 written in BCD to its decimal and binary equivalents.

P18–4 Convert each of the following *decimal* numbers to its binary equivalent:
(a) 11.
(b) 561.
(c) 1701.

P18–5 Draw the truth table for a three-input
(a) NAND gate.
(b) NOR gate.

P18–6 The following binary numbers correspond to pulse trains applied to a three-input AND gate: $A = 1001$, $B = 0101$, and $C = 1101$. Determine the output pulse train.

P18–7 Repeat prob. P18–6 for pulse trains A, B, and C applied to a three-input NOR gate.

P18–8 Using a truth table, verify that the redundancy properties listed in Table 18–6 are valid.

P18–9 Using a truth table, show that $(\overline{A + B}) = \bar{A} \cdot \bar{B}$.

Construct truth tables for the following three problems:

P18–10 (a) $\bar{A} \cdot B$.
(b) $\overline{A + B}$.
(c) $(A + B)\bar{A}$.

P18–11 (a) $\bar{A} \cdot B + \bar{C}$.
(b) $(A + \bar{B})C$.
(c) $(X \cdot Y)\bar{Z}$.

P18–12 $(X + Y\bar{X})(WY + \bar{X}) + (W + \bar{Y})$.

P18–13 Using a truth table, verify that $(A\bar{B} + \bar{C})B = B\bar{C}$.

For the following three problems, use, where possible, the properties of Boolean algebra to simplify the logic expressions. Then use the truth table to verify your results.

P18–14 (a) $(X + \bar{Y})\bar{X}$.
(b) $(\bar{X} + \bar{Y})'$.
(c) $(\bar{A} \cdot B)A$.

P18–15 (a) $A \cdot B \cdot C + \bar{A} \cdot \bar{C} \cdot B + \bar{B} \cdot C \cdot A$.
(b) $\overline{AB} \cdot C + AB \cdot \bar{C} + A \cdot \bar{B} \cdot C$.
(c) $(\overline{XY} \cdot Z)'$.

P18–16 (a) $(\bar{A} \cdot \bar{B} + A \cdot B)(A \cdot \bar{B})$.
(b) $XYZ + \bar{X}\bar{Y}\bar{Z} + \bar{X}Y\bar{Z} + X\bar{Y}Z$.

P18–17 Draw logic diagrams for the expressions of
(a) prob. P18–14.
(b) prob. P18–15.
(c) prob. P18–16.
Assume that the negated variables are available.

P18–18 Implement the expressions of prob. P18–14 with NAND gates only.

P18–19 Implement the expressions of prob. P18–15 with NOR gates only.

P18–20 Simplify the expression of prob. P18–16(b) using the Karnaugh map.

19

Diodes and Transistors as Switches

The first digital computer contained a multitude of relays and switches. Because of these electromechanical devices, the computer was slow in operation and had poor reliability. The vacuum-tube computer that followed, the first to employ true electronic components, also had some shortcomings. Recall that the architecture of a digital computer from the previous chapter (Fig. 18–1) required that thousands of vacuum tubes be used. The amount of heat dissipated was excessive. Think of the heat generated in a vacuum-tube television receiver containing only 18 vacuum tubes. Multiply that figure by 1000 for a vacuum-tube computer.

The potential of semiconductor devices for digital circuit elements was recognized during their early stages of development. Their small size, low power consumption, and high reliability all pointed to the adoption of these devices in computers. At one time, IBM Corporation was the largest manufacturer of semiconductor devices in the world. All the devices the company produced were for use in its computers.

To reduce further the size of computers, and to increase their capabilities, integrated circuits were produced and are widely used today. Entire sections have been reduced in size. For example, the arithmetic section may occupy a 9-in. by 12-in. plug-in card.

In this chapter, we shall examine how the diode and the transistor are used as switches in logic gates. Their dynamic response to digital signals (pulses) also will be considered.

19.1 Semiconductor Switches

Many devices are available which answer the description of a switch. The requirements for a true electronic switch in digital applications can be met by semiconductor devices. These requirements include fast switching, high repetition rate, and long life.

A diode meets these requirements because of its unidirectional characteristics. Diodes also can be made to switch very rapidly. Because of these characteristics, early logic circuits employed diodes as their principal elements.

As we saw in Chapter 18, a transistor also lends itself to switching applications and, in addition, provides power and voltage gain. Further, inversion is inherent between input and output of such a device when a BJT is in the *C-E* and a FET in the *C-S* configuration. Figure 19–1A shows a basic transistor switching circuit, the INVERTER. The collector characteristics for the device are provided in Fig. 19–1B.

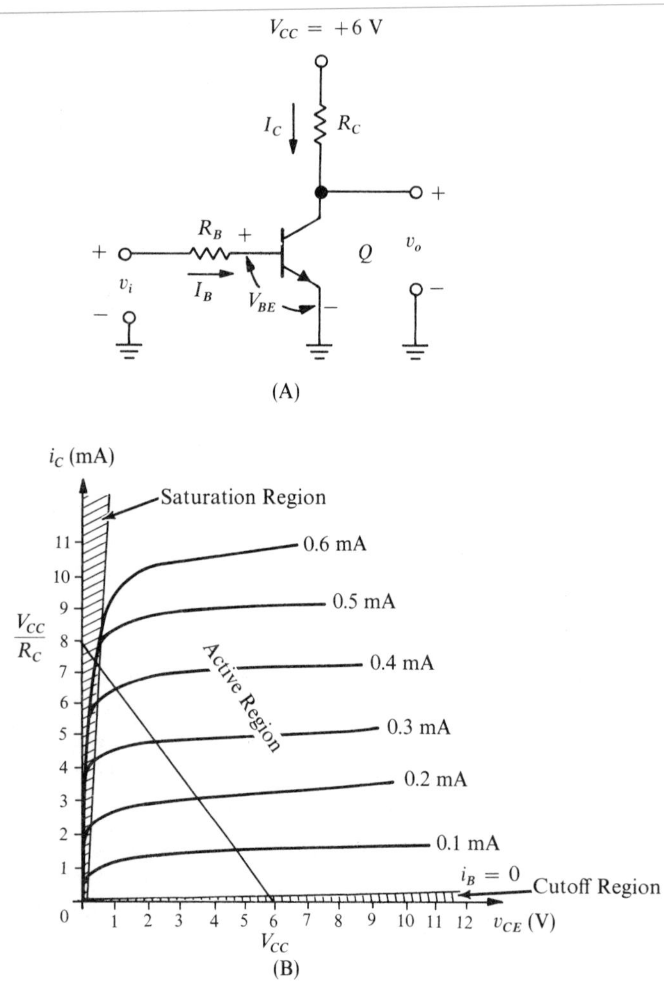

Fig. 19–1. *Basic transistor switch (INVERTER). (A) Basic circuit. (B) Collector characteristics.*

A logic circuit delivers an output signal that assumes two distinct voltage levels: a "high" and a "low." The transistor switch, therefore, is generally operated in either the cutoff (high) or the saturation (low) region. Operation in the active region is avoided because of variations in the output with changes in device parameters and loading.

With zero input, the transistor is OFF. No base or collector current flows other than a small leakage current,

I_{CO}. The leakage current may be in the order of a few nanoamperes, resulting in a negligible drop across R_C. Under this condition, the output voltage, v_o, is

$$v_o = V_{CC} - I_{CO}R_C \simeq V_{CC} \tag{19–1}$$

An input voltage greater than zero is applied to turn ON the transistor. The voltage level of the input must be at least 0.7 V to overcome the base-emitter voltage drop and to maintain a silicon transistor ON. In this case, the base current, I_B, is

$$I_B = \frac{v_i - V_{BE(ON)}}{R_B} \tag{19–2}$$

where v_i is the input voltage and $V_{BE(ON)}$ is the base-emitter voltage for the transistor to be in saturation.

In saturation, the collector current, $I_{C(sat)}$, is

$$I_{C(sat)} = \frac{V_{CC} - V_{sat}}{R_C} \tag{19–3}$$

where V_{sat} is the collector-emitter voltage of a transistor in saturation and R_C is the value of the collector resistor. The saturation voltage, V_{sat}, varies from less than 0.1 to 0.3 V, depending upon the transistor used and circuit conditions.

The output voltage of a transistor switch assumes a value of V_{CC} corresponding to a high, and V_{sat} indicating a low (Fig. 19–1B). A low value of saturation voltage is desirable for a switching transistor. Saturation may be defined by

$$h_{FE}I_B > I_{C(sat)} \tag{19–4}$$

EXAMPLE 19–1.

For the transistor switch of Fig. 19–1A, $V_{CC} = 6\,\text{V}$, $R_C = 750\,\Omega$, $R_B = 10\,\text{k}\Omega$, $h_{FE} = 25$, and $V_{sat} = 0.2\,\text{V}$. Determine the minimum value of v_i to saturate the transistor.

Solution:

By Eq. (19–3),

$$I_{C(sat)} = \frac{V_{CC} - V_{sat}}{R_C} = \frac{6 - 0.2}{750} = 7.85\,\text{mA}$$

The minimum value of base current to saturate the transistor is, by Eq. (19–4),

$$I_{B(min)} = \frac{I_{C(sat)}}{h_{FE}} = \frac{7.85}{25} = 0.313\,\text{mA}$$

Solving for the minimum input voltage, $v_{i(min)}$, by Eq. (19–2),

$$v_{i(min)} = I_{B(min)}R_B + V_{BE(ON)} = 0.313 \times 10 + 0.7 = 3.83\,\text{V}$$

We conclude that an input of at least 3.83 V is required for saturation. An output of 6 V corresponds to cutoff and 0.2 V to saturation.

To measure the degree of saturation a transistor is in, a ratio of collector current to base current is defined:

$$h_{FE(\text{sat})} = \frac{I_{C(\text{sat})}}{I_B} \tag{19–5}$$

where $h_{FE(\text{sat})}$ is the dc current gain of a transistor in saturation. The lower its value, the greater is the transistor in saturation. In saturation, $h_{FE(\text{sat})}$ is less than h_{FE} of a transistor in the active region:

$$h_{FE(\text{sat})} < h_{FE} \tag{19–6}$$

EXAMPLE 19–2.

Determine if the circuit of Fig. 19–2 is in saturation.

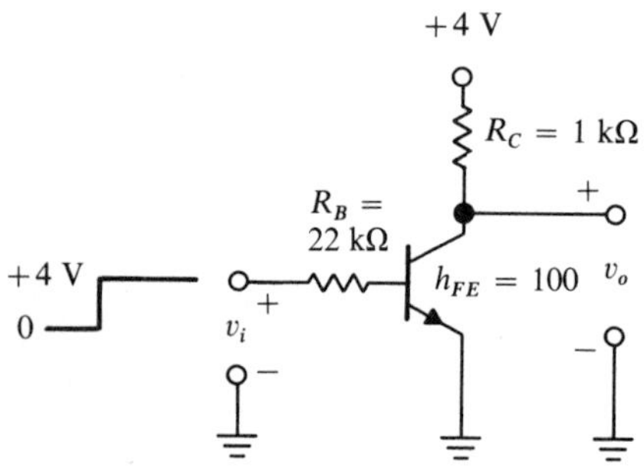

Fig. 19–2. *INVERTER circuit of Example 19–2.*

Solution:

By Eq. (19–2),

$$I_B = \frac{v_i - V_{BE(\text{ON})}}{R_B} = \frac{4 - 0.7}{22} = 0.15\,\text{mA}$$

By Eq. (19–3),

$$I_{C(\text{sat})} = \frac{V_{CC} - V_{\text{sat}}}{R_C} = \frac{4 - 0.2}{1} = 3.8\,\text{mA}$$

The value of $h_{FE(\text{sat})}$ is determined from Eq. (19–5):

$$h_{FE(\text{sat})} = \frac{I_{C(\text{sat})}}{I_B} = \frac{3.8}{0.15} = 25.3$$

By Eq. (19–6), $25.3 < 100$. The transistor, therefore, is in saturation.

19.2 Pulse Characteristics

Information in the form of pulses travels through a computer. Pulses are generated within the computer, and their shape is distorted as they travel from circuit to circuit. The distortion is introduced by the active devices and impedance mismatches in the connecting lines.

A perfect pulse (Fig. 19–3A) applied to a transistor switch, such as an INVERTER, will emerge distorted. The collector current and output voltage are shown in Figs. 19–3B and 19–3C, respectively. The input pulse is assumed to be of sufficient magnitude to saturate the transistor. Hence, the output varies between V_{CC} and V_{sat} volts as indicated by the output waveform. The output voltage waveform is identical to the collector current waveform except for the inversion.

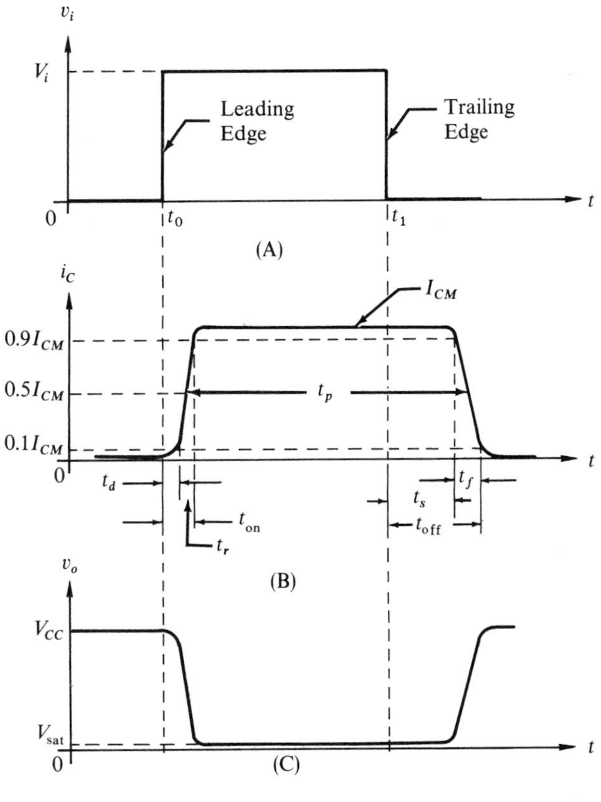

Fig. 19–3. *Dynamic response of a transistor switch. (A) Ideal (perfect) input pulse. (B) Collector current waveform. (C) Output voltage waveform.*

The collector current does not respond instantaneously to changes in the input. This accounts for *delay time*, t_d. Delay time, t_d, is defined as the time necessary for the current to rise to one-tenth (10 percent) of the maximum current, I_{CM}. The value of I_{CM} is approximately equal to V_{CC}/R_C. Delay t_d occurs because of

1. The time required to charge the base-emitter capacitance.
2. The time required for minority carriers to travel from the emitter to the collector.
3. The time necessary for the current to build up to one-tenth of its maximum value.

The collector current continues to rise until the transistor reaches saturation. It takes a finite time for the current to sweep through the active region. The time it takes the collector current to rise, exponentially, from 10 percent to 90 percent of its maximum value is defined as the *rise time*, t_r. Total time required for the current to reach 90 percent of its maximum value is the *turn-on time*, t_{on}. It is equal to the sum of the delay and rise times:

$$t_{on} = t_d + t_r \qquad \textbf{(19–7)}$$

The collector current finally reaches its maximum value, I_{CM}. For a transistor in saturation, excess minority carriers are stored in the base. When the input returns to zero at $t = t_1$, the stored charge causes current to continue to flow in the collector until the excess charge is depleted in the base. *Storage time*, t_s, is defined as the time required for the current to drop to 90 percent of the maximum value. It is measured from the trailing edge of the input pulse.

For a transistor to turn OFF completely, the collector current must once again sweep through the active region. This sweep results in an exponential decay of collector current. The time interval in which this occurs is called the *fall time*, t_f. It is defined as the time required for the collector current to fall from 90 percent to 10 percent of its maximum value.

The turn-off time, t_{off}, is defined as the sum of the storage and fall times:

$$t_{off} = t_s + t_f \qquad \textbf{(19–8)}$$

Although the definitions of the different time intervals were given in terms of collector current, the same definitions apply to the collector voltage. The voltage waveform is inverted but has the same shape as the current waveform.

Propagation Delay

The propagation delay, t_{pd}, indicates the switching speed of a logic gate. As we will see in the following chapter, t_{pd} is used as a figure of merit in comparing different families of logic.

Referring to Fig. 19–4, we see that the output of a gate is delayed with respect to the input pulse. Using 50 percent

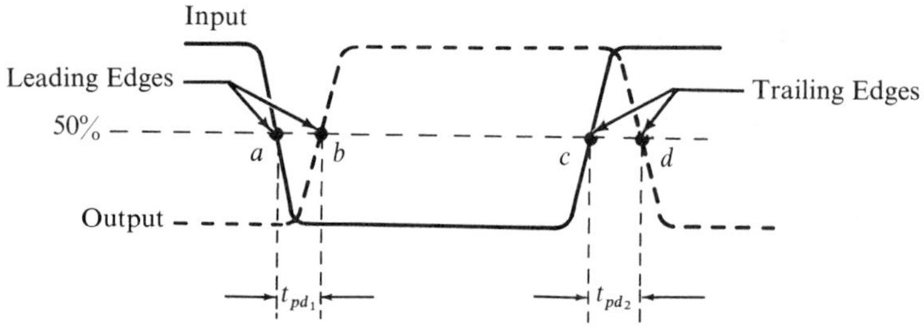

Fig. 19–4. *Defining propagation delay, t_{pd}.*

of the final value as reference, the delay between the leading edges of the input and output waveforms is denoted by t_{pd_1}. Similarly, the delay between the trailing edges of the waveforms is denoted by t_{pd_2}. The average of the two delays is defined as the propagation delay, t_{pd}. It is expressed by

$$t_{pd} = \frac{t_{pd_1} + t_{pd_2}}{2} \qquad \textbf{(19–9)}$$

19.3 Improving Dynamic Response

Distortion of the input signal pulse is undesirable. The rise time may be reduced by lowering the value of base resistor R_B in Fig. 19–1A. A high-voltage input pulse will reduce the turn-on time, but it drives the transistor harder into saturation, thereby increasing the turn-off time.

The storage time is most critical. Under certain conditions, the storage time can be several times longer than the rise or fall time. One method of reducing storage time is to connect a capacitor across resistor R_B. Referred to as a *speed-up*, or *commutating*, capacitor, the capacitor "transfers" the full signal to the base during the leading edge of the input pulse. When the pulse returns to zero, the capacitor provides a discharge path for the charge stored in the transistor base.

A practical INVERTER is shown in Fig. 19–5. Resistor R_1 and voltage supply $-V_{BB}$ ensure that the transistor is in cutoff when the input is zero. Speed-up capacitor C_s is connected across R_B to reduce the turn-on and turn-off times. The value of C_s may be chosen such that the time constant R_BC_s is equal to the time constant of the base-emitter junction. Under this condition, the circuit is said to be *fully compensated*.

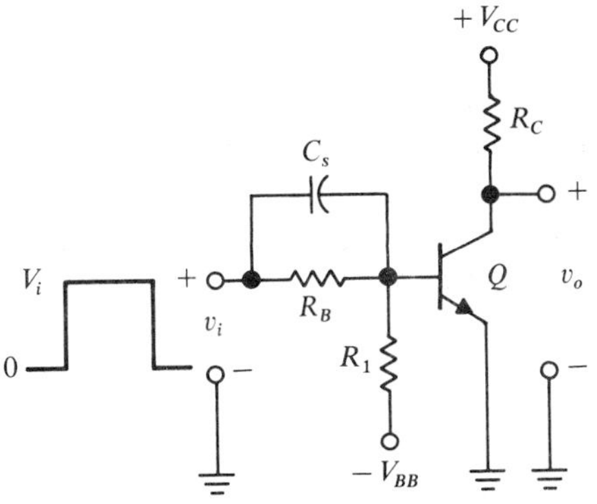

Fig. 19–5. *Practical INVERTER circuit employing a commutating capacitor, C_s.*

Figure 19–6 provides a model of the compensated network. The time constant of the base-emitter junction is $r_{b'e}C_i$, where $r_{b'e}$ is the base-emitter resistance and C_i is the input capacitance of the transistor. The effect of the base-spreading resistance, $r_{bb'}$, is neglected; hence, for full compensation,

$$R_BC_s = r_{b'e}C_i \qquad \textbf{(19–10a)}$$

Because of the compensation, the pulse is attenuated at the base of the transistor. The amount of attenuation, a, is given by

$$a = \frac{r_{b'e}}{r_{b'e} + R_B} \qquad \textbf{(19–10b)}$$

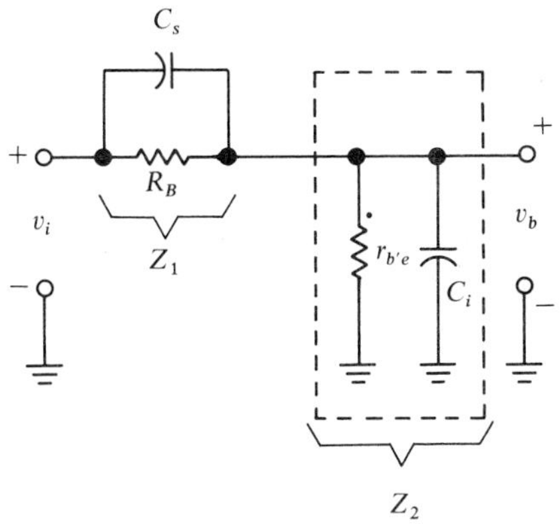

Fig. 19–6. *Model of a compensated network.*

The appearance of a pulse at a transistor base under different conditions is illustrated in Fig. 19–7. In Fig. 19–7A, no compensation was employed. The leading and trailing edges of the pulse are distorted. A longer time, therefore, is required to turn ON or turn OFF the transistor. If $R_B C_s < r_{b'e} C_i$ (the condition for an *undercompensated* network), the result is the same as if no compensation were used.

For full compensation ($R_B C_s = r_{b'e} C_i$), the input signal at the base reaches its maximum level instantaneously, as shown in Fig. 19–7B. In practice, $R_B C_s > r_{b'e} C_i$, and the network is *overcompensated.* The result for this condition appears in Fig. 19–7C. Note that positive and negative spikes exist at the leading and trailing edges, respectively. This helps reduce the turn-on and turn-off times of a transistor switch.

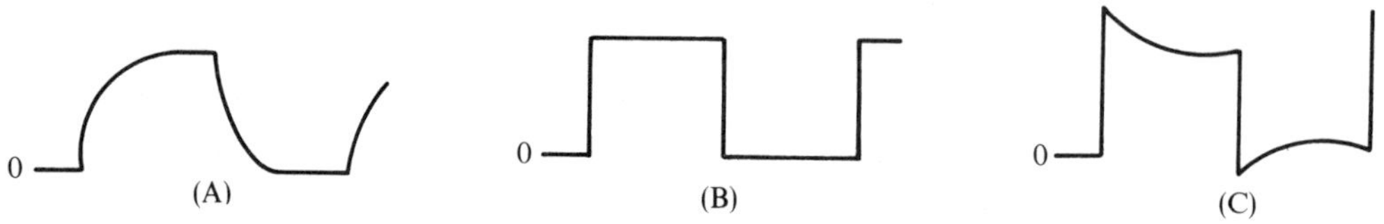

Fig. 19–7. *Waveforms at the base of a transistor. (A) No compensation or undercompensation. (B) Full compensation. (C) Overcompensation.*

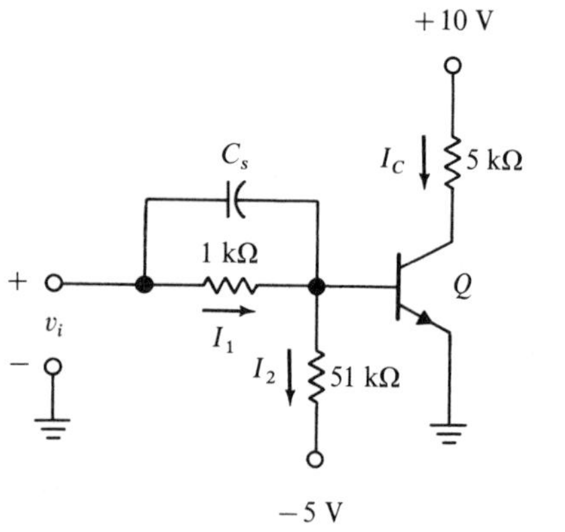

Fig. 19–8. *INVERTER circuit for Example 19–3.*

EXAMPLE 19–3.

For the INVERTER of Fig. 19–8,

(a) Show that the transistor is OFF when $v_i = 0$ and saturated when a suitable pulse is present.

(b) Find the value of C_s for full compensation.

For the transistor, $h_{FE(\text{min})} = 60$, $r_{b'e} = 1200\,\Omega$, $C_i = 100\,\text{pF}$, $V_{BE(\text{ON})} = 0.7\,\text{V}$, and $V_{\text{sat}} = 0.2\,\text{V}$.

Solutions:

(a) For $v_i = 0$, by voltage division, the base-emitter voltage, V_{BE}, is

$$V_{BE} = -5 \times \frac{1}{1 + 51} = -0.096\,\text{V}$$

With V_{BE} negative, an NPN transistor is indeed OFF. When the transistor is ON,

$$I_1 = \frac{6 - 0.7}{1} = 5.3\,\text{mA}$$

and

$$I_2 = \frac{0.7 - (-5)}{51} = 0.112\,\text{mA}$$

$$I_B = I_1 - I_2$$
$$= 5.3 - 0.112 = 5.188\,\text{mA}$$

$$I_{C(\text{sat})} = \frac{10 - 0.2}{5} = 1.96\,\text{mA}$$

Hence,

$$h_{FE(\text{sat})} = \frac{1.96}{5.188} = 0.378$$

Because $h_{FE(\text{sat})}$ is less than $h_{FE} = 60$, the transistor is in saturation.

(b) Solving Eq. (19–10a) for C_s,

$$C_s = \frac{r_{b'e}C_i}{R_B}$$

$$= 1200 \times \frac{100}{1000} = 120\,\text{pF}$$

19.4 Nonsaturated Transistor Switches

A transistor that is not saturated when ON exhibits practically no storage time delay. To produce nonsaturated operation, the collector-base junction must be prevented from becoming forward biased when the transistor is ON. A method for achieving this is the use of a *clamping diode*, illustrated in Fig. 19–9.

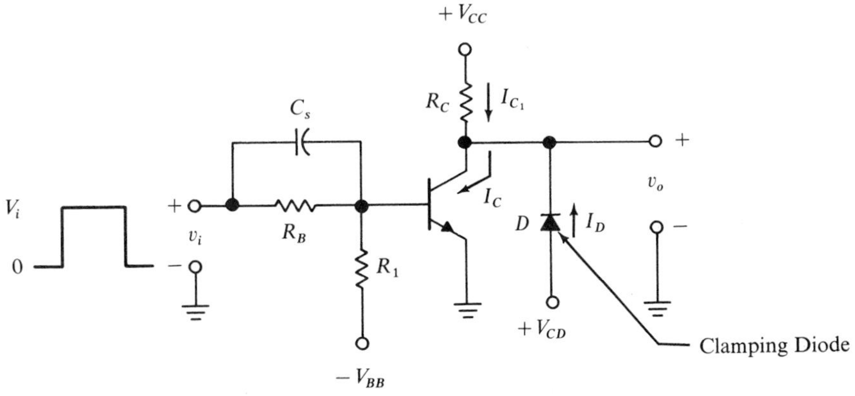

Fig. 19–9. *Nonsaturated switch using a clamping diode.*

The cathode of clamping diode D is connected to the collector, and the anode to supply V_{CD}. The value of V_{CD} is less than the collector supply voltage, V_{CC}. When the input is zero, the transistor is OFF. The collector voltage is equal to V_{CC} volts, and diode D is reverse biased. For this condition, the behavior of the circuit is no different from that of a saturated switch. When the input rises to v_i volts, the transistor turns ON, and the collector-emitter voltage drops. The value of V_{CE} is limited to a minimum of

$$V_{CE} = V_{CD} - V_D \qquad \textbf{(19–11)}$$

where V_D is the forward voltage drop across the diode.

The value of V_{CD} is selected to ensure that V_{CE} is greater than the base-emitter voltage, V_{BE}. Because a nonsaturated switch is operating in the active region when ON, the collector current is a function of the base current and h_{FE}.

The output voltage for a logic 0 in the circuit of Fig. 19–9 is 0.7 V or higher. On the other hand, the output voltage corresponding to a logic 0 in a saturated switch is in the order of 0.1 V. As a result, a nonsaturated switch dissipates much more power when ON than does a saturated switch.

Another type of nonsaturated switch employs a *Schottky diode*. The Schottky diode is connected between the collector and base of a transistor (Fig. 19–10A). A metal semiconductor device, the Schottky diode lends itself to monolithic IC fabrication. Since, when forward biased, only majority carriers flow, storage time is almost nonexistent. No minority carriers have to be removed when the device is turned OFF, as in the case of a junction diode. The voltage drop across a conducting Schottky diode is approximately 0.4 V; for a junction diode, it is 0.7 V.

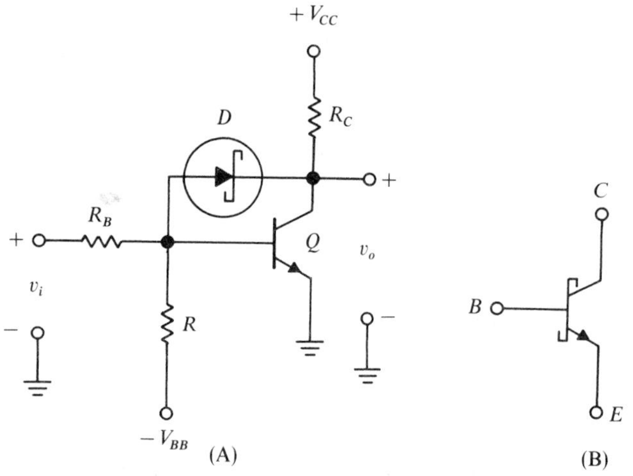

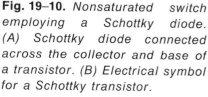

Fig. 19–10. *Nonsaturated switch employing a Schottky diode. (A) Schottky diode connected across the collector and base of a transistor. (B) Electrical symbol for a Schottky transistor.*

In Fig. 19–10A, if the collector current is increased, the collector voltage decreases, and the diode turns ON. A constant voltage of 0.4 V is maintained across the device. This results in the collector being negative with respect to the base by 0.4 V, which is insufficient to forward bias the collector-base junction. The transistor, therefore, is kept out of saturation.

A Schottky diode can be manufactured simultaneously with the transistor. The combined device is known as a *Schottky transistor*. Its electrical symbol is given in Fig. 19–10B.

The circuit of Fig. 19–11A is an INVERTER that employs only two P-channel MOSFETs. Such a circuit is ideal for

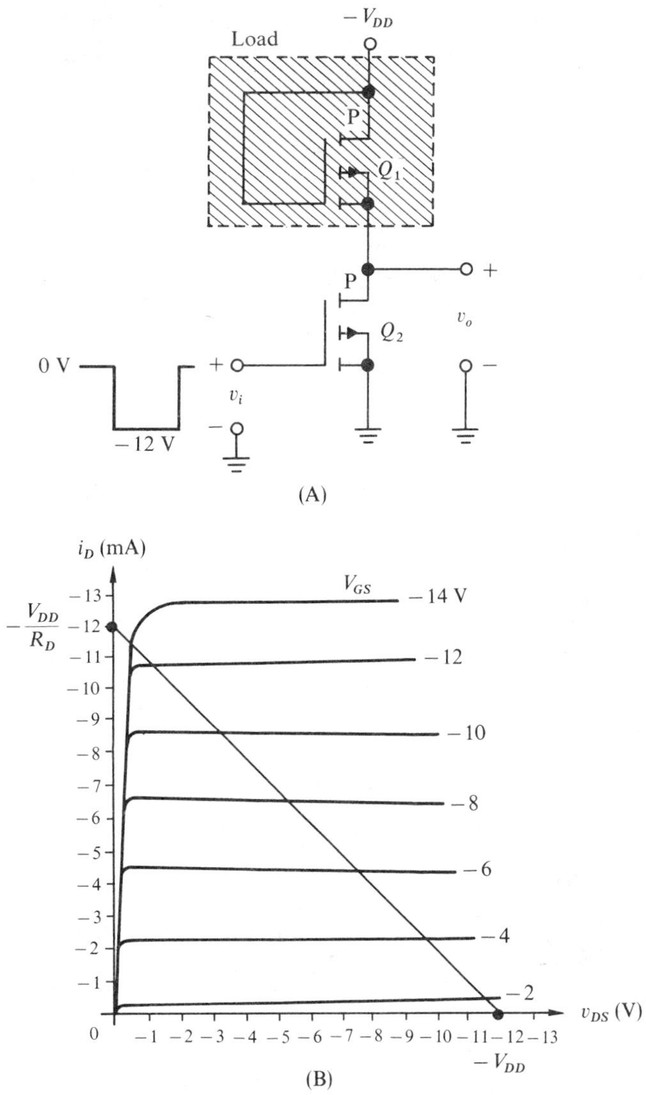

Fig. 19–11. *INVERTER using two P-channel MOSFETs. (A) Circuit. (B) Drain characteristics.*

IC fabrication because of its high packing density. Although MOSFET switches are generally slower than BJT switches, they consume less power.

Transistor Q_1 in Fig. 19–11A acts like a load resistor (R_D) and Q_2 as an inverting transistor. Actually, Q_1 behaves like a nonlinear resistance. For the sake of understanding how the circuit operates as an INVERTER, however, we shall assume that Q_1 is a linear resistance. Figure 19–11B shows the load line plotted on the drain characteristics. For zero input, $v_o = v_{DS} = -12\,\text{V}$. For $v_i = -12\,\text{V}$, $v_o = -2\,\text{V}$. The circuit is also adaptable to negative logic. In this case, a logic 0 corresponds to -2 V and a logic 1 to -12 V.

A widely used type of nonsaturating logic switches current from one transistor to another. Called *current mode switching*, these circuits have delays of a few nanoseconds.

They form the basis for the emitter-coupled logic (ECL) family, which is discussed in Chapter 20.

19.5 Diodes as Switches

A simple two-input diode OR gate is illustrated in Fig. 19–12A. For review of its operation, a truth table is provided

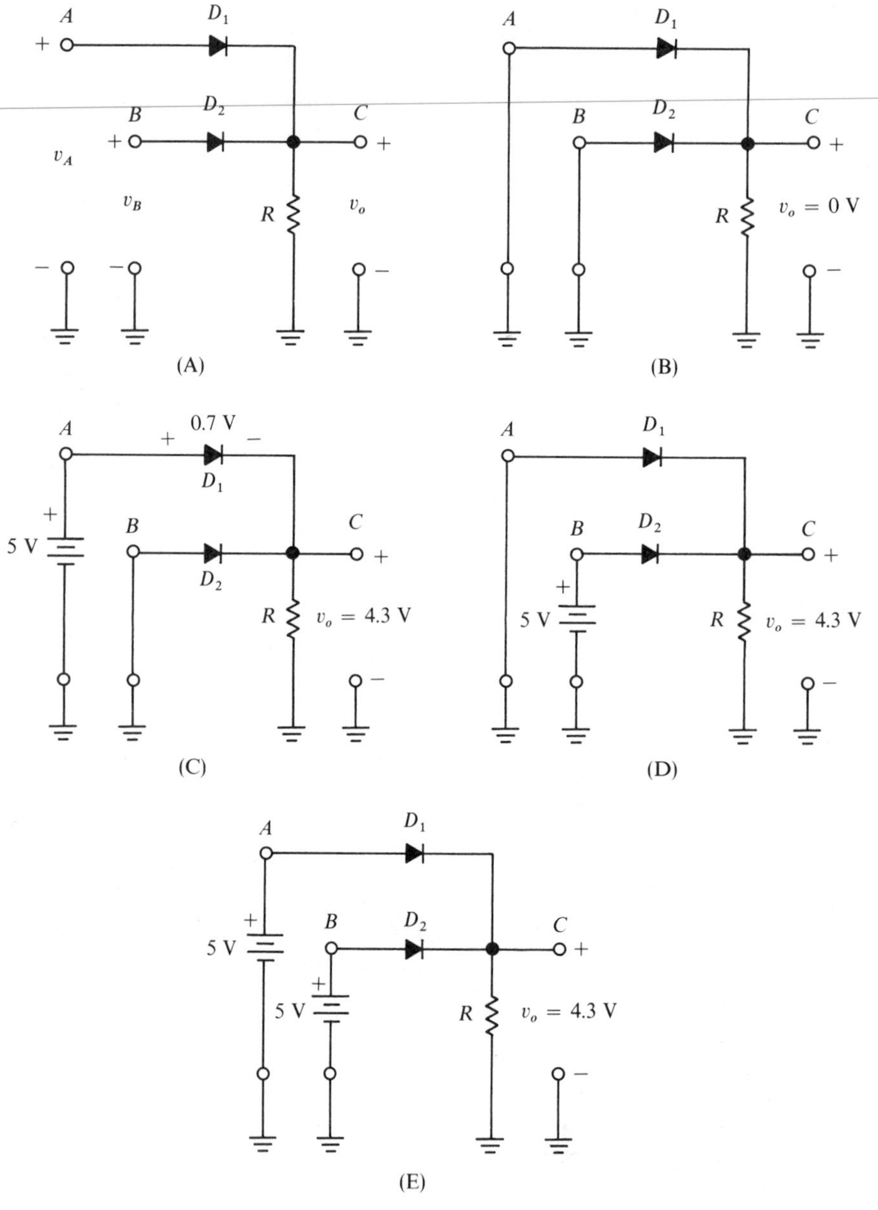

Fig. 19–12. *Two-input diode OR gate. (A) Basic circuit. (B) $v_A = v_B = 0$ (0 V). (C) $v_A = 1$ (5 V) and $v_B = 0$ (0 V). (D) $v_A = 0$ (0 V) and $v_B = 1$ (5 V). (E) $v_A = v_B = 1$ (5 V).*

in Table 19–1A. When both inputs are at logic 0, the output is also a logic 0. For this condition, inputs v_A and v_B are shorted to ground (Fig. 19–12B). The diodes are nonconducting, and the output voltage is indeed zero.

TABLE 19–1. Truth tables for a two-input OR gate. (A) Logic truth table. (B) Voltage truth table.

A	B	C
0	0	0
0	1	1
1	0	1
1	1	1

(A)

v_A	v_B	v_o
0 V	0 V	0 V
0 V	5 V	4.3 V
5 V	0 V	4.3 V
5 V	5 V	4.3 V

(B)

Assume a logic 1 corresponds to 5 V. With $v_A = 5$ V and $v_B = 0$ V (Fig. 19–12C), diode D_1 conducts. A forward voltage drop of 0.7 V is measured across D_1 (identical silicon diodes are assumed). The output voltage is given by

$$v_o = 5 - 0.7 = 4.3 \text{ V}$$

which now corresponds to a logic 1. Because the cathode of D_2 is 4.3 V positive with respect to ground, it is reverse biased. The same results are obtained for $v_A = 0$ V and $v_B = 5$ V (Fig. 19–12D).

With both inputs at a logic 1, $v_A = v_B = 5$ V (Fig. 19–12E), diodes D_1 and D_2 conduct. The output is 4.3 V (logic 1). The current in any conducting diode is limited by resistor R. Our discussion can be extended to include OR gates with more than two inputs. When several inputs are excited, only the diode in the branch with the highest input voltage conducts current. A voltage truth table for the two-input OR gate is provided in Table 19–1B.

A basic two-input AND gate is illustrated in Fig. 19–13A. For review, the truth table for the circuit is given in Table 19–2A. For $v_A = v_B = 0$, which correspond to a logic 0, both diodes are forward biased (Fig. 19–13B). The output voltage is equal to the forward voltage of a conducting diode (0.7 V for silicon).

In Fig. 19–13C, $v_A = 5$ V and $v_B = 0$ V. Diode D_2 is forward biased, and D_1 is reverse biased; $v_o = 0.7$ V. The same result holds for $v_A = 0$ V and $v_B = 5$ V (Fig. 19–13D). When both inputs are at a logic 1 ($v_A = v_B = 5$ V), diodes D_1 and D_2 are reverse biased; $v_o = 5$ V. A voltage truth table for the circuit is provided in Table 19–2B.

For a diode AND gate having more than two inputs, the output voltage is determined by the lowest input. Only the diode in the branch connected to the lowest input voltage conducts current.

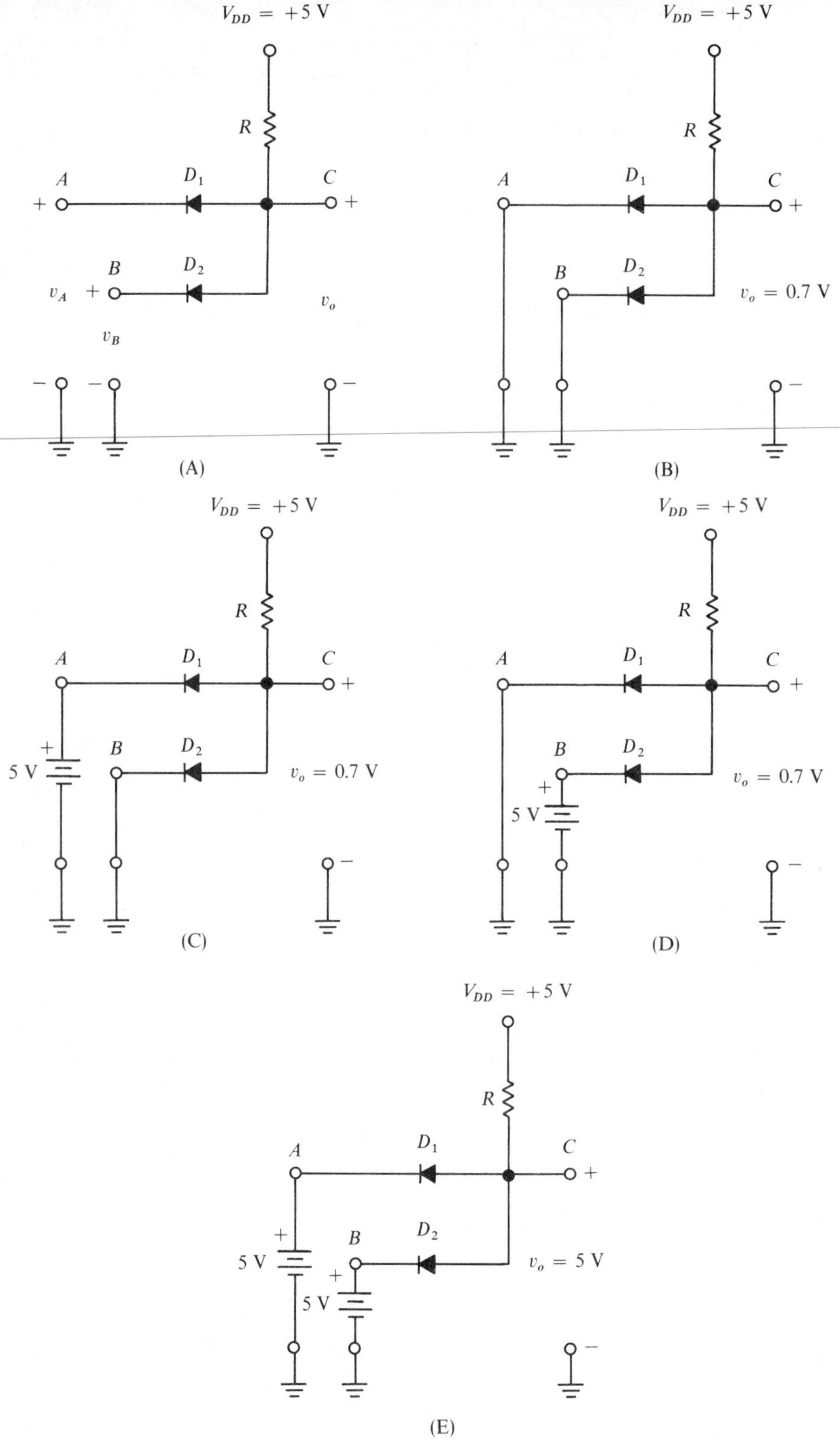

Fig. 19–13. *Two-input diode AND gate. (A) Basic circuit. (B) $v_A = v_B = 0$. (C) $v_A = 1$ and $v_B = 0$. (D) $v_A = 0$ and $v_B = 1$. (E) $v_A = v_B = 1$.*

TABLE 19–2. Truth tables for a two-input AND gate. (A) Logic truth table. (B) Voltage truth table.

A	B	C	v_A	v_B	v_o
0	0	0	0 V	0 V	0.7 V
0	1	0	0 V	5 V	0.7 V
1	0	0	5 V	0 V	0.7 V
1	1	1	5 V	5 V	5 V

(A) (B)

A value of 0.7 V for a logic 0 at the output of the AND gate may be too high for some applications. To reduce the value to 0 V, a *pull-down* diode may be added to the circuit of Fig. 19–13A, as illustrated in Fig. 19–14. The analysis of the new circuit is developed in the next example.

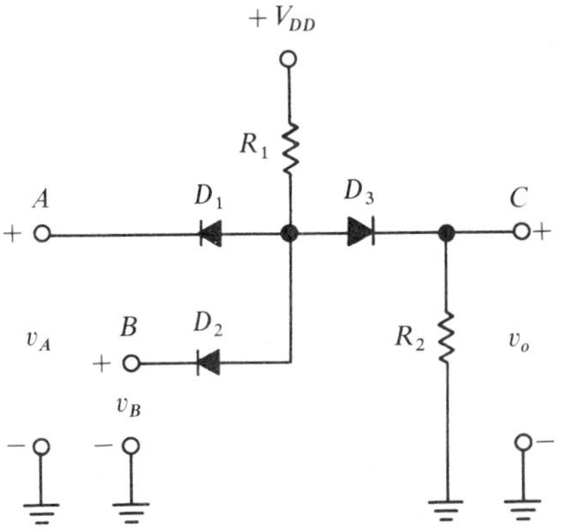

Fig. 19–14. *Improved AND gate employing a pull-down diode, D_3.*

EXAMPLE 19–4.

Determine the voltage truth table for the circuit of Fig. 19–14. Assume that $V_{DD} = 12$ V, $R_1 = R_2 = 10\,\text{k}\Omega$, a logic 0 equals 0 V, and a logic 1 equals 5 V.

Solution:

In Fig. 19–15A, $v_A = v_B = 0$ V, and both inputs are therefore at logic 0. Diodes D_1 and D_2 conduct, and the voltage across each diode is 0.7 V. This is also the voltage at point D with respect to ground. Pull-down diode D_3 also conducts, and 0.7 V is across it. The two voltages cancel, and the output is 0 V. This illustrates the "pull-down" action of D_3.

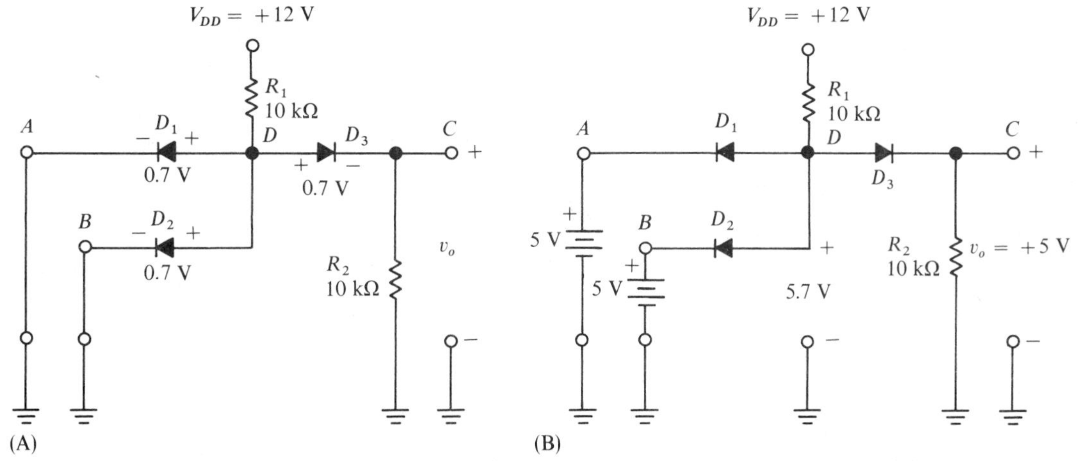

Fig. 19–15. *Two-input diode AND gate of Example 19–4. (A) Both inputs at logic 0. (B) Both inputs at logic 1.*

Assume that $v_A = 5$ V and $v_B = 0$ V. Current flows in D_2, and the voltage across point D with respect to ground is 0.7 V. Diode D_3 compensates for the voltage drop, and an output of 0 V is realized. The result is the same if $v_A = 0$ V and $v_B = 5$ V.

When $v_A = v_B = 5$ V, the circuit appears as shown in Fig. 19–15B. Diodes D_1 and D_2 conduct, and the voltage across point D and ground is 5.7 V. Diode D_3 is forward biased, and the voltage across it is 0.7 V. The output, then, is $5.7 - 0.7 = 5$ V. A voltage truth table for the circuit is provided in Table 19–3.

TABLE 19–3. Voltage truth table for the AND gate of Fig. 19–14. (See Example 19–4.)

v_A	v_B	v_o
0 V	0 V	0 V
0 V	5 V	0 V
5 V	0 V	0 V
5 V	5 V	5 V

19.6 Interconnecting Logic Gates

Logic gates are interconnected to perform various logic and arithmetic operations. Their use to implement Boolean expressions was covered in Chapter 18. The limitations of diode logic gates become apparent when they are interconnected.

Figure 19–16 shows two AND gates connected in cascade to form a three-input AND gate. A careful examination of the circuit reveals the following: When all three inputs are at 0 V, D_1, D_2, and D_4 conduct. A potential of 0.7 V is

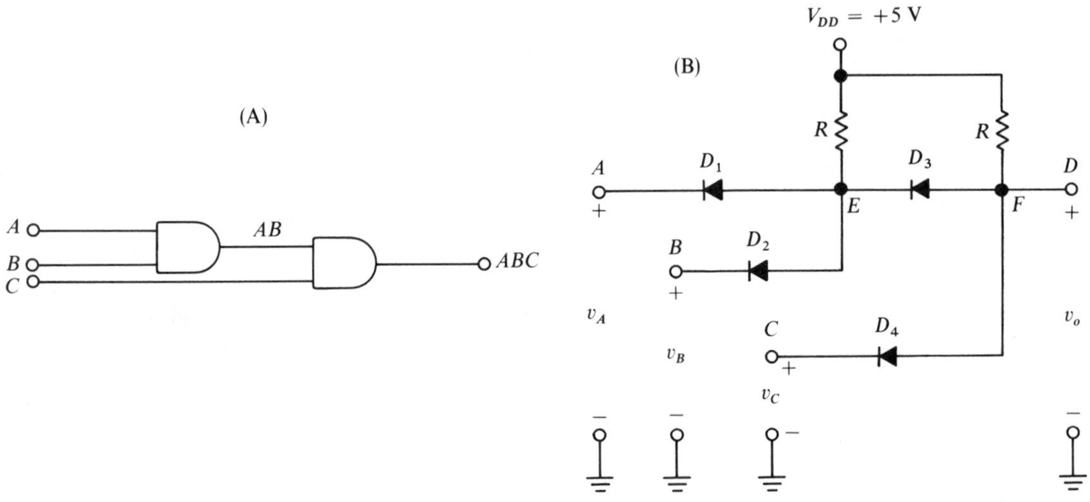

Fig. 19–16. *Cascade connection of two AND gates. (A) Logic diagram. (B) Circuit schematic.*

established at points E and F with respect to ground. Diode D_3 is reverse biased, and $v_o = 0.7\,\text{V}$.

Under the condition $v_A = v_B = 0\,\text{V}$ and $v_C = 5\,\text{V}$, the voltage at point E is 0.7 V. Diode D_4 is reverse biased, and D_3 is forward biased. These conditions result in a voltage of 1.4 V at point F. From Table 19–4, we expect a logic 0 for this condition. In this circuit, however, for 0 V as a logic 0 at the input, 0.7 V and 1.4 V are obtained for a logic 0 at the output. If another AND gate were cascaded with the circuit, 2.1 V would become a logic 0.

TABLE 19–4. Truth table for two AND gates connected in cascade. (See Fig. 19–16.)

A	B	C	D	v_o
0	0	0	0	0.7 V
0	0	1	0	1.4 V
0	1	0	0	0.7 V
0	1	1	0	1.4 V
1	0	0	0	0.7 V
1	0	1	0	1.4 V
1	1	0	0	0.7 V
1	1	1	1	5 V

The characteristics of a diode gate can be improved by the addition of an INVERTER. Such a circuit provides an inverted output of the logic function and is called a NAND gate (see Chapter 18). A NAND gate is shown in Fig. 19–17. Resistors R_B and R_1 and base source $-V_{BB}$ are chosen to keep the transistor OFF when a logic 0 is applied to an input. When both inputs are at a logic 1, the voltage at point C is sufficient to saturate the transistor.

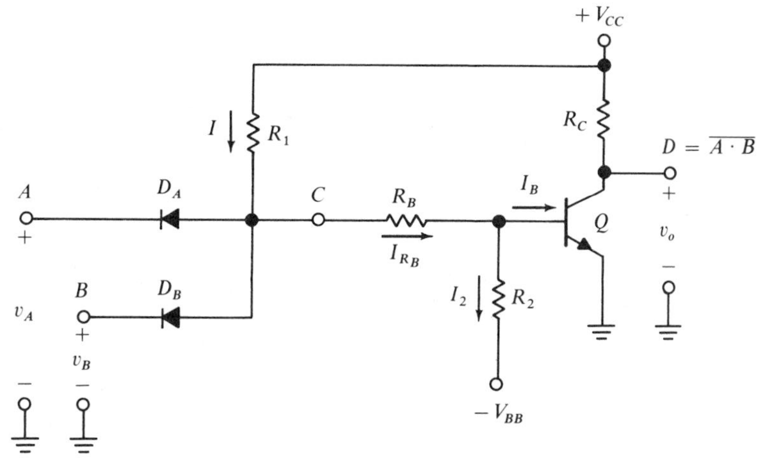

Fig. 19–17. *NAND gate.*

Assume that one NAND gate drives other NAND gates, as illustrated in Fig. 19–18. With at least one input "low," point D is "high" and remains "high" because diodes D_1–D_n are reverse biased. When both inputs are "high" and Q is saturated, current flows in one or more of the diodes (D_1, $D_2, \ldots, D_n$). Transistor Q of the previous stage acts as a *current sink* for these gates.

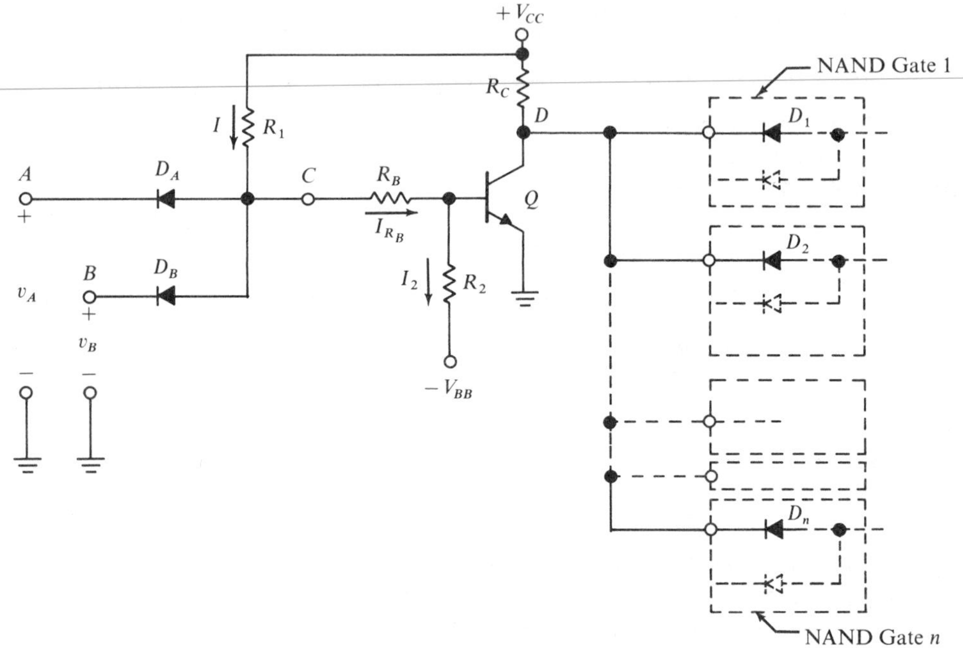

Fig. 19–18. *NAND gate driving n similar NAND gates.*

Fan-Out and Fan-In

The number of similar gates a gate can drive without an appreciable change in its output characteristics is called *fan-out*. *Fan-in* is the number of inputs a logic gate can accommodate.

EXAMPLE 19–5.

In the circuit of Fig. 19–18, $R_1 = R_C = 3.3\,\text{k}\Omega$, $R_B = 5\,\text{k}\Omega$, $R_2 = 22\,\text{k}\Omega$, $V_{sat} = 0.2\,\text{V}$, $V_{CC} = 6\,\text{V}$, $-V_{BB} = -6\,\text{V}$, and $h_{FE} = 50$. Determine

(a) Fan-out.

(b) Fan-in.

(c) Minimum input voltage required to turn ON the transistor.

Solutions:

(a) In determining fan-out, we must first calculate the input current corresponding to a "low" input. Assuming $v_A = 0\,\text{V}$, diode D_A conducts. Current I in R_1 is

$$I = \frac{V_{CC} - V_{BE}}{R_1} = \frac{6 - 0.7}{3.3} = 1.6\,\text{mA}$$

To determine the saturation current of the transistor, assume both inputs are "high" (6 V). The input diodes, then, are reverse biased. Current in R_B, I_{R_B}, is

$$I_{R_B} = \frac{V_{CC} - V_{BE}}{R_1 + R_B} = \frac{6 - 0.7}{3.3 + 5} = 0.633\,\text{mA}$$

Current I_2 in R_2 is

$$I_2 = \frac{V_{BE} - (-V_{BB})}{R_2} = \frac{0.7 - (-6)}{22} = 0.304\,\text{mA}$$

Base current I_B is equal to the difference in I_{R_B} and I_2; hence,

$$I_B = 0.633 - 0.304 = 0.329\,\text{mA}$$

The collector saturation current, $I_{C(\text{sat})}$, is

$$I_{C(\text{sat})} = \frac{V_{CC} - V_{\text{sat}}}{R_C} = \frac{6 - 0.2}{3.3} = 1.76\,\text{mA}$$

Maximum available current in the collector, I_{CM}, is

$$I_{CM} = h_{FE}I_B = 50 \times 0.329 = 16.4\,\text{mA}$$

The maximum sink current, I_{SM}, is equal to the difference in I_{CM} and $I_{C(\text{sat})}$:

$$I_{SM} = 16.4 - 1.76 = 14.64\,\text{mA}$$

The number of inputs the circuit can drive, that is, the fan-out, F.O., is

$$\text{F.O.} = \frac{I_{SM}}{I} = \frac{14.61}{1.6} = 9.13$$

Because the lower whole number is used, the fan-out is 9.

(b) The fan-in is 2 because there are two inputs to the gate.

(c) To calculate the input voltage necessary to turn the transistor ON, the cut-in voltage, $V_{\text{cut-in}}$, must be considered. For a silicon transistor, $V_{\text{cut-in}} = 0.6\,\text{V}$. Then,

$$V_{\text{cut-in}} = \frac{(-V_{BB} - V_D - v_i)R_B}{R_B + R_2} + v_i + V_D$$

$$0.6 = \frac{(-6.7 - v_i)5}{22 + 5} + v_i + 0.7$$

Solving for v_i,

$$v_i = \frac{1.14}{0.82} = 1.39\,\text{V}$$

Noise Margin

The minimum voltage calculated in Example 19–5(c) is known as the *noise margin*, N.M., of the circuit. If, in the example, the input voltage exceeded 1.39 V, the input would be a "high" instead of a "low." The noise margin may be calculated from the following expression:

$$\text{N.M.} = (V_{\text{cut-in}} - V_D)\frac{R_B + R_2}{R_2} + \frac{(V_{BB} + V_D)R_B}{R_2} \qquad \textbf{(19–12)}$$

Neglecting $V_{\text{cut-in}}$ and V_D,

$$\text{N.M.} \simeq \frac{V_{BB}R_B}{R_2} \qquad \textbf{(19–13)}$$

SUMMARY

Simple OR and AND gates may be designed using diodes as the main switching elements. An INVERTER employs a single transistor. A diode OR gate followed by an INVERTER yields a NOR gate. Similarly, an AND gate followed by an INVERTER results in a NAND gate.

Signals found in logic circuits are pulses. A pulse appearing at the output of a logic gate is delayed, and its leading and trailing edges are distorted. The delay is expressed as the propagation delay, t_{pd}. The distortion of the leading edge is measured in terms of the delay and rise times, t_d and t_r, respectively. Their sum is equal to the turn-on time, t_{on}.

Fall time, t_f, refers to the trailing edge. In addition, if a transistor is operated as a saturated switch, a storage time delay, t_s, also exists. The sum of the storage and fall times is equal to the turn-off time, t_{off}.

Fan-out is a loading parameter of a logic gate. It defines the number of gates which can be driven by the output of a similar gate. Fan-in denotes the number of inputs to a gate. Noise margin describes the vulnerability of a logic gate to noise. It defines a maximum logic 0 level and a minimum 1 level that ensure reliable operation in the presence of noise.

Further Reading

Millman, J., and H. Taub. *Pulse, Digital, and Switching Waveforms.* New York: McGraw-Hill Book Company, 1965, Chapters 8 and 9.

Nashelsky, L. *Introduction to Digital Computer Technology.* New York: John Wiley and Sons, 1972, Chapter 7.

Oppenheimer, S. L. *Semiconductor Logic and Switching Circuits.* 2nd ed. Columbus, Ohio: Charles E. Merrill Publishing Company, 1973, Chapters 3 and 4.

Robinson, V. *Basic Principles of Digital Computers.* Reston, Va.: Reston Publishing Co., Inc., 1974, Chapter 5.

Tocci, R. J. *Fundamentals of Pulse and Digital Circuits.* 2nd ed. Columbus, Ohio: Charles E. Merrill Publishing Company, 1977, Chapters 6, 7, and 8.

REVIEW QUESTIONS

19.1 Describe the characteristics of an electronic switch.

19.2 Why is the integrated circuit ideally suited for computer applications?

19.3 Provide another name for a transistor switch.

19.4 What causes a pulse signal to become distorted as it travels through computer circuits?

19.5 Define (a) delay, (b) rise, (c) storage, and (d) fall times of a pulse.

19.6 Define propagation delay time.

19.7 Explain the function of a commutating capacitor.

19.8 What is meant by a fully compensated network?

19.9 Discuss the advantages and disadvantages of saturated over nonsaturated operation.

19.10 Describe how a Schottky diode is used in switching circuits.

19.11 What is meant by current sink and current source in logic circuits? Give an example of each type of element.

19.12 Define fan-in and fan-out.

19.13 Why is the MOSFET considered ideal for the fabrication of logic integrated circuits?

19.14 What is the function of resistor R_1 in the circuit of Fig. 19–5?

19.15 Explain the function of the clamping diode in the circuit of Fig. 19–9.

19.16 Identify the pull-down diode in the circuit of Fig. 19–14. What is its function in the circuit?

19.17 What is the purpose of the inverter stage in Fig. 19–17, other than to provide inversion of the signal?

19.18 Define noise margin.

PROBLEMS

P19–1 For the INVERTER of Fig. 19–1A, $V_{CC} = 10\,\text{V}$, $R_C = 1\,\text{k}\Omega$, $R_B = 33\,\text{k}\Omega$, $h_{FE} = 50$, $V_{\text{sat}} = 0.2\,\text{V}$, and $V_{BE(\text{ON})} = 0.7\,\text{V}$. If $v_i = 5\,\text{V}$, determine whether the transistor is in saturation.

P19–2 Repeat prob. P19–1 for $h_{FE} = 30$.

P19–3 For the conditions stated in prob. P19–1, what is the minimum input voltage required to keep the transistor saturated?

P19–4 In the INVERTER of Fig. 19–2, what is the maximum value of R_B which can be used so that the transistor still is saturated?

P19–5 Design a transistor switch similar to that of Fig. 19–1A that operates from a 5-V dc source. Assume the transistor has an h_{FE} in the range of 20–60. A logic 1 corresponds to 5 V and a logic 0 to 0 V.

P19–6 Repeat prob. P19–5 using a 12-V dc source.

P19–7 Referring to the pulse description in Fig. 19–3, calculate the width of the actual input pulse if the following times were measured at the output: $t_d = 20\,\text{ns}$, $t_r = 10\,\text{ns}$, $t_f = 12\,\text{ns}$, and $t_s = 25\,\text{ns}$. The pulse width at $0.9I_{CM}$ is $2\,\mu\text{s}$.

P19–8 The following measurements were taken for the waveforms of Fig. 19–4: point a corresponds to 0, point b to 35 ns, point c to 120 ns, and point d to 150 ns. Calculate the average propatation delay, t_{pd}.

P19–9 For the INVERTER of Fig. 19–5, $R_C = 2.2\,\text{k}\Omega$, $R_B = 3.3\,\text{k}\Omega$, $R_1 = 47\,\text{k}\Omega$, $V_{CC} = 6\,\text{V}$, $-V_{BB} = -6\,\text{V}$, $h_{FE(\text{min})} = 40$, $V_{BE(\text{ON})} = 0.7\,\text{V}$, and $V_{\text{sat}} = 0.2\,\text{V}$. Calculate the minimum input voltage for reliable switching.

P19–10 Repeat prob. P19–9 for $V_{CC} = 10\,\text{V}$ and $-V_{BB} = -10\,\text{V}$.

P19–11 For the INVERTER of prob. P19–9, determine the maximum value of R_B for a 3-V input pulse.

P19–12 If the transistor in Fig. 19–5 has a $C_i = 60\,\text{pF}$ and $r_{b'e} = 2\,\text{k}\Omega$, determine the value of C_s for a base resistor R_B of
(a) $3.3\,\text{k}\Omega$.
(b) $8\,\text{k}\Omega$.

P19–13 Design the component values for the INVERTER of Fig. 19–5 to operate as a saturated switch from ± 12-V supplies. The pulse $= 6\,\text{V}$, $h_{FE(\text{min})} = 30$, $r_{b'e} = 1.5\,\text{k}\Omega$ and $C_i = 120\,\text{pF}$.

P19–14 Repeat prob. P19–13 for an input pulse that varies between $-2\,\text{V}$ and $+2\,\text{V}$.

P19–15 Construct a voltage truth table for the AND gate of Fig. 19–14. Assume that $V_{DD} = 5\,\text{V}$, $R_1 = R_2 = 1\,\text{k}\Omega$, and that a logic 0 corresponds to 0 V and a logic 1 to 5 V.

P19–16 Construct a voltage truth table for the AND gate of Fig. 19–16B. Assume that $V_{DD} = 10\,\text{V}$, $R = 2.2\,\text{k}\Omega$, and that a logic 0 corresponds to 0 V and a logic 1 to 10 V.

P19–17 For the circuit of Fig. 19–17, $R_1 = 4.7\,\text{k}\Omega$, $R_B = 10\,\text{k}\Omega$, $R_2 = 47\,\text{k}\Omega$, $R_C = 1\,\text{k}\Omega$, $V_{\text{sat}} = 0.2\,\text{V}$, $V_{BE(\text{ON})} = 0.7\,\text{V}$, $V_{CC} = 10\,\text{V}$, $-V_{BB} = -10\,\text{V}$, and $h_{FE(\text{min})} = 40$. What is the fan-out for the circuit?

P19–18 Repeat prob. P19–17 for $R_B = 22\,\text{k}\Omega$.

P19–19 The value of R_C in prob. P19–17 is changed to $10\,\text{k}\Omega$. What is the new fan-out?

P19–20 Calculate the noise margin for the circuit of prob. P19–17.

20

Integrated (IC) Logic

Electronic logic gates have gone through a remarkable evolution. Today's logic circuits are much faster and more versatile than the early diode gates. They are available in endless combinations of internally connected circuits which form entire logic blocks. Their reliability has improved, and the space formerly occupied by one gate can now accommodate many gates. This progress has been achieved through IC technology.

Integrated circuits bear little resemblance to the discrete circuits from which they evolved. To produce a high packing density, a high ratio of active to passive elements is necessary. Active devices occupy less space on a chip than do resistors and capacitors (see Chapter 10).

IC gates are available in a variety of packages (*encapsulations*). They are regarded as components by the logic designer and technician. When an integrated circuit becomes defective, the chip is not repaired—it is replaced. This necessitates a simple removal of the defective integrated circuit and its replacement by a new integrated circuit of the same type.

In this chapter, we shall consider the different types of IC logic, known as logic families. A comparison of their performance and specific applications also will be made.

20.1 DTL and HTL

The acronyms DTL and HTL stand for *D*iode *T*ransistor *L*ogic and *H*igh *T*hreshold *L*ogic, respectively. They represent two logic families. Different kinds of gates and related circuits with the same types of configurations and general specifications constitute a family. The NAND gate considered in Chapter 19 (Fig. 19–17) may be considered as an example of DTL. The input elements are diodes, and the output element is a transistor.

The circuit of Fig. 20–1A is an example of a practical DTL integrated circuit. Although the circuit bears the Motorola designation MC930, it is also manufactured by

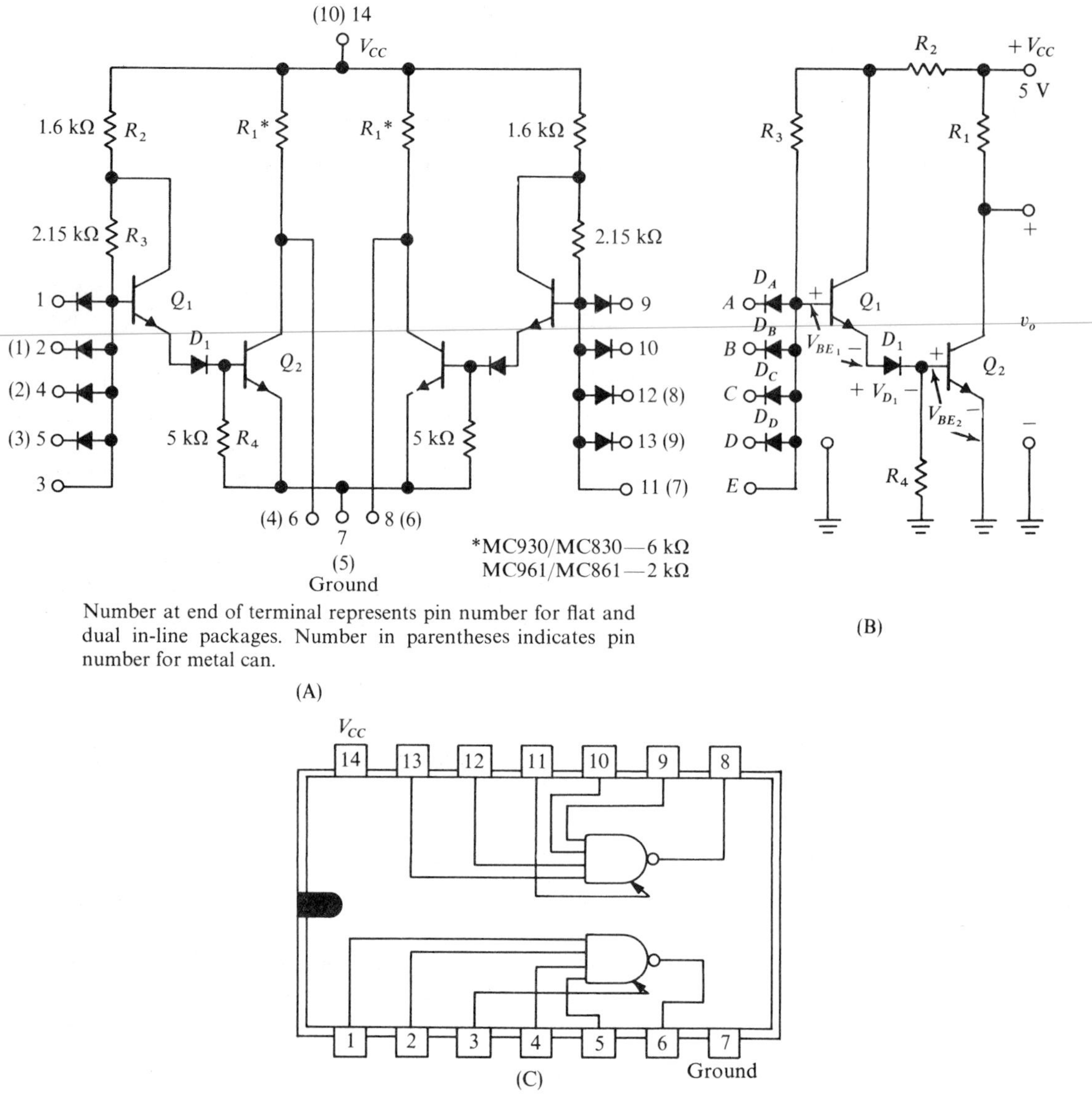

Fig. 20–1. *Practical DTL integrated circuit. (A) Dual four-input NAND gate. (B) Single four-input NAND gate. (C) Dual in-line plastic package showing pin configuration. (Courtesy Motorola Semiconductor Products, Inc.)*

other companies. It comes in three different package styles (Fig. 20–2): a flat-pack, a plastic dual in-line package, and a round metal can. The circuit is described as an expandable dual four-input gate. Note that there are two identical four-input gates in each package. The word *expandable* denotes that the circuit can be interconnected in ways to extend its capabilities.

One of the gates is redrawn in Fig. 20–1B. Only one power supply (typically $V_{CC} = 5\,\text{V}$) is required. This is an improvement over the discrete circuit of Fig. 19–17. The negative source, $-V_{BB}$, was used in the discrete circuit to improve the noise margin and to provide a small turn-off

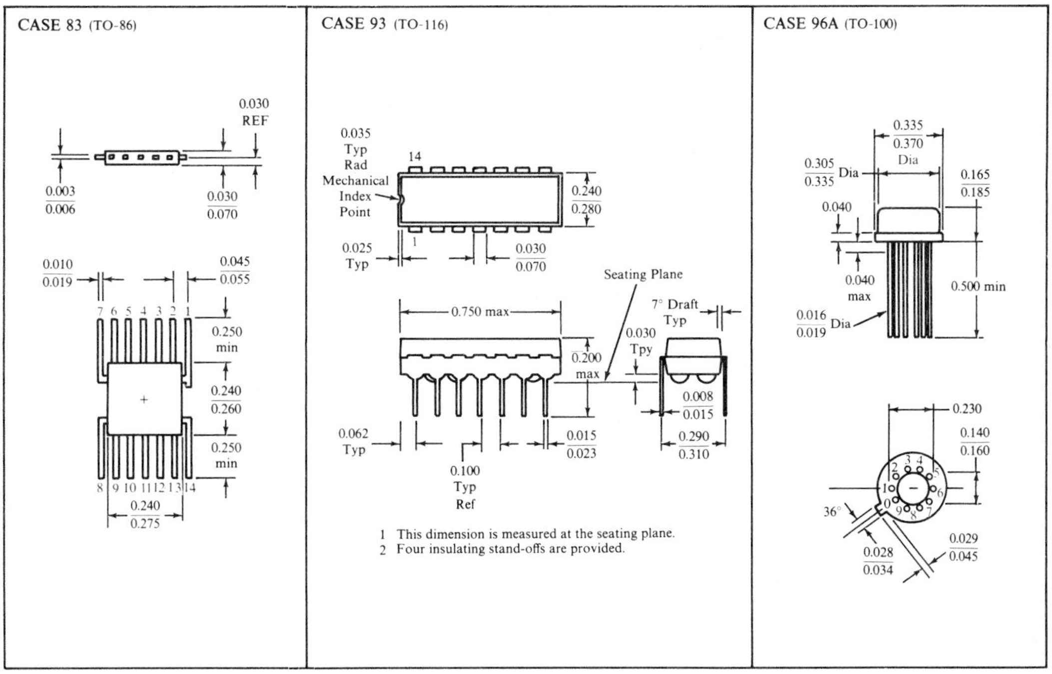

(A) (B) (C)

Fig. 20–2. *Examples of integrated circuit package (case) styles. (A) Flat-pack. (B) Dual in-line plastic package. (C) Round metal can. (Courtesy Motorola Semiconductor Products, Inc.)*

time. In Fig. 20–1B, the added transistor, Q_1, provides isolation between the input and R_4. The resistance of R_4 can then be made small to achieve a rapid turn-off time. Transistor Q_1 also supplies the input current to drive Q_2 hard into saturation. Terminal E is the expander input through which the circuit can accept additional inputs.

When all inputs are at logic 0, or grounded, current flows through the input diodes. Voltage V_{B_1} is approximately equal to 0.7 V (the forward voltage drop across a diode). Transistor Q_1, diode D_1, and transistor Q_2 are OFF. For these to conduct, V_{B_1} must be equal to approximately 2.1 V. This is equal to the sum $V_{BE_1} + V_{D_1} + V_{BE_2}$. With Q_2 OFF, the output is approximately V_{CC} volts, or a logic 1. The same line of reasoning applies when at least one of the inputs is "low," yielding a "high" at the output.

If all inputs are "high," transistors Q_1 and Q_2 are ON, as is D_1. Voltage V_{B_1} is approximately 2.1 V. None of the input diodes conduct. Transistor Q_2 is saturated because of the current from Q_1. Output voltage $V_o = V_{\text{sat}}$, or a "low" (approximately 0.2 V).

The circuit has a fan-out of 8 and a total package power dissipation rating of 22 mW. Propagation delay time is 30 ns, and the noise margin is 1.1 V. The circuit may be used as a positive logic NAND gate or a negative logic NOR gate.

HTL is an IC family with high noise immunity. It is used in applications in which high levels of noise are present, and high noise immunity is necessary to prevent unwanted switching. An example of an HTL NAND gate is shown in Fig. 20–3. The high noise immunity is achieved by the use of zener diode D_1. Actually, D_1 is a reverse-biased, base-emitter junction which exhibits a reverse breakdown voltage of approximately 7 V. The input voltage needed to turn Q_2 ON, therefore, is high, in the order of 7.5 V.

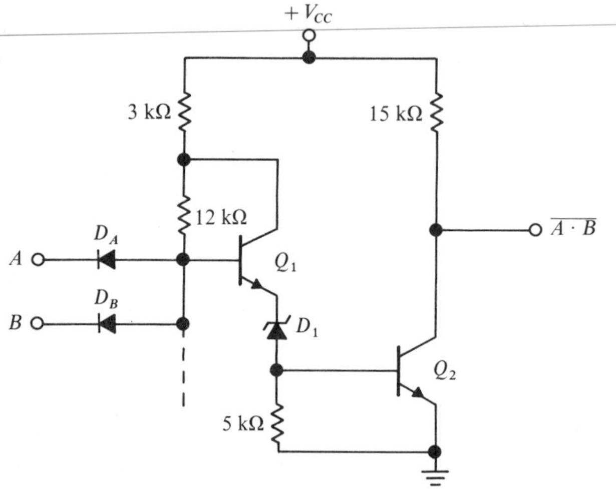

Fig. 20–3. *HTL NAND gate with passive pull-up.*

Supply voltage V_{CC} is higher than that required for the DTL gate; it is specified at 15 V ± 1 V. Consequently, a logic 1 corresponds to 15 V. For a logic 0, the output is equal to V_{sat}. The propagation delay is in the order of 110 ns, which makes it a slower logic family than DTL.

In addition to the resistance of the load, output capacitance always must be considered for the HTL as well as for other logic circuits. The output capacitance is made up of the load, wiring, and inherent transistor capacitances. In the discussion following, the total output capacitance will be called C_o.

When the output switches from a "high" to a "low," the output transistor turns ON. A discharge path is provided through the ON transistor for the stored charge in C_o. The time constant is small, resulting in a rapid discharge. Because the discharge path includes a transistor, it is referred to as an *active pull-down.*

When transistor Q_2 turns OFF, C_o is charged to V_{CC} volts. The charging path is through the 15-kΩ collector resistor; therefore, the time constant is much longer than the discharge cycle. This arrangement of the output capacitance charging through a resistor is called *passive pull-up.*

To decrease the charge cycle time constant, an *active pull-up* transistor, Q_3, is added to the basic circuit in Fig. 20–4. When Q_2 turns OFF, transistor Q_3 turns ON and provides a low-resistance charging path for C_o. The fan-out of a typical HTL circuit with active pull-up is 10. Total power dissipation is 88 mW with inputs at "high" and 26 mW with inputs at "low."

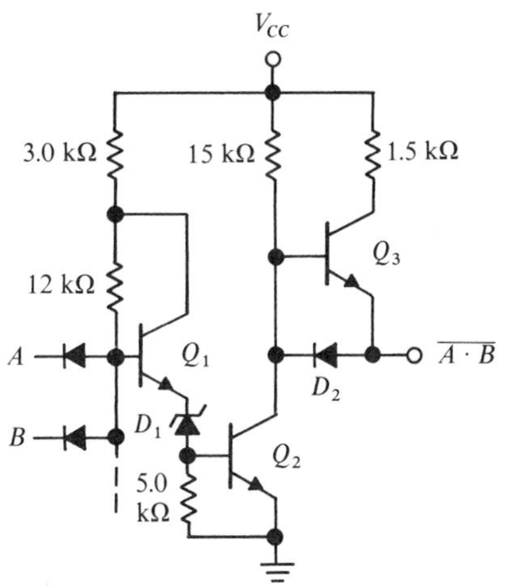

Fig. 20–4. *HTL NAND gate with active pull-up transistor Q_3. (Courtesy Motorola Semiconductor Products, Inc.)*

20.2 Resistor Transistor Logic (RTL)

The RTL family gained its popularity as the first digital IC. A three-input RTL NOR gate is illustrated in Fig. 20–5. The circuit operates as follows: With all three inputs grounded (logic 0), each transistor is OFF. The output equals V_{CC} volts (logic 1). If at least one input is at a logic 1, the transistor turns ON. The output falls to V_{sat} volts (logic 0).

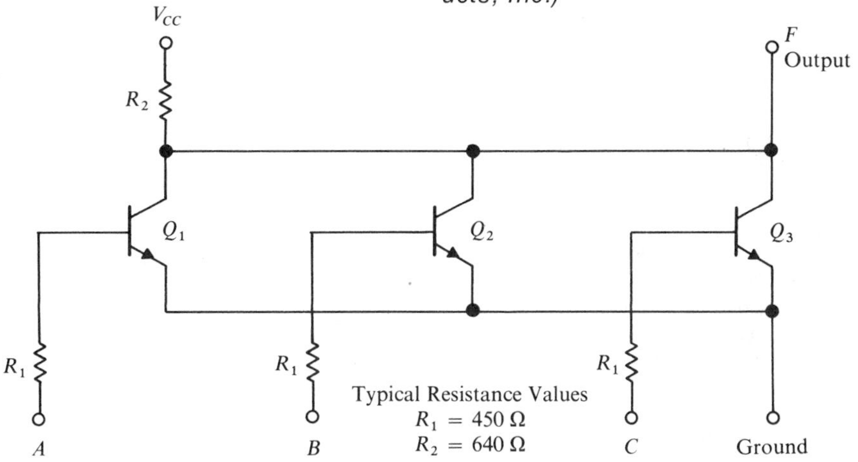

Fig. 20–5. *Three-input RTL NOR gate. (Courtesy Motorola Semiconductor Products, Inc.)*

The RTL gate has several shortcomings. It is a low threshold circuit with a noise immunity of approximately 0.3 V. Because of the base resistor in each input leg, which affects the turn-on and turn-off times, RTL is a relatively low-speed logic. The fan-out is also low. On the other hand, it consumes only 12 mW of power per gate, is inexpensive, and may operate from a single low-voltage source of 3.6 V.

An attempt was made to improve the characteristics of RTL by increasing its switching speed. Speed was increased by connecting speed-up capacitors across the base resistors. This resulted in a new logic family, RCTL (*r*esistor-*c*apacitor *t*ransistor *l*ogic). Because the new circuit did not lend itself to monolithic fabrication, RCTL never materialized commercially.

20.3 Transistor-Transistor Logic (TTL, T^2L)

The transistor-transistor logic (TTL, T^2L) family evolved directly from DTL. Because of monolithic technology, a transistor with multiple emitters can be manufactured, as shown in Fig. 20–6. The multiple emitters replace the input diodes of a DTL gate, resulting in a substantial savings in space per gate. A smaller geometry also exhibits less capacitance to the substrate, and, therefore, increased switching speed is realized.

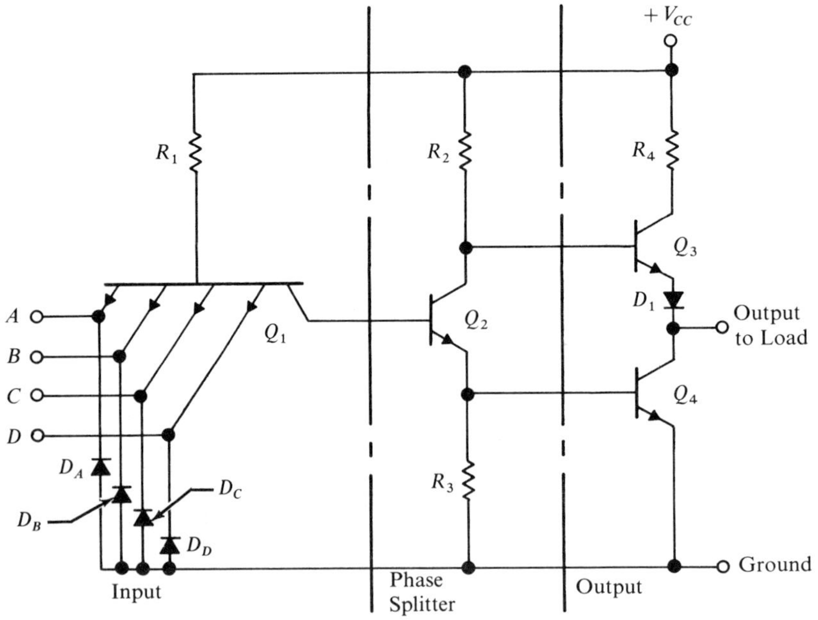

Fig. 20–6. *T^2L medium-speed (conventional) NAND gate. (Courtesy Motorola Semiconductor Products, Inc.)*

The emitters of the input transistor present light loading to the driving circuit. This results in a good fan-out. Transistor Q_1 provides a low-impedance discharge path for the base of Q_2, thereby reducing the turn-off time of the circuit. Because the collector voltage of Q_2 is 180° out of phase with the voltage at the emitter, it acts as a phase splitter. Transistor Q_3, diode D_1, and transistor Q_4 are connected in a totem-pole configuration. This provides active pull-up and pull-down operation, making the circuit suitable for driving capacitive loads.

The four-input NAND gate of Fig. 20–6 can be divided into three basic circuits: the input, phase splitter, and output circuit. Diodes D_A, D_B, D_C, and D_D are normally nonconducting. They are turned ON only when a spurious signal, such as a negative spike, appears at an input. The diode associated with that particular input conducts and shorts the unwanted signal to ground. The diodes act as clamps to prevent the input from becoming excessively negative, thereby protecting Q_1.

To understand the operation of T^2L, we consider three cases of input signal conditions:

1. *All inputs are low.* Transistor Q_1 conducts, and its base-emitter voltage is 0.7 V. For Q_2 to turn ON, the sum $V_{BC_1} + V_{BE_2} + V_{BE_4} = 0.7 + 0.7 + 0.7 = 2.1$ V must exist. Because the voltage at the base of Q_1 is only 0.7 V, transistors Q_2 and Q_4 are OFF. A "high" (V_{CC} volts) is present at the base of Q_3. Transistor Q_3 acts as an emitter follower, producing a "high" at the output as diode D_1 conducts. In this case, Q_3 behaves like a *current source.*
2. *At least one input is low.* The "low" input forces Q_1 to conduct, and the operation is identical to case 1. The output is again a "high." Note that with some inputs "low" and others "high," transistor action can occur between their respective emitters and the base of the transistor. For example, if A is "low" and B is "high," terminal A still acts as an emitter. Terminal B, however, assumes the role of a collector. Fortunately, the h_{FE} of such a transistor is negligible (0.01). In effect, the original signal between the "low" and "high" emitters is attenuated. For all practical purposes, transistor action does not occur between emitters.
3. *All inputs are high.* When all inputs are "high," Q_1 is OFF. Its base-collector junction is forward biased, and Q_1 supplies base current to Q_2. Transistors Q_2 and Q_4 turn ON and saturate. The output is equal to V_{sat} volts (logic 0). Transistor Q_4 in this case behaves like a *current sink.*

The voltage at the collector of Q_2 with respect to ground, V_{C_2}, is

$$\begin{aligned} V_{C_2} &= V_{BE_4} + V_{sat_2} \\ &= 0.7 + 0.2 = 0.9 \text{ V} \end{aligned} \tag{20–1}$$

(In our discussion, it is assumed that $V_{sat} = 0.2$ V.) Because the collector of Q_2 is directly connected to the base of Q_3, the base voltage of Q_3 with respect to ground is also 0.9 V. The minimum base voltage required to turn ON Q_3, $V_{B_3(min)}$, is

$$\begin{aligned} V_{B_3(min)} &= V_{BE_3} + V_{D_1} + V_{sat_4} \\ &= 0.7 + 0.7 + 0.2 = 1.6 \text{ V} \end{aligned} \tag{20–2}$$

Transistor Q_3 is therefore OFF because the voltage at its base is insufficient to turn it ON.

EXAMPLE 20–1.

For the two-input NAND gate of Fig. 20–7, find

(a) The output voltage when at least one input is at a "low."

(b) The fan-out with both inputs "high."

Assume $h_{FE(\min)} = 30$ and $V_{sat} = 0.2$ V. For simplicity, the input clamping diodes have been deleted from the circuit.

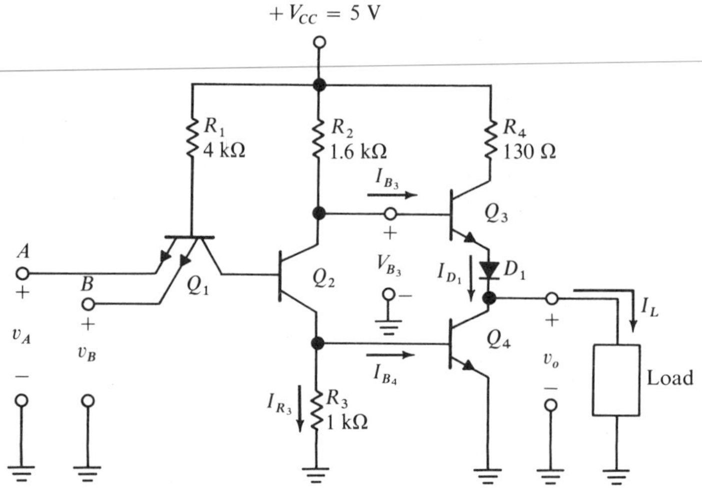

Fig. 20–7. *Two-input T²L gate. (See Example 20–1.)*

Solutions:

(a) Let $v_A = 0$ V ("low") and $v_B = 5$ V ("high"). Transistor Q_1 conducts, and its low voltage at the collector keeps Q_2 OFF. Transistor Q_3 is ON, and the voltage at its base with respect to ground, V_{B_3}, may be calculated from

$$V_{B_3} = V_{CC} - I_{B_3}R_2 \qquad \textbf{(20–3)}$$

The load, diode, and emitter current of Q_3 are equal:

$$I_L = I_{D_1} = I_{E_3}$$

The base current in Q_3 is

$$I_{B_3} \simeq \frac{I_{E_3}}{h_{FE}}$$

Assuming a load current of 0.7 mA,

$$I_{B_3} = \frac{0.7}{30} = 0.0233 \text{ mA}$$

By Eq. (20–3),

$$V_{B_3} = 5 - 0.0233 \times 1.6 = 4.96 \text{ V}$$

The output voltage is

$$v_o = V_{B_3} - V_{BE_3} - V_{D_1} \qquad \textbf{(20–4)}$$
$$= 4.96 - 0.7 - 0.7 = 3.56 \text{ V}$$

(b) With both inputs "high," the base-emitter junctions are reverse biased, and the base-collector junction of Q_1 is forward biased. Transistor Q_2 saturates, and

$$I_{B_2} = \frac{V_{CC} - (V_{BC_1} + V_{BE_2} + V_{BE_4})}{R_1} \qquad \textbf{(20–5)}$$

$$= \frac{5 - 2.1}{4} = 0.725\,\text{mA}$$

The maximum available collector current in Q_2, $I_{C_2(\max)}$ is

$$I_{C_2(\max)} = I_{B_2} h_{FE(\min)}$$
$$= 0.725 \times 30 = 21.75\,\text{mA}$$

The current in Q_2 for saturation, $I_{C_2(\text{sat})}$, is

$$I_{C_2(\text{sat})} = \frac{V_{CC} - V_{BE_4} - V_{\text{sat}_2}}{R_2} \qquad \textbf{(20–6)}$$

$$= \frac{5 - 0.7 - 0.2}{1.6} = 2.56\,\text{mA}$$

Comparing $I_{C_2(\max)}$ with $I_{C_2(\text{sat})}$, we conclude that Q_2 is indeed saturated.

The emitter voltage of Q_2, V_{E_2}, is equal to the base-emitter voltage of Q_4, $V_{BE_4} = 0.7\,\text{V}$. The current in R_3, I_{R_3}, is

$$I_{R_3} = \frac{V_{E_2}}{R_3}$$
$$= \frac{0.7}{1} = 0.7\,\text{mA}$$

Base current I_{B_4} is given by

$$I_{B_4} = I_{E_2} - I_{R_3} \qquad \textbf{(20–7)}$$
$$= 2.56 - 0.7 = 1.86\,\text{mA}$$

This results in a value of $I_{C_4} = 1.86 \times 30 = 55.8\,\text{mA}$.

The maximum load current that can be switched by the gate is 55.8 mA. Assuming that each input of a connected gate requires a current of 1.33 mA, the fan-out, F.O., is

$$\text{F.O.} = \frac{55.8}{1.33} = 41.8$$

Because the fan-out must be a whole number, the answer is 41.

A fan-out of 41 is a large number. In reality, the current and power limitations of the devices in the chip reduce the fan-out. For this particular circuit, the fan-out is 10.

The circuit discussed thus far is known as medium-speed T²L. It is powered typically from a 5-V dc supply, and the maximum allowable input signal is 5.5 V. The unused inputs of the same gate are either connected to the used inputs or returned to the dc supply through a resistor. This avoids external noise from appearing on an open input line and accidentally triggering the gate. With more than one gate in a package, the inputs of the unused gates are returned to ground.

The typical output swing of a T^2L gate is between 0.2 V and 3.5 V; power dissipation is 10–15 mW/gate. The average propagation delay is 10 ns–12 ns. Typical rise and fall times are 3.5 and 1.5 ns, respectively.

The speed of a T^2L circuit may be increased by modifying the basic circuit. In Fig. 20–8, the new circuit features a Darlington active pull-up circuit (Q_4, Q_5) and an active bypass network (Q_3) in the base of Q_6. (The operation of the active bypass network is described later.) Diode D_1 of Fig. 20–6 is not required because of Q_4. Transistor Q_4 provides an additional diode drop to keep Q_5 turned OFF when Q_6 is in saturation. The Darlington pair exhibits a low output impedance which allows the circuit to drive capacitive loads at higher speeds with improved noise immunity.

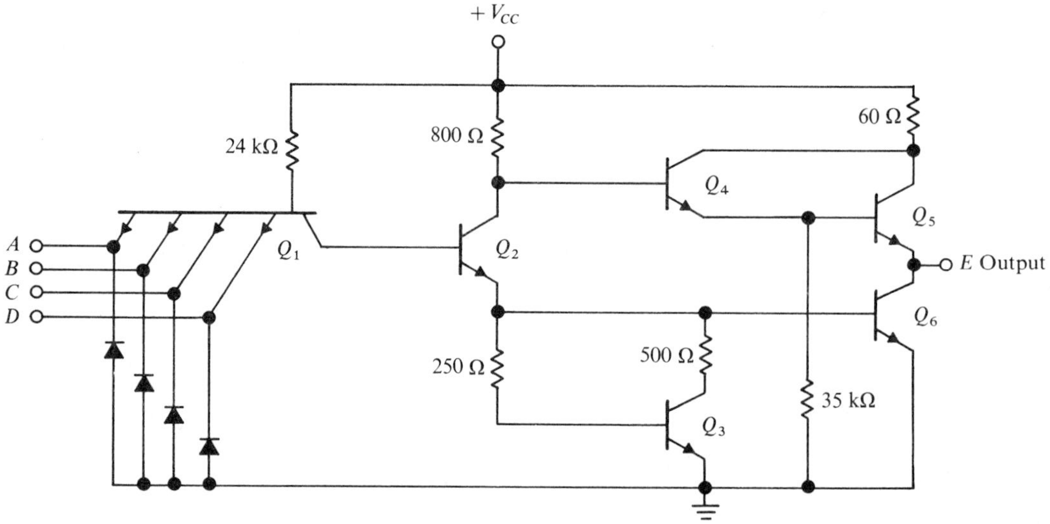

Fig. 20–8. *High-speed T^2L gate. (Courtesy Motorola Semiconductor Products, Inc.)*

Transistor Q_3 holds the phase-splitter transistor (Q_2) OFF until the input signal is sufficient to switch the transistor. This results in an improved transfer characteristic. The transfer characteristics of a conventional and a high-speed T^2L gate are compared in Fig. 20–9. Note the sharper changeover from one state to the other for the high-speed T^2L gate.

For a high-speed T^2L gate, the output impedance is typically 10 Ω in both states; the propagation delay is 6 ns. The rise and fall times are 1 and 1.3 ns, respectively. Power dissipation per gate is 22 mW, and the fan-out is 10. From Fig. 20–9, the noise margin is approximately 1.5 V.

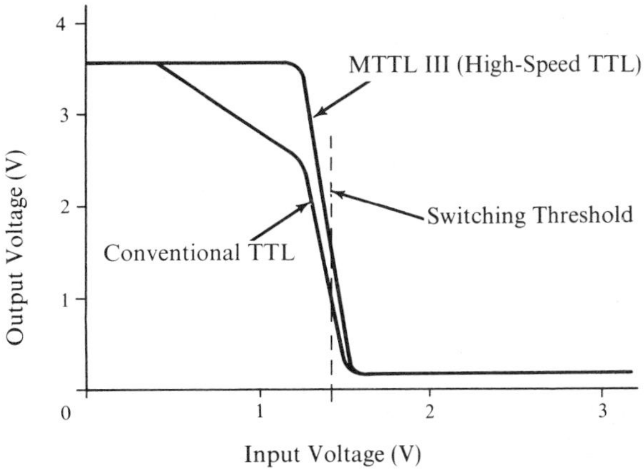

Fig. 20–9. *Comparison of transfer curves for conventional and high-speed T²L. (Courtesy Motorola Semiconductor Products, Inc.)*

Low-Power T²L

Low-power T²L was developed for aerospace, military, and other applications where low power consumption is of utmost importance. Illustrated in Fig. 20–10, the circuit is identical to that of medium-speed T²L, except for the resistance values, which are higher.

Low-power T²L sacrifices speed. The propagation delay for the circuit is typically 35 ns, or three times greater than conventional T²L. Power dissipation per gate is typically 1 mW, which is a remarkable improvement over other T²L gates. It becomes apparent that, in order to achieve high-speed operation, one must sacrifice power, and vice versa. Low-power gates do not have high speeds, and trade-offs between speed and power are made by the circuit designer.

The *speed-power product* is a measure of the combined performance, in terms of speed and power, of a gate. A plot of propagation delay time versus power dissipation for different members of the T²L family is given in Fig. 20–11.

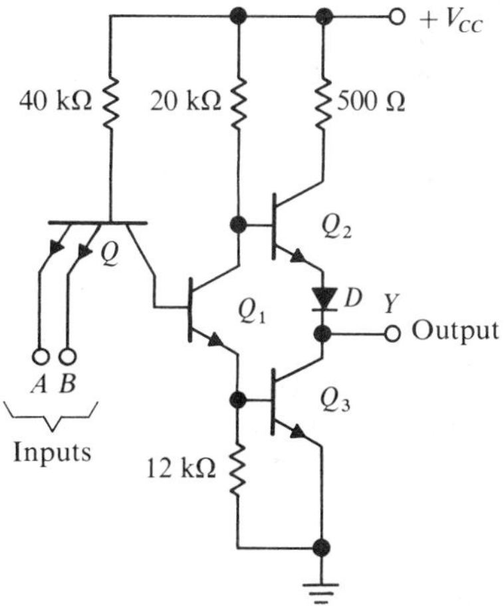

Fig. 20–10. *Low-power T²L.*

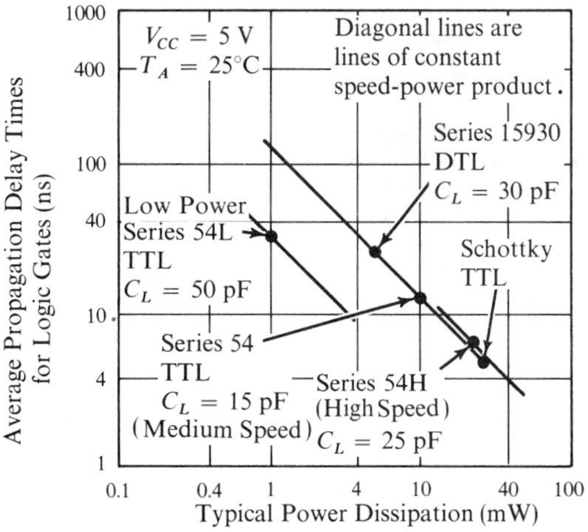

Fig. 20–11. *Speed-power relationships of T²L gates. (Courtesy Texas Instruments, Inc.)*

The speed-power product is expressed by

$$\text{Speed-power product} = t_{pd} \times P_D \qquad \textbf{(20–8)}$$

where t_{pd} is the propagation delay time and P_D is the power dissipated by the gate. The unit for the speed-power product is the joule (J).

EXAMPLE 20–2.

From Fig. 20–11, determine which T^2L gate considered thus far has the lowest speed-power product.

Solution:

Medium-speed T^2L:

$$t_{pd} \times P_D = 12\,\text{ns} \times 10\,\text{mW}$$
$$= 120 \times 10^{-12}\,\text{Ws} \doteq 120\,\text{pJ} \quad \text{(picojoules)}$$

(1 Ws = 1 J)

High-speed T^2L:

$$6\,\text{ns} \times 22\,\text{mW} = 132\,\text{pJ}$$

Low-power T^2L:

$$30\,\text{ns} \times 1\,\text{mW} = 30\,\text{pJ}$$

The low-power T^2L has the lowest speed-power product.

Schottky T^2L

To further increase the speed of a T^2L gate, the circuit of Fig. 20–8 is implemented with Schottky devices in place of conventional transistors and diodes (Fig. 20–12). As discussed in Chapter 19, the use of Schottky transistors results

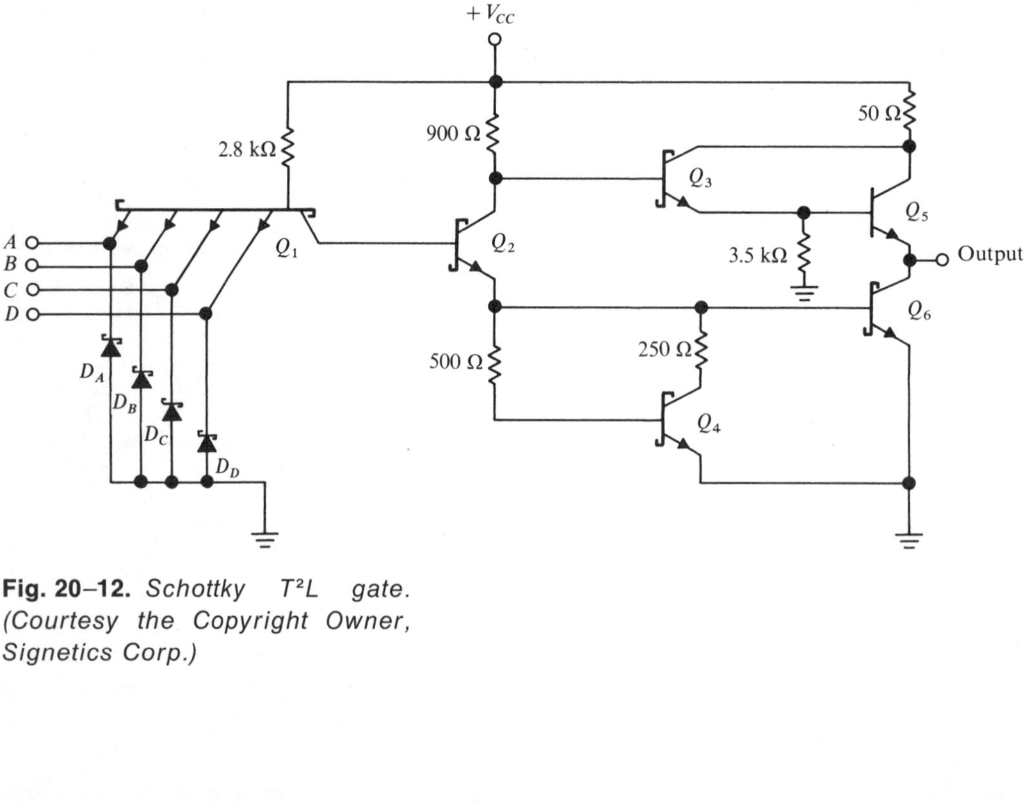

Fig. 20–12. *Schottky T^2L gate. (Courtesy the Copyright Owner, Signetics Corp.)*

in a nonsaturated logic. The effect is a reduction in storage time and increased switching speeds.

Schottky T^2L has a propagation delay of 5 ns, and a typical power dissipation of 19 mW/gate. This results in a speed-power product of 95 pJ. Because transistor Q_5 does not saturate, it is not replaced with a Schottky transistor.

20.4 Emitter Coupled Logic (ECL)

The ECL family of logic is the most popular nonsaturating type of logic. Sometimes called *current mode logic* (CML), it exhibits high speed and fan-out and provides simultaneously OR and NOR logic functions. The circuit of a four-input ECL gate is illustrated in Fig. 20–13A; the logic symbol is provided in Fig. 20–13B.

High switching speeds are achieved because ECL is a nonsaturating logic. Because of the high input impedance of the differential amplifier (Q_1, Q_8), which is the heart of the ECL gate, and the low output impedance of emitter

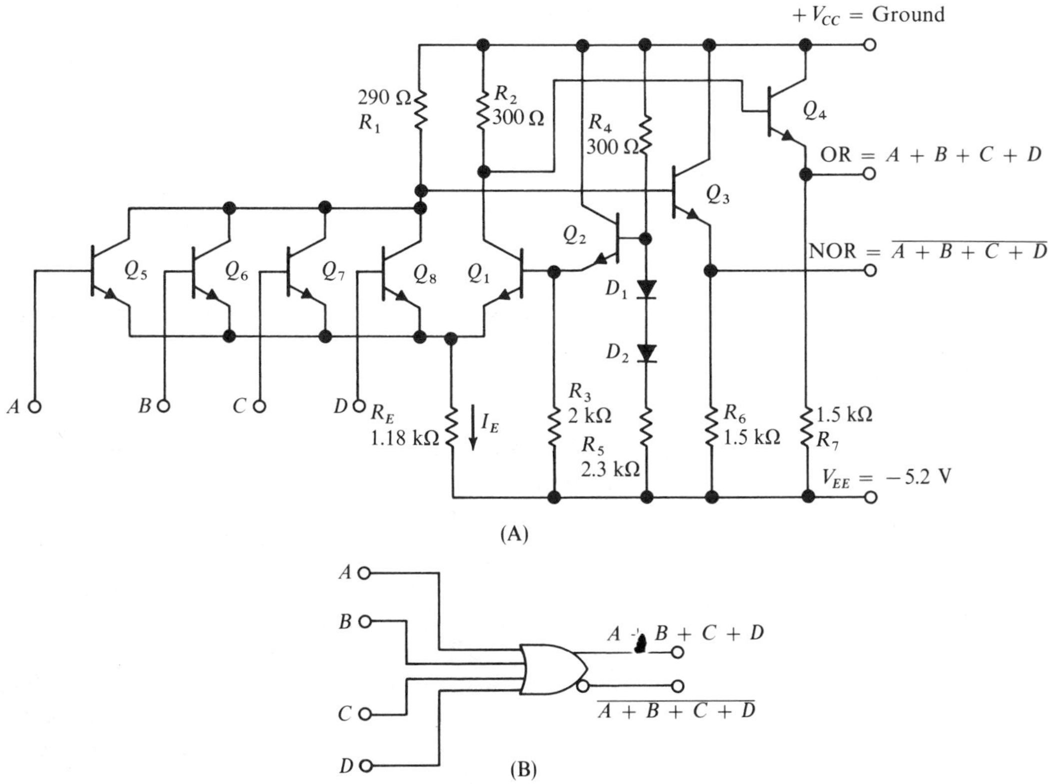

Fig. 20–13. *Example of a four-input ECL OR/NOR gate. (A) Circuit. (B) Logic symbol. (Courtesy Motorola Semiconductor Products, Inc.)*

followers Q_3 and Q_4, a high fan-out is realized. The differential amplifier draws a constant current from the supply. As a result, spikes that usually exist at the supply terminals during switching are eliminated.

We now explain the operation of the circuit. With all inputs "low," the input transistors are OFF because each base is negative with respect to its emitter. Diodes D_1 and D_2 and resistors R_4 and R_5 provide a bias reference for Q_2. The value of the base voltage of Q_2 with respect to ground, V_{B_2}, is

$$V_{B_2} = \frac{(V_{EE} + V_{D_1} + V_{D_2})R_4}{R_4 + R_5}$$

$$= \frac{(-5.2 + 0.7 + 0.7) \times 0.3}{2.3 + 0.3} = -0.45\,\text{V}$$

The voltage at the base of Q_1 with respect to ground, V_{B_1}, is

$$V_{B_1} = V_{E_2} = V_{B_2} - V_{BE_2}$$

$$= -0.45 - 0.7 = -1.15\,\text{V}$$

and the emitter voltage of Q_1, V_{E_1}, is

$$V_{E_1} = V_{E_2} - V_{BE_1}$$

$$= -1.15 - 0.7 = -1.85\,\text{V}$$

Current flowing in R_E, I_E, is expressed by

$$I_E = \frac{V_{E_1} - V_{EE}}{R_E}$$

$$= \frac{-1.85 - (-5.2)}{1.18} = 2.85\,\text{mA}$$

The voltage at the collector of Q_1 with respect to ground, V_{C_1}, is

$$V_{C_1} = -I_{C_1}R_2 \simeq -I_E R_2$$

$$= -2.5 \times 0.3 = -0.85\,\text{V}$$

The OR output, V_{OR}, is taken at the emitter of Q_4 with respect to ground. Its value is determined by

$$V_{\text{OR}} = -0.85 - 0.7 = -1.55\,\text{V}$$

which corresponds to a logic 0.

Because no current flows in R_1 when all inputs are "low," the collectors of the input transistors are at ground potential. The NOR output voltage is one base-emitter junction drop below ground, or -0.7 V. This level is considered a "high," or logic 1. Note the small difference between a "high" and a "low." This difference makes ECL a low-noise immunity logic.

Assume now that at least one input is "high" (-0.7 V). The input transistor with a "high" at its base turns ON, causing a voltage of -1.4 V to appear at the emitter of Q_1. Because the base-emitter voltage of Q_1 is $-1.15 - (-1.4) = 0.25$ V, Q_1 is OFF. The collector of Q_1 is at ground potential, and the OR output is reduced by the base-emitter voltage drop of Q_4 to -0.7 V ("high").

The current I_E in R_E is now equal to

$$I_E = \frac{-1.4 - (-5.2)}{1.18} = 3.24\,\text{mA}$$

and

$$V_{C_1} = -3.24 \times 0.29 = -0.94\,\text{V}$$

resulting in a NOR output of

$$V_{\text{NOR}} = -0.94 - 0.7 = -1.64\,\text{V}$$

which corresponds to a logic 0.

From the preceding analysis, we see that the "high" output is independent of variations in the power supply voltage. Variations in the supply voltage affect the "low" by only a slight amount. This may be attributed to the excellent common-mode rejection of power supply changes by a differential-amplifier type circuit. Manufacturers specify a wide allowable supply tolerance of ± 20 percent. The family of ECL gates has a propagation delay of from 1 to 8 ns; the power dissipated per gate is approximately 50 mW.

20.5 CMOS Logic

Before CMOS logic is discussed, we will consider other types of logic that employ the MOSFET. As we explained in Chapter 19, logic gates can be fabricated with MOSFETs only. No other components, such as resistors, are necessary. The power dissipation is extremely low for a MOSFET gate. Because of the MOSFETs' high input impedance, negligible input current flows, resulting in a high fan-out with excellent noise immunity. Several MOSFET fabrication techniques are used, each having its own special characteristics.

The *metal-gate PMOS* was the first type of MOSFET logic used. Composed of P-channel devices, the circuits were produced at low cost and high packing density. These gates are fairly slow, with a typical propagation delay time of 300 ns.

To increase the speed of a PMOS gate, the *silicon gate* device was developed. In this device, the aluminum gate is replaced by polycrystalline silicon. In addition to increased speed, it dissipates less power, can be made smaller, and is fully compatible with other types of logic (mainly T^2L).

A circuit that uses both P- and N-channel devices is called *complementary-symmetry* MOS (CMOS or COS/MOS) logic. The CMOS gate has an extremely low power dissipation, making it ideal as a memory device (see Chapter 22). CMOS circuits are found in many electronic watches where all functions are produced in a single chip.

MOSFET devices used in logic gates are enhancement type. Operation in the enhancement mode requires only a single dc power supply. A two-input CMOS NOR gate is

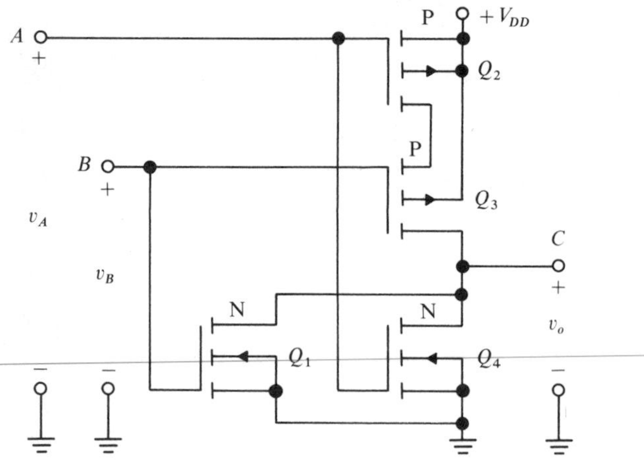

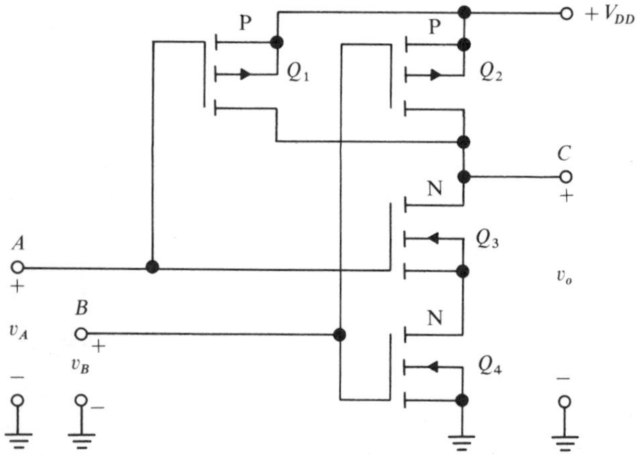

Fig. 20–14. (Above) *Two-input CMOS NOR gate.*

Fig. 20–15. (Below) *Two-input CMOS NAND gate.*

illustrated in Fig. 20–14. Two P-channel MOSFETs are in series, and two N-channel devices are connected in parallel.

Assume that both inputs are "low" (0 V). Both gates are negative with respect to the supply voltage, V_{DD}. Hence, the P-channel devices (Q_2, Q_3) are ON, and the N-channel transistors (Q_1, Q_4) are OFF. The output voltage is close to V_{DD} volts ("high"), because of the low voltage drop across Q_2 and Q_3 in conduction.

If one or both inputs are "high," the N-channel devices are ON, and the P-channel devices are OFF. Because the output is taken across the N-channel transistors, the output is "low."

From our discussion, it appears that a CMOS gate operates in a push-pull manner. If a P-channel device is ON, an N-channel device is OFF, and vice versa. This results in sharply defined switching characteristics. CMOS logic gates may be operated from a positive as well as a negative source, over a wide range of supply voltages.

A circuit of a CMOS NAND gate is shown in Fig. 20–15. In this circuit, the N-channel transistors are in series, and the P-channel devices are in parallel. With at least one input "low," Q_1 or Q_2, or both, are ON. Transistors Q_3 and Q_4 are OFF, and the output is slightly less than V_{DD} voltage, which corresponds to a logic 1.

With both inputs at a logic 1, transistors Q_3 and Q_4 are ON, and Q_1 and Q_2 are OFF. The output corresponds to a logic 0. A comparison of the logic families discussed in the chapter is provided in Table 20–1.

TABLE 20–1. Comparison of IC logic families.

Logic Family	Gate Function	Gate Density on Chip	t_{pd} (ns)	Power Diss./Gate (mW)	Speed-Power Product (pJ)	Fan-out	Noise Immunity	Supply Voltage (V)
DTL	NAND	Fair	30	8–12	240–360	8	Medium	5
HTL	NAND	Fair	90	26–88	4950	10	Very good	15
RTL	NOR	High	12	12	144	5	Fair	3.6
T^2L	NAND	Medium	6–12	12–22	144	10	Good	5
ECL	OR/NOR	Medium	1–8	40–55	55	25	Fair	−5.2
MOS	NAND	High	300	0.2–10	60–3000	20	Excellent	4–15
CMOS	NOR/NAND	Very high	70	0.01–1	0.7–70	> 50	Excellent	3–18
I^2L	OR/NOR	Very high	< 30	1–7	0.1–0.7	Variable	Fair	1–15

EXAMPLE 20–3.

Design a CMOS INVERTER. The power supply voltage $V_{DD} = 5\text{ V}$.

Solution:

From the analysis of the CMOS NOR and NAND gates, we see that a P-channel device turns ON when the input is "low," and an N-channel device turns ON when the input is "high." By connecting a P-channel MOSFET in series with an N-channel MOSFET, an INVERTER is produced (Fig. 20–16).

With a "low" input, Q_1 turns ON, resulting in a "high" output (5 V). When the input is "high," Q_1 is turned OFF and Q_2 ON. An output of approximately 0 V ("low") results.

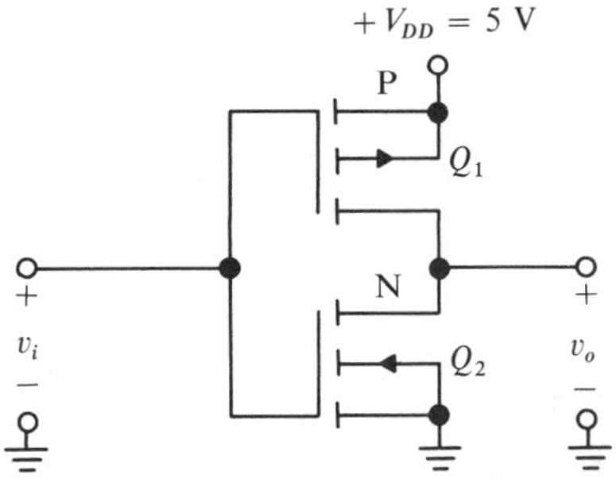

Fig. 20–16. *CMOS INVERTER. (See Example 20–3.)*

20.6 SSI, MSI, and LSI

Logic gates are contained in packages, such as those illustrated in Fig. 20–2. The number of gates per package is limited by the space occupied by each gate and the number of available pins. The second limitation determines the number of gates per chip. For example, in Fig. 20–1C, the dual four-input NAND gate is encapsulated in a dual in-line plastic package requiring a total of 14 pins. All available pins of the package are used. Thus, this standard package can accommodate only two four-input NAND gates.

A dual in-line package also can accommodate a maximum of six inverters. Each inverter requires a separate input and output pin, and one pin each for ground and the supply voltage. Gates can be internally interconnected to perform different functions. In this case, a minimum of external connections is required.

If fewer than 12 gates appear on a chip, it is called *small-scale integration* (SSI). A chip containing more than 12 but fewer than 100 gates is called *medium-scale integration* (MSI). Finally, arrays of over 100 gates on a chip are defined as *large-scale integration* (LSI).

20.7 Integrated Injection Logic (I^2L)

Integrated injection logic (I^2L) is ideally suited for large-scale integration. As many as 1000–3000 gates can occupy a single chip. The basic circuit is extremely versatile, permitting both digital and analog functions to be incorporated in the same chip. The speed-power product is as low as 0.1 pJ, which is considerably less than that for other types of logic. It also requires fewer processing steps than conventional T^2L, making it less costly to manufacture.

The basic I^2L element consists of a complementary bipolar transistor pair. In Fig. 20–17, *current injection transistor* Q_1 serves as a constant current source. Transistor Q_2, having *multiple collectors*, acts as an INVERTER. No resistors are required. Furthermore, the base of Q_1 is connected to the emitter of Q_2, and the collector of Q_1 is connected to the base of Q_2. This makes it possible to fabricate the circuit in the space normally occupied by a single transistor without electrical isolation between them. This results in an increased packing density.

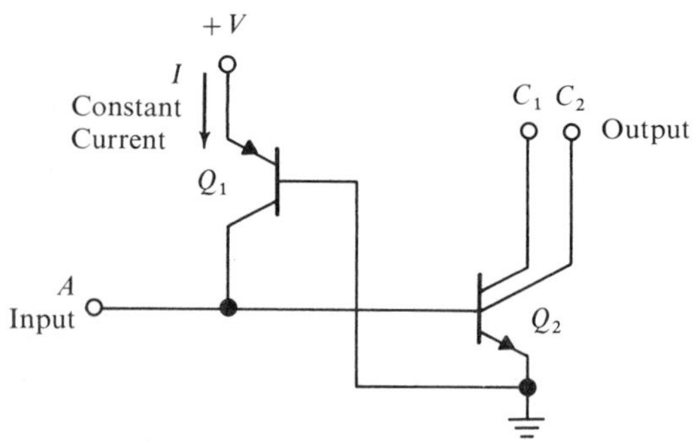

Fig. 20–17. *Basic I^2L element.*

A basic I^2L NOR gate is shown in Fig. 20–18. Inversion of the signal is provided by Q_2 and Q_4, resulting in $\overline{A}$ and $\overline{B}$ outputs. At point C, therefore, $\overline{A} \cdot \overline{B}$ is obtained. This is equivalent to $\overline{A + B}$, which is the NOR operation.

A logic 1 corresponds to approximately 0.7 V and a logic 0 to 0.05 V. Switching is accomplished by steering *injector*

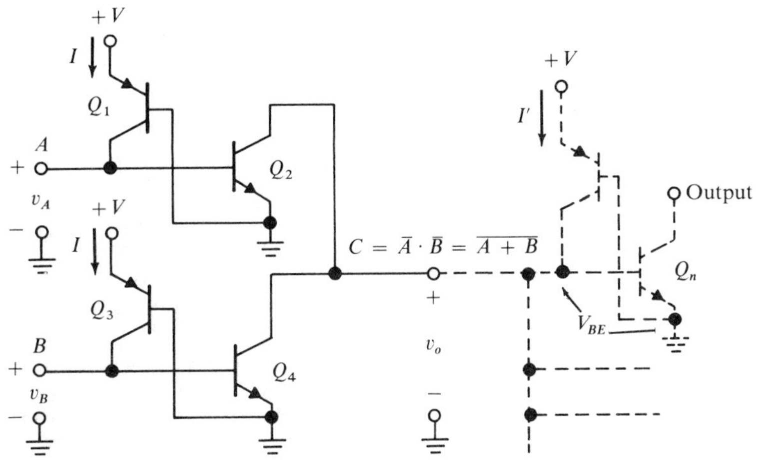

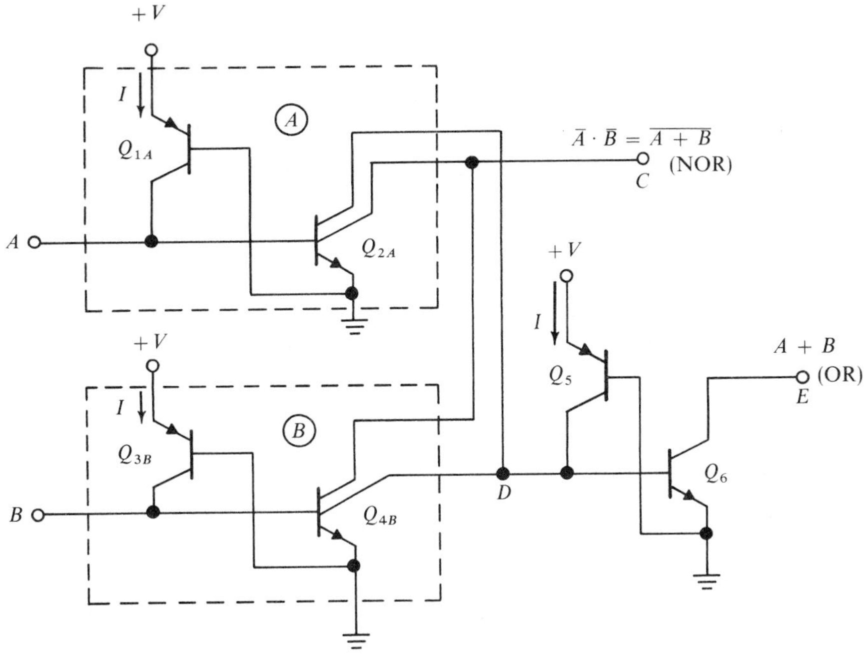

Fig. 20–18. (Above) *I²L NOR gate.*

Fig. 20–19. (Below) *I²L gate that yields NOR and OR outputs.*

current I to appropriate transistor bases. Assume both inputs are "low." Current I flows into the driving sources at the inputs, and Q_2 and Q_4 are deprived of base current. Both transistors, therefore, are OFF.

With transistors Q_2 and Q_4 OFF, the injector current of the following stage, I', flows into the base of Q_n. The transistor is turned ON, and the output is 0.7 V, which corresponds to the base-emitter voltage of Q_n. This corresponds to a logic 1. If one of the inputs is "high" and the other is "low" (for example, $v_A = 0.05$ V and $v_B = 0.7$ V), injector current I turns ON Q_4. This results in an output of $v_0 = 0.05$ V. Similarly, when both inputs are "high," the output is "low." The preceding analysis verifies the NOR operation for the circuit.

The circuit of Fig. 20–18 is modified in Fig. 20–19 to yield NOR and OR outputs simultaneously. This is an example of how multicollector outputs are generally utilized. Inputs A and B are inverted in circuits Ⓐ and Ⓑ, respectively. By interconnecting the collectors of Q_{2A} and Q_{4B}, the NOR function is obtained at output C. Transistors Q_5 and Q_6 form another I^2L element. In this case, they are used as an INVERTER to yield an OR function at terminal E.

The major factors that make I^2L a high-performance logic are summarized in Table 20–1. Note particularly the extremely low speed-power product and the high packing density.

SUMMARY

IC logic gates are divided into groups called logic families. A logic family is based on a common configuration of a gate. Examples of logic families considered in this chapter include T^2L, ECL, CMOS, and I^2L.

The important factors to consider in evaluating IC logic gates include:

1. Gate density on the chip.
2. Speed and power dissipated per gate, which is combined to yield the speed-power product.
3. Fan-out.
4. Noise immunity.

The gate density on a chip is divided into three groups: SSI (fewer than 12 gates per chip); MSI (fewer than 100 gates per chip); and LSI (more than 100 gates per chip).

MOS, CMOS, and I^2L families of logic are most suitable for large-scale integration. ECL is a nonsaturated type of logic. It is extremely fast, but its power dissipation per gate is fairly high. The lowest speed-power product is exhibited by I^2L and CMOS gates. T^2L is the most widely used logic.

Further Reading

Hart, C. M., A. Slob, and H. E. J. Wulms. "Bipolar LSI Takes a New Direction with Integrated Injection Logic." *Electronics*, Oct. 1974, pp. 111–18.

Kaufman, M., and A. H. Seidman, eds. *Handbook for Electronics Engineering Technicians*. New York: McGraw-Hill Book Company, 1976, Chapter 15.

Motorola. *The Integrated Circuit Data Book*, Phoenix, Ariz.: Motorola Semiconductor Products, Inc., 1968.

Oppenheimer, S. L. *Semiconductor Logic and Switching Circuits.* 2nd ed. Columbus, Ohio: Charles E. Merrill Publishing Company, 1973, Chapter 6.

RCA. *COS/MOS Integrated Circuits Manual.* Somerville, N.J.: RCA Corporation, 1971.

Texas Instruments. *The Integrated Circuits Catalog for Design Engineers.* Dallas, Tex.: Texas Instruments, Inc., 1971.

REVIEW QUESTIONS

20.1 What are the characteristics of HTL circuits?

20.2 What type of logic circuit results if diode D_1 in the circuit of Fig. 20–3 is replaced with a junction diode?

20.3 Define passive pull-up.

20.4 What is meant by active pull-up and pull-down?

20.5 What are the shortcomings of RTL gates?

20.6 Describe the three major sections of a T^2L gate.

20.7 Identify the output circuit used in the T^2L NAND gate of Fig. 20–6.

20.8 What is the purpose of diodes D_A–D_D in the circuit of Fig. 20–6?

20.9 How is the operation of the circuit affected when diode D_1 is shorted out in Fig. 20–6?

20.10 What is the effect on the output of the circuit in Fig. 20–6 if diode D_A is shorted out?

20.11 Compare the increase in speed of a high-speed T^2L gate with that of a standard T^2L gate.

20.12 What major characteristic is sacrified in a low-power T^2L gate?

20.13 Define the unit of the speed-power product of a gate.

20.14 Identify two types of nonsaturated logic gates.

20.15 What are the corresponding voltages of a "low" and a "high" for ECL?

20.16 Compare MOS and BJT logic devices.

20.17 Describe the differences between SSI, MSI, and LSI.

20.18 What are the characteristics of I^2L?

20.19 Describe the basic logic functions performed by
(a) RTL gates.
(b) T^2L gates.
(c) ECL gates.

20.20 What are the three standard package styles of a digital IC?

20.21 Why is transistor Q_5 in the circuit of Fig. 20–12 not a Schottky transistor?

20.22 Diode D_1 is open in the ECL circuit of Fig. 20–13A. How does this affect the output?

PROBLEMS

P20–1 For the RTL gate of Fig. 20–5, verify, by constructing a voltage truth table, that the gate performs the NOR operation. Assume that $R_1 = 450\,\Omega$, $R_2 = 640\,\Omega$, $V_{CC} = 3.6\,\text{V}$, $h_{FE(\text{min})} = 40$, $V_{BE(\text{ON})} = 0.7\,\text{V}$, and $V_{\text{sat}} = 0.1\,\text{V}$.

P20–2 For the circuit in prob. P20–1, determine the minimum voltage level for a "high" at the input to cause a "low" at the output.

P20–3 Calculate the fan-out for the circuit of prob. P20–1.

P20–4 Find the output voltage across the load in Fig. 20–7 with both inputs "high." Assume that $I_L = 1\,\text{mA}$, $h_{FE} = 30$, $V_{\text{sat}} = 0.1\,\text{V}$ and $V_{BE(\text{ON})} = 0.7\,\text{V}$.

P20–5 In the circuit of Fig. 20–10, determine the fan-out with both inputs "high." Assume that $V_{CC} = 5\,\text{V}$, a "high" corresponds to 5 V, $h_{FE(\text{min})} = 25$, $V_{\text{sat}} = 0.2\,\text{V}$, and $V_{BE(\text{ON})} = 0.7\,\text{V}$.

P20–6 For the circuit of prob. P20–5, calculate the output voltage with both inputs "low." Assume a load current of 0.1 mA.

P20–7 The speed-power product for a certain gate is given as 600 pJ. What is the propagation delay time for a power dissipation of 25 mW?

P20–8 Construct a voltage truth table for the DTL gate of Fig. 20–1A. Assume that the gate has two inputs, $V_{CC} = 5\,\text{V}$, $R_1 = 6\,\text{k}\Omega$, $h_{FE(\text{min})} = 40$, and $V_D = V_{BE(\text{ON})} = 0.7\,\text{V}$.

P20–9 Repeat prob. P20–8 for $h_{FE(\text{min})} = 20$.

P20–10 With all inputs "low," calculate the output voltage for the gate of Fig. 20–3. Assume there is no external loading, $V_{CC} = 15\,\text{V}$, the breakdown voltage for D_1 is 7 V, $h_{FE(\text{min})} = 30$, $V_{\text{sat}} = 0.1\,\text{V}$, and $V_{BE(\text{ON})} = 0.7\,\text{V}$.

P20–11 Repeat prob. P20–10 for $h_{FE(\text{min})} = 20$ with inputs "high."

P20–12 Calculate the total current through input diodes D_A and D_B with all inputs "low" in Fig. 20–3.

P20–13 Determine the power dissipated in transistors Q_1, Q_2, and Q_3 in the circuit of Fig. 20–10. Assume that $h_{FE_1} = h_{FE_2} = h_{FE_3} = 30$.

P20–14 Calculate the current in diodes D_1 and D_2 in Fig. 20–13A for the following input conditions:
(a) All inputs "high."
(b) All inputs "low."

P20–15 Design a CMOS three-input NOR gate.

P20–16 Design a CMOS three-input NAND gate.

21

Multivibrators

Multivibrators constitute a family of electronic circuits widely used in digital systems. A multivibrator (MV) is a *regenerative switching circuit*. (A regenerative switching circuit is one that employs positive feedback. The output is switched from a "high" to a "low" and vice versa.) There are three types of multivibrators, with many variations in each category.

The *bistable* MV, *flip-flop* (FF), or *binary* as it is sometimes called, is an important circuit found in virtually all digital systems. It exhibits two stable states and can be switched from one state to the other with appropriate external signals. The flip-flop, for example, is used as a storage device. It can store one bit of information and may be viewed as a one-bit memory.

The *monostable* MV (one-shot), as its name suggests, has only one stable state. An external input signal causes the circuit to switch from the stable state to a *transitional*, or *quasi-stable*, state. After a predetermined time, it reverts to its stable state. Monostable multivibrators are used primarily in phase delay, pulse shaping, and pulse restoration applications.

The *astable*, or *free running*, MV has no stable states. In fact, it is an oscillator that provides an approximate square waveform. Free running multivibrators are used to generate clock pulses in digital systems.

The various multivibrators are analyzed in this chapter. Their operations will be explained, and applications shown.

21.1 The Bistable MV (Flip-Flop)

A bistable MV (flip-flop) may be produced by interconnecting two INVERTERs as shown in Fig. 21–1A. The output of each INVERTER is connected to the input of the other. If output Q of INVERTER I_1 is a logic 1, then the input to INVERTER I_2 is also a 1. As a result, the output of I_2 is a logic 0 ($\bar{Q} = 0$). If $\bar{Q} = 0$, a 0 is present at the input of I_1; the output of I_1, therefore, is a logic 1. With no external signals, the circuit remains in its stable state with $Q = 1$ and $\bar{Q} = 0$.

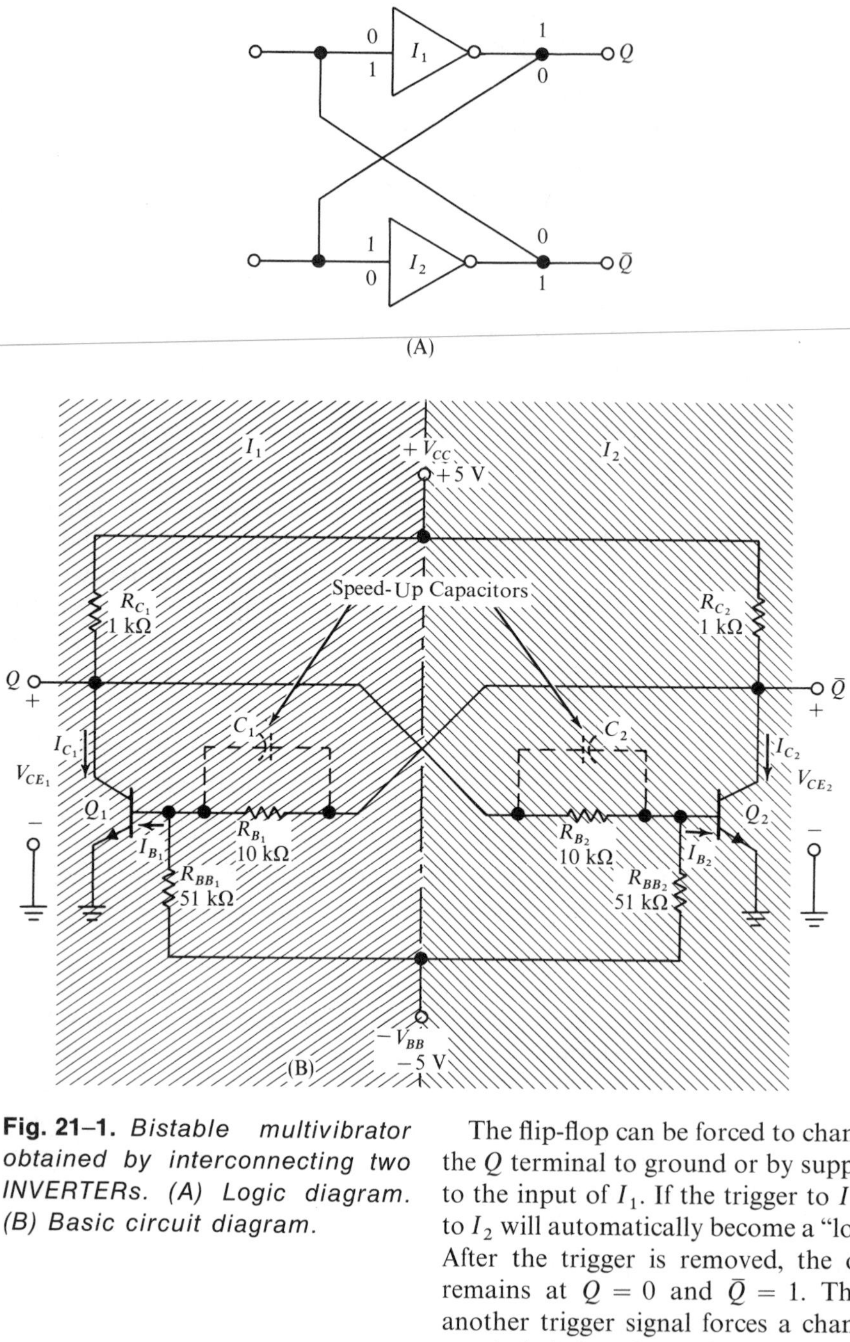

Fig. 21–1. *Bistable multivibrator obtained by interconnecting two INVERTERs. (A) Logic diagram. (B) Basic circuit diagram.*

The flip-flop can be forced to change its state by shorting the Q terminal to ground or by supplying a suitable trigger to the input of I_1. If the trigger to I_1 is a "high," the input to I_2 will automatically become a "low," resulting in $\bar{Q} = 1$. After the trigger is removed, the output of the flip-flop remains at $Q = 0$ and $\bar{Q} = 1$. This state prevails until another trigger signal forces a change of state. It may be concluded that Q equals a logic 0 or 1 when $\bar{Q}$ equals a logic 1 or 0, respectively. Note that Q and $\bar{Q}$ cannot be both at a logic 0 or a logic 1 simultaneously.

The circuit of Fig. 21–1B illustrates how two identical saturated switches (discussed in Chapter 19) are connected to yield a flip-flop. At the instant power is applied to the circuit, both transistors attempt to turn ON and conduct. Since components cannot be manufactured to be perfectly identical, one transistor tends to conduct more current than the other.

Assuming that quiescent current I_{C_2} is initially greater than I_{C_1}, voltage V_{CE_2} will be less than V_{CE_1}. The current to the base of Q_1 is diminished, resulting in a reduction in I_{C_1}, and an increase in V_{CE_1}. An increase in the collector voltage of Q_1 increases I_{B_2}, which, in turn, increases I_{C_2}. This causes a further drop in V_{CE_2}. This action continues until a limit is reached where Q_2 is saturated and Q_1 is cut off. The result is a "high" across Q_1 and a "low" across Q_2 ($Q = 1$ and $\bar{Q} = 0$).

The preceding description illustrates the regenerative feedback action of the circuit. Speed-up, or commutating, capacitors (C_1 and C_2) may be used to reflect the changes from the collector of one transistor to the base of the other with minimum delay. Under certain extreme conditions, both transistors may be ON simultaneously. This condition is known as *lock-up*.

EXAMPLE 21–1.

For the indicated component values, verify that the circuit of Fig. 21–1B operates as a flip-flop, exhibiting two stable states. The transistors are silicon, each having an $h_{FE(\text{min})} = 40$, $V_{\text{sat}} = 0.2$ V, and negligible reverse saturation current.

Solution:

To determine the state of a bistable MV, the assumption that one of the transistors is saturated (ON) is made. Under this condition, we prove that the other transistor is OFF. Assuming that Q_2 is saturated, we draw a model of Fig. 21–1B in Fig. 21–2. The collector-emitter circuit of Q_1 is represented by an open switch, and that of Q_2 by a battery of V_{sat} equal to 0.2 V.

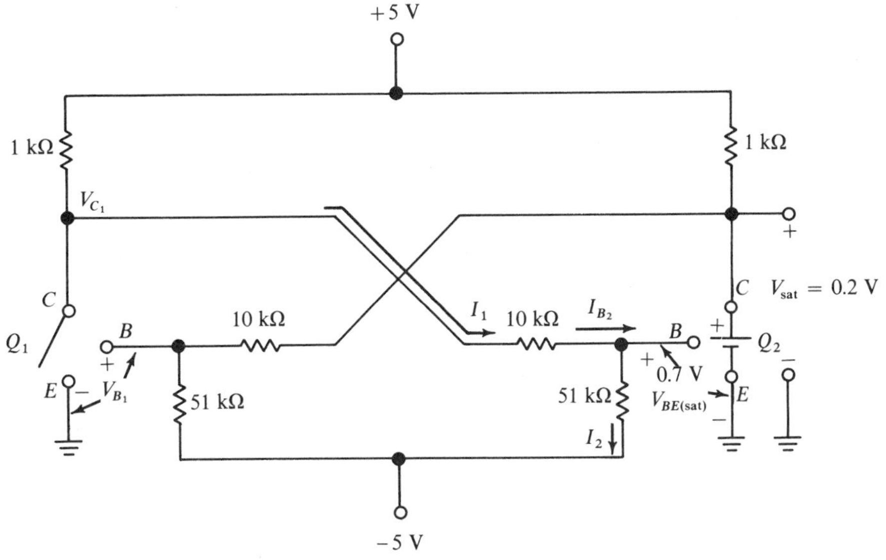

Fig. 21–2. *Equivalent circuit of a flip-flop with Q_1 cut off and Q_2 in saturation. (See Example 21–1.)*

By superposition, the voltage at the base of Q_1 with respect to ground, V_{B_1}, is

$$V_{B_1} = -5 \times \frac{10}{10 + 51} + 0.2 \times \frac{51}{10 + 51}$$
$$= -0.65\ \text{V}$$

A negative base-emitter voltage of -0.65 V is more than sufficient to ensure that an NPN transistor is cut off. Hence, Q_1 is OFF.

Let us now verify our assumption that Q_2 is saturated. For Q_2 to be saturated, it must have sufficient base current, $I_{B_2(\text{min})}$ to ensure that maximum collector current, $I_{C_2(\text{sat})}$, for a transistor in saturation flows:

$$I_{B_2(\text{min})} = \frac{I_{C_2(\text{sat})}}{h_{FE(\text{min})}}$$
$$= \frac{\dfrac{5 - 0.2}{1}}{40} = 0.12\ \text{mA}$$

Current I_1 in the 10-kΩ resistor is

$$I_1 = \frac{5 - 0.7}{10 + 1} = 0.39\ \text{mA}$$

and current I_2 in the 51-kΩ resistor is

$$I_2 = \frac{0.7 - (-5)}{51} = 0.112\ \text{mA}$$

Therefore,

$$I_{B_2} = I_1 - I_2$$
$$= 0.39 - 0.112 = 0.278\ \text{mA}$$

Because I_{B_2} is greater than $I_{B_2(\text{min})}$, transistor Q_2 is saturated (ON). The "low" is equal to $V_{\text{sat}} = 0.2$ V. The "high" is a function of the circuit component and dc supply values. Again, using superposition,

$$V_{C_1} = 5 \times \frac{10}{10 + 1} + 0.7 \times \frac{1}{10 + 1}$$
$$= 4.6\ \text{V}$$

Loading effects must be considered when using flip-flops. Bistable action must not be impaired under maximum load.

21.2 Triggering a Flip-Flop

For a flip-flop to change its state, an external signal must be supplied to the circuit. The external signal, called a *trigger*, is generally in the form of a pulse. Two triggering schemes are used; these are *symmetrical* and *unsymmetrical* triggering.

With symmetrical triggering, the flip-flop switches states with each successive trigger, regardless of the state of the flip-flop. Unsymmetrical triggering causes a change in state

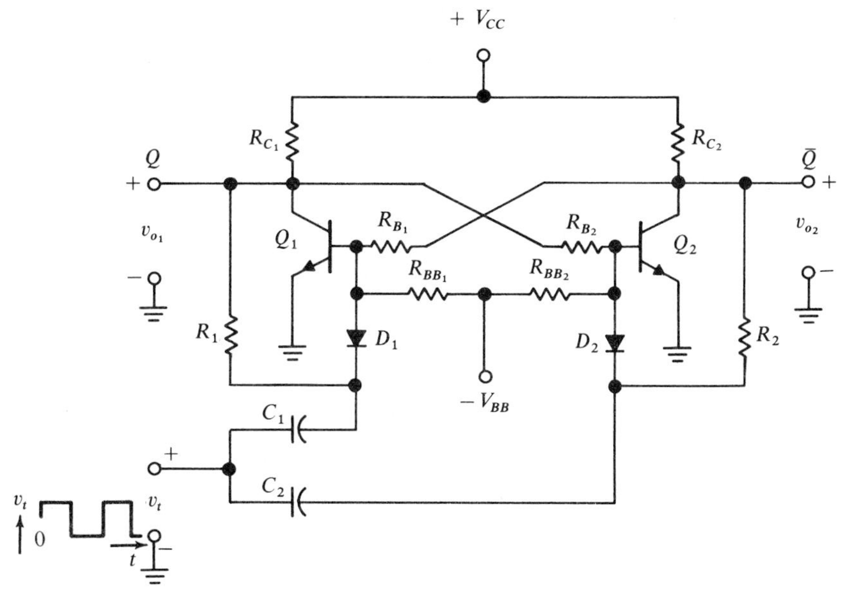

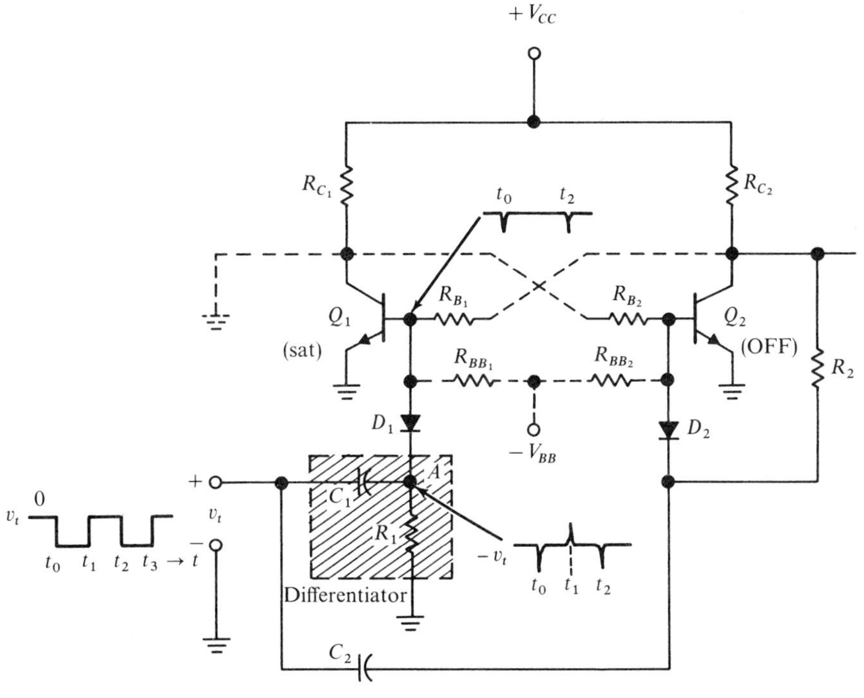

in only one direction. To return the binary to its initial state, a second trigger from a different source, applied to a different input terminal, is required.

Let us examine the flip-flop of Fig. 21–3. This circuit incorporates symmetrical triggering. Diodes D_1 and D_2 are called *steering diodes*. Assume that Q_1 is ON and, therefore, Q_2 is OFF. Also, assume that V_{sat} is equal to 0 V. An equivalent circuit (model) is drawn in Fig. 21–4 to illustrate that R_1 and C_1 form a differentiating network (see Chapter 5).

Fig. 21–3. (Above) *Symmetrical triggering employing collector steering.*

Fig. 21–4. (Below) *Resistor R_1 and capacitor C_1 form a differentiator.*

Using negative trigger pulses, the output of the differentiator at point A contains positive, as well as negative, spikes. Diode D_1 conducts only on negative spikes. Therefore, at time t_0, a negative spike appears at the base of Q_1. The transistor is turned OFF, and Q_2 is turned ON. With Q_2 OFF, R_2 is returned to a "high" (collector of Q_2). The differentiating action of C_2 and R_2 is minimal because R_2 is in series with the very high collector resistance of Q_2. Transistor Q_2, therefore, is not affected.

When the next negative trigger appears at the input, C_2 and R_2 act as the differentiating network. Transistor Q_2 turns OFF, and Q_1 turns ON. Hence, each incoming trigger causes a change in state of the flip-flop. In our example, the change of state occurred on the negative-going edge of the input trigger. The values of R_1, R_2, C_1, and C_2 must be chosen carefully to ensure differentiating action.

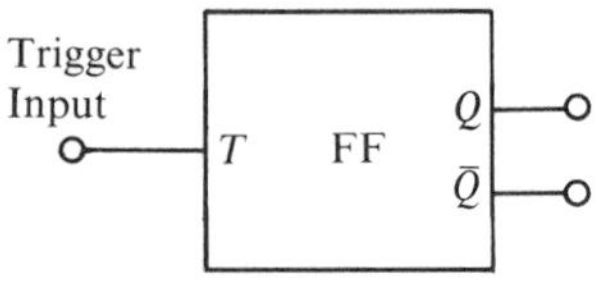

Fig. 21–5. *Logic symbol for a T flip-flop.*

The Flip-Flop as a Logic Element

The flip-flop of Fig. 21–3 is represented by its logic symbol in Fig. 21–5. It is known as a *T flip-flop*, where T denotes *trigger*, or *toggle*. Connecting a number of T flip-flops, as shown in Fig. 21–6A, results in a *counter*. A counter yields

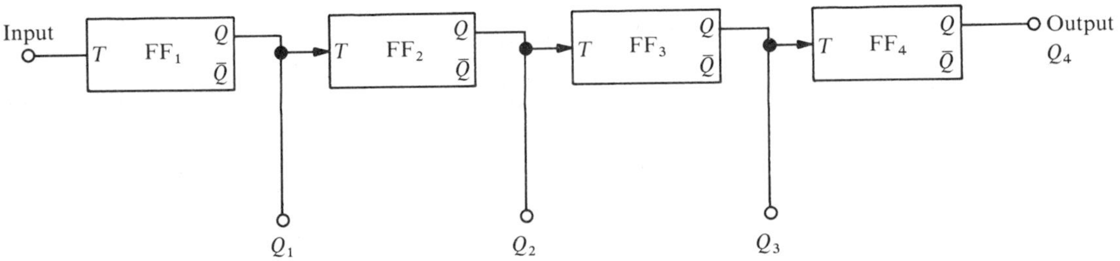

(A)

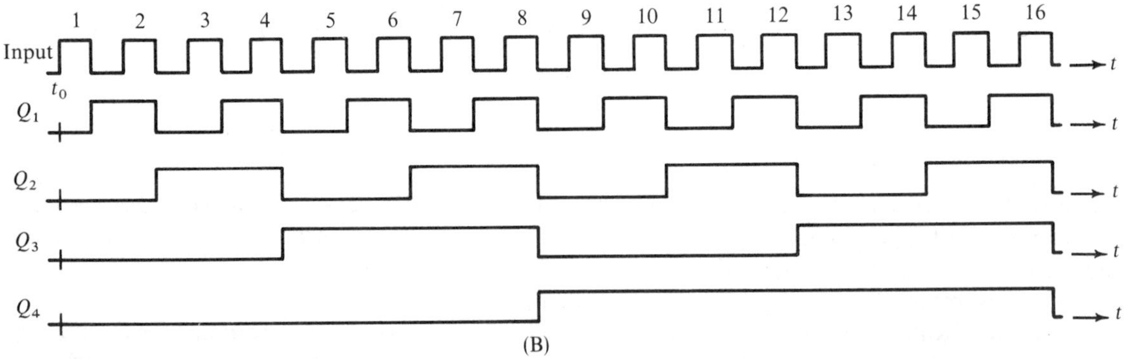

(B)

Fig. 21–6. *Counter comprised of T flip-flops. (A) Circuit. (B) Input-output timing waveforms.*

an output pulse after a predetermined number of consecutive input pulses. Such a circuit is used to *count* pulses. The number of incoming pulses, N, for one output pulse is related to the number of flip-flops, x, by

$$N = 2^x \qquad \textbf{(21-1)}$$

For example, if three flip-flops are connected as a counter, $x = 3$, and $N = 2^3 = 8$.

In Fig. 21-6B, note that the frequency of the input signal is divided by a factor of two as it passes through each flip-flop. This circuit, therefore, can also be used as a *frequency divider* or a *pulse-time multiplier*.

SET-RESET (S-R) FLIP-FLOP. The S-R flip-flop is used to store a bit of information (a 0 or a 1). A logic diagram of an S-R flip-flop is shown in Fig. 21-7A. It may be implemented by only NAND or NOR gates; NAND gates are used in Fig. 21-7A. From the truth table of Fig. 21-7B, when the S (SET, PRESET) input is a 1 and the R (RESET, CLEAR) input is a 0, $Q = 1$ and $\bar{Q} = 0$. To change the state of the flip-flop, S must become a 0 and R a 1. The condition $R = S = 1$ is not permitted because the output under this set of inputs is indeterminate. This gives rise to an *illegal*, or *ambiguous*, state.

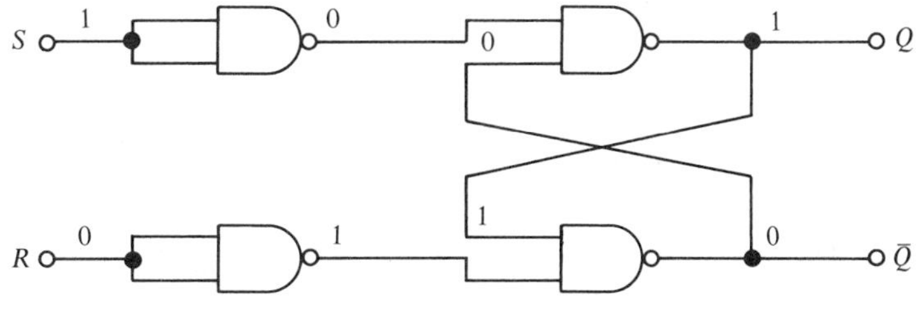

(A)

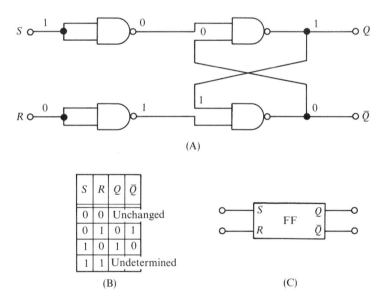

S	R	Q	$\bar{Q}$
0	0	Unchanged	
0	1	0	1
1	0	1	0
1	1	Undetermined	

(B)

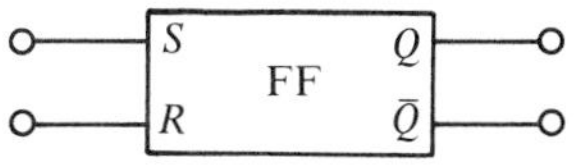

(C)

Fig. 21-7. *S-R flip-flop using NAND gates. (A) Logic diagram. (B) Truth table. (C) Logic symbol.*

CLOCKED S-R FLIP-FLOP. When operations are performed in a predetermined sequence controlled by clock pulses, a *clocked S-R* flip-flop is employed. This is an example of *synchronous operation*. For this operation, a change in state occurs only when appropriate signals are fed to the S and R terminals and a clock pulse is present. The flip-flop will not change state without a clock pulse, nor will there be a transition with a clock pulse alone.

Using two NAND gates in place of the two INVERTERs in Fig. 21–7A, the clocked *S-R* flip-flop of Fig. 21–8A is realized. The logic symbol is provided in Fig. 21–8B. Assume that a clock pulse is not present ($C = 0$). Then, regardless of what the *S* and *R* inputs are, the logic levels at *A* and *B* are always 1, and the output remains unchanged. To produce a change in state, a clock pulse must be present.

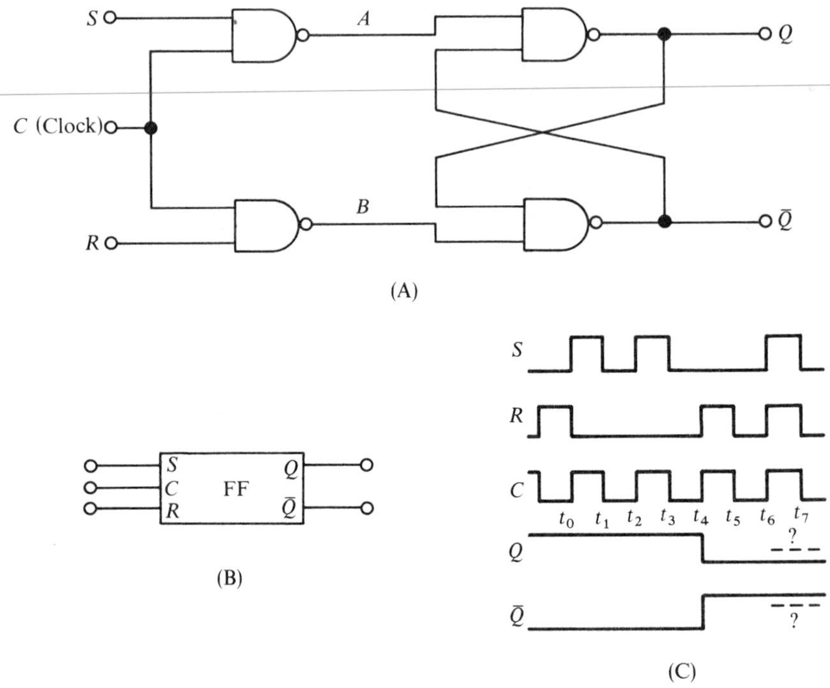

Fig. 21–8. *Clocked S-R flip-flop. (A) Logic diagram. (B) Logic symbol. (C) Input-output timing waveforms.*

Examine the waveforms of Fig. 21–8C. Assume that the initial state of the flip-flop is such that $Q = 1$ and $\bar{Q} = 0$. Because at t_0 the inputs are $S = 1$ and $R = 0$, the initial state remains the same ($Q = 1$ and $\bar{Q} = 0$) even if a clock pulse is present. At t_1, both inputs are equal to zero, and the output is still the same. Also, at t_2, *S* and *R* revert to their initial levels ($S = 1$ and $R = 0$), and the output is unaffected.

At t_4, $S = 0$, $R = 1$, and $C = 1$. A change of state occurs, resulting in $Q = 0$ and $\bar{Q} = 1$. For time t_6, $S = R = C = 1$. This state is not permitted because an ambiguous condition exists in which either a 1 or a 0 can appear at each output. The outputs during the time duration of the ambiguous state are indicated by question marks in Fig. 21–8C.

J-K FLIP-FLOP. The *J-K* flip-flop of Fig. 21–9A (its logic symbol is shown in Fig. 21–9B) is a modified version of the *S-R* flip-flop. The ambiguous state inherent in the *S-R* flip-flop is eliminated in the *J-K* flip-flop. Because of its versatility, the *J-K* flip-flop is often called the universal flip-flop. Its operation is summarized in Table 21–1. All

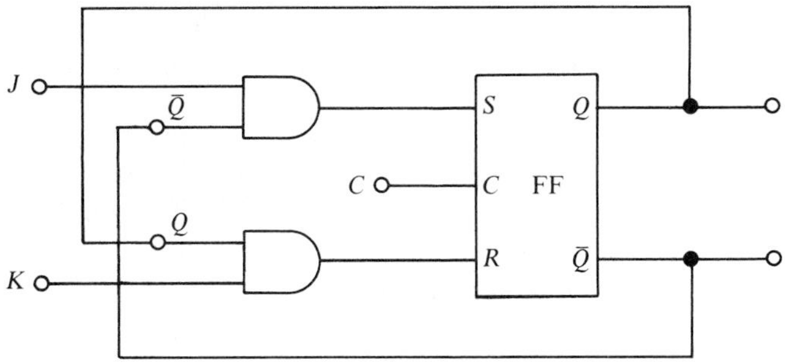

(A)

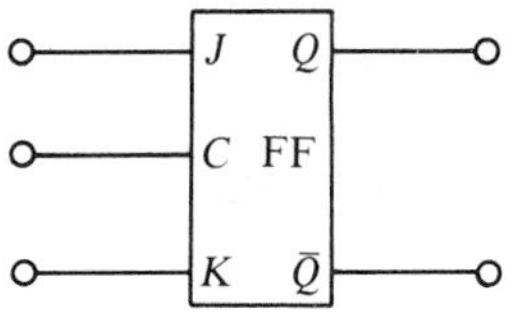

(B)

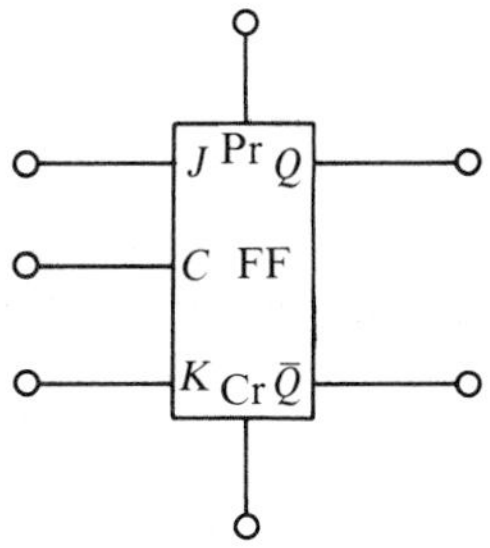

(C)

Fig. 21–9. *The J-K flip-flop. (A) Obtained by modifying an S-R flip-flop. (B) Logic symbol for a J-K flip-flop. (C) Logic symbol for a J-K flip-flop with clear (Cr) and preset (Pr) inputs.*

TABLE 21–1. Truth tables for a *J-K* flip-flop. (A) Outputs as a function of data inputs. (B) Outputs as a function of Cr and Pr inputs.

J	K	C	Q	$\bar{Q}$
0	0	1	No change	
1	0	1	1	0
0	1	1	0	1
1	1	1	Change	

(A)

Cr	Pr	C	Q	$\bar{Q}$
0	1	0	0	1
1	0	0	1	0
1	1	1	*	*

* Outputs obtained from (A).

(B)

states are well defined, including the $S = R = 1$ input state. In addition, the *J-K* flip-flop may be cleared or preset between clock pulses.

A logic diagram showing the additional CLEAR (Cr) and PRESET (Pr) terminals is provided in Fig. 21–9C. Owing to these inputs, *asynchronous* operation may be realized, in which the flip-flop is triggered without the presence of a clock pulse. From Table 21–1B, the condition

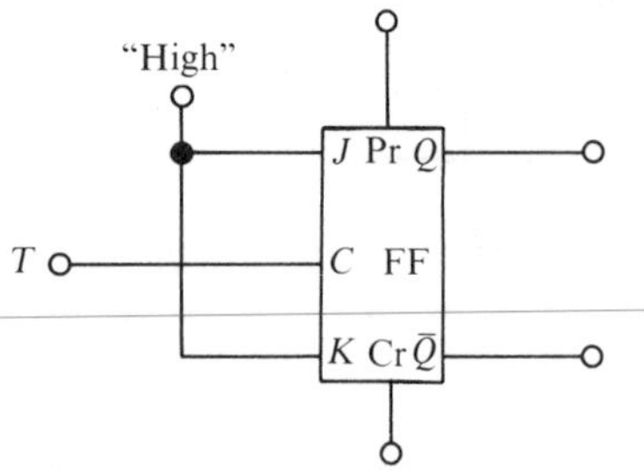

Fig. 21–10. *J-K flip-flop converted to function as a T flip-flop.*

of Pr = 1 and Cr = 0 results in $Q = 0$ and $\bar{Q} = 1$. Conversely, if Cr = 1 and Pr = 0, $Q = 1$ and $\bar{Q} = 0$. If Cr = Pr = 1, the output obtained is in accordance with the *J*, *K*, and *C* inputs given in Table 21–1A. To prevent the ambiguous state of the *S-R* flip-flop, the condition Cr = Pr = 0 should be avoided. Hence, when the Cr and Pr inputs are not used, they should be returned to a "high" in the circuit.

A *J-K* flip-flop may be converted to a *T* flip-flop by connecting the *J* and *K* terminals to a "high," as shown in Fig. 21–10. A circuit schematic of the Motorola MC515 T^2L *J-K* flip-flop is given in Fig. 21–11A. This unit has three *J* and three *K* inputs, each ANDed together for increased versatility. It also has direct SET and RESET terminals. The logic diagram is shown in Fig. 20–11B, and the truth table in Fig. 21–11C.

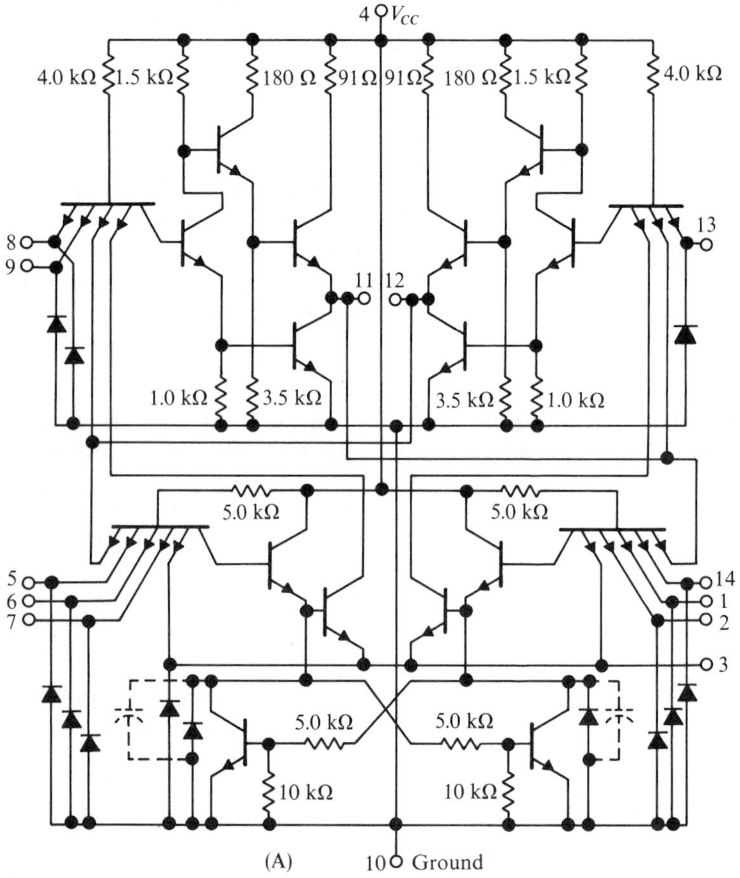

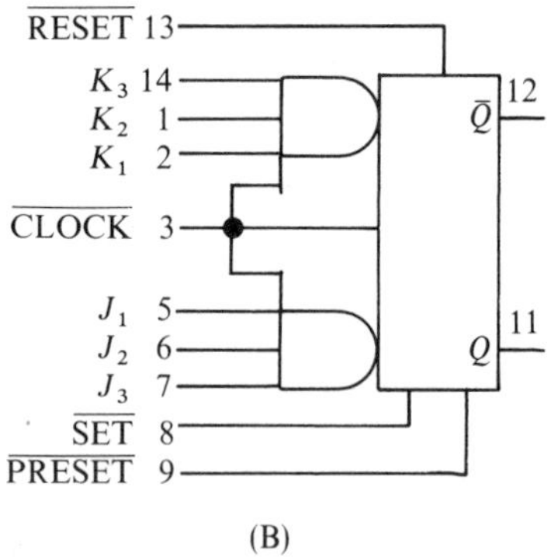

J	K	Q_n	Q_{n+1}
0	0	0	0
0	0	1	1
0	1	0	0
0	1	1	0
1	0	0	1
1	0	1	1
1	1	0	1
1	1	1	0

Where $J = J_1 \cdot J_2 \cdot J_3$
$K = K_1 \cdot K_2 \cdot K_3$

(C)

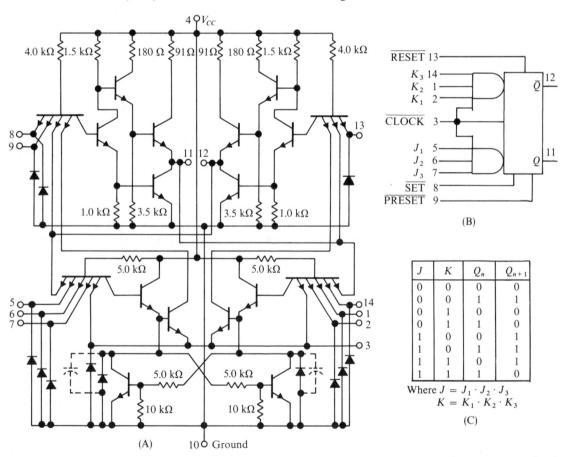

Fig. 21–11. *The Motorola MC515 J-K flip-flop. (A) Circuit diagram. (B) Logic diagram. (C) Truth table. (Courtesy Motorola Semiconductor Products Inc.)*

RACE-AROUND CONDITION. Race-around refers to an unstable condition in a *J-K* flip-flop which results in an ambiguous output. It occurs in the *J-K* flip-flop because of the very short propagation delay time compared with the duration of the trigger pulse. The output reflects the input state almost instantaneously. Because the output is returned to the input, a new input state arises which forces a transition and a new output state. Several changes in the output may occur during the duration of a clock pulse.

MASTER-SLAVE FLIP-FLOP. To eliminate the race-around condition, a master-slave flip-flop is used. This circuit is also free of the ambiguous states discussed previously. It consists of two flip-flops. The input flip-flop is the "master" and the output flip-flop the "slave." The logic diagram of a *J-K*, master-slave flip-flop is shown in Fig. 21–12. Note that a conventional *J-K* flip-flop is joined with an *S-R* flip-flop. Feedback connections exist between the "slave" and "master." Furthermore, the clock pulse is applied to both, with the "slave" receiving an inverted clock pulse. Information is transferred on the trailing edge of the clock pulse. Since the slave of the flip-flop acts on the trailing edge of the clock pulse, the possibility of a race-around condition is removed.

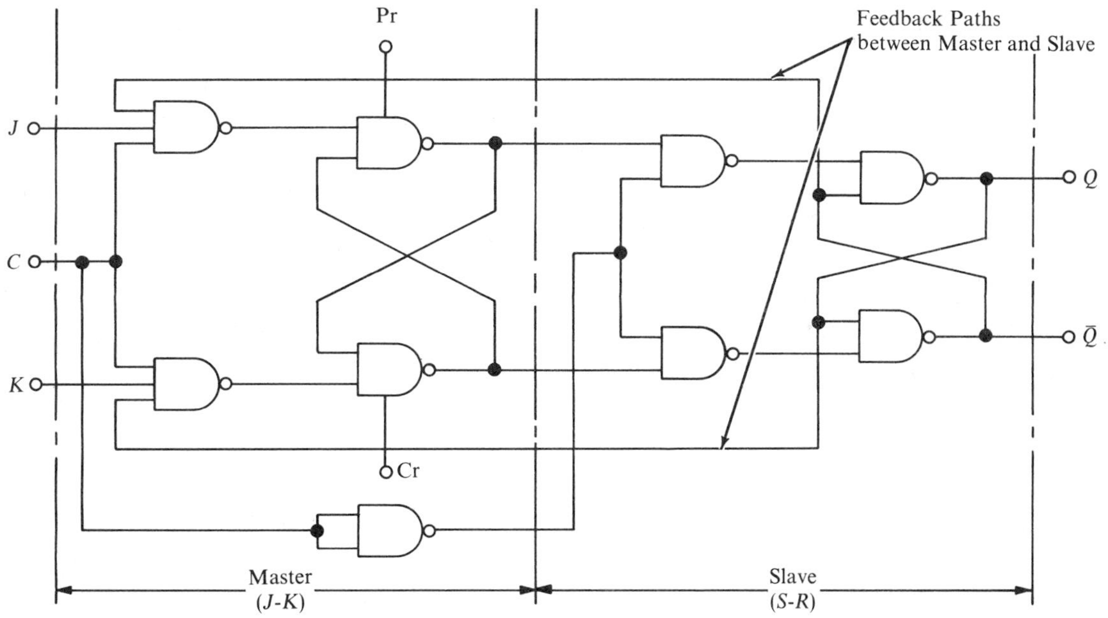

Fig. 21–12. *Master-slave flip-flop.*

21.3 Schmitt Trigger

The Schmitt trigger is an emitter-coupled bistable multivibrator. It is used as a pulse shaper and a level shifter. Because of its ability to act as a signal comparator, it is also employed as a level detector. The pulse shaping and restoration properties of the circuit occur since the output of a Schmitt trigger is always a rectangular waveform. Hence, a distorted pulse at the input is reshaped, and a rectangular pulse appears at the output.

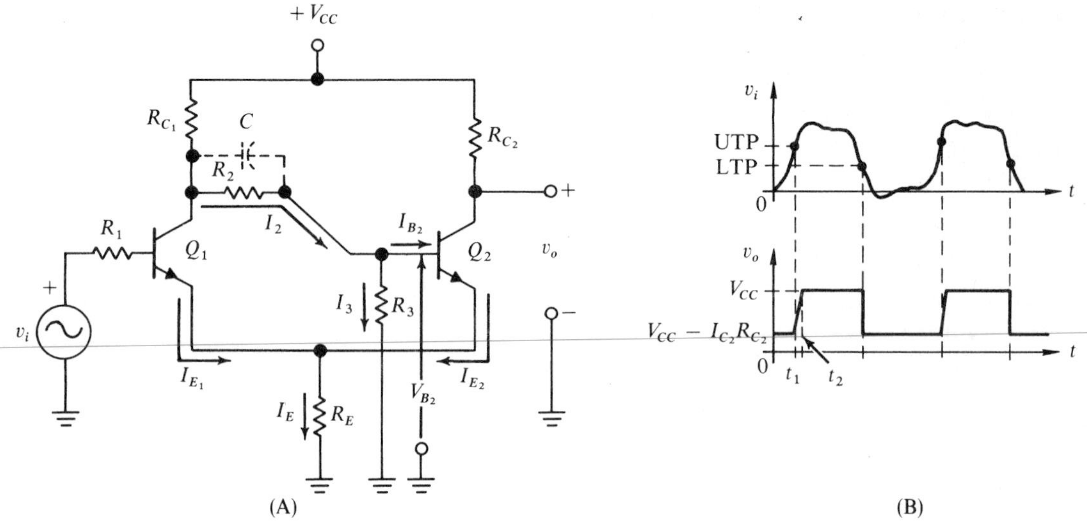

Fig. 21–13. *Schmitt trigger. (A) Basic circuit. (B) Input and output waveforms.*

The basic circuit of a Schmitt trigger is illustrated in Fig. 21–13A. Transistor Q_1 is the input transistor, and Q_2 is the output transistor. The two emitters share a common emitter resistor, R_E. For either transistor to be in a conducting state, the base voltage must be equal to the sum of the emitter voltage (V_E) and the base-emitter voltage (V_{BE}):

$$V_B = V_E + V_{BE} \tag{21–2}$$

With the input $v_i = 0$, Q_1 is OFF and Q_2 is ON. The base current of Q_2, I_{B_2}, is given by

$$I_{B_2} = I_2 - I_3 \tag{21–3}$$

where I_2 is the current in R_2 and I_3 is the current in R_3. The emitter voltage is expressed by

$$V_E = I_{E_2} R_E \tag{21–4}$$

where

$$I_{E_2} = (h_{FE} + 1) I_{B_2} \tag{21–5}$$

if Q_2 is in the active region of operation. If Q_2 is in saturation,

$$I_{E_2(\max)} = \frac{V_{CC} - V_{sat}}{R_{C_2} + R_E} \tag{21–6}$$

To analyze further the Schmitt trigger, an equivalent circuit for the condition $v_i = 0$ is illustrated in Fig. 21–14A. Voltage V_{Th} is the Thevenin equivalent voltage at the base of Q_2. From Fig. 21–14B,

$$V_{Th} = \frac{V_{CC} R_3}{R_{C_1} + R_2 + R_3} \tag{21–7a}$$

The Thevenin resistance, R_{Th}, is given by

$$R_{Th} = R_3 \| (R_{C_1} + R_2) \tag{21–7b}$$

The base current in Q_2 is

$$I_{B_2} = \frac{V_{Th} - V_{BE(ON)}}{R_{Th} + (h_{FE} + 1) R_E} \tag{21–8}$$

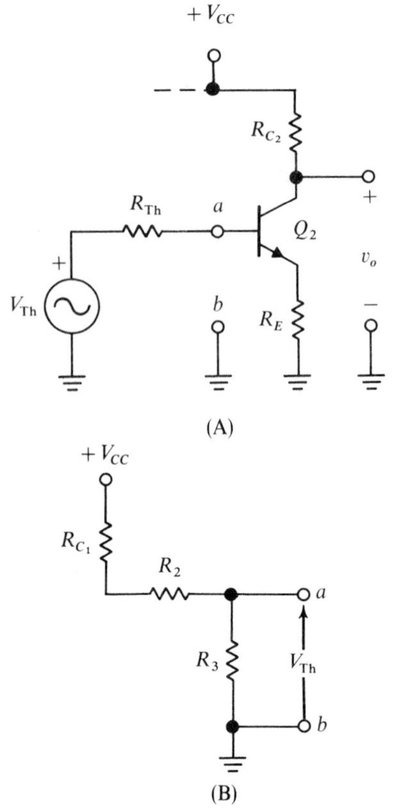

Fig. 21–14. *Equivalent circuits for the Schmitt trigger. (A) Input voltage $v_i = 0$. (B) Obtaining the Thevenin voltage at the base of Q_2.*

Substitution of Eq. (21–6) and Eq. (21–8) in Eq. (21–4) yields

$$V_E = (h_{FE} + 1)\frac{(V_{\mathrm{Th}} - V_{BE(\mathrm{ON})})R_E}{R_{\mathrm{Th}} + (h_{FE} + 1)R_E} \qquad \textbf{(21–9a)}$$

for Q_2 in the active region, or

$$V_E = I_{E_2(\max)}R_E \qquad \textbf{(21–9b)}$$

for Q_2 in saturation.

For Q_1 to turn ON, a sufficiently large input signal is required. The minimum, or threshold, voltage is called the *u*pper *t*riggering *p*otential (UTP):

$$\mathrm{UTP} = V_E + V_{BE(\mathrm{ON})} \qquad \textbf{(21–10)}$$

where $V_{BE(\mathrm{ON})}$ is approximately equal to 0.7 V.

We now show that when Q_1 turns ON, Q_2 turns OFF. As Q_1 starts to turn ON, the collector voltage of Q_1 begins to fall. This results in a reduction in I_{B_2}, causing the collector voltage of Q_2 to rise. During these changes, the emitter current is constant and is equal to the sum of the emitter currents in Q_1 and Q_2. Finally, when Q_1 saturates, Q_2 turns OFF. The collector voltage of Q_1 is now only slightly positive with respect to the emitter voltage and is not sufficient to turn ON Q_2. The transition time is very short and is indicated as the interval between t_1 and t_2 in Fig. 21–13B. The output level remains at V_{CC} volts as long as Q_2 is OFF.

The input level required to turn OFF Q_1 and turn ON Q_2 is known as the *l*ower *t*riggering *p*otential (LTP). When the input level drops to a point where Q_1 starts to turn OFF, the collector voltage of Q_1 increases until it is high enough to supply current to the base of Q_2. Then, transistor Q_2 turns ON. Again, a transition period exists, with both transistors conducting until Q_1 turns OFF.

The LTP level of the circuit is computed with the aid of the equivalent circuits of Fig. 21–15. From Fig. 21–15A,

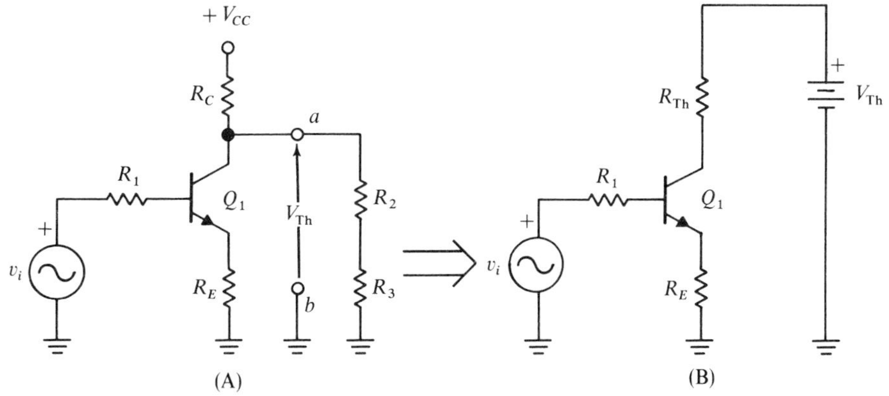

Fig. 21–15. *Determining the LTP of a Schmitt trigger. (A) Equivalent circuit. (B) Further simplification.*

the Thevenin voltage and resistance at the collector of Q_1 are

$$V_{\text{Th}} = \frac{(R_2 + R_3)V_{CC}}{R_{C_1} + R_2 + R_2} \tag{21–11a}$$

and

$$R_{\text{Th}} = R_{C_1} \| (R_2 + R_3) \tag{21–11b}$$

For transistor Q_2 to turn ON,

$$V_{B_2} = V_E + V_{BE(\text{ON})}$$

where

$$V_E = \frac{V_{C_1} R_3}{R_2 + R_3} - V_{BE(\text{ON})} \tag{21–12}$$

and the collector voltage of Q_1, V_{C_1}, is

$$V_{C_1} = V_{\text{Th}} - R_{\text{Th}} I_{C_1} \tag{21–13}$$

Substitution of Eqs. (21–11a) and (21–11b) in Eq. (21–13) yields

$$V_{C_1} = \frac{(V_{CC} - I_{C_1} R_{C_1})(R_2 + R_3)}{R_{C_1} + R_2 + R_3}$$

Hence,

$$V_E = \frac{(V_{CC} - I_{C_1} R_{C_1}) R_3}{(R_{C_1} + R_2 + R_3)} - V_{BE(\text{ON})}$$

Substituting V_E/R_E for I_{C_1} and solving for V_E, we have

$$V_E = \frac{V_{CC} R_E R_3 - V_{BE(\text{ON})} R_E (R_{C_1} + R_2 + R_3)}{R_E (R_{C_1} + R_2 + R_3) + R_{C_1} R_3} \tag{21–14}$$

The lower triggering potential is

$$\text{LTP} = V_E + V_{BE_1} \tag{21–15}$$

Examples of input and output waveforms for a Schmitt trigger are shown in Fig. 21–13B. Whereas the input is a distorted square wave, the output is a very "clean" square wave. As a matter of fact, for nearly any input waveform, the output will be a rectangular waveform.

A significant difference between the Schmitt trigger and a flip-flop is that the Schmitt trigger has no memory. It does not remain in its switched state when the input trigger is removed. Also, the UTP and LTP inputs are not equal. The difference between these two levels defines a *hysteresis* zone.

A plot of output voltage versus input voltage for a Schmitt trigger is shown in Fig. 21–16. Arrows indicate the switching sequence. The hysteresis zone may be reduced to zero by adjusting the loop gain to unity. A minimum loop gain of one must be maintained for switching to occur. To ensure a loop gain of one or greater, the following relationships must hold true:

$$R_{C_1} \geqslant R_{C_2} \tag{21–16a}$$

and

$$R_{C_1} \geqslant \frac{R_2}{h_{FE} - 1} \tag{21–16b}$$

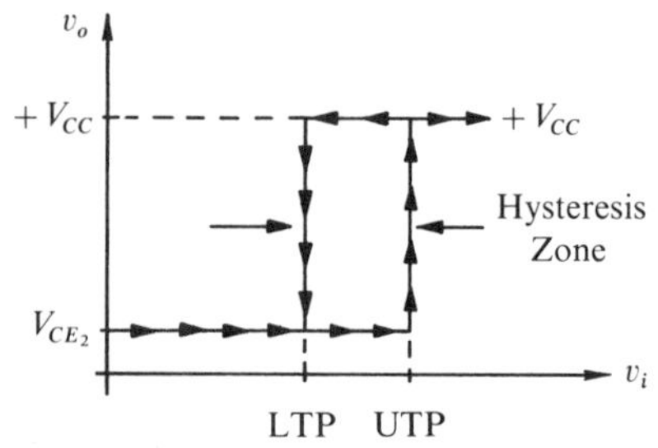

Fig. 21–16. *Hysteresis zone of a Schmitt trigger.*

The value of R_1, which equals the sum of the source and external base resistance, is important in hysteresis considerations. The loop gain is affected by its value. To ensure proper switching,

$$R_1 \ll h_{FE}R_E \qquad \textbf{(21–16c)}$$

In practice, a loop gain greater than one is maintained. Setting the gain to exactly one, and maintaining it at that value, is not possible under operating conditions.

EXAMPLE 21–2.

For the Schmitt trigger of Fig. 21–13A,

$$\begin{aligned} V_{CC} &= 10\,\text{V} \\ V_{sat} &= 0.2\,\text{V} \\ h_{FE_1} &= h_{FE_2} = 100 \\ R_{C_1} &= 1.3\,\text{k}\Omega \\ R_{C_2} &= R_1 = 1\,\text{k}\Omega \\ R_2 &= 6.8\,\text{k}\Omega \\ R_3 &= 8.2\,\text{k}\Omega \\ R_E &= 240\,\Omega. \end{aligned}$$

Determine
- **(a)** If switching occurs.
- **(b)** UTP.
- **(c)** LTP.
- **(d)** The output levels.

Solutions:

(a) For switching to occur, the loop gain must be greater than one. By Eq. (21–16b),

$$\frac{R_2}{h_{FE} - 1} = \frac{6.8\,\text{k}\Omega}{100 - 1} \simeq 68\,\Omega$$

The value of $R_{C_1} = 1.3\,\text{k}\Omega$ is much greater than $68\,\Omega$. By Eq. (21–16c),

$$h_{FE}R_E = 100 \times 240 = 24\,\text{k}\Omega$$

This value is much greater than $R_1 = 1\,\text{k}\Omega$. We therefore conclude that switching will occur.

(b) By Eq. (21–7a) and Eq. (21–7b),

$$V_{Th} = \frac{10 \times 8.2}{1.3 + 6.8 + 8.2} = 5.03\,\text{V}$$

and

$$R_{Th} = 8.2 \,\|\, (1.3 + 6.8) = 4.07\,\text{k}\Omega$$

We now determine if Q_2 operates in its active or saturation region. For saturation,

$$\begin{aligned} I_{B_2(\min)} &= \frac{I_{C_2(\max)}}{h_{FE}} \\ &= \frac{V_{CC} - V_{sat}}{(R_{C_2} + R_E)h_{FE}} \\ &= \frac{10 - 0.2}{(1 + 0.24)100} \simeq 80\,\mu\text{A} \end{aligned}$$

By Eq. (21–8),

$$I_{B_2} = \frac{V_{\text{Th}} - V_{BE(\text{ON})}}{R_{\text{Th}} + (h_{FE} + 1)R_E}$$
$$= \frac{5.03 - 0.7}{4.07 + (100 + 1)0.24} = 153\ \mu\text{A}$$

Because $I_{B_2} > I_{B_2(\text{min})}$, Q_2 is in saturation.

The upper triggering potential is equal to $V_E + V_{BE(\text{ON})}$. The value of $V_{BE(\text{ON})}$ may be taken as 0.7 V. The value of V_E is

$$V_E = \left(\frac{V_{CC} - V_{\text{sat}}}{R_{C_2} + R_E}\right) R_E$$
$$= \left(\frac{10 - 0.2}{1 + 0.24}\right) 0.24 = 2\ \text{V}$$

Hence, UTP = 2 + 0.7 = 2.7 V.

When v_i reaches UTP, Q_1 starts conducting and goes into saturation. The emitter voltage is

$$V_{E_1} = I_{E1(\text{max})} R_E$$
$$= \frac{(10 - 0.2) \times 0.24}{1.3 + 0.24} = 1.53\ \text{V}$$

Assuming that Q_1 eventually becomes saturated, by voltage division,

$$V_{B_2} = \frac{(1.53 + 0.2) \times 8.2}{8.2 + 6.8} = 0.95\ \text{V}$$

Because $V_{B_2} < V_{E_1}$, Q_2 is indeed OFF.

(c) By Eq. (21–14),

$$V_E = \frac{10(0.24)(8.2) - 0.7(0.24)(1.2 + 6.8 + 8.2)}{0.24(1.3 + 6.8 + 8.2) + 1.3(8.2)}$$
$$= 1.16\ \text{V}$$

By Eq. (21–15),

$$\text{LTP} = 1.16 + 0.7 = 1.86\ \text{V}$$

(d) With Q_1 conducting, $v_o = V_{CC}$ volts. With Q_2 conducting, $v_o = V_{CC} - I_C R_{C_2}$. In this example,

$$I_{C_2} = I_{C2(\text{max})} = 80\ \mu\text{A} \times 100 = 8\ \text{mA}$$

and

$$v_o = 10 - 8 \times 1 = 2\ \text{V}$$

Voltage Comparator

An op amp can be used to perform the voltage comparator function of a Schmitt trigger. Voltage comparators, or sense amplifiers, may be used to distinguish between a logic 0 or a logic 1. A reference source is connected to the noninverting terminal of an op amp to establish the triggering level. Input signals above the reference level cause the output to switch, and signals below the level force the output to return to its original state.

The Fairchild μA710 op amp is manufactured especially for this application. A functional diagram of the circuit is provided in Fig. 21–17A. The hysteresis zone is a few millivolts. The circuit of Fig. 21–17B, however, has a controlled hysteresis zone. The zone is a function of feedback resistors R_1 and R_2 and is expressed by

$$\text{UTP} - \text{LTP} = \frac{\Delta v_o R_1}{R_1 + R_2} \qquad \textbf{(21–17)}$$

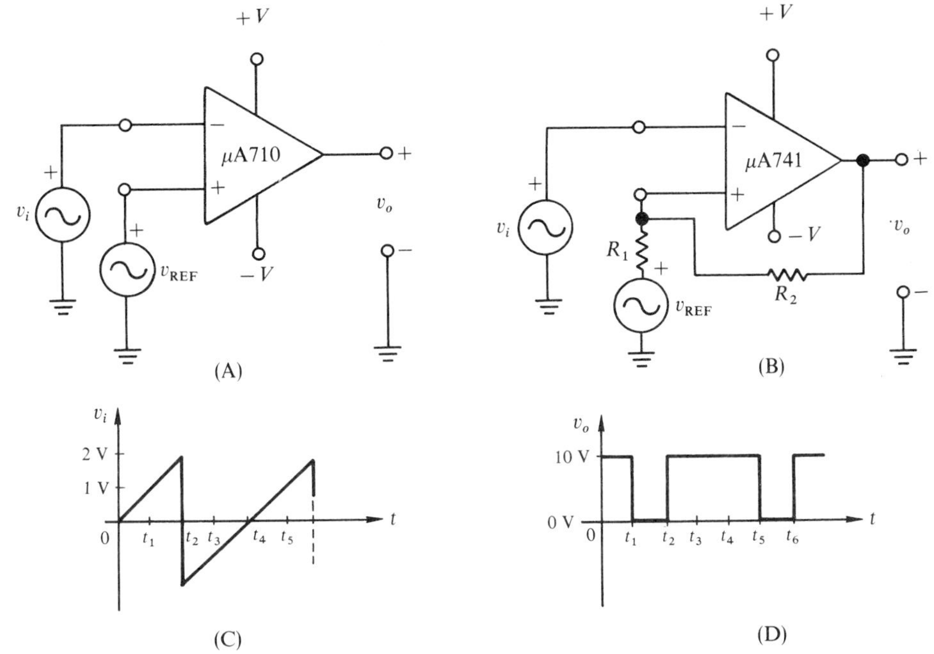

Fig. 21–17. *Op-amp voltage comparator. (A) Functional diagram. (B) Circuit with controlled hysteresis. (C), (D) Input and output waveforms, respectively, for Example 21–3.*

EXAMPLE 21–3.

The comparator of Fig. 21–17A is fed with the sawtooth wave of Fig. 21–17C. The reference voltage $v_{REF} = 1$ V, $+V = 10$ V, and $-V = 0$ V. Draw and label the output waveform.

Solution:

The solution is divided into several time intervals. For $0 < t < t_1$, the input rises from 0 to 1 V. Because the reference is constant at 1 V, the input is at a lower level than the reference. The op amp, because of its very high gain, provides an output of 10 V. A small difference in voltage between the input terminals (terminal 2 negative with respect to terminal 3) causes the op amp to saturate and deliver the maximum output of 10 V.

For $t_1 < t < t_2$, the inverting input is more positive than the reference voltage. The output, therefore, is at 0 V.

For $t_2 < t < t_5$, the input is again less than the reference. The output is now at 10 V. The output waveform is drawn in Fig. 21–17D.

21.4 The Monostable Multivibrator (One-Shot)

The monostable MV is used to generate a rectangular waveform having a width determined essentially by the values of a few circuit components. It has a single stable state, and one quasi-stable state. The output remains in its stable state until an input trigger causes the circuit to switch to its quasi-stable state. The circuit remains in this state for a time, t_w, and then switches back to its stable state. A discrete monostable MV and its waveforms are shown in Fig. 21–18.

Fig. 21–18. (Below) *The monostable multivibrator. (A) Basic circuit. (B) Collector and base voltage waveforms.*

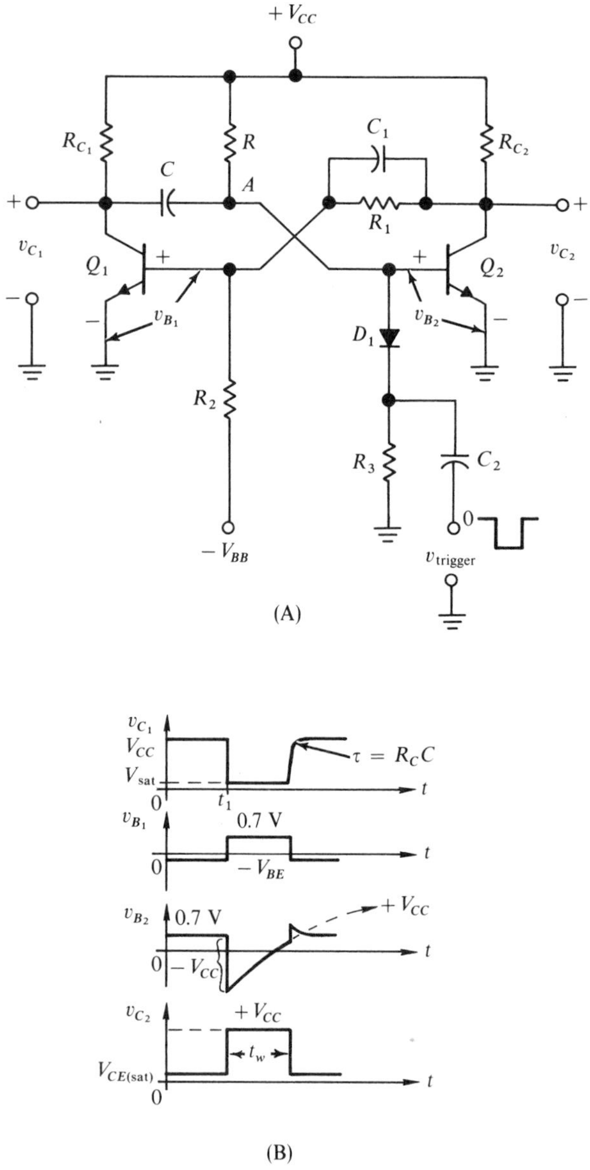

The stable state exists when Q_2 is ON and Q_1 is OFF. A negative trigger applied to the base of Q_2 at time t_1 causes the transistor to turn OFF. The voltage at the collector of Q_2 rises, forcing Q_1 to turn ON. As Q_1 turns ON and saturates, the collector voltage of Q_1, v_{C1}, drops from V_{CC} to V_{sat} volts. Because the voltage across a capacitor (C) cannot change instantaneously, the voltage at the base of Q_2, v_{B_2}, experiences a drop of the same magnitude. Before time t_1, $v_{B_2} = 0.7\,\text{V}$; now, it is approximately equal to $0.7 - V_{CC}$ volts. The voltage is negative and keeps Q_2 OFF.

An equivalent circuit for the one-shot in its quasi-stable state is given in Fig. 21–19. Capacitor C starts charging toward V_{CC} volts with a time constant equal to RC seconds. When $v_{B_2} = 0.6\,\text{V}$, the threshold voltage for a silicon transistor, Q_2 turns ON and Q_1 turns OFF. The circuit is now in its stable state. To a very good approximation, the width of the rectangular pulse, t_w, at the collector of Q_2 is

$$t_w = 0.69RC \qquad \textbf{(21–18)}$$

The width t_w is independent of the duration of the trigger pulse as long as the width of the trigger is less than t_w.

For proper operation of the one-shot, the following conditions must be satisfied:

1. The value of R is chosen so that Q_2 is saturated in its stable state. This is realized if

$$R < h_{FE(\min)}R_{C_2} \qquad \textbf{(21–19)}$$

(Commonly, $R_{C_1} = R_{C_2} = R_C$.)

2. The values of R_1 and R_2 are chosen so that Q_1 is OFF in the stable state and is saturated in the quasi-stable state.
3. To avoid switching delays,

$$R_C \ll R \qquad \textbf{(21–20)}$$

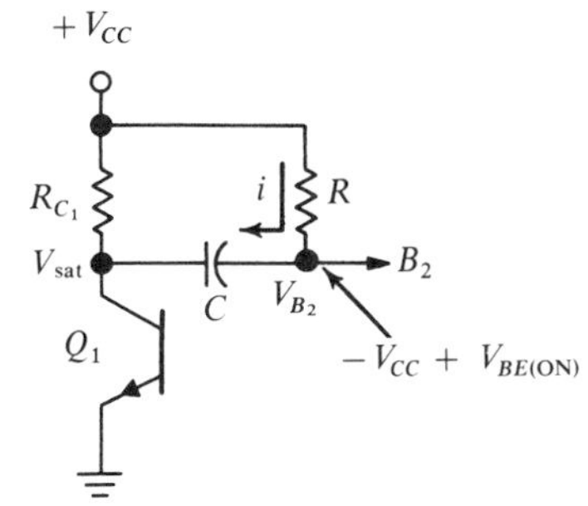

Fig. 21–19. *Equivalent circuit of a monostable multivibrator in its quasi-stable state.*

A one-shot using an op amp as its principal element is illustrated in Fig. 21–20A. The circuit is in its stable state with the output at V volts, and the voltage across the inverting terminal, v_c, is equal to the voltage across diode D_1. Voltage v_x is

$$v_x = \frac{v_o R_2}{R_1 + R_2} \qquad \textbf{(21–21)}$$

A trigger pulse larger than $v_x - V_{D_2}$ causes the output to switch to $-V$ volts. Capacitor C begins to charge through R_F, and D_1 becomes reverse biased. When the voltage across the capacitor reaches $-v_x$ volts, the output returns to V volts. The pulse width of this circuit is given by

$$t_w = R_F C \ln\left(\frac{R_1 + R_2}{R_1}\right) \qquad \textbf{(21–22)}$$

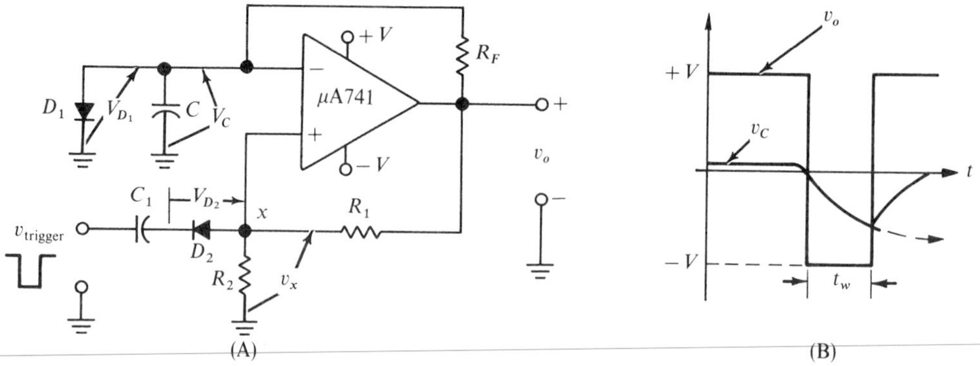

Fig. 21–20. *Op-amp monostable multivibrator. (A) Circuit diagram. (B) Voltage waveforms.*

EXAMPLE 21–4.

For what values of R_1 and R_2 will $t_w = 0.69R_FC$ in the op amp one-shot of Fig. 21–20A?

Solution:

Equating Eqs. (21–18) and (21–22), we have

$$0.69R_FC = R_FC \ln\left(\frac{R_1 + R_2}{R_1}\right)$$

$$0.69 = \ln\left(\frac{R_1 + R_2}{R_1}\right) = \ln 2$$

(because $0.69 = \ln 2$). Hence,

$$2 = \frac{R_1 + R_2}{R_1}$$

Solving, $R_1 = R_2$.

21.5 The Astable Multivibrator

The astable MV has no stable states. Instead, it has two quasi-stable states and oscillates continuously between them. The result is an approximate square wave output (Fig. 21–21A). If base-capacitor coupling is provided for both halves of the monostable MV of Fig. 21–18A, the astable MV of Fig. 21–21B is produced.

The frequency of oscillation, f, for the astable MV is

$$f = \frac{1}{t_{w1} + t_{w2}} \qquad \textbf{(21–23a)}$$

where $t_{w1} = 0.69R_1C_1$ and $t_{w2} = 0.69R_2C_2$. If $R_1 = R_2 = R$ and $C_1 = C_2 = C$, a symmetrical output is realized with $t_{w1} = t_{w2} = 0.69RC$. Hence, Eq. (21–23a) reduces to

$$f = \frac{1}{1.38RC} \qquad \textbf{(21–23b)}$$

The restrictions for proper circuit operation listed for the one-shot also apply to the astable MV.

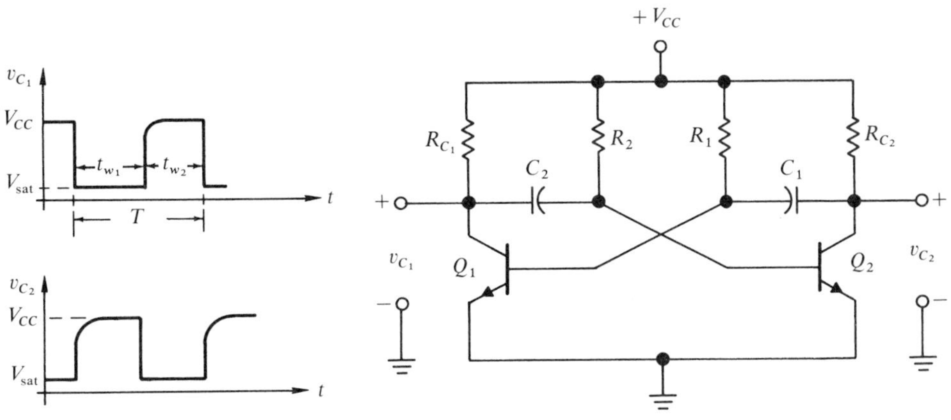

(A) (B)

Fig. 21–21. *Astable multivibrator. (A) Collector voltage waveforms. (B) Basic circuit.*

An op amp version of an astable MV is shown in Fig. 21–22A. It is the same basic circuit as that used for the one-shot of Fig. 21–20A. Diode D_1 and the trigger circuit, however, are deleted. Voltage v_x is the reference voltage and is equal to $\pm VR_2/(R_1 + R_2)$. When $v_c > v_x$, $v_o = -V$ volts; when $v_c < v_x$, $v_o = +V$ volts.

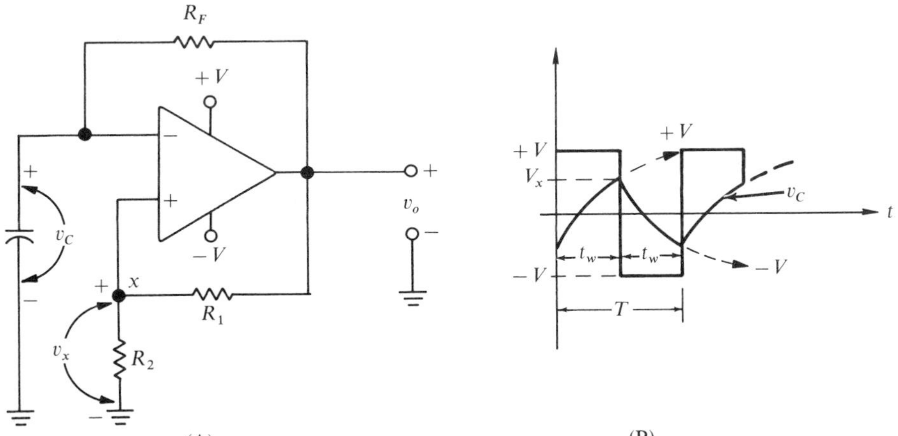

(A) (B)

Fig. 21–22. *Op-amp astable multivibrator. (A) Circuit diagram. (B) Voltage waveforms.*

Let us assume that at some instant of time, $v_c > v_x$. Then, the output voltage, v_o, is equal to $-V$ volts, and capacitor C charges through R_F to the $-V$ level. The capacitor never reaches this level because, as soon as $v_c = v_x$, the output switches to $+V$ volts. The polarity of v_x reverses, and the capacitor starts charging in the reverse direction. It now charges toward $+V$ volts and stops charging at $v_c = v_x$. The output switches between $+V$ and $-V$ volts (Fig. 21–22B). The period, T, may be calculated from the following expression:

$$T = 2R_F C \ln\left(\frac{R_1 + 2R_2}{R_1}\right) \qquad \textbf{(21–24)}$$

The circuit delivers only a symmetrical waveform.

EXAMPLE 21–5.

Determine the frequency of oscillation for the astable MV of Fig. 21–22A for the following component values: $R_F = 10\,\text{k}\Omega$, $R_1 = 7.5\,\text{k}\Omega$, $R_2 = 3.3\,\text{k}\Omega$, and $C = 0.1\,\mu\text{F}$.

Solution:

By Eq. (21–24),

$$T = 2 \times 10^4 \times 10^{-7} \times \ln\left(\frac{7.5 + 2 \times 3.3}{7.5}\right)$$
$$= 1.27 \times 10^{-3}\,\text{s}$$
$$f = \frac{1}{T}$$
$$= \frac{1}{1.27 \times 10^{-3}} = 787.4\,\text{Hz}$$

21.6 An Electronic Timer

The NE/SE 555* monolithic IC timer is a very versatile unit. It functions as a monostable MV to provide accurate time delays, and as an astable MV to generate clock pulses. Further, it is capable of supplying up to 200 mA of load current and may be operated over a wide voltage range, from 4 V to 18 V. Its popularity stems from its ability to generate accurately timing pulses having a duration of from microseconds through hours. The duty cycle is also adjustable.

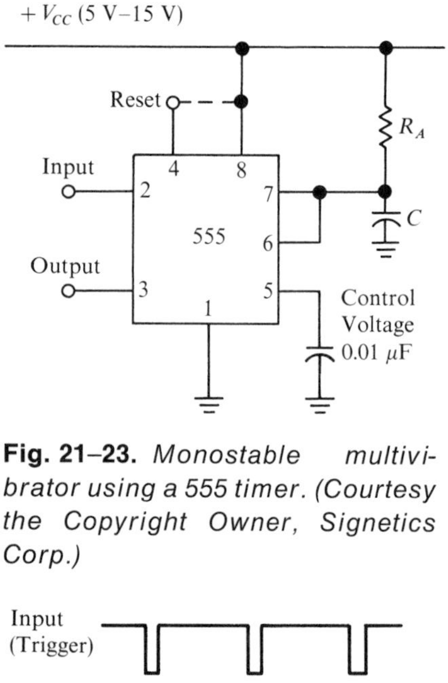

Fig. 21–23. *Monostable multivibrator using a 555 timer. (Courtesy the Copyright Owner, Signetics Corp.)*

The circuit of Fig. 21–23 is an example of how the 555 timer can be connected to function as a one-shot. External components R_A and C determine the output pulse width. When a negative-going trigger is applied to pin 2, capacitor C starts to charge exponentially with a time constant equal to R_AC. The output stays "high" during the charging cycle. When the voltage across the capacitor reaches the value of two-thirds V_{CC}, the capacitor is rapidly discharged, and the output drops to a "low." It remains in the "low" state until a new trigger arrives.

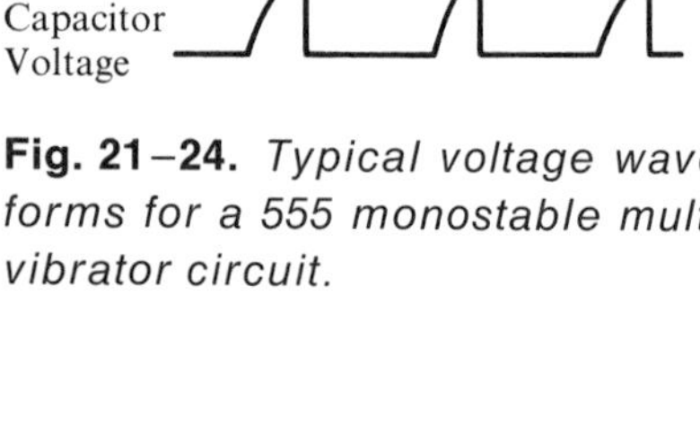

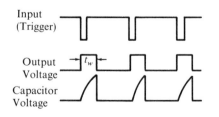

Fig. 21–24. *Typical voltage waveforms for a 555 monostable multivibrator circuit.*

Waveforms of trigger, capacitor, and output voltage pulses are drawn in Fig. 21–24. The time t_w at which the output is "high" is given by

$$t_w = 1.1R_AC \qquad \textbf{(21–25)}$$

and is independent of the supply voltage. The relationship

*NE/SE 555 is a Signetics Corporation designation. The same unit is available as MC1555 from Motorola.

between pulse width, resistance R_A, and capacitance C is provided by the manufacturer in the graphs of Fig. 21–25.

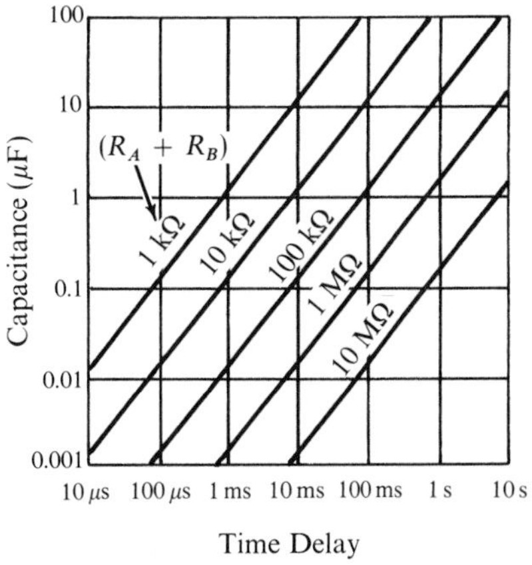

Fig. 21–25. *Time delay versus circuit component values for a 555 monostable multivibrator. (Courtesy the Copyright Owner, Signetics Corp.)*

EXAMPLE 21–6.

Determine the values of R_A and C for the circuit of Fig. 21–23 to generate a 1-ms output pulse.

Solution:

By Eq. (21–25),

$$R_A C = \frac{t_w}{1.1} = \frac{10^{-3}}{1.1} = 0.91 \times 10^{-3}\,\text{s}$$

Assuming a capacitor value of 0.1 μF,

$$R_A = \frac{0.91 \times 10^{-3}}{0.1 \times 10^{-6}} = 9.1\,\text{k}\Omega$$

In Fig. 21–26, the timer is connected as an astable MV. Charging is accomplished through R_A, R_B, and C. The discharge path passes through only R_B and C. Hence, the duty cycle is a function of R_A and R_B. It is calculated as a percentage duty cycle, $\%D$:

$$\%D = \left(\frac{R_B}{R_A + 2R_B}\right) \times 100\% \qquad \textbf{(21–26)}$$

$$= \frac{t_2}{T} \times 100\%$$

where t_2 is the OFF time.

Duty cycles from 0 percent to almost 50 percent can be obtained. The output stays "high" when capacitor C is charging. It remains at a "low" during discharge. Typical waveforms are provided in Fig. 21–27.

The pulse width when the output is "high," t_1, is given by

$$t_1 = 0.693(R_A + R_B)C \qquad \textbf{(21–27)}$$

The OFF time, t_2, is

$$t_2 = 0.693 R_B C \qquad \textbf{(21–28)}$$

Because the period T is the sum of t_1 and t_2, the frequency of oscillation, f, is

$$f = \frac{1}{T} = \frac{1.44}{(R_A + 2R_B)C} \qquad \textbf{(21–29)}$$

The recommended minimum value for resistor R_A is 1 kΩ, and the maximum for $R_A + R_B$ is 3.3 MΩ. Capacitor C has a low limit of 500 pF. The upper limit is determined

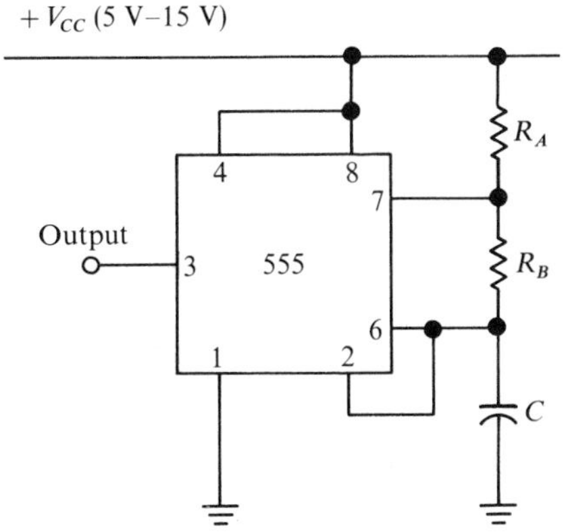

Fig. 21–26. *The 555 timer connected as an astable multivibrator. (Courtesy the Copyright Owner, Signetics Corp.)*

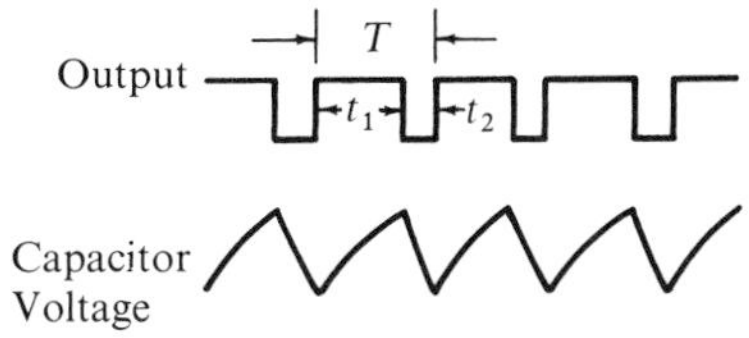

Fig. 21–27. *Typical waveforms for a 555 astable multivibrator.*

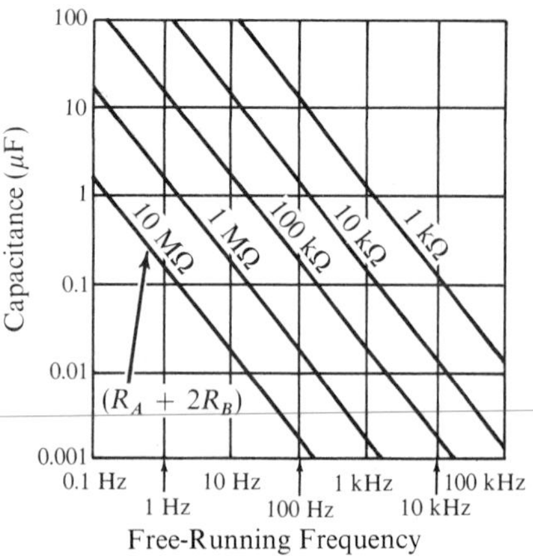

Fig. 21–28. *Curves used for the calculation of the free running frequency of a 555 astable multivibrator. (Courtesy the Copyright Owner, Signetics Corp.)*

by capacitor leakage. Calculation of resistance and capacitance values may be done with the graphs of Fig. 21–28.

EXAMPLE 21–7.

The circuit of Fig. 21–26 has the following component values: $R_A = 1.5\,\mathrm{k\Omega}$, $R_B = 8.6\,\mathrm{k\Omega}$, and $C = 0.1\,\mu\mathrm{F}$. Calculate

(a) Pulse width.
(b) Frequency of oscillation.
(c) Duty cycle.

Solutions:

(a) By Eq. (21–27),

$$t_1 = 0.693(1.5 + 8.6) \times 0.1 \times 10^{-6}$$
$$= 0.7\,\mathrm{ms}$$

(b) By Eq. (21–29),

$$f = \frac{1.44}{(1.5 + 2 \times 8.6) \times 0.1 \times 10^{-6}}$$
$$= 0.77\,\mathrm{kHz}$$

(c) The duty cycle is determined by Eq. (21–26):

$$\%D = \left(\frac{8.6}{1.5 + 2 \times 8.6}\right) \times 100\%$$
$$= 46\%$$

SUMMARY

Multivibrators are found in numerous applications in digital systems. The flip-flop (bistable MV) is used primarily as a storage element and is found in counters, shift registers, and memories. Various IC flip-flops are available, with the *J-K* type being the most popular.

The Schmitt trigger is a multivibrator that is used as a pulse shaper, comparator, and level shifter. The output of the Schmitt trigger is always a rectangular waveform, regardless of the shape of the input signal. It may, therefore, be used to reshape pulses.

A monostable MV, or one-shot, is used to generate rectangular pulses of a determined width. The pulse width is determined by circuit capacitor and resistor values. An astable, or free running, MV delivers an approximate square wave output with no external input signal. The frequency of an astable MV is a function of circuit component values. It is used as a clock to provide timing pulses in digital systems, as well as in other applications.

Further Reading

Deem, W., K. Muchow, and A. Zeppa. *Digital Computers: Circuits and Concepts*. Reston, Va.: Reston Publishing Company, Inc., 1974, Chapter 8.

Metzger, D. *Electronic Circuit Behavior*. Englewood Cliffs, N.J.: Prentice-Hall, 1975, Chapter 5.

Millman, J., and H. Taub. *Pulse, Digital, and Switching Waveforms*. New York: McGraw-Hill Book Company, 1965, Chapters 10 and 11.

Oppenheimer, S. L. *Semiconductor Logic and Switching Circuits*. 2nd ed. Columbus, Ohio: Charles E. Merrill Publishing Company, 1973, Chapters 5 and 7.

Tocci, R. J. *Fundamentals of Pulse and Digital Circuits*. 2nd ed. Columbus, Ohio: Charles E. Merrill Publishing Company, 1977, Chapters 9, 10, and 12.

REVIEW QUESTIONS

21.1 Describe the structure and function of the three types of multivibrator circuits.

21.2 What type of MV can be formed by the direct interconnection of two INVERTERs?

21.3 Describe the regenerative action in a bistable MV.

21.4 Explain the function of a trigger circuit in a flip-flop.

21.5 What is the function of the differentiator in Fig. 21–4?

21.6 Describe two MV triggering schemes.

21.7 What is the function of a counter?

21.8 Explain how a counter can be used as a frequency divider.

21.9 List three types of flip-flops.

21.10 What is the advantage of a *J-K* over an *S-R* flip-flop?

21.11 How does a master-slave flip-flop eliminate the race-around condition?

21.12 Identify two applications in which a Schmitt trigger is used.

21.13 Define hysteresis zone in a Schmitt trigger.

21.14 Which circuit components in Fig. 21–18A determine the width of the output pulse?

21.15 What is the function of capacitor C_1 in Fig. 21–18A?

21.16 What is the relationship between the output pulse width and frequency of the trigger signal in the circuit of Fig. 21–20A?

21.17 Which components must be of the same value to assure symmetrical operation of the astable MV of Fig. 21–21?

21.18 Is it possible to achieve a nonsymmetrical output from the circuit of Fig. 21–22A?

21.19 If a variable duty cycle clock is to be designed, which component would most likely be varied in the circuit of Fig. 21–26 to accomplish this task? Why?

21.20 What type of output waveform, regardless of its input, does a Schmitt trigger deliver?

PROBLEMS

P21–1 In the circuit of Fig. 21–1B, the $-V_{BB}$ source is changed to -3 V. Determine if the circuit operates as a bistable MV. Assume that $h_{FE(\text{min})} = 40$, $V_{\text{sat}} = 0.2$ V, and $V_{BE(\text{ON})} = 0.7$ V.

P21–2 Design a discrete bistable MV similar to Fig. 20–1B to operate from ± 12-V sources. Use NPN transistors having an $h_{FE(\text{min})} = 50$ and $V_{\text{sat}} = 0.1$ V. Assume that $I_{C(\text{ON})} = 10$ mA.

P21–3 Repeat prob. P21–2 for ± 5-V sources.

P21–4 Draw a schematic diagram of a bistable MV with symmetrical triggering. Use PNP transistors, and show all source polarities.

P21–5 Determine the number of *T* flip-flops required to construct a counter that counts
(a) 64 pulses.
(b) 1024 pulses.

P21–6 For the waveforms shown in Fig. 21–8C, draw the output waveform at the *Q* and *Q′* terminals of an *S-R* flip-flop.

P21–7 For the Schmitt trigger of Fig. 21–13A,

$$\begin{aligned} V_{CC} &= 24\text{ V} \\ h_{FE_1} &= h_{FE_2} = 60 \\ V_{\text{sat}} &= 0.1\text{ V} \\ R_{C_1} &= 2.2\text{ k}\Omega \\ R_{C_2} &= 1.5\text{ k}\Omega \\ R_E &= 680\ \Omega \\ R_1 &= 2.2\text{ k}\Omega \\ R_2 &= 10\text{ k}\Omega \\ R_3 &= 22\text{ k}\Omega \end{aligned}$$

Determine if proper switching of the output signal occurs.

P21–8 Repeat prob. P21–7 for $h_{FE_1} = h_{FE_2} = 25$.

P21–9 Calculate the (a) UTP, (b) LTP, and (c) output levels of the circuit in prob. P21–7.

P21–10 The comparator of Fig. 21–17A is fed by a 5-V peak sinusoid. Reference supply $v_{\text{REF}} = 2$ V, and $\pm V = \pm 12$ V. Draw and label the output waveform.

P21–11 For the circuit of Fig. 21–17B, the output switches between 12 V and 8 V. Resistor $R_1 = 1\text{ k}\Omega$, and $R_2 = 22\text{ k}\Omega$. Calculate the magnitude of the hysteresis zone.

P21–12 In prob. P21–11, what values of R_1 and R_2 are necessary for a hysteresis zone of 100 mV?

P21–13 The monostable MV of Fig. 21–18A produces a 100-μs pulse.
(a) Calculate the value of capacitor C for $R = 33\,\text{k}\Omega$.
(b) Determine suitable values for R_{C_1} and R_{C_2}.

P21–14 Repeat prob. P21–13 for $R = 22\,\text{k}\Omega$.

P21–15 In the circuit of Fig. 21–20A, $R_1 = R_2 = R_F = 10\,\text{k}\Omega$, and $C = 0.01\,\mu\text{F}$. Calculate the pulse width.

P21–16 Solve for the value of R_F in the monstable MV of Fig. 21–20A, if $R_1 = 10\,\text{k}\Omega$, $R_2 = 22\,\text{k}\Omega$, and $C = 0.47\,\mu\text{F}$, to yield a 1-ms pulse.

P21–17 Repeat prob. P21–16 for a 100-μs pulse.

P21–18 Determine the frequency of oscillation for the astable MV of Fig. 21–21B if $R_1 = R_2 = 5.1\,\text{k}\Omega$ and $C_1 = C_2 = 0.1\,\mu\text{F}$.

P21–19 Design the values of R_1, R_2, C_1, and C_2 for the astable MV of Fig. 21–21B to yield an asymmetrical output of $t_{w_1} = 0.2$ ms and $t_{w_2} = 0.4$ ms.

P21–20 The op amp astable MV of Fig. 21–22 is to generate 10-μs-wide pulses. The component values are $R_1 = R_2 = 4.7\,\text{k}\Omega$ and $R_F = 2\,\text{k}\Omega$. Calculate the value of capacitor C.

P21–21 Determine the pulse width delivered by the monostable MV of Fig. 21–23 if $R_A = 22\,\text{k}\Omega$ and $C = 0.047\,\mu\text{F}$.

P21–22 Calculate the values of C and R_B necessary to generate an output frequency of 100 Hz in the circuit of Fig. 21–26. The duty cycle is 40 percent, and $R_A = 5\,\text{k}\Omega$.

P21–23 Repeat prob. P21–22 for a 30 percent duty cycle.

22

Counters, Registers, and Memories

Flip-flops and logic circuits are connected to form *counters* and *registers*. Counters perform various operations in a computer; registers are used as devices for temporarily storing binary information. Registers also play a considerable role in the transfer of information from one point to another in a digital system.

A simple binary ripple counter made of T flip-flops was examined in Chapter 21. This counter, also known as a direct counter, is found in applications where exact counts are required. Another type of counter can be made to deliver an output and resets after a specified count. This and other kinds of counters are discussed in the chapter.

Binary information is generally fed into shift registers, either in a serial or parallel manner. The first method refers to shifting, in sequence, one bit of information at a time. In the latter method, all data are shifted into the register simultaneously. Both types of shift registers are examined in the chapter.

22.1 Types of Memories

It was pointed out in Chapter 18 that the memory section of a computer stores information. Such information may be in the form of data for the problem to be solved, programming instructions, or partial results obtained during the solution of the problem. All memories, regardless of their construction, are specified by their storage capacity. *Storage capacity* is the maximum number of bits a memory can retain.

Another parameter, *access time*, refers to the time it takes to locate data or an instruction in the memory and transfer it to the arithmetic section, or vice versa. The *mode of access* is also an important parameter. It denotes the manner in which data are retrieved from the memory. In the *parallel mode* of access the bits of a word are retrieved simultaneously. *Sequential access* refers to obtaining information serially, one bit at a time.

The *random-access memory* (RAM) is an example of a read/write memory. Data are constantly written into and read out of this type of memory.

Another kind of memory is the *read-only memory* (ROM). Information is stored permanently in the ROM, and its contents cannot be changed during operation. The ROM is used for dedicated computer applications such as the storing of programs, subroutines, etc., to be described later.

22.2 The Decade Counter

A counter that counts up to ten pulses and resets automatically on the tenth pulse is known as a *decade counter*. It is also called a *base-10*, or a *modulus-10*, counter. The modulus of a counter is defined as the highest number of pulses counted before resetting.

Consider a counter that counts up to 2^n pulses, where n is the number of flip-flops in the counter. Such a counter is known as a modulus-2^n, or simply, a MOD-2^n, counter. Several techniques may be used to cause a counter to reset after a predetermined count. We shall use the decade counter of Fig. 22–1A to illustrate some of these methods.

The first method calls for a modification of a simple ripple counter by providing a feedback connection for resetting the counter. To determine the number of flip-flops required in the design of a specific counter, the following relationship must be true:

$$2^n \geqslant M \qquad \textbf{(22–1)}$$

where n is defined as in the preceding discussion, and M is the modulus. In the case of a MOD-10 counter, $M = 10$, requiring an n of 4 ($2^4 = 16$). If $n = 3$ is chosen, $2^3 = 8$, which is less than 10, and Eq. (22–1) is violated.

The decade counter of Fig. 22–1A uses four *J-K* flip-flops. Outputs $\bar{Q}_B$ and $\bar{Q}_D$ are connected to an OR gate. Feedback is realized by connecting the output of the OR gate to the clear (Cr) input of each flip-flop.

Assume that all flip-flops are cleared (all Q outputs equal zero). The first clock pulse (Fig. 22–1B) causes flip-flop A to change state on the trailing edge of the pulse. Output Q_A remains at 1 until the trailing edge of the second pulse appears. The output pulse Q_A becomes a logic 0, causing Q_B to become a logic 1. This represents the count of 2.

So far, the counter behaves like the simple ripple counter described in the previous chapter. The operation of the counter continues in this manner with a flip-flop changing states only if the preceding flip-flop goes from a "high" to a "low" state, until the tenth pulse arrives. When this occurs, $Q_A = 0$, $Q_B = 1$, $Q_C = 0$, and $Q_D = 1$. The two inputs to

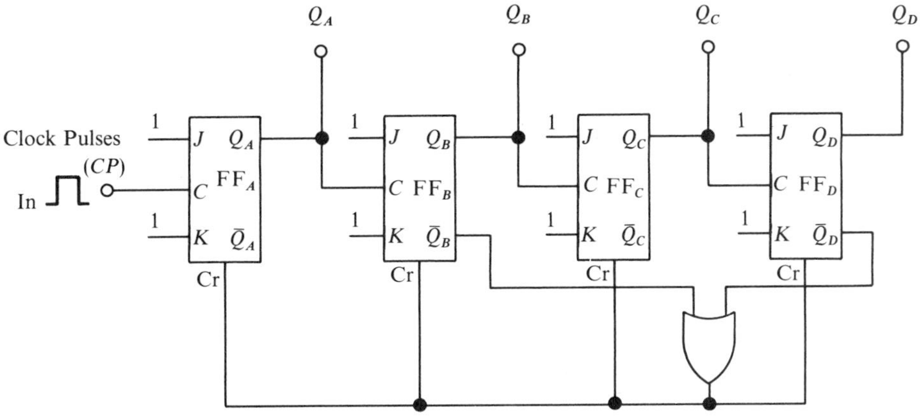

(A)

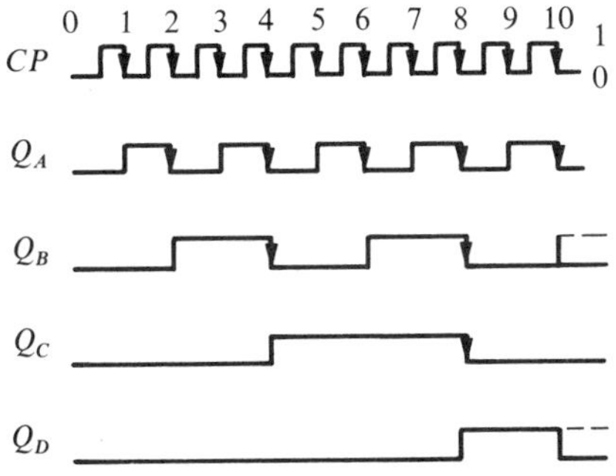

(B)

	Outputs					
CP	Q_D	Q_C	Q_B	Q_A	$\bar{Q}_D$	$\bar{Q}_B$
0	0	0	0	0	1	1
1	0	0	0	1	1	1
2	0	0	1	0	1	0
3	0	0	1	1	1	0
4	0	1	0	0	1	1
5	0	1	0	1	1	1
6	0	1	1	0	1	0
7	0	1	1	1	1	0
8	1	0	0	0	0	1
9	1	0	0	1	0	1
10	1	0	1	0	0	0
↓	↓	↓	↓	↓		
0	0	0	0	0		

(C)

Fig. 22–1. *Decade counter using J-K flip-flops. (A) Logic diagram. (B) Waveforms. (C) Truth table.*

the OR gate, $\bar{Q}_B$ and $\bar{Q}_D$, are now at logic 0. The output of the OR gate, therefore, is also a logic 0.

From the truth table of Fig. 22–1C, only under this condition (at the count of ten) is the output of the OR gate a logic 0. Because the output of the OR gate is returned to the clear input of each flip-flop, the counter resets to zero. With the arrival of the eleventh pulse, the counter begins a new count cycle.

Examining the waveforms in Fig. 22–1B, we observe that a single pulse at the output corresponds to ten input pulses. In other words, the output frequency is one-tenth the input frequency. A modulus counter, therefore, may be used as a frequency divider circuit. This property of counters is utilized, for example, in the design of digital clocks.

EXAMPLE 22–1.

Design a modulus-5 counter using *J-K* flip-flops.

Solution:

First we determine the number of flip-flops required. By Eq. (22–1) with $M = 5$, n must be equal to 3 ($2^3 = 8 > 5$). If $n = 2$ were chosen, $2^2 = 4 < 5$. Hence, three flip-flops are required, as illustrated in Fig. 22–2.

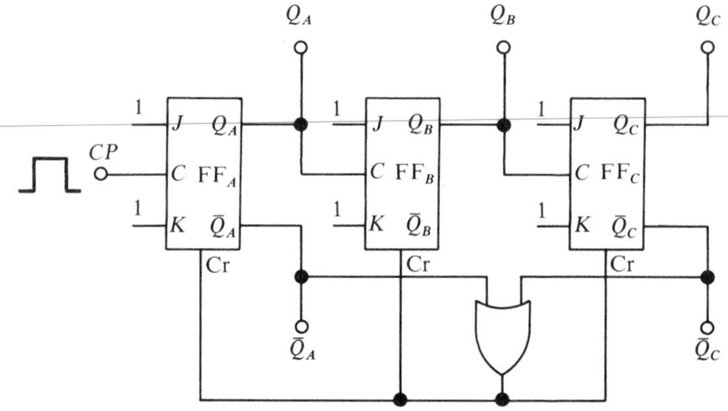

Fig. 22–2. *MOD-5 counter. (See Example 22–1.)*

The feedback connection is derived from outputs $\bar{Q}_A$ and $\bar{Q}_C$, which equal a logic 0 on the fifth count. The output of the OR gate is returned to the Cr terminal of each flip-flop. A logic 0 therefore exists at each clear terminal, and all flip-flops are reset on count 5.

A commercial MSI four-bit ripple counter is illustrated in Fig. 22–3. Employing T^2L, the SN5493 counter is manufactured by Texas Instruments, Inc. For use as a four-bit

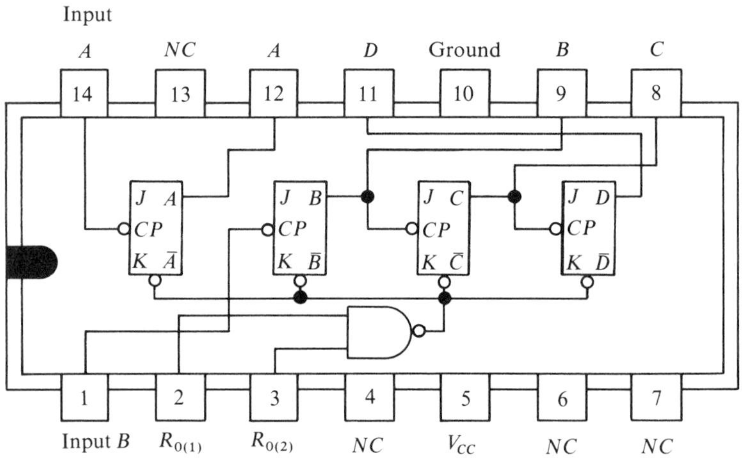

Fig. 22–3. *Example of a commercial four-bit ripple counter. (Courtesy Texas Instruments, Inc.)*

counter, output A is connected to input B. To obtain frequency division by 2, flip-flop A is used alone. The use of flip-flops B, C, and D (with input to pin 1 and output to pin 11) results in frequency division by 8.

22.3 The Synchronous Counter

The modulus counters considered thus far have a significant drawback: the switching of flip-flops occurs serially. A transition of a preceding flip-flop must occur before the next binary changes state. Because each flip-flop has an inherent time delay, the total delay time of the counter may become appreciable. It is equal to the sum of the individual delay times. This makes the ripple counter relatively slow, thereby limiting its operating frequency.

The *synchronous counter* is designed to overcome this drawback. In this counter, all flip-flops change their state upon the application of a clock pulse. Because the same pulse is applied to all flip-flops, the state transitions occur simultaneously. The total delay time of the synchronous counter is, therefore, equivalent to the delay of a single stage. Because not all flip-flops have equal delay times, the total delay is taken as the delay of the slowest stage.

A synchronous four-bit counter is illustrated in Fig. 22–4A. The pulses to be counted are applied to AND gates A_1, A_2, and A_3. Each AND gate is connected to the clock (C) input of a J-K flip-flop. The truth table and waveforms of Figs. 22–4B and C describe the state of flip-flops for each clock pulse. All flip-flops are assumed to switch ON the trailing edge of a pulse.

The first pulse sets only flip-flop A to a 1; the other flip-flops are unaffected. Because both inputs to AND gate A_1 are 1's, the second clock pulse results in a 1 output from A_1. As the second pulse returns to zero, flip-flop B changes state, and a 1 appears at its output ($Q_B = 1$). Flip-flop A reverts to zero ($Q_A = 0$). After the second pulse, the count is 0010 (decimal 2). The counting continues in the same manner until the sixteenth pulse arrives. At the sixteenth clock pulse, all flip-flops are reset to zero.

EXAMPLE 22–2.

Design a synchronous decade counter.

Solution:

As in the ripple decade counter, a synchronous decade counter requires four flip-flops. Figure 22–5A shows

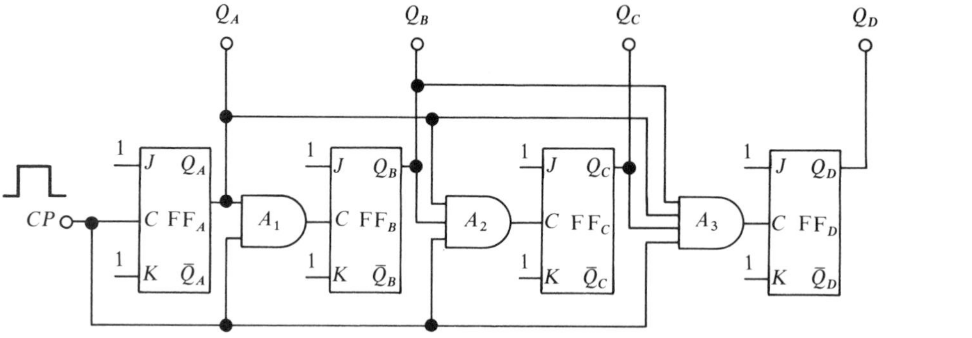

(A)

CP	Q_D	Q_C	Q_B	Q_A
	Outputs			
0	0	0	0	0
1	0	0	0	1
2	0	0	1	0
3	0	0	1	1
4	0	1	0	0
5	0	1	0	1
6	0	1	1	0
7	0	1	1	1
8	1	0	0	0
9	1	0	0	1
10	1	0	1	0
11	1	0	1	1
12	1	1	0	0
13	1	1	0	1
14	1	1	1	0
15	1	1	1	1
16 / 0	0	0	0	0

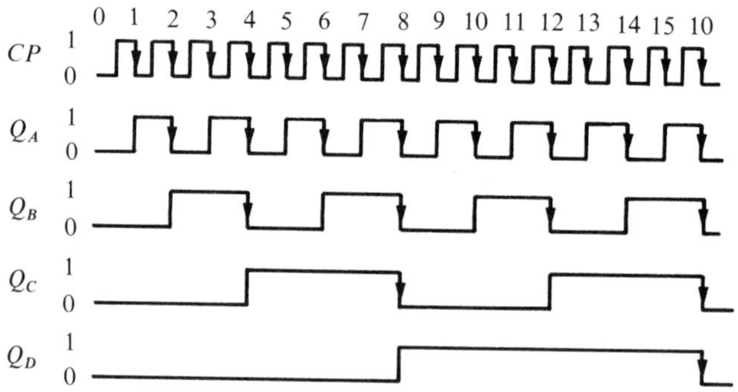

(C)

(B)

Fig. 22–4. *Four-bit synchronous counter. (A) Logic diagram. (B) Truth table. (C) Waveforms.*

a synchronous decade counter employing four flip-flops. Feedback is realized through the NAND gate. Inputs to the NAND gate are derived from Q_B and Q_D. The output of the NAND gate is returned to the K input of each flip-flop.

When Q_B and Q_D are at a logic 1 (Q_A and Q_C are at a logic 0), the count is 1010 (decimal 10). The output of the NAND gate is now a logic 0. A 0 at each K terminal and a 1 at each J terminal forces the flip-flops to reset to 0. The state of each flip-flop after every clock pulse is summarized in the truth table of Fig. 22–5B.

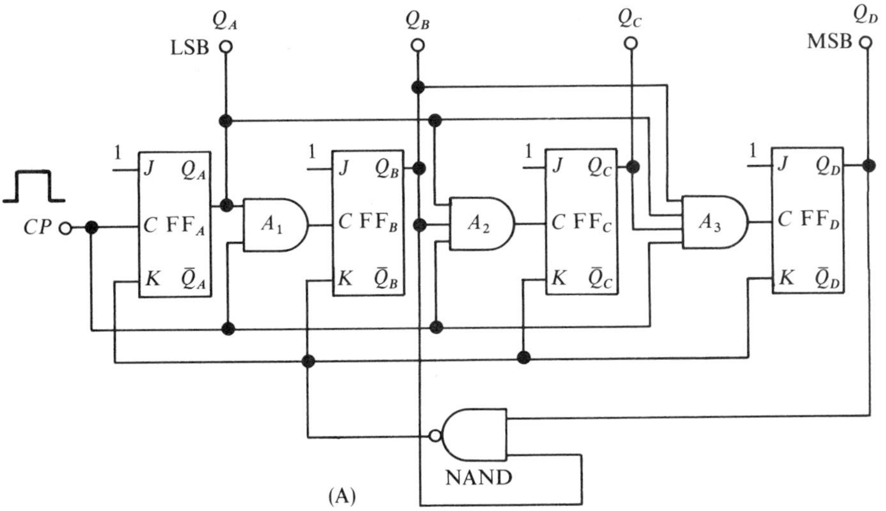

(A)

CP	Outputs Q_D	Q_C	Q_B	Q_A
0	0	0	0	0
1	0	0	0	1
2	0	0	1	0
3	0	0	1	1
4	0	1	0	0
5	0	1	0	1
6	0	1	1	0
7	0	1	1	1
8	1	0	0	0
9	1	0	0	1
10	1 ↓	0 ↓	1 ↓	0 ↓
0	0	0	0	0

(B)

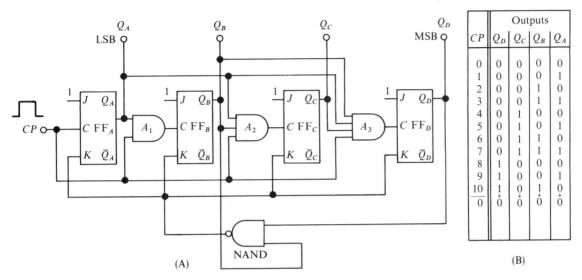

Fig. 22–5. *Synchronous decade counter. (A) Logic diagram. (B) Truth table. (See Example 22–2.)*

22.4 MSI Counters

A number of MSI counters are available. In addition to the four-bit ripple counter of Fig. 22–3, there are decade, hexadecimal (modulus-16), and modulus-12 counters. A MSI decade counter is shown in Fig. 22–6. Four master-slave flip-flops provide divide-by-2 (modulus-2) and divide-by-5 (modulus-5) counts.

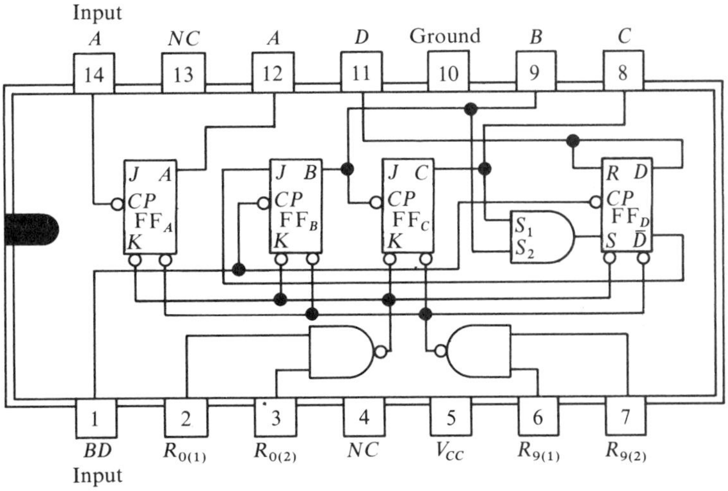

Fig. 22–6. *Example of an MSI decade counter (SN5490/SN7490). (Courtesy Texas Instruments, Inc.)*

Flip-flop A yields a divide-by-2 count, and the divide-by-5 count is obtained from the B, C, and D outputs. For a true decade (divide-by-10) count, the output of flip-flop D is externally connected to the input of flip-flop A (pin 11 to pin 14). The input is applied to pin 1, and the output is derived from pin 12.

22.5 Digital Clocks

Digital clocks operate on the principle of frequency division of a suitable input signal by a counter. Two methods are generally used to derive the input, or clock, signal. In ac powered clocks, the 60-Hz line frequency is converted to a square wave of the same frequency. The 60-Hz square wave is applied to a divide-by-60 (modulus-60) counter. A 1-Hz square wave is obtained at the output of the counter. An output pulse is present once every second.

Applying the 1-Hz wave to another divide-by-60 counter results in an output pulse once every minute. The hour count is obtained by dividing the minutes by another divide-by-60 counter. Additional counters, for example, can be used to generate a calendar.

A battery-operated digital clock derives its input pulses from a crystal oscillator. The oscillator is designed to provide a relatively high frequency signal. The higher the frequency, the more accurate is the clock. As in the ac clock, a series of counters is used to divide the oscillator frequency to yield seconds, minutes, and hours.

The RCA COS/MOS CD4024A counter of Fig. 22–7A is a versatile unit. It contains seven flip-flops, and an external output connection is provided for each stage. With seven stages, we can count up to $2^7 = 128$ pulses. The CD4024A counter is used in many clock applications and as a divide-by-60 counter.

EXAMPLE 22–3.

Design a MOD-60 counter using the CD4024A chip.

Solution:

The design that follows is only one of many for a MOD-60 counter. A block diagram of the counter is illustrated in Fig. 22–7B.

We first examine the outputs of the CD4024A chip after the fifty-ninth pulse. The resultant output is a combination of the following counts: 1, 2, 8, 16, and 32 (a total of 59). Therefore, outputs Q_1, Q_2, $\bar{Q}_3$, Q_4, Q_5, Q_6, and $\bar{Q}_7$ are 1. The output of NAND gate A_1 is a 0. Because a fifty-ninth count occurs before any change occurs in Q_7, output Q_7 is not connected to the NAND gate. The output of A_1 is inverted and fed to a D flip-flop.* The D flip-flop yields a "low" output upon the arrival of the sixtieth pulse. A final output pulse appears when both the clock pulse and the $\bar{Q}$ output of the D flip-flop are "low." This occurs immediately after the sixtieth pulse has returned to 0.

* The D flip-flop provides a one-bit delay. When $D = 1$, $Q = 1$; when $D = 0$, $Q = 0$.

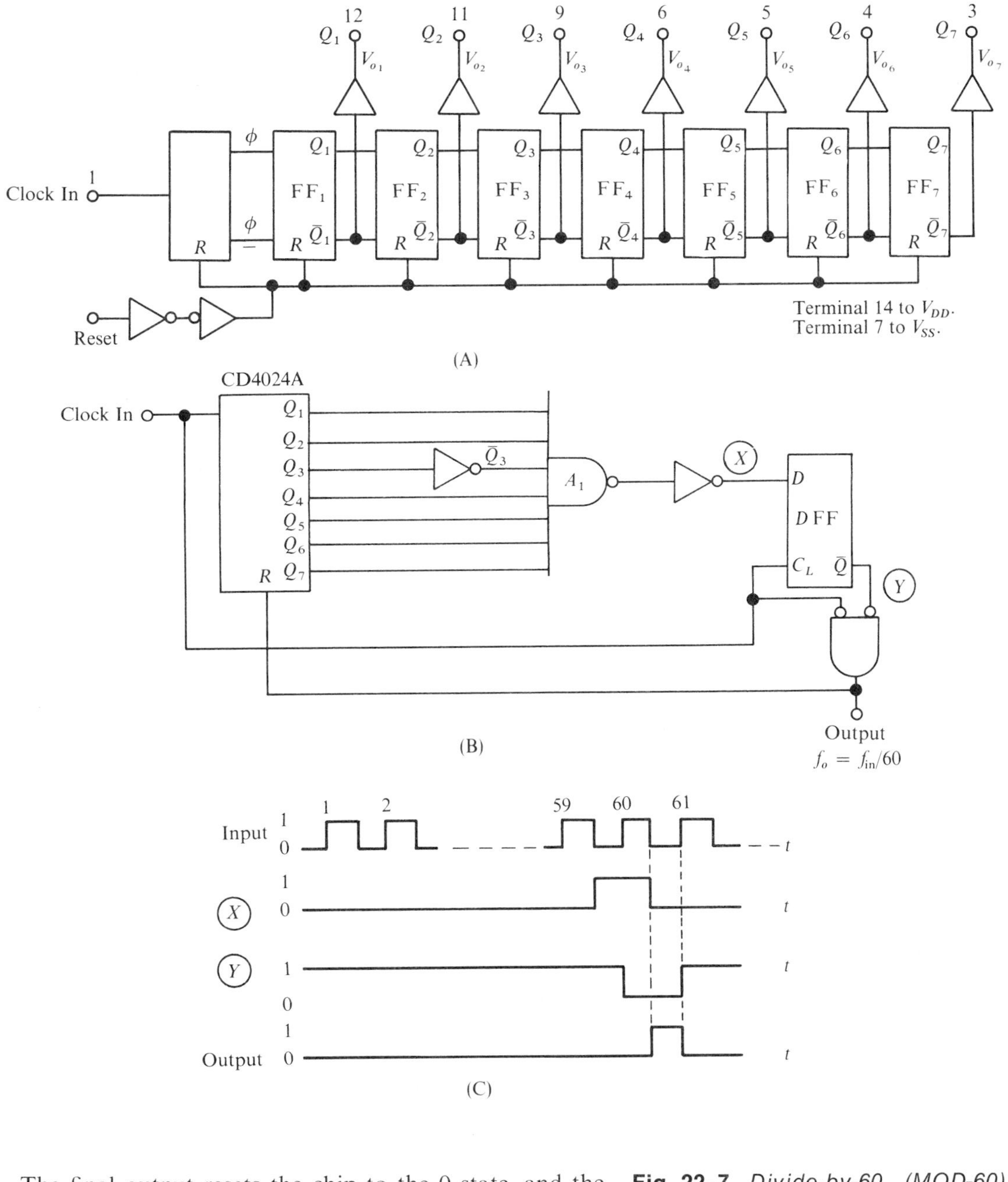

The final output resets the chip to the 0 state, and the counts starts anew. The waveforms at different points in the counter are provided in Fig. 22–7C.

Fig. 22–7. *Divide-by-60 (MOD-60) counter. (A) Type CD4024A counter. (B) Block diagram of the counter. (C) Waveforms at various points of interest in the circuit. (Courtesy RCA Solid State Division.)*

22.6 Shift Registers

As mentioned earlier in this chapter, a shift register stores binary data and may be regarded as a temporary storage device. The number of bits that can be stored is equal to the number of flip-flops contained in the register. Registers, like counters, may operate in a serial or parallel manner. When data are accepted serially, flip-flops are set one at a time. In parallel operation, all flip-flops are set simultaneously.

An example of a parallel entry register is shown in Fig. 22–8. Using *J-K* flip-flops, the register is capable of storing four bits of binary data. Each bit of data is introduced through a NAND gate and an INVERTER. All flip-flops are cleared when a "high" appears on the clear line. Data are fed to input terminals *A*, *B*, *C*, and *D* of the NAND gates.

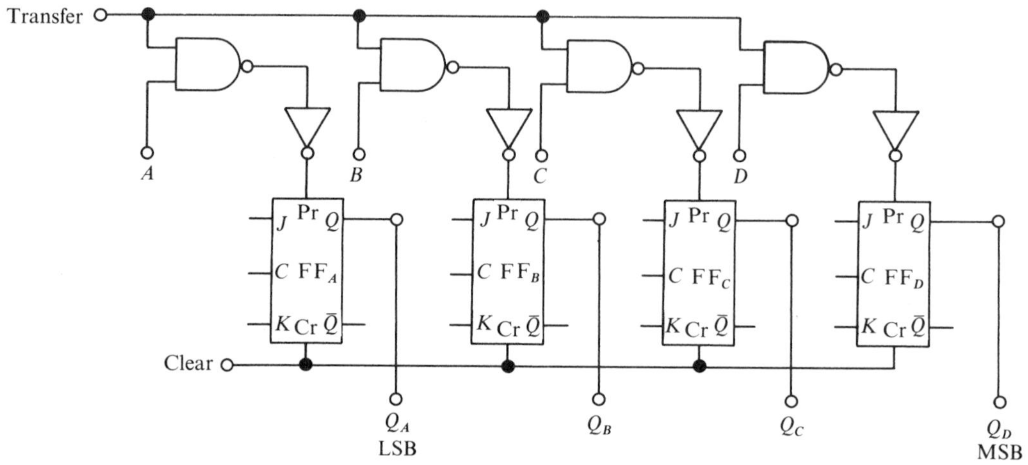

Fig. 22–8. *Parallel entry register.*

If, for example, the quantity 0101 is to be stored in the register, a "high" appears on *B* and *D* and a "low" on *A* and *C*. To shift the information into the register, a "high" must be present on the transfer line and a "low" on the clear line. One's, therefore, appear on the preset (Pr terminals of flip-flops *B* and *D*. As a result, Q_B and Q_D are at a "high," and Q_A and Q_C are at a "low." The data stored in the register are 0101.

Consider now the serial *shift-right* register of Fig. 22–9. A 0 or 1 is shifted one place to the right during each clock pulse. The MSB is the leading bit in the shift sequence.

Assume that the binary number 1011 is to be stored in the register. The "high" of the MSB and the presence of a clock pulse cause flip-flop *A* to change its state. This results in $Q_A = 1$; all the other flip-flops remain in their cleared state. The next significant bit is a 0. Hence, during the second clock pulse, a "low" is present at the *J* terminal of flip-flop *A*. The status of flip-flop *A* does not change; however, flip-flop *B* changes its state, resulting in $Q_B = 1$. Again, Q_C and Q_D are unaffected.

The next input bit is a 1, and, during the third clock pulse, flip-flop A is set. Flip-flop B remains unchanged, and the state of flip-flop C is changed to a 1. Output Q_D is still at a 0. When the LSB (a 1) is fed to the register during the fourth clock pulse, $Q_A = 1$, $Q_B = 1$, $Q_C = 0$, and Q_D is changed to a 1. The number 1011 is stored in the register in the proper sequence. A truth table depicting the state of each flip-flop is provided in Fig. 22–9B.

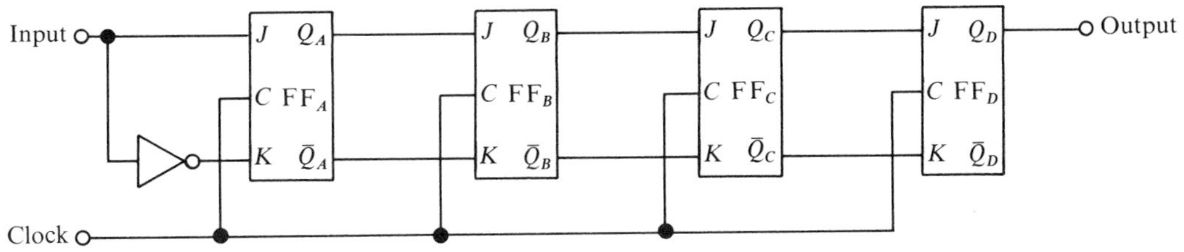

(A)

Clock Pulse	LSB Q_A	Q_B	Q_C	MSB Q_D
0	0	0	0	0
1	1	0	0	0
2	0	1	0	0
3	1	0	1	0
4	1	1	0	1

(B)

Clock Pulse	LSB Q_A	Q_B	Q_C	MSB Q_D	
0	1	1	0	1	← MSB
1	0	1	1	0	
2	0	0	1	1	
3	0	0	0	1	← LSB
4	0	0	0	0	

(C)

Fig. 22–9. *Shift-right register. (A) Logic diagram. (B) Truth table for shift-in sequence of number 1011. (C) Truth table for shift-out sequence of number 1011.*

In the serial register of Fig. 22–9A, a total of four pulses was required to shift in a four-bit number. All flip-flops received the clock pulse simultaneously. The bits, however, were shifted in, one bit at a time. Data in the register may be read out in two different ways:

1. By sensing the Q output of each flip-flop.
2. By applying four more clock pulses, causing the data to "spill out" from the register, bit by bit. During this operation, flip-flop D is sensed.

The second method for reading a register requires a constant 0 on the input line and four clock pulses. From the truth table of Fig. 22–9C, with the contents of the register still 1011, the first clock pulse results in $Q_A = 0$, $Q_B = 1$, $Q_C = 1$, and $Q_D = 0$. The second clock pulse shifts the contents of the register another place to the right; the results are $Q_A = 0$, $Q_B = 0$, $Q_C = 1$, and $Q_D = 1$. Following the third clock pulse, $Q_A = 0$, $Q_B = 0$, $Q_C = 0$, and $Q_D = 1$. The fourth clock pulse resets the register, and $Q_A = Q_B = Q_C = Q_D = 0$.

In a *shift-left* register, data are shifted from right to left. The LSB is the first bit to be shifted in or out. Shift registers can be built with individual gates and flip-flops, or an entire register can be fabricated on a single chip.

In some applications, it is necessary to employ a shift-right, shift-left register. This permits the shifting of data in either direction. The TTL/MSI 7495 chip of Fig. 22–10 is an example of such a register. In this register, *R-S* flip-flops are used to store information. The gating circuitry controls the shift direction. A number of these four-bit registers may be connected to form an *N*-bit shift register.

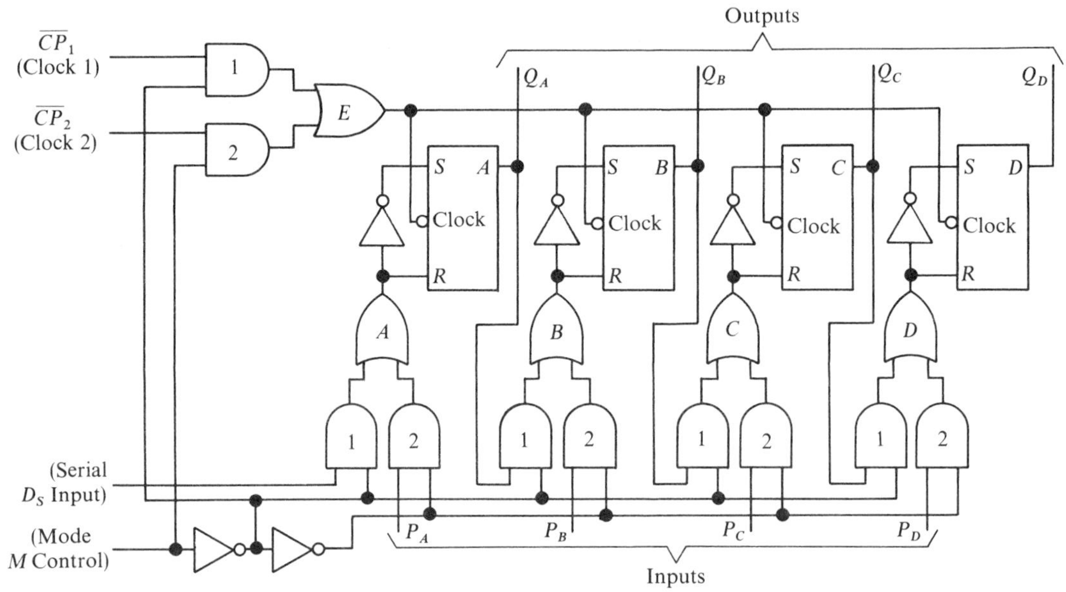

Fig. 22–10. *Type 7495 shift-right, shift-left register. (Courtesy Fairchild Camera and Instrument Corp.)*

The 7495 register features a serial input line (D_S) and four parallel input terminals (P_A, P_B, P_C, and P_D). Data may be entered serially or in parallel. Two clock input terminals and individual output terminals from each flip-flop (Q_A, Q_B, Q_C, and Q_D) are available. The shift direction (left or right) is controlled through the mode control input terminal, *M*.

For a shift-right operation, a "low" is applied to the mode control input terminal. Under this condition, the output of the first INVERTER is a "high," and all number 1 AND gates are enabled. Because of the second INVERTER, all number 2 AND gates are inhibited. With the occurrence of a clock pulse at CP_1, a shift-right operation is performed. Data are applied to the serial data input line, D_S.

For a shift-left operation, each parallel input is connected externally to the output of the next flip-flop. For example, P_A is connected to Q_B. A "high" on the mode control line enables all number 2 AND gates and inhibits all number 1 gates. Data (now applied to the P_D input terminal) are shifted one stage to the left for every clock pulse at terminal CP_2.

The 7495 also can be used as a parallel-input, parallel-output register. In this case, the input is fed to the P_A, P_B, P_C, and P_D terminals. The output is obtained from the Q_A, Q_B, Q_C, and Q_D terminals. In addition, a clock pulse must be present on the CP_2 terminal. Serial-input, parallel-output and parallel-input, serial-output registers are also available.

A CMOS dual four-stage serial-input, parallel-output register (RCA CD4015A) is shown in Fig. 22–11. Each of the two identical registers contains four *D*-type flip-flops and a number of INVERTERs. In addition, each register has its own clock (*CL*) and reset (*R*) input terminals.

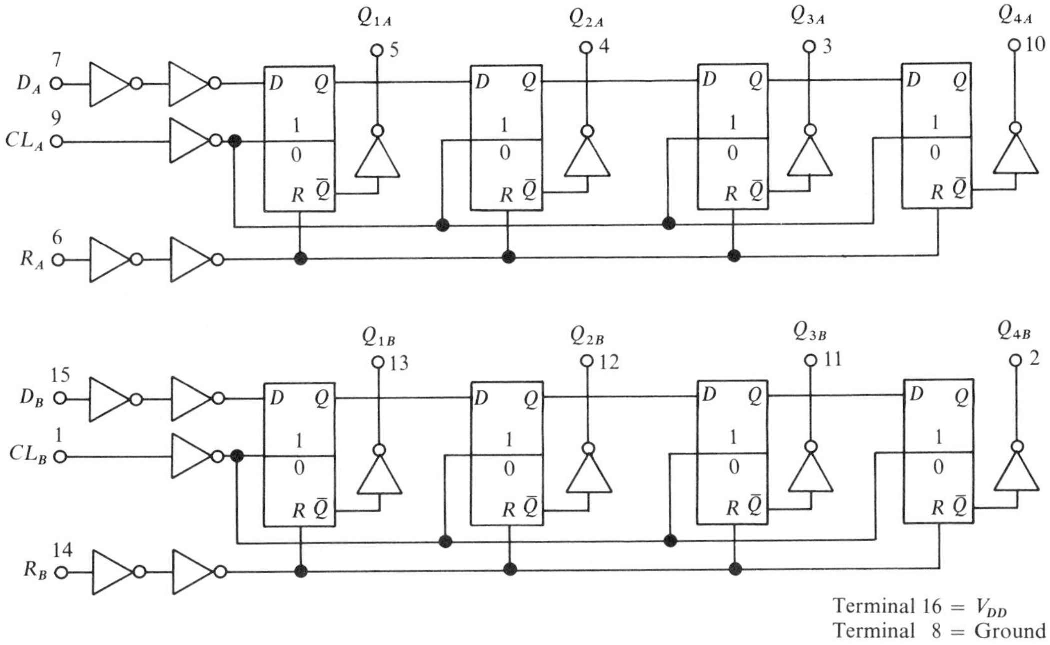

Fig. 22–11. *CMOS-type CD4015A dual four-stage serial-input, parallel-output register. (Courtesy RCA Solid State Division.)*

The operation of the register is similar to the operation of the shift-right register discussed in the previous section. Data bits are entered serially through the D_A or D_B lines. Each clock pulse shifts in a new bit. All stages are reset simultaneously by a pulse on the R_A or R_B lines. The content of each stage may be read by sensing the appropriate *Q* output terminal.

22.7 Semiconductor Memories

Flip-flops are used as basic storage elements in semiconductor memories. Various types of semiconductor memories have been, and continue to be, developed. They are divided into two groups: *bipolar* and *MOS* types. To increase the number of storage cells for a given geometry, LSI technology is employed. These memories are capable of storing thousands of bits of information. In addition to the storage cells, the LSI memory also contains decoder circuits for entering and retrieving data.

Both the bipolar and MOS technologies lend themselves to the fabrication of RAM and ROM memories. As mentioned earlier, data in the RAM can be written in and read out repeatedly. The ROM is programmed once and stores the data indefinitely. The programmable read-only memory (PROM) is a varation of the ROM. The PROM can be programmed by the user in the field. For this reason, the PROM is also called a *field programmable* ROM.

22.8 Bipolar RAM

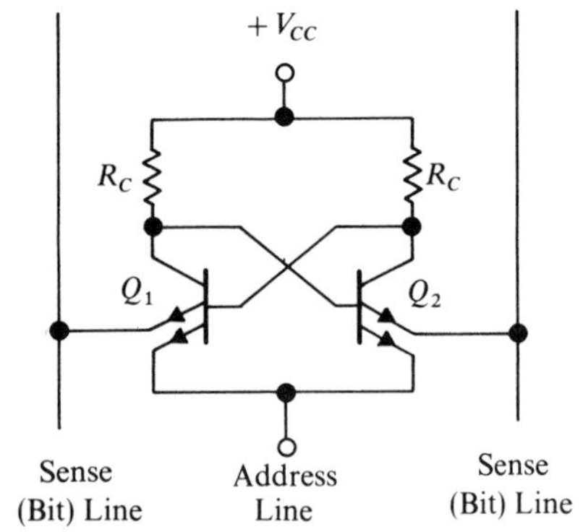

Fig. 22–12. *Bipolar memory cell.*

Most bipolar memories employ a two-transistor flip-flop for the storage cell. Such a cell is illustrated in Fig. 22–12. Multiemitter transistors are not new to us; they are standard in T^2L. One emitter of each transistor is connected to a sense (bit) line. The lines are used to sense the state of the flip-flop for writing in and reading out data. Connected to the other emitters is the address line.

A "low" on the address line forces the current in the flip-flop to flow through that line. Raising the address line to a "high" forces the current to flow through one of the bit lines. A current sensor in the bit line senses the content of the cell.

To change the state of the cell, the address line is raised to a "high." Two opposite signals on the bit lines force the flip-flop either to remain unchanged or to alter its state. When a number of these cells are combined to form a memory array, a particular cell is addressed by raising the address line of the cell to a "high."

Memory arrays are arranged in a matrix configuration by distributing the cells in *rows* and *columns*. The Fairchild T^2L READ/WRITE memory is an example of such an array. A logic diagram of the memory is given in Fig. 22–13A, and its logic symbol is provided in Fig. 22–13B.

This particular memory can store 16 bits of data; hence, it utilizes 16 cells. Each cell consists of an *R-S* flip-flop with two address lines (X and Y) instead of a single address line for the basic cell of Fig. 22–12. (The address line is also called a *word line* because a number of cells making up a particular word can be sensed simultaneously.)

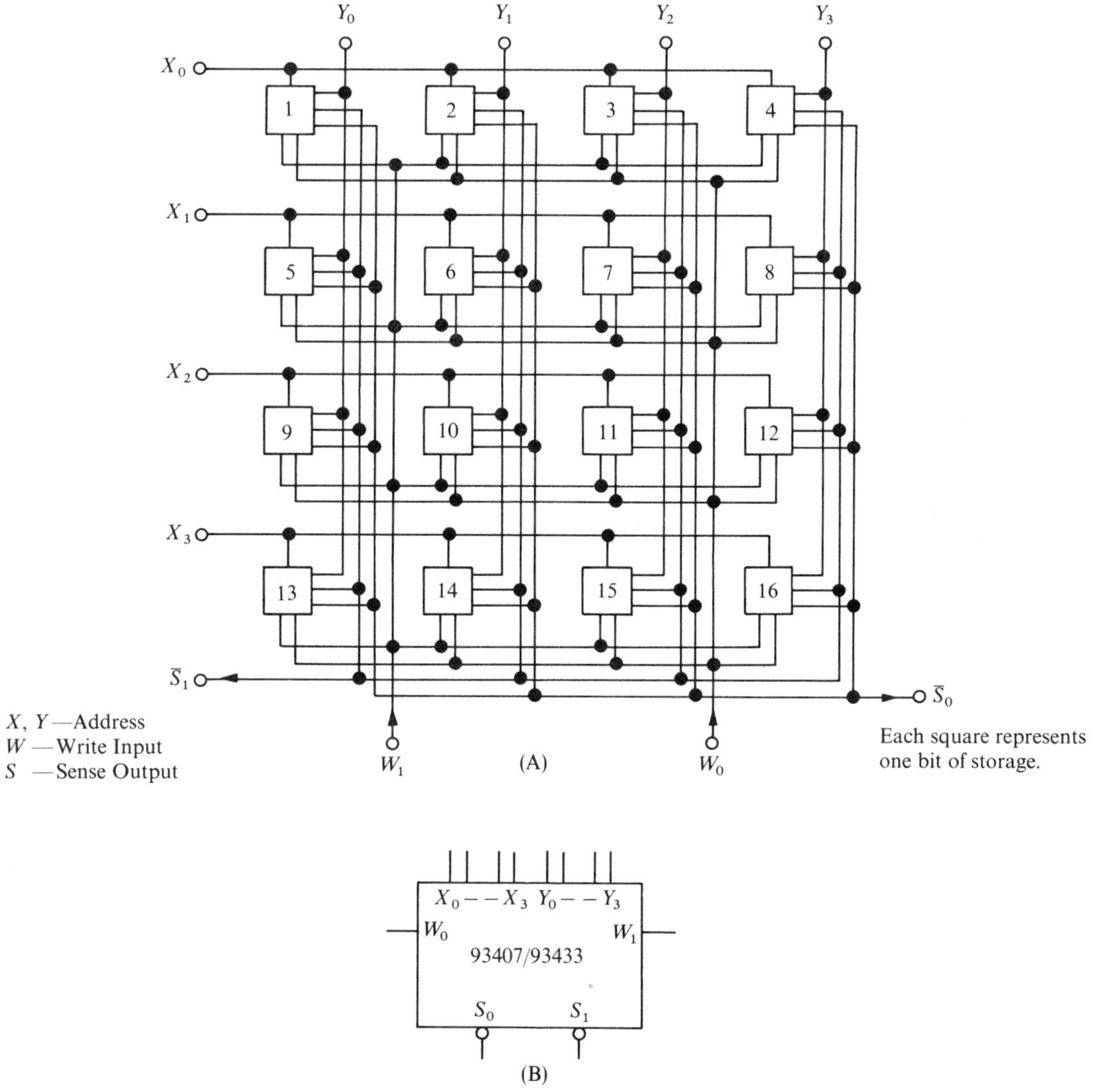

Fig. 22–13. *Example of a T²L read/write memory. (A) Logic diagram. (B) Logic symbol. (Courtesy Fairchild Camera and Instrument Corp.)*

By using two word lines per cell, it is possible to address 16 cells by eight input word lines. To address a particular cell for either reading out or writing in, both word lines for the cell are set at a "high." For example, to address cell 6, the X_1 and Y_1 lines are raised to a "high."

The content of a cell is read out through sense output terminals $\overline{S}_1$ and $\overline{S}_0$. If the addressed cell is in the 1 state, $\overline{S}_1$ is "low," and S_0 is "high." For a 0, $\overline{S}_1$ is "high," and $\overline{S}_0$ is "low."

Data are written into the memory by setting the address lines to a "high." To write a 1 into an addressed cell, a "high" is placed on the W_1 input terminal. For writing in a 0, a "high" must be present on the W_0 terminal.

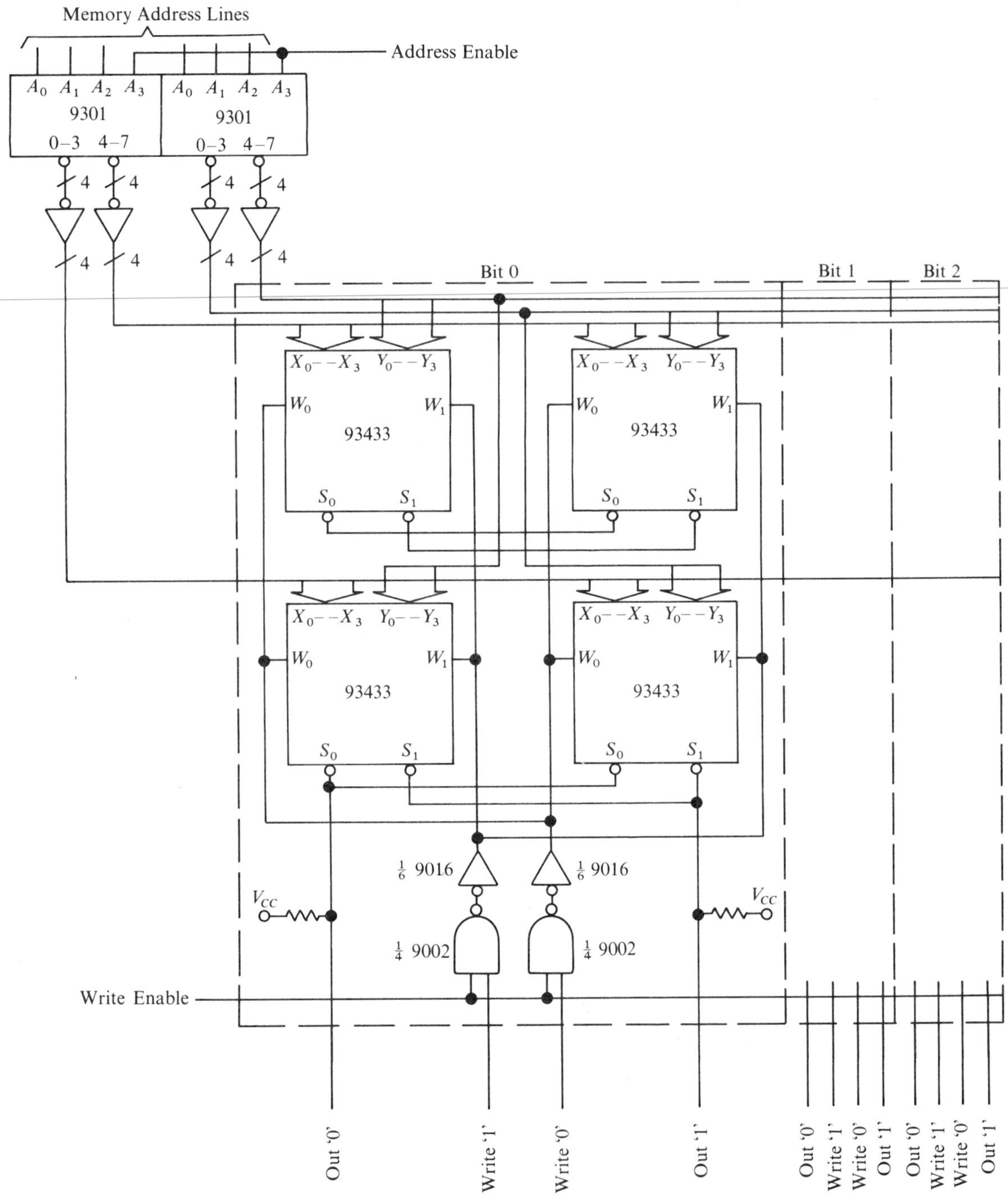

Fig. 22–14. *A 64-word memory. (Courtesy Fairchild Camera and Instrument Corp.)*

Memories such as the Fairchild 93407/93433 may be expanded by connecting a number of similar chips to yield a large memory array. For example, a 64-bit memory is illustrated in Fig. 22–14. Four chips (each containing 16 cells) are connected to store 64 bits. Using three such groups with appropriate external connections, a memory which stores 64 three-bit (64 × 3) words is formed. If N groups of four 16-bit chips are used, a 64 word × N bit memory can be created.

In Fig. 22–14, note that two decoders (93011) are used to provide proper address signals. All 64 addresses are available through the six input lines to the two decoders. This should not be too surprising, because $2^6 = 64$.

The *address enable input* functions as follows: If a "high" is present on the address enable line, the outputs of the decoders are also "high," and none of the cells are addressed. When the enable line is "low," only one of the cells can be addressed. The outputs of the two decoders serve as the X and Y addressing lines.

Bipolar RAM memories are available with a storage capacity of up to 1024 bits on a single chip employing T^2L and larger capacities for I^2L operation. Typical access time is 35 ns–45 ns. Some high-speed Schottky devices have an access time less than 25 ns.

22.9 Bipolar ROM

In general, data are only read out from a ROM. Information may be written in, or programmed, during the processing of the chip. The customer supplies the manufacturer with a specification sheet, or punched tape, specifying how the memory is to be programmed.

The PROM can be programmed by the user in the field. There are two types of PROMs. In one type, electrical signals are applied to permanently program the memory. This process is irreversible. In the second type, the content of the memory can be electrically rewritten, thereby permitting more than one program change. Such a memory is called an *electrically alterable ROM* (EAROM).

In programming a bipolar PROM of the first type, an electrical voltage or current is applied to a selected cell to *open circuit* ("blow out") a fusible resistor. The fusible resistor is made of a material such as nichrome. An example of the second type is considered under the MOS ROM section of this chapter.

The basic ROM cell is much simpler than that of a RAM. Hence, for the same physical size of an LSI chip, the ROM has a larger capacity. An example of high packing density is the Signetics 4096-bit bipolar ROM (type 8228). Organized as a 1024 word × 4 bits/word memory, the 8228, including decoder circuits, is contained in a 16-pin dual in-line package.

A 16 word × 4 bits/word ROM is illustrated in Fig. 22–15. Note the fusible resistors connected to the emitters of some transistors. A word is selected by activating the appropriate word select line. For example, if word W_0 is to be read, a "high" is placed on the W_0 word select line. This activates all four cells that constitute word W_0. It is assumed that a 0 is stored in the cell if a 1 appears on the sense line. If a 0 appears on the line, the bit stored is a 1.

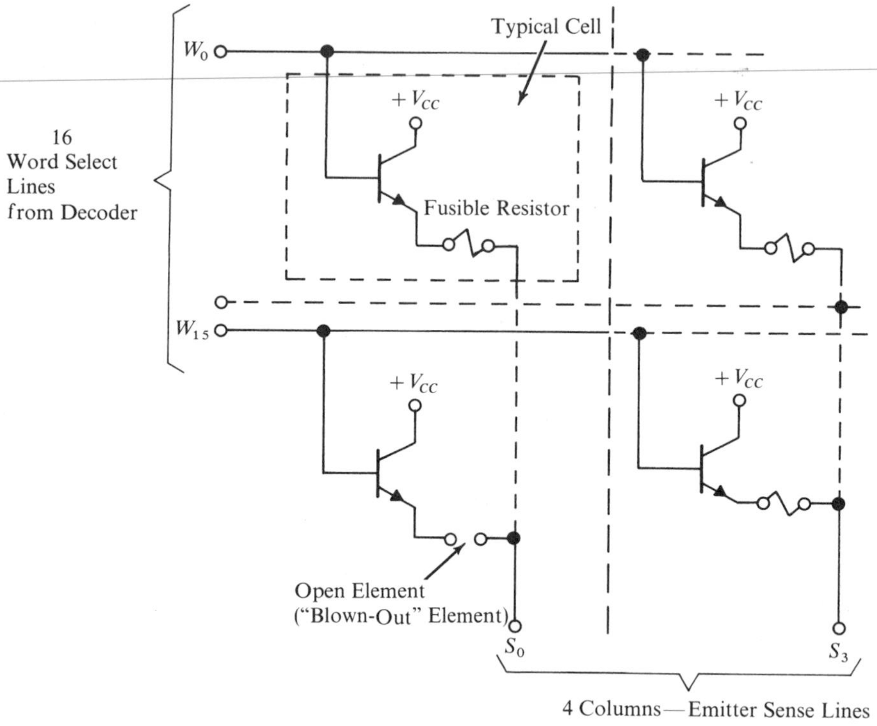

Fig. 22–15. *A 16 bit × 4 word ROM.*

If a fusible resistor is present, the sense line is at a "high." If the resistor was open circuited (blown out), the sense line is at a "low." We may then conclude that a cell with an emitter resistor stores a 0, and a cell with a blown resistor stores a 1. When the user plans to field program a PROM, all cells in the memory delivered to him are in the "low" state. In other words, each cell contains an emitter resistor. The user also receives a set of instructions on how to program the memory either cell by cell or word by word.

To access each cell individually, a decoder similar to the one used in Fig. 22–14 is required. A block diagram of the Signetics 82S26/82S29 256 × 4 bit PROM is shown in Fig. 22–16. The heart of this unit is four 32 × 8 storage arrays. The addressing is accomplished through the A terminals (A_0–A_7); the output is obtained from the B terminals (B_0–B_3).

To field program a particular cell in this memory, the word containing the cell is addressed through the appro-

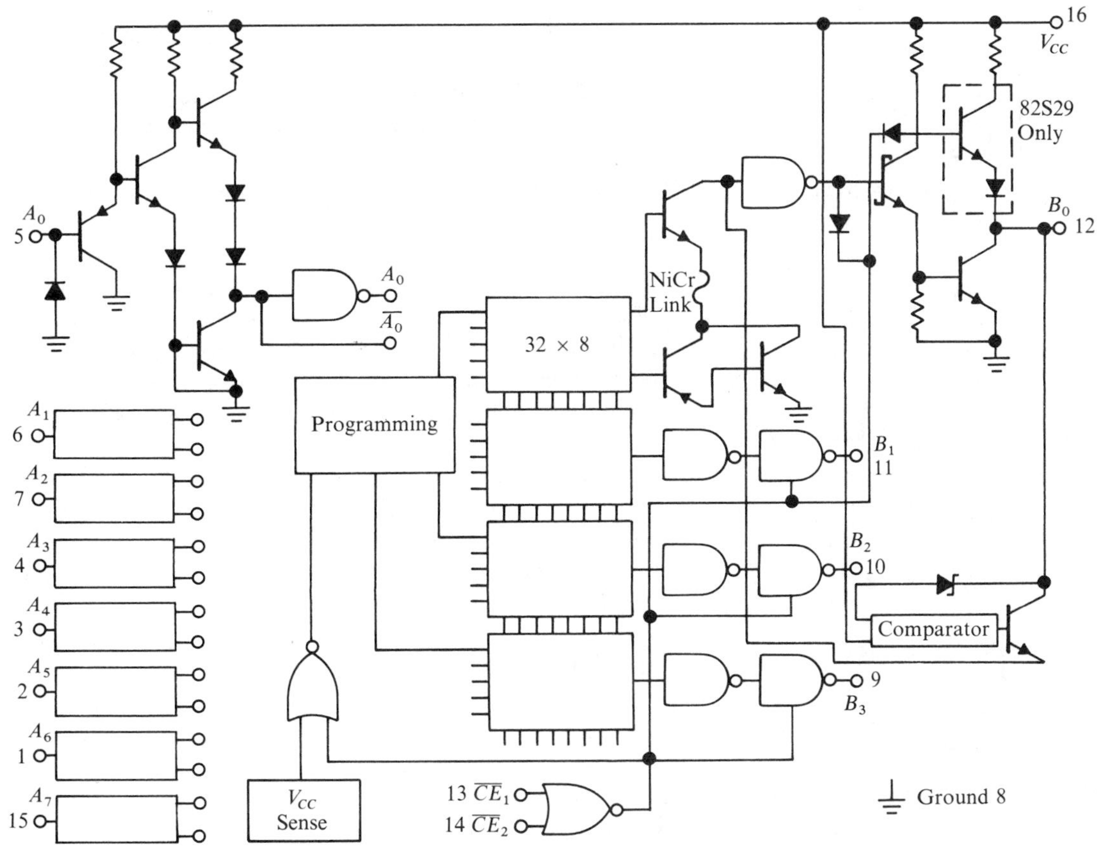

Fig. 22–16. *A 256 × 4 bipolar PROM. (Courtesy the Copyright Owner, Signetics Corp.)*

priate A terminal. A current of 85 mA is sent to one of the four outputs. Feeding a current through one of the outputs addresses a particular cell of the selected word.

To execute the programming of the cell, both *chip enable* terminals ($\overline{CE}_1$ and $\overline{CE}_2$) are reduced to 0 V. The fusible resistor is blown out, and the cell is now permanently stored with a 1. This procedure is repeated to store 1's in other cells of the memory. Cells that store a 0 are left untouched.

22.10 MOS Memories

The MOS device lends itself ideally to MSI and LSI fabrication, as was pointed out in Chapters 10 and 20. The ability to construct a MOS digital circuit without the use of resistors or capacitors provides very high packing density. Many different types of MOS memories, including the RAM and ROM, are commercially available. Generally speaking, PMOS, NMOS, and CMOS logics are used.

The MOS memory is also classified as a *static* or *dynamic* type memory. To understand the differences between the two, let us first compare a static and a dynamic INVERTER, shown in Fig. 22–17. In the static MOS INVERTER of Fig. 22–17A, transistor Q_1 is used as the load resistor. The

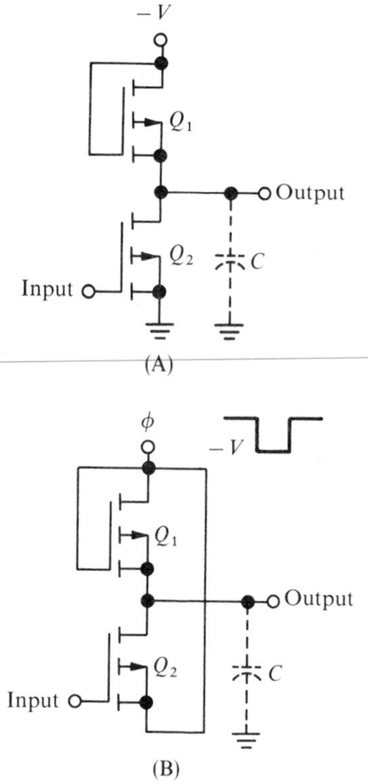

Fig. 22–17. *Basic MOS INVERTERs. (A) Static. (B) Dynamic.*

gate of Q_1 is connected to V_{DD}, which is negative because the devices shown are P-channel type. The resistance exhibited by Q_1 connected as a load resistor is many times greater than the internal resistance of switching transistor Q_2.

The realization of a proper resistance ratio between Q_1 and Q_2 necessitates the use of transistor geometries that do not utilize the IC chip area efficiently. To keep the power dissipation down, low current levels are desirable. This implies high circuit resistances. The load for the INVERTER is the input of a similar circuit. Such a load has a capacitive component (indicated by dashed lines in Fig. 22–17). A large time constant (RC) reduces the switching speed of the circuit.

Dynamic MOS circuits dissipate very low power and exhibit good switching characteristics. These properties result since the circuit is operated in a pulsed mode rather than continuously. The load that these circuits drive is also considered to be capacitive.

In Fig. 22–17B, pulses are applied to the *phase* (ϕ) terminal. When the ϕ input goes negative, load C is charged through Q_1 to a negative potential. When the negative pulse returns to zero, the charge stored in C remains unchanged because Q_1 does not conduct. Transistor Q_2 conducts when a 1 appears on the input. The capacitor discharges through Q_2, and the output is 0. If a 0 appears on the input, Q_2 is OFF, and the output is a 1. Because the MOSFETs in Fig. 22–17 are P-channel type, a 1 level corresponds to a negative potential.

The dynamic INVERTER consumes power only during the presence of the phase pulse. The devices occupy a minimum of space on a chip because there is no need for special geometry considerations. Comparing the dynamic to the static circuit, the dynamic INVERTER has a higher packing density, is faster, and less costly to manufacture. On the other hand, it requires a more complex drive signal.

Examples of storage cells employed in MOS memories are illustrated in Fig. 22–18. The static storage cell of Fig. 22–18A consists of six P-channel enhancement-type MOSFETs. Transistors Q_1 with Q_3 and Q_2 with Q_4 are INVERTERs (see Fig. 22–17). They are cross-coupled to form a bistable MV. Transistors Q_5 and Q_6 are used as *transmission gates.* A transmission gate is used for the selection of a particular memory cell in a word, and for reading out and writing in data of a cell. Reading and writing is accomplished through the data lines.

To read the content of a cell, the address select line is enabled. The side of the flip-flop that conducts deposits a 0 on the data line through the corresponding transmission gate (Q_5 or Q_6). Information is written in by impressing it

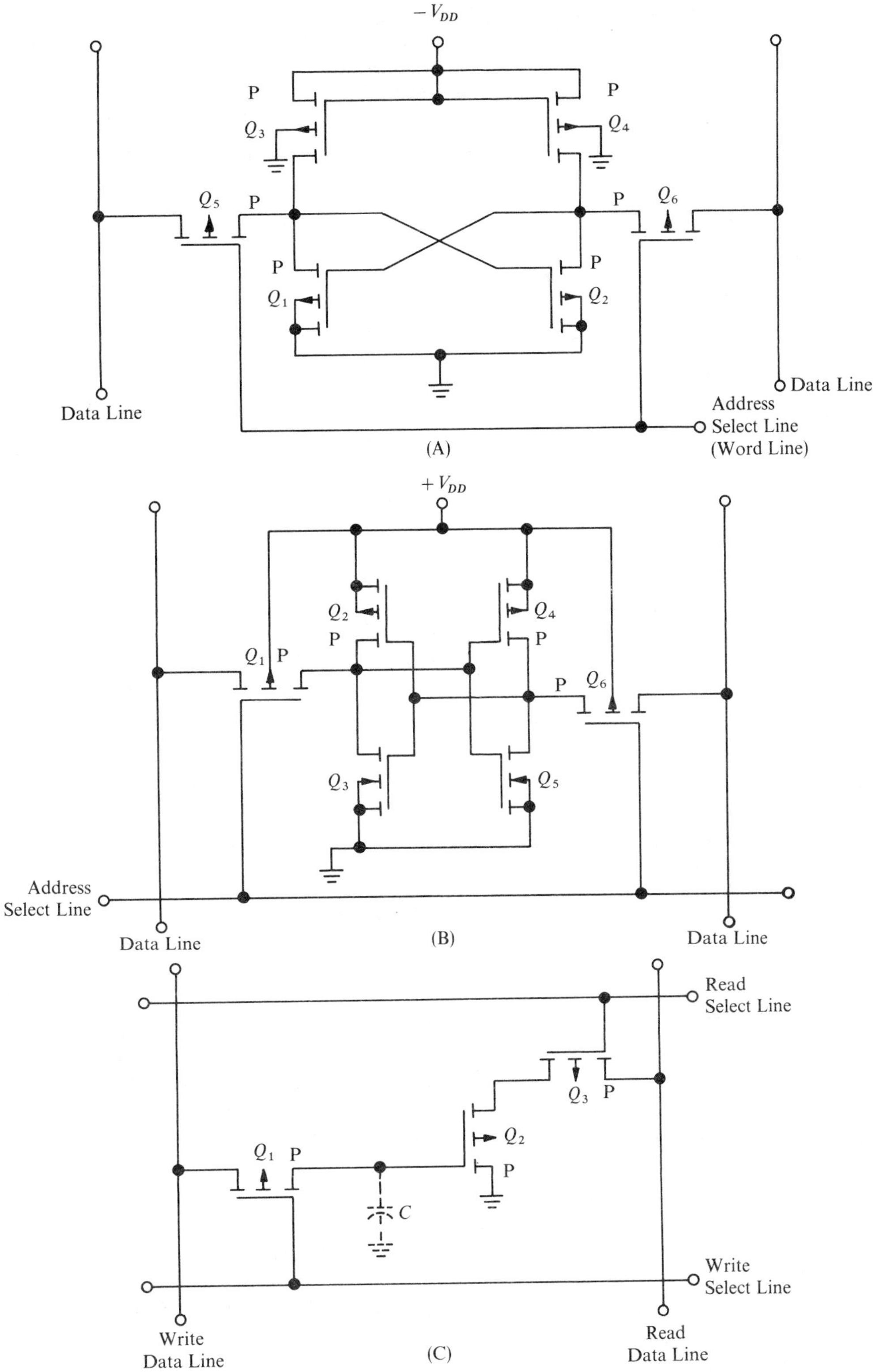

Fig. 22–18. *Types of MOS memory cells. (A) Static PMOS. (B) Static CMOS. (C) Dynamic PMOS.*

on the data lines. When the address select line is enabled, the flip-flop changes state in accordance with the information on the data lines.

An array of such static cells may be fabricated in a manner similar to bipolar memories. Using one address line, a single word is selected at a time.

The CMOS memory cell of Fig. 22–18B contains six transistors for word organized storage (an entire word is selected at a time). Transistors Q_2, Q_3, Q_4, and Q_5 constitute the flip-flop; Q_1 and Q_6 serve as transmission gates. A similar eight-transistor cell is used for X-Y addressing. For this type of addressing, the memory is said to be *bit organized*. It permits each cell to be addressed independently of the other cells in the array.

The CMOS cell in Fig. 22–18B operates in a manner similar to the static cell of Fig. 22–18A. Addressing is accomplished by activating the address select line. Data are read out or written in through the data lines. The CMOS memory is faster than conventional MOS memories and dissipates less power.

The PMOS dynamic storage cell of Fig. 22–18C is an example of a very popular cell design. It is popular because only three transistors are needed for a cell, resulting in an extremely high packing density. Capacitor C represents parasitic capacitance at the gate of Q_2. When C is sufficiently charged to make transistor Q_2 conduct (gate of Q_2 is negative), the cell stores a 1. When C is insufficiently charged for Q_2 to conduct, the cell is in the 0 state.

The content of a cell is read out by sensing the charge on capacitor C. This is done by applying a negative voltage to the read data line. A negative potential is also applied to the read select line to turn ON Q_3. If the content of a cell is a 1, transistor Q_2 is also ON. The voltage on the read data line drops to zero (ground level) as C discharges through Q_2 and Q_3. If the content of the cell is a 0, Q_2 is OFF, and no discharge path exists for the negative voltage on the read data line. In summary, the voltage on the read data line immediately after the application of a voltage on the read select line is the *complement* of the previous state of the cell.

Data are written into a cell by impressing a negative voltage (corresponding to a 1) or ground level (corresponding to a 0) on the write data line. The write select line is enabled by placing a negative potential on the line. This, in turn, activates Q_1, and capacitor C charges to the voltage on the write data line. After the write select line is returned to ground, C remains charged to preserve the content of the cell.

In practice, it is difficult to retain a charge across capacitor C. Because of leakage, the charge on C is gradually lost. It is therefore necessary that the charge on C be continuously *refreshed*.

The dynamic MOS memory array is arranged in matrix form (in rows and columns), similar to bipolar memories. Rows are connected to common select lines, and columns share the two data lines. In such an organization, an entire row in the array is addressed by activating the read select or write select line of a particular row. Enabling a particular read data or write data line in a given column permits the reading or writing of data in a particular cell. To read out or write in an entire row, all read data or all write data lines are activated simultaneously.

A *refresh amplifier* for such an array is placed in each column. During the refresh operation, all refresh amplifiers are activated to restore the cell content of one row at a time. The refresh cycle must be fast enough to allow the content of each cell to be restored between successive read and write operations. A refresh operation, required in a dynamic memory, is not necessary for a static memory.

Although the basic storage cells of Figs. 22–18A and B show P-channel devices, both P- and N-type MOS memories are manufactured. The NMOS-type memory operates at higher speeds, and dissipates less power, than the PMOS memory.

22.11 The MOS RAM

A block diagram of the Signetics 2602 RAM is shown in Fig. 22–19. It is a 1024-bit static memory using N-channel silicon gate devices. (Silicon gate MOSFETs are discussed in Chapter 19.) Because it is a static memory, no refresh

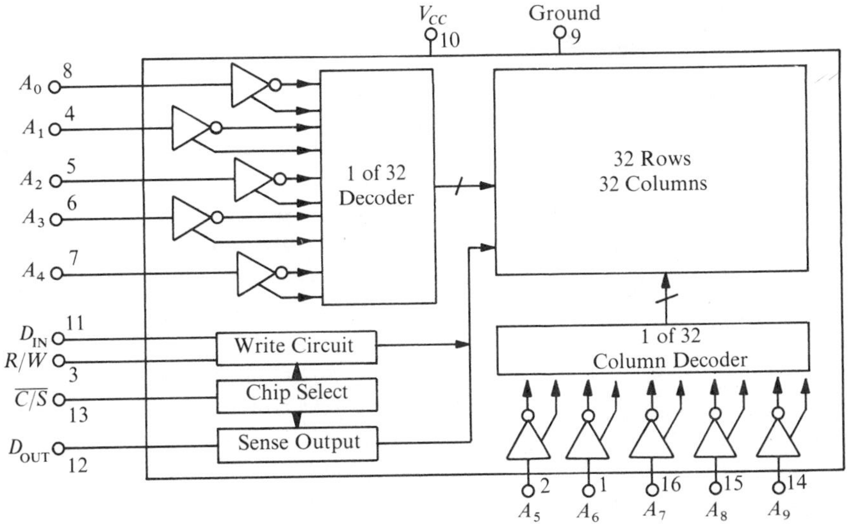

Fig. 22–19. *Block diagram of a 1024-bit static RAM. (Courtesy the Copyright Owner, Signetics Corp.)*

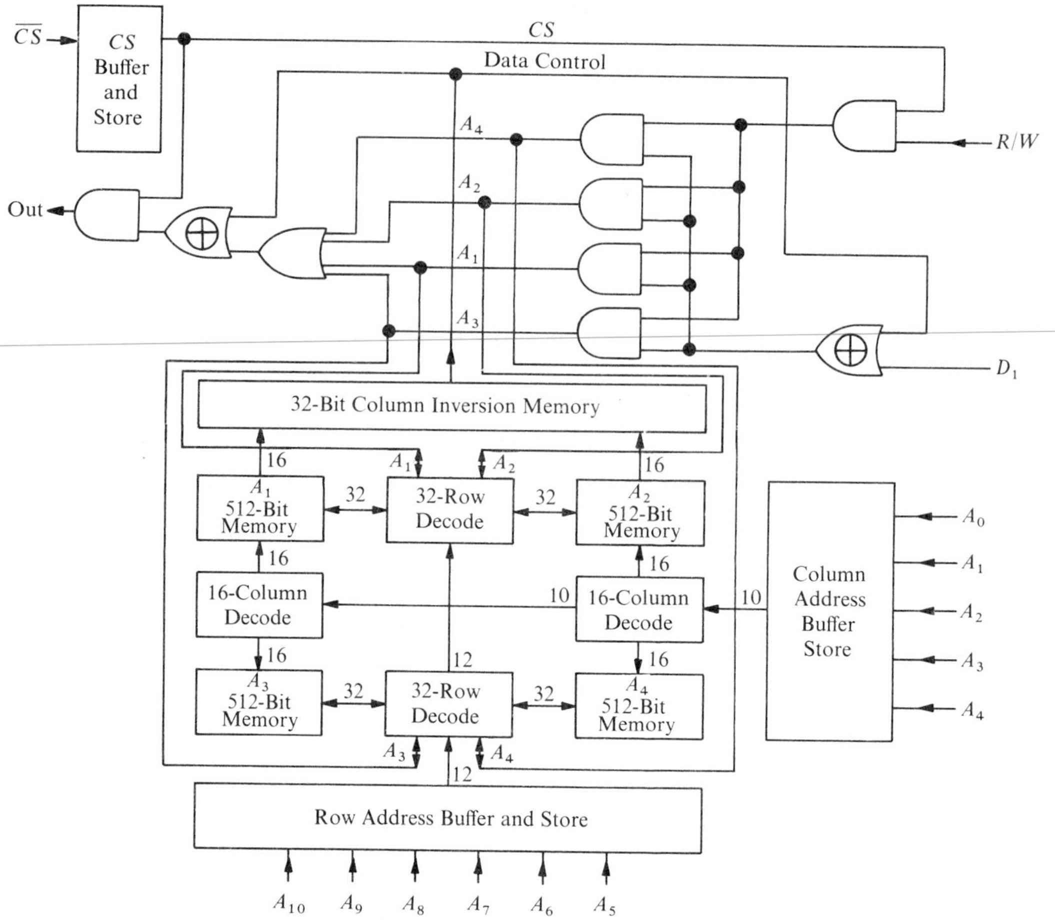

Fig. 22–20. *Block diagram of a 2048-bit dynamic RAM. (Courtesy the Copyright Owner, Signetics Corp.)*

operation is needed, nor is there a need for phase signals. Only one 5-V supply is required to operate the memory, making it compatible with T^2L.

The content of the memory is read by addressing a given cell through the A terminals. Two decoders are used to facilitate the selection of a cell with only ten (A_0–A_9) address inputs. The internal organization of the memory is 32 rows by 32 columns. To initiate the read cycle, the $R/\overline{W}$ ($\overline{\text{READ/WRITE}}$) line must be at a "high." The content of the addressed cell is read at the D_{OUT} (data-out) terminal.

To write, the proper cell is selected, and the $R/\overline{W}$ line is write-enabled. This allows data to be shifted in on the D_{IN} (data-in) line. In both the read and write operations, the $\overline{C/S}$ (chip-select) line must be enabled to operate the memory. The access time is 500 ns, making it a slower memory than the bipolar type. The 2602 is packaged in a 16-pin dual in-line package. By connecting a number of such chips, a larger bit-capacity memory may be realized.

The Signetics 2548 (Fig. 22–20) is an example of a dynamic RAM. Note the complexity of this unit compared with the static memory of Fig. 22–19. The 2548 is a 2048-bit memory that uses P-channel devices. It contains four 512-bit arrays with an elaborate address decoding system. In addition, there is input storage buffers and output gating circuitry.

Three separate power sources and three phase signals are needed to operate the memory. An automatic refresh operation is executed during each read cycle. The read/write cycle time for the memory is 560 ns.

22.12 The MOS ROM

The MOS ROM, like the bipolar ROM, is preprogrammed to store a given set of data. MOS technology lends itself to the fabrication of large ROM arrays, because of the small size of these devices. In addition to the permanent ROM, we can obtain a MOS ROM that can be electrically altered.

The basic storage cell of an MOS ROM contains only one transistor. Such cells, like bipolar ROM cells, are grouped in arrays. Decoding circuitry is included on the chip to keep the number of pins per package to a minimum. The memory is preprogrammed during manufacture either by including a transistor in the location where a 1 is to be stored or by eliminating the transistor for a 0. The elimination of a transistor is actually achieved by etching away the gate of the MOSFET.

Another programming technique is based on the use of two levels of thickness for the oxide layer between the gate and channel of the device. A thick oxide layer renders a MOSFET inactive; hence a 0 is stored. A thin oxide layer allows normal operation for storing a 1.

The Signetics 2530 (Fig. 22–21) is an example of a 4096-bit static ROM. It is organized as a 512 × 8 memory and

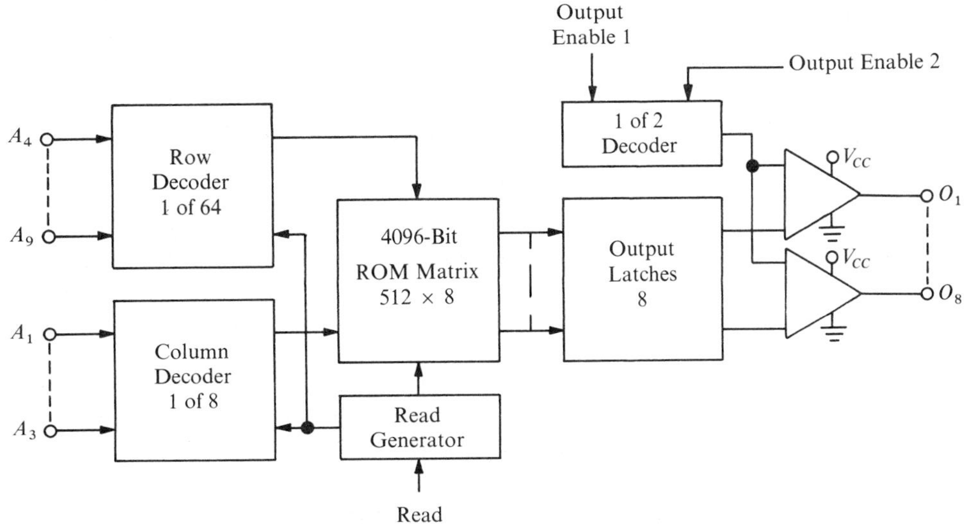

Fig. 22–21. *Block diagram of a 4096-bit static ROM. (Courtesy the Copyright Owner, Signetics Corp.)*

employs silicon gate PMOS devices with on-chip decoding. The memory cells are addressed through the A terminals. Data are transferred to the output latches when the READ line is enabled.* For a particular word to be read at the output terminals, O_1–O_8, it is necessary to activate the two OUTPUT ENABLE lines. This memory is programmed for the user by the manufacturer.

A MOS PROM which can be electrically reprogrammed employs devices with a unique structure. It is called the *f*loating *a*valanche-injection MOS (FAMOS). It is basically a charge storage device in which a charge is stored in the gate region, and retained for a very long time.

To reprogram this type of memory, the data must be erased before new data can be written in. The old data are erased by a nonelectrical method. The memory is exposed to ultraviolet (UV) light. A discharge path between the gate and channel is thereby produced, and the stored charge is lost. New data are written in by applying a suitable charging potential to the gate.

22.13 Applications of ROMs

Because of its versatility, the ROM is used in many applications. A very common application is the mathematical *lookup table.* For example, a multiplication table or a table of sine function values can be stored in a ROM. Such lookup tables save enormous amounts of computing time. The alternatives are the recalculation of each single value or the storing of such tables in the main memory of the computer.

A block diagram of a bipolar ROM multiplication table is illustrated in Fig. 22–22. The circuit employs two 256×4 bipolar ROMs and is capable of storing the entire multiplication table for products up to 15×15. Four-bit binary numbers are fed to the ROM through the A terminals. The product is read, as a binary number, across the eight output terminals, B_1–B_8.

A sine lookup table which provides the value y of the sine function whose argument is x ($y = \sin x$) can also be designed using a ROM. Such a table requires a large storage-capacity ROM to provide accurate values of the sine function.

The ROM also is used in *microprogramming.* Microprogramming is a technique used for controlling various types of digital functions by means of data stored in a memory. The lookup tables are, in a sense, examples of microprogramming applications.

* An S-R flip-flop also is called a latch.

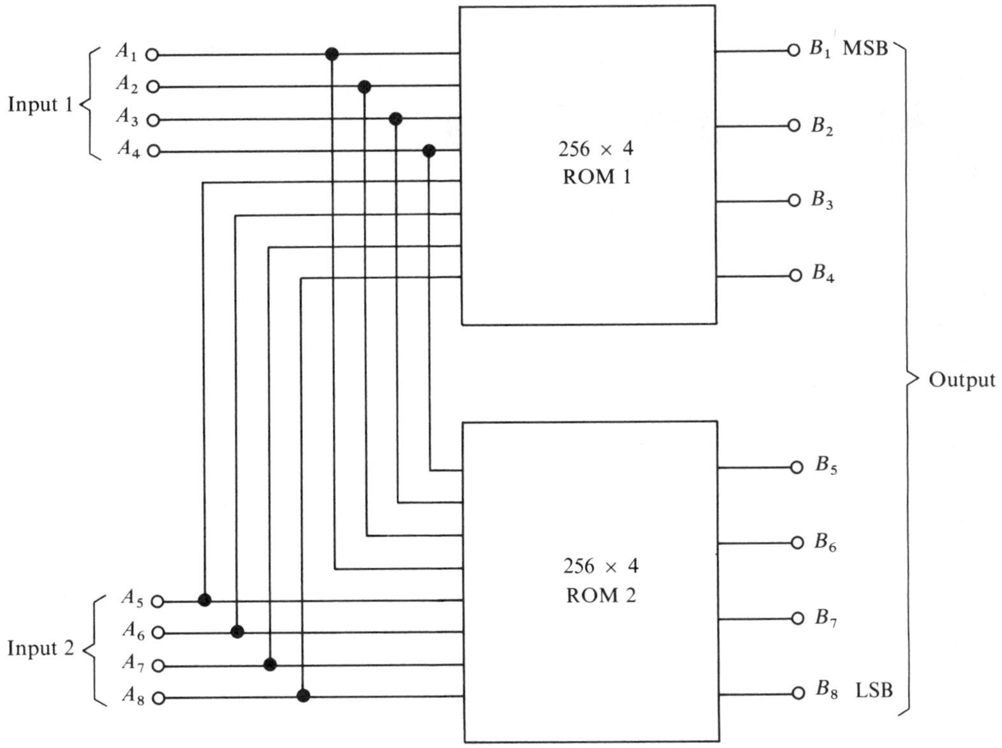

Fig. 22–22. *ROM multiplication table that yields products of 0 × 0 to 15 × 15.*

Generally speaking, routine tasks in a computer can be accomplished with the aid of a ROM. It is possible to perform repeated operations by wiring many logic circuits. A more efficient method is to program a ROM to store all the instructions for the sequence of operations to be executed.

The ROM also is used in the generation of characters for CRT displays, light-emitting diode matrices, and printers. In each of these examples, the ROM converts electronic codes into display information.

22.14 Charge-Coupled Device (CCD)

The charge-coupled device (CCD) is a MOS-type capacitor that stores and transfers electric charge. This device is only possible in IC form; it cannot be made from discrete components. The IC geometry for the CCD consists of an array of closely spaced metal electrodes deposited on an insulating layer of silicon dioxide. A cross-section of a CCD is shown in Fig. 22–23.

The CCD's principle of operation is the storage of minority carriers in the depletion region, or *potential well*, near the surface of the semiconductor below the insulating layer. The charge in a well can be transferred to the next well by the application of a higher potential to its electrode. In

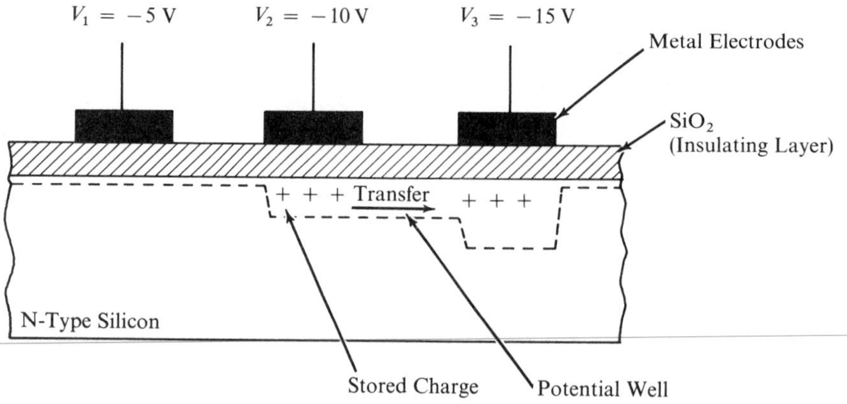

Fig. 22–23. *Cross-section of a charge-coupled device (CCD).*

Fig. 22–23, the semiconductor material is N-type silicon. Negative voltages applied to the electrodes create minority carriers (holes, indicated by the + signs) below the metal electrode, in the potential well. A greater negative voltage on the third electrode causes the charge to transfer from the second to the third potential well. The potential on the first electrode is at the normal biasing level of -5 V. The voltage on the second electrode is at the store level of -10 V, and the voltage on the third electrode is at the transfer level of -15 V. The three voltages may be derived from a three-phase voltage supply.

A CCD is used as a memory in which each well represents a storage cell. Because no transistors are needed, the fabrication is relatively simple and inexpensive. The bit capacity of such a memory is extremely high.

Data are written into the memory by applying a pulse to a given cell, creating a potential well which contains holes. A store level of -10 V at the electrode of the selected cell ensures that the charge remains in the cell until it is transferred to the adjacent cell.

Data are read out of the memory by sensing the charge transferred to the third cell (electrode at -15 V). This operation indicates that the CCD is inherently a serial device having a relatively slow access time. Manufacturers are developing fast CCDs for use as memories. A current example of such a memory is Fairchild's *l*ine *a*ddressable RAM (LARAM), which has an access time as low as 25 ns.

22.15 Volatility

Volatility refers to the ability of a memory to retain data after power to it is disconnected. The RAM is an example of a volatile memory in which the stored information is destroyed when its power is removed. To circumvent this, a standby battery system may be incorporated to provide power to the RAM when the main power is turned off. The

ROM, on the other hand, is nonvolatile because it is preprogrammed in the manner discussed earlier in this chapter.

22.16 Comparison of Semiconductor Memories

The performance characteristics of the different bipolar and MOS-type memories discussed in this chapter are compared in Table 22–1. Bipolar memories are the fastest, overall; however, they do not exhibit the high packing density of the MOS memory. The power dissipation per bit of the bipolar memory, with the exception of I^2L, is several times greater than that of MOS devices. The CCD-type memory exhibits the highest packing density and lowest power dissipation of all memories listed in the table.

TABLE 22–1. Comparison of semiconductor memories.

	Type	Access Time (ns)	Cycle Time* (ns)	Power Diss. per Bit (μW)	Packing Density (Bits/Chip)
Bipolar	TTL	35–60	80–100	500	1,024
	I^2L	50	100	100	4,096
MOS	PMOS	300–400	500–600	100	4,096
	NMOS	150–250	350–450	100	4,096
	CMOS	50–60	500–600	20	1,024
	CCD	80–250	120–500	10	16,384

* Cycle time is 1 divided by the rate at which a word is selected for writing or reading.

22.17 Nonsemiconductor-Type Memories

Magnetic-core memories have occupied a prominent place among computer memories since the development of the modern computer. Before the advent of the semiconductor memory, core memories were found in virtually all large-scale computers. The basic element in this memory is a tiny ferrite ring, shown in Fig. 22–24. A current is passed in a wire strung through the hollow center of the ring. It magnetizes the core in either a clockwise or counterclockwise direction, depending on the direction of current in the wire. If the core is magnetized in the clockwise direction, we assume that the 1 state is induced. Magnetization of the core in the counterclockwise direction means that a 0 is stored in the core. A core storing a 1 and a 0 is shown in Figs. 22–24A and B, respectively.

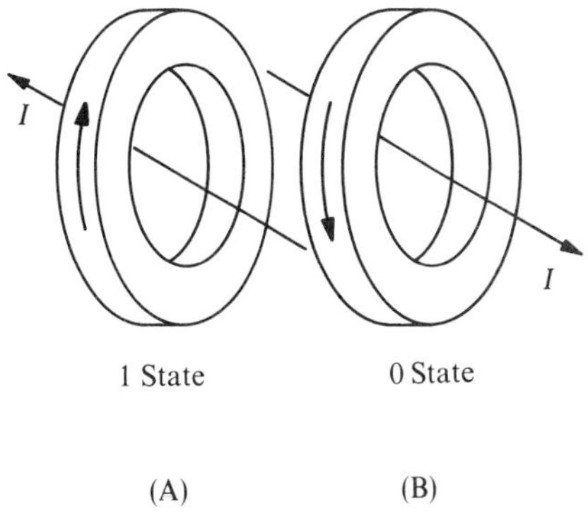

Fig. 22–24. Basic ferrite core. Current flows in a direction to induce (A) a 1 state and (B) a 0 state.

Small ferrite cores, each representing a memory cell, are arranged in planes. These planes, in turn, are arranged in stacks to comprise a complete memory. A plane containing

16 magnetic cores is shown in Fig. 22–25. A popular organization of a core memory is one in which each plane contains one bit of a word. The number of bits per word corresponds to the number of planes. The plane of Fig. 22–25 is part of a memory which has a total of 16 words. Connecting N such planes together yields an N bit × 16 word memory.

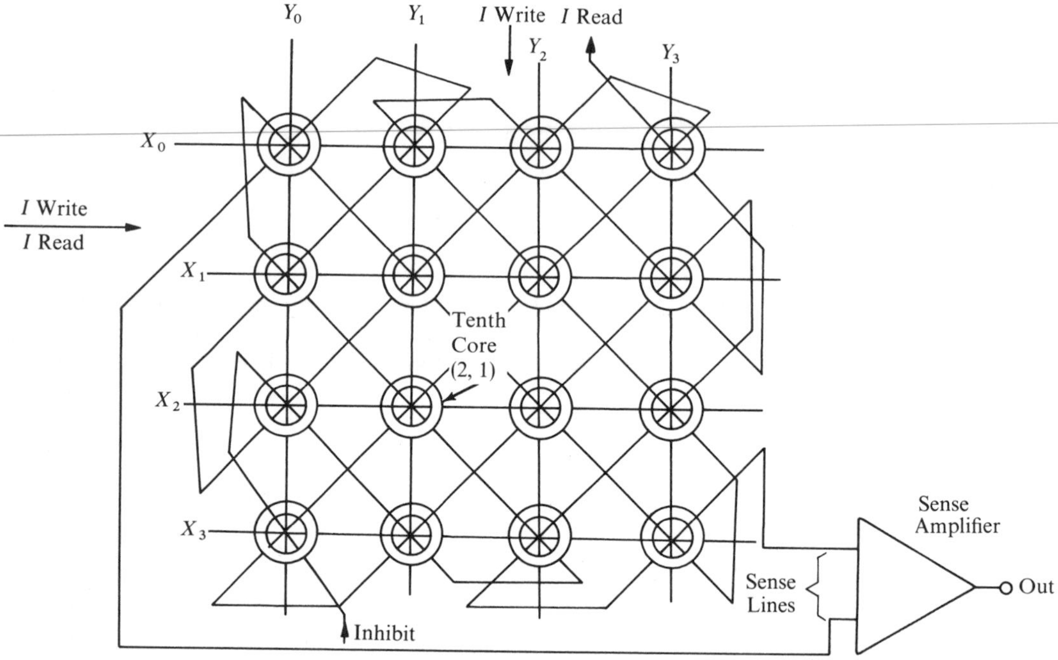

Fig. 22–25. *Core memory plane organized in a 16 word × 1 bit array.*

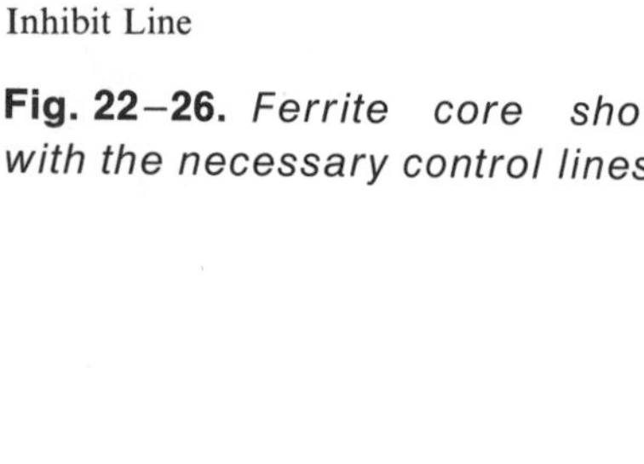

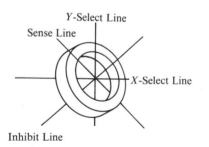

Fig. 22–26. *Ferrite core shown with the necessary control lines.*

An individual ferrite core (Fig. 22–26) contains four control lines. The X-select and Y-select lines are used to address a particular core in the plane. The sense line *senses*, or *reads out*, the content of a core. Finally, the inhibit line prevents a 1 from being induced in a core when its content is to remain at zero.

To select a particular word in the memory, the cores corresponding to that word must be enabled. (One cell of each plane corresponding to the word is selected.) The selection of a core is accomplished by passing a current through the corresponding X and Y lines.

For example, to select the tenth core in the plane of Fig. 22–25, a current of magnitude I is made to flow through lines X_2 and Y_1. The core selected therefore "sees" a magnetization current of $2I$. Other cores that are not addressed "see" only a current of I. The cores are so designed that a magnitude of $2I$ is needed to magnetize the core. Current I alone is insufficient to change the state of a core.

We now consider how data are written into a core memory. Assume that all cores are in the 0 state initially. The word is selected by passing a current through the appropriate X and Y lines. One core in each plane is now selected. Each selected core stores a 1. To prevent the cores that must remain at 0 from being set to a 1, a current of $-I$ is sent to the inhibit line. A core that is to remain at 0 now "sees" a current of $2I$ from the X and Y lines, and $-I$ from the inhibit line. The net current is I, which is insufficient to change the state of a core from a 0 to a 1.

To read a particular core, each select line (X and Y) conducts a current of $-I$. All cores in the 0 state are not affected; those in the 1 state, however, switch. A change in state from a 0 to a 1 induces a current in the sense line. The change on the sense line is fed to a sense amplifier.

An output from the sense amplifier implies that the core was in the 1 state. This type of readout is *destructive* because the core is in the 0 state following the READ operation. To avoid this, the output of the sense line is redeposited to the core which was read. Magnetic-core memories have good speed (access time of about 1 μs), are relatively inexpensive, and occupy a reasonable volume even at a megabit capacity.

The *magnetic-drum* memory is another example of a magnetic memory. It is made of a cylinder having a large magnetic storage surface. Drum memories have many drawbacks. For one, they are slow. To access a cell in a drum memory, the drum is rotated until the cell lines up with the READ or WRITE head. Hence, access time is a function of speed of rotation of the drum. An advantage of the drum memory that must not be overlooked is its relatively low cost.

The *plated-wire* memory is also a magnetic-type memory which is faster than a core memory and has a large storage capacity. In this memory, a magnetic, conductive wire is plated with a coating of a nickel-iron alloy to create a magnetic film. The coating of the film is applied so as to allow for an "easy" magnetization in one direction, and a "difficult" magnetization in the other direction. In Fig. 22–27, the conductive portion of the wire acts as the bit line.

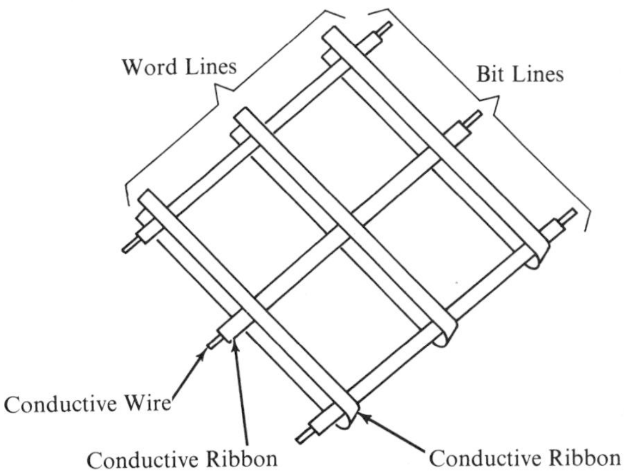

Fig. 22–27. *Section of a plated-wire memory.*

Conductive ribbons wrapped around the bit lines serve as word lines. In addition to its high speed and large capacity, the plated-wire memory is also nondestructive.

22.18 Magnetic-Bubble Memory

The magnetic-bubble memory has a theoretical capacity of millions of bits per square inch. Owing to limitations in its manufacture, however, such high densities have not yet been achieved. The magnetic-bubble memory is nondestructive, much slower than most other types of memories, and the cost per bit is extremely low.

In this memory, a bit of data is represented by a *magnetic domain* called a *bubble*. The medium in which the magnetic bubble exists is a single-crystal magnetic oxide called an *orthoferrite*. Orthoferrites are man-made and can be magnetized easily by the application of a magnetic field. Magnetic domains, when properly formed, have well-defined dimensions and remain stable in a cylindrical shape. The presence or absence of a bubble in a particular location determines if a 1 or a 0 is stored.

Domain diameters can be as small as 0.04 mil (0.00004 in.). A separation distance, however, of at least three domain diameters is maintained to avoid ambiguities. Such a distance is necessary because the bubble has a tendency to spread when the field is reduced. A magnetic bubble can be moved to an adjacent location by the application of a field to the adjacent area. This property lends itself to the fabrication of shift registers and counters employing magnetic bubbles.

SUMMARY

Counters are used to count incoming pulses, and as frequency divider circuits. A modulus counter contains a number of flip-flops and a feedback circuit. A single output pulse exists for a given number of input pulses. The modulus number of a counter is the number of input pulses for which one output pulse is generated.

Because of its frequency division capabilities, counters are utilized in such applications as electronic clocks and watches. In an electronic clock, a basic clock pulse signal is generated which is subsequently divided by a number of counters to yield seconds, minutes, and hours.

Registers are temporary storage elements which employ flip-flops for storage. Each flip-flop stores one bit of data. Data are entered into the register in parallel or serial manner. Parallel entry means that all data are shifted into the register simultaneously. In serial entry, data enter one bit at a time during each clock pulse. Serial entry is slower than parallel entry but requires less gating circuitry.

The output of a register can be read out serially or in parallel. MSI registers are manufactured to operate in all modes, that is, parallel in-parallel out, serial in-parallel out, etc. Practical shift registers transfer information to the right or to the left. Both T^2L- and MOS-type shift registers are available.

Computer memories can be grouped into semiconductor and nonsemiconductor categories. Semiconductor memories are either of the random access (RAM) or read only (ROM) type. Data are written in and read out repeatedly with a RAM. The ROM is permanently programmed, and data can only be read out.

Both bipolar- and MOS-type memories are available. Bipolar memories are faster, but consume more power, and cannot be packed as densely as MOS devices. The MOS-type memory is either static or dynamic. Static memories are simpler to operate because no elaborate clocking and refreshing are needed as with the MOS memory. On the other hand, static memories consume more power and cannot be packed as densely.

Because of its structure, the CCD memory is relatively simple to manufacture. Its main features are extremely high packing density and very low power consumption.

Nonsemiconductor memories discussed in this chapter are basically magnetic-type devices. Magnetic-core memories have been the most popular type of memory for many years. They are, however, being replaced by semiconductor memories. The magnetic-bubble memory shows great promise for the future.

Further Reading

Allan, R. "Semiconductor Memories." *IEEE Spectrum*, Aug. 1975, pp. 40–45.

Eimbinder, J., ed. *Semiconductor Memories*. New York: John Wiley and Sons, 1971.

Hodges, D. A., ed. *Semiconductor Memories*. New York: IEEE Press, 1971.

Lenk, J. D. *Handbook of Logic Circuits*. Reston, Va.: Reston Publishing Company, Inc., 1972, Chapters 3, 4, and 5.

Weber, S., ed. *Large Scale and Medium Scale Integration*. New York: McGraw-Hill Book Company, 1972.

REVIEW QUESTIONS

22.1 Define
(a) Storage capacity.
(b) Access time.
(c) Mode of access.

22.2 Describe the differences between a RAM and a ROM.

22.3 What is the advantage of a synchronous over a ripple counter?

22.4 How does a battery-operated clock derive its basic timing pulses?

22.5 What is the function of a shift register?

22.6 Describe the sequence of operations in a shift-left register.

22.7 Discuss the differences between a ROM and a PROM.

22.8 What is a typical access time of bipolar memories?

22.9 Compare the structures of bipolar RAM and ROM cells.

22.10 Discuss the advantages and disadvantages of a dynamic MOS memory cell over a static MOS memory cell.

22.11 Why is it necessary to *refresh* the contents of a dynamic MOS cell?

22.12 Describe a method for reprogramming a MOS PROM.

22.13 Provide examples of mathematical lookup tables that can be implemented with a ROM.

22.14 Define microprogramming.

22.15 Describe how a charge-coupled device can be used for a memory element.

22.16 Define volatile memory.

22.17 Compare the bipolar and MOS memories.

22.18 Identify four different types of magnetic memories.

22.19 Describe the function of the four control lines in Fig. 22–26.

22.20 What is the major drawback of a magnetic-drum memory?

22.21 Describe the principle of operation of the magnetic-bubble memory.

PROBLEMS

P22–1 Design a modulus-6 counter using *J-K* flip-flops.

P22–2 Repeat prob. P22–1 for a modulus-60 counter.

P22–3 Designate the input and output terminals and internal connections of the SN5493 counter of Fig. 22–3 for a
(a) Four-bit counter.
(b) Three-bit counter.

P22–4 Show how two SN5493 chips can be used to form a modulus-128 counter.

P22–5 Design a synchronous three-bit counter. Provide a truth table for the circuit.

P22–6 Design a synchronous modulus-12 counter.

P22–7 Show how two chips of the type illustrated in Fig. 22–6 can be connected to form a divide-by-50 counter.

P22–8 Using the modulus-60 counter of Example 22–3, design a digital clock to operate from a 60-Hz square wave. The clock must deliver seconds, minutes, and hours pulses.

P22–9 Repeat prob. P22–8 for a square-wave source of 43,200 Hz.

P22–10 Show how the quantity 1101 is shifted into a register with a single pulse on the transfer line.

P22–11 Show the states of all input terminals for shifting serially the number 1100 into a register.

P22–12 Referring to Fig. 22–13A, show the steps involved for
(a) Reading the content of cell number 15.
(b) Writing into cell number 11.

P22–13 Provide a block diagram of a 7 × 7 ROM multiplication table. Use the block diagram of Fig. 22–22 for a guide.

P22–14 Describe the steps for writing in, and reading out, data of the second core on the top horizontal line of the memory plane in Fig. 22–25.

23

Displays, Converters, and the Microprocessor

This chapter is devoted to a number of topics. First, *alphanumeric* displays are considered. A large variety of display devices are available, with the LED (*l*ight-*e*mitting *d*iode) and the LCD (*l*iquid *c*rystal *d*isplay) being the most widely used. These devices are inexpensive, low-voltage, general-purpose indicators. Incandescent tube displays, although much slower and consuming more power than the LED or LCD, are still employed. Gas discharge and cathode ray tubes are used for displaying a large number of characters.

Analog-to-digital (A/D) and *digital-to-analog* (D/A) *converters* play an important role in systems containing both analog and digital signals. In such systems, for example, input data may be analog signals, but their processing is accomplished digitally. An A/D converter is therefore required to change the data from an analog to a digital form. The opposite need, in which a digital signal is converted to an analog signal by a D/A converter, also arises.

The *microprocessor*, in one or more LSI chips, contains thousands of transistors for performing arithmetic and control operations. It functions as a central processor unit (CPU) of a computer. Digital systems which have a computerlike organization can be replaced by the microprocessor. A wired logic system is drastically simplified when substituted with a microprocessor based system. A continuously growing area of applications, from calculators through automotive to communications, use microprocessors. The microprocessor has revolutionized the field of digital controls.

An example of a practical electronic system concludes the chapter. The system considered is a digital multimeter (DMM). It contains analog circuits, an A/D converter, circuitry for processing digital data, and a display. An examination of the DMM should enable the reader to see how a number of basic elements considered in this chapter are brought together to form an electronic system.

23.1 Alphanumeric Displays

In digital systems, the display of data is accomplished either by direct-illumination devices or by the printing of characters on various media, generally paper. Printers produce a permanent display, called *hard copy*. Illumination devices provide only a temporary display.

A direct display is used in numerous applications such as calculators, clocks, and instrumentation. The printer-type display is generally employed where a permanent record of data is necessary. This section of the text is devoted to different types of direct-illumination displays. These include the LED, LCD, CRT, and gas-filled tubes.

The operation of the LED is based on the principle that when a current flows in a PN junction, light is emitted from its surface. This phenomenon is known as *electroluminescence.* For the emission of visible light, materials such as GaAsP (gallium arsenide phosphide) and GaP (gallium phosphide) are used. Depending on the material and doping levels used, display colors such as red, amber, yellow, green, and blue are available. The red LED is most efficient, where efficiency is rated in lumens/watt. (The *lumen* is the unit for the time rate of flow of light.) The human eye is most sensitive to green light.

Generally speaking, the LED is a low-efficiency device. The percentage efficiency of converting electrical energy to light is less than 10 percent. The average red LED emits light with a voltage drop of 1.2 V across it, and a current of 10 mA or higher. Special optical lenses may be used to enhance its efficiency.

Alphanumeric LEDs have *segmented* characters. In order to display all the numerals and some of the letters in the alphabet, a minimum of seven segments is used. This requires up to seven PN junction diodes to display a character.

A seven-segment display is shown in Fig. 23–1A. The generation of different characters requires the activation of various diodes. Not all segments need be displayed. For example, a 3 is lit up when segments A, B, C, D, and G are energized. An 8, however, requires the energization of all seven segments. The possible characters that can be generated with a seven-segment display are provided in Fig. 23–1B. To display all alphanumeric characters, it is necessary to use a diode matrix array or a highly segmented display, such as a 16-segment device. The diode matrix display is generally a 5×7 matrix which contains 35 LEDs.

In addressing the various diodes to display a character of a seven-segment unit, a *decoder* and *driver* are required. The decoder accepts binary data in a coded form and converts it to a signal on one of seven output lines. Each line activates one segment of the display. A driver is inserted between the decoder output line and segment to provide sufficient drive current for the display.

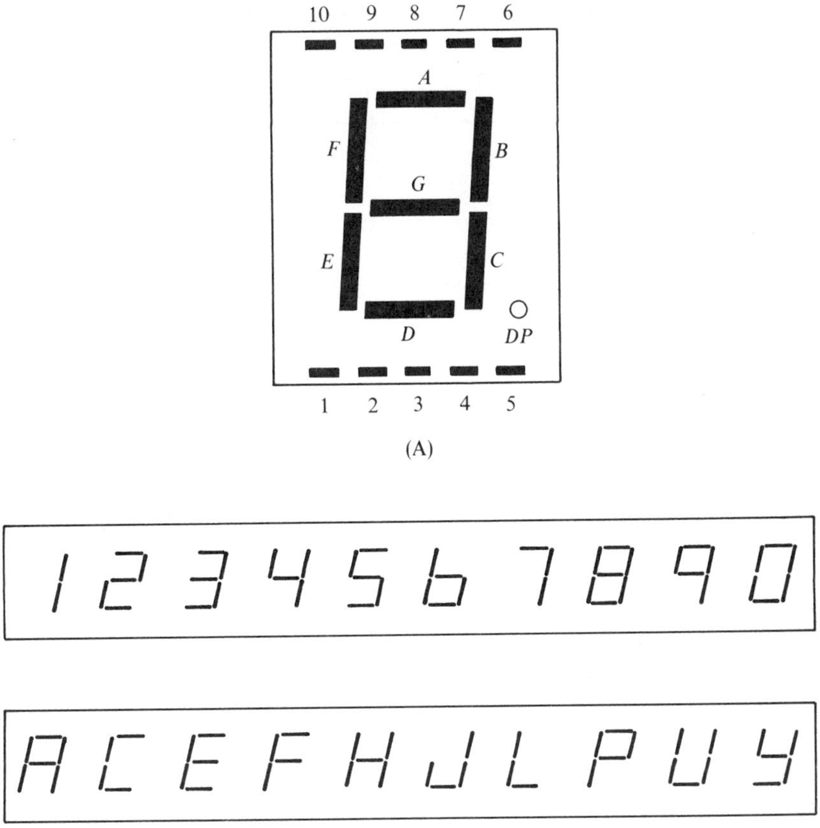

(B)

Fig. 23–1. *Alphanumeric LED. (A) Seven-segment display. (B) Possible characters generated by a seven-segment display.*

The binary data are applied to the decoder in BCD (*b*inary *c*oded *d*ecimal) form. In BCD, a decimal number is represented by a four-bit binary number. For example, binary number 1001 represents decimal 9. In this code, binary numbers from 1010 (decimal 10) through 1111 (decimal 15) are not used because only decimals 0 through 9 are necessary. BCD-to-seven-segment decoder/driver circuits are commercially available on a single chip.

An example of such a circuit is the Signetics 7447 unit. Employing T^2L, the device is capable of driving LED-, incandescent-, and flourescent-type displays. The pin configuration, logic diagram, and display characters are illustrated in Figs. 23–2A, B, and C, respectively.

The unit is designed to activate a segment as its output goes "low." It is used with displays which have the positive supply lead (up to 15 V) returned to one side of a display segment. When the output of the 7447 goes "low," the segment lights up. The driver is capable of delivering up to 20 mA per segment.

The truth table (Table 23–1) lists the input and output relationships for the device. The input labeled *LT* (lamp test) is normally kept at a "high." A "low" at LT causes all segments to light up. Ripple blanking input (RBI) and ripple

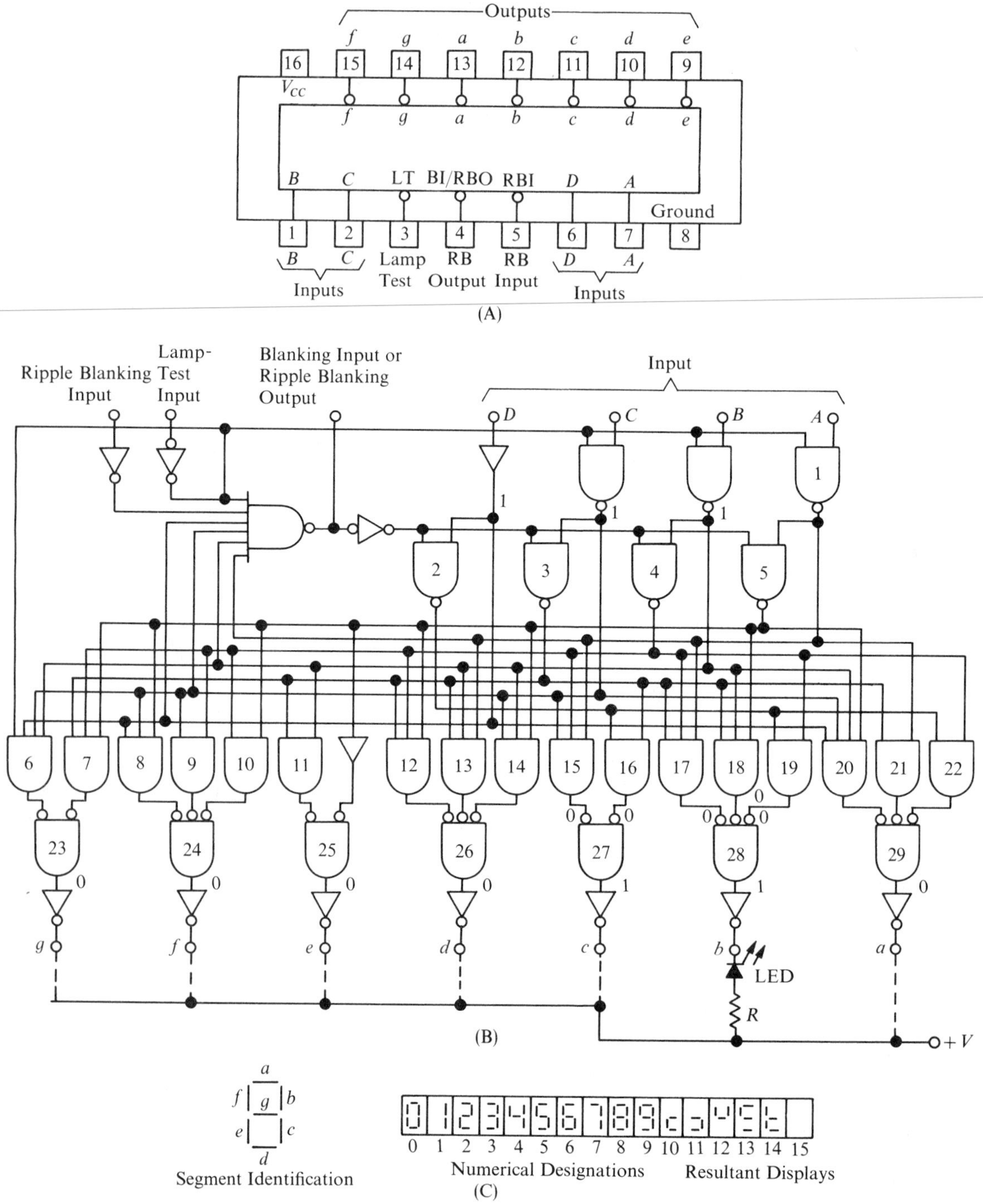

Fig. 23–2. *A 7447 BCD-to-seven-segment decoder/driver. (A) Pin configuration. (B) Logic diagram. (C) Displayed characters. (Courtesy the Copyright Owner, Signetics Corp.)*

blanking output (BI/RBO) are returned to a "high" or simply left open.

A "low" on RBI prevents the character 0 from lighting up. Character 0 is also prevented from lighting up in a multidigit display if BI/RBO is at a "low." This blanking capability permits a more direct display of numbers. For example, with blanking, the four-digit number 0341 can be displayed as 341, and .4000 as .4.

TABLE 23–1. Truth table for the 7447 decoder/driver. (Courtesy the Copyright Owner, Signetics Corp.)

	Inputs							Outputs						
Decimal or Function	LT	RBI	*D*	*C*	*B*	*A*	BI/RBO	*a*	*b*	*c*	*d*	*e*	*f*	*g*
0	1	1	0	0	0	0	1	0	0	0	0	0	0	1
1	1		0	0	0	1	1	1	0	0	1	1	1	1
2	1		0	0	1	0	1	0	0	1	0	0	1	0
3	1		0	0	1	1	1	0	0	0	0	1	1	0
4	1		0	1	0	0	1	1	0	0	1	1	0	0
5	1		0	1	0	1	1	0	1	0	0	1	0	0
6	1		0	1	1	0	1	1	1	0	0	0	0	0
7	1		0	1	1	1	1	0	0	0	1	1	1	1
8	1		1	0	0	0	1	0	0	0	0	0	0	0
9	1		1	0	0	1	1	0	0	0	1	1	0	0
10	1		1	0	1	0	1	1	1	1	0	0	1	0
11	1		1	0	1	1	1	1	1	0	0	1	1	0
12	1		1	1	0	0	1	1	0	1	1	1	0	0
13	1		1	1	0	1	1	0	1	1	0	1	0	0
14	1		1	1	1	0	1	1	1	1	0	0	0	0
15	1		1	1	1	1	1	1	1	1	1	1	1	1

EXAMPLE 23–1.

Referring to the logic diagram of Fig. 23–2B, show how number 1 is displayed.

Solution:

From Table 23–1, the corresponding BCD input is 0001. Thus, input *A* is "high," and inputs *B*, *C*, and *D* are "low." Terminals LT and RBI are at a "high." The inputs to NAND gate 1 are both "high," resulting in a "low" output. Both inputs to gate 2 are "high," and, therefore, its output is "low." The same is true for gates 3 and 4. The output of gate 5 is "high" because one of its inputs is "low."

AND gate 15 receives two "low" signals from gates 1 and 4, resulting in a "low" output. Gate 16 receives "lows" from gates 2 and 3, thereby also yielding a "low" output. When these "low" signals are applied to gate 27, the result is a "high" which is inverted. The final "low" on terminal *C* activates segment *c* in the display.

AND gates 17, 18, and 19 all receive at least one "low" input, resulting in a "high" at the output of gate 28. This output is inverted to activate segment *b*. According to Table 23–1, only segments *b* and *c* are activated to display numeral 1.

It is left as an exercise for the reader to show that all other segments are OFF when BCD 0001 is applied to the decoder.

The addressing of a diode matrix display is accomplished through a *scanning* technique. This method is similar to the addressing of a memory. Each diode is energized by selecting a given row and column.

The LCD is a widely used alphanumeric display. Because it is an electric field-operated device, it consumes extremely low power. The LCD requires a suitable potential for establishing an electric field but virtually no current to operate. A liquid crystal material is contained between two sheets of glass. The front glass is made totally conductive; the conduction surface on the back glass, however, is shaped to resemble the character to be displayed.

When a potential is applied between the plates, the crystalline structure of the liquid is altered, creating an image which is a duplicate of the pattern on the rear plate. To display the characters, the front plate of the LCD must be exposed to light. This is one of the disadvantages of this type of display. To operate an LCD in the dark, a lamp is usually included to illuminate the display surface.

Liquid crystal displays are either of the *field-effect* or *dynamic-scattering* type. The field-effect LCD operates from a low voltage (7–9 V), and it responds to rapid ON-OFF changes. It is, however, limited in display color and has a narrow viewing angle. Dynamic-scattering LCDs can be made with almost any color background and a wider viewing angle. They require, however, a larger operating potential. Both types yield a continuous display of various sizes. A typical LCD for indicating time is shown in Fig. 23–3.

Fig. 23–3. *Example of a LCD time indicator. (Courtesy Optel Corp.)*

Incandescent bulb displays are still in use. They provide a very bright image at low cost. Although more efficient than the LED, and available in a variety of shapes and sizes, the incandescent bulb consumes more power, has a shorter life, and a slower ON-OFF response. Some typical incandescent bulb displays are illustrated in Fig. 23–4.

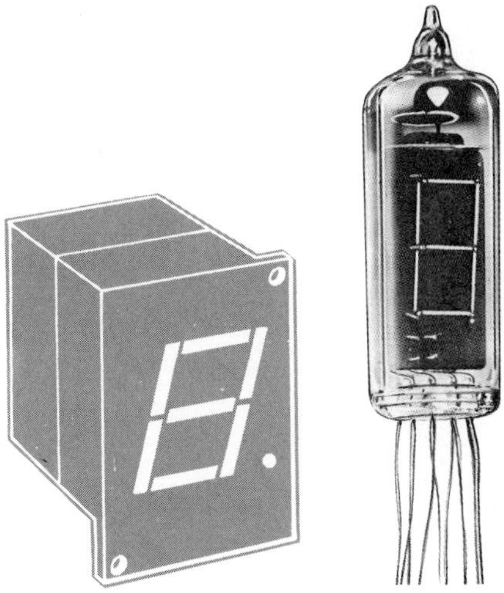

(A) (B)

Fig. 23–4. *Examples of incandescent bulb displays. [(A) Courtesy Dialight Corp. (B) Courtesy Mura Corp.]*

Nixie* tubes, used almost exclusively as numerical displays, are cold cathode gas-filled tubes. Each of the tubes shown in Fig. 23–5 contains ten different gas-filled tubes shaped as a numeral (0–9). In operation, each tube is activated separately. Its main disadvantage is the need for a high operating voltage, which generally implies a separate power supply.

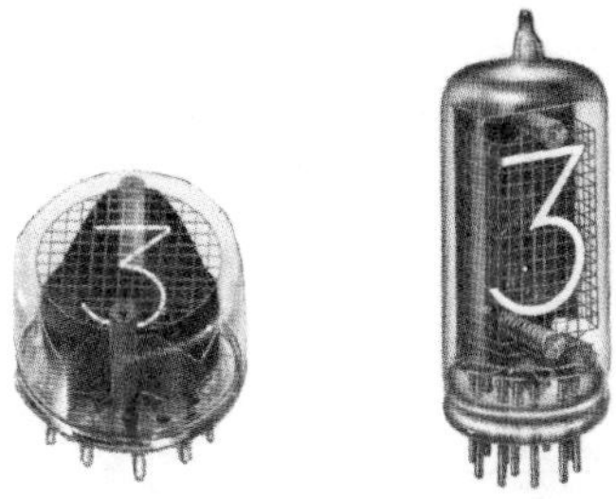

(A) (B)

Fig. 23–5. *Cold cathode gas-filled discharge tubes. (A) Wide-angle tube. (B) Side-viewing tube. (Courtesy National Electronics, Inc.)*

Various other types of gas discharge displays have been developed and are currently in use. One such unit used to display as many as 12 digits is the Panaplex II, manufactured by the Burroughs Corp. The advantage of this unit is that it can display 12 digits with only 19 external connections. A similar LED display requires at least 85 (12×7 segments + power) connections.

Several types of *planar* gas discharge displays are available. These are entire panels capable of displaying up to thousands of characters. Each character is displayed through a matrix pattern (generally a 5×7 matrix), providing a continuous display. To circumvent the problem of high dc voltage required to operate gas discharge displays, some manufacturers offer dc-to-dc converters. These units convert the standard 5 V used with T^2L to 250 V or whatever is necessary to drive the display.

Vacuum-flourescent devices are also used as numerical displays. They are attractive indicators that glow with a blue-green color. They also can be filtered to produce other colors. This type of display requires a continuous filament supply and an additional dc voltage of 12 V–25 V to produce the glow.

---

* Trade name of Burroughs Corp.

Cathode ray tubes (CRTs) are generally used in computer terminals to display large amounts of alphanumeric data. The CRT display is generated in a number of ways. The simplest method uses a conventional CRT. Digital data are converted to an analog signal which is applied to the deflection plates of the tube. The displayed pattern is then constantly refreshed to yield a continuous image.

Another type of CRT display uses no deflection components (plates or coils). Instead, it uses a metal mask with etched characters to shape an electron beam. Other systems contain preprogrammed memory lists. These lists supply the tube with the appropriate display signals to drive its deflection components.

23.2 A/D and D/A Converters

As mentioned earlier in this chapter, an A/D converter is a circuit which converts continuous (analog) signals to a train of pulses (digital signals). The D/A converter performs the opposite function. It converts a digital to an analog signal. These conversions are needed because some signals can be processed more efficiently if they are in digital form. In other cases, analog processing is the preferred method. The system designer must have access to both types of conversions. Because of advances in IC technology, many digital circuits are available to replace functions traditionally performed by analog circuits.

A/D and D/A converters are used in digital controls, digital communication, hybrid computers, and measuring instruments. A simplified block diagram of a hybrid computer is shown in Fig. 23–6. It consists of an analog com-

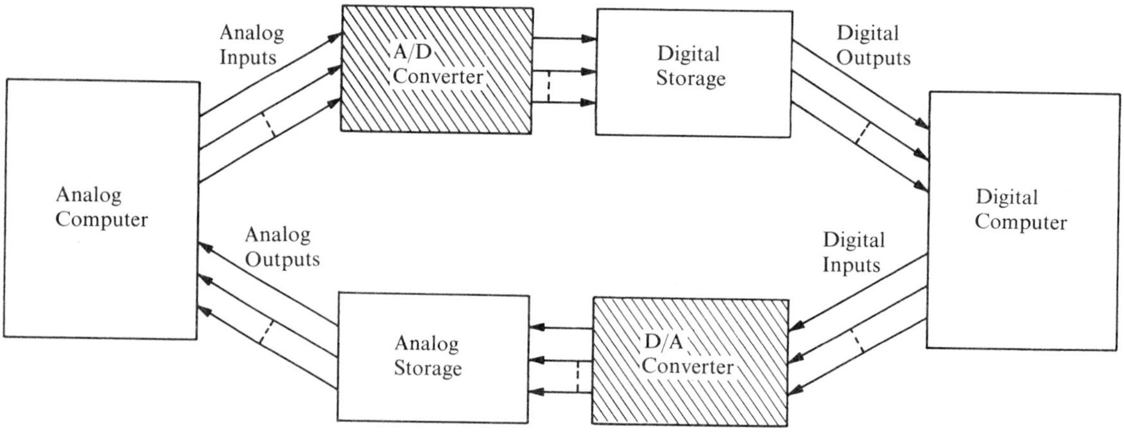

Fig. 23–6. *Simplified block diagram of a hybrid computer.*

puter, a digital computer, and interfacing circuitry which contains an A/D and a D/A converter. In this system, computations are shared between the two computers. Another example of a system which requires conversion is the digital multimeter, which is discussed later in this chapter. Converters are available in monolithic and hybrid IC forms.

23.3 The D/A Converter

The digital-to-analog (D/A) converter is the simpler of the two types. It consists of a resistive divider network, a reference voltage source, a level amplifier (usually an op amp), and a register for storing the digital input signal. A block diagram of a D/A converter is shown in Fig. 23–7. Digital data are fed to the register when the conversion enable input is activated.

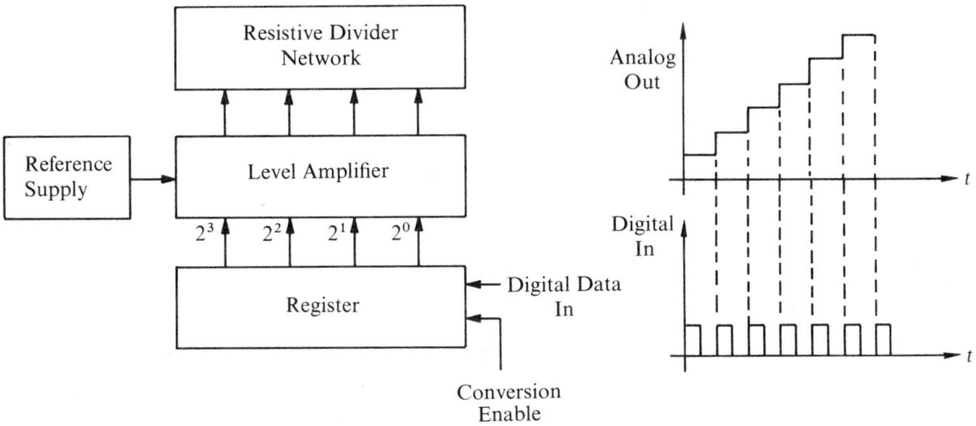

Fig. 23–7. *Block diagram of a basic D/A converter.*

The digital signal can be entered in the register in parallel or serial form. Because the levels of all 1's and 0's at the input are not necessarily the same, the level amplifier is used to ensure that precise levels enter the divider network. In most cases, 10 V correspond to a 1, and 0 V to a 0.

The resistive divider network is the key to the operation of a D/A converter. Two types of resistive divider networks are used: the *weighted resistor* and the *R*-2*R* networks of Fig. 23–8.

In the weighted resistor network of Fig. 23–8A, the current through the MSB (most significant bit) resistor is twice as large as that through the next bit resistor. The current decreases by a factor of two through each consecutive resistor. At the output of the divider, the total current equals the sum of the currents contributed by all the inputs in a weighted manner. The output voltage, V_o, is therefore proportional to the digital quantity at the input.

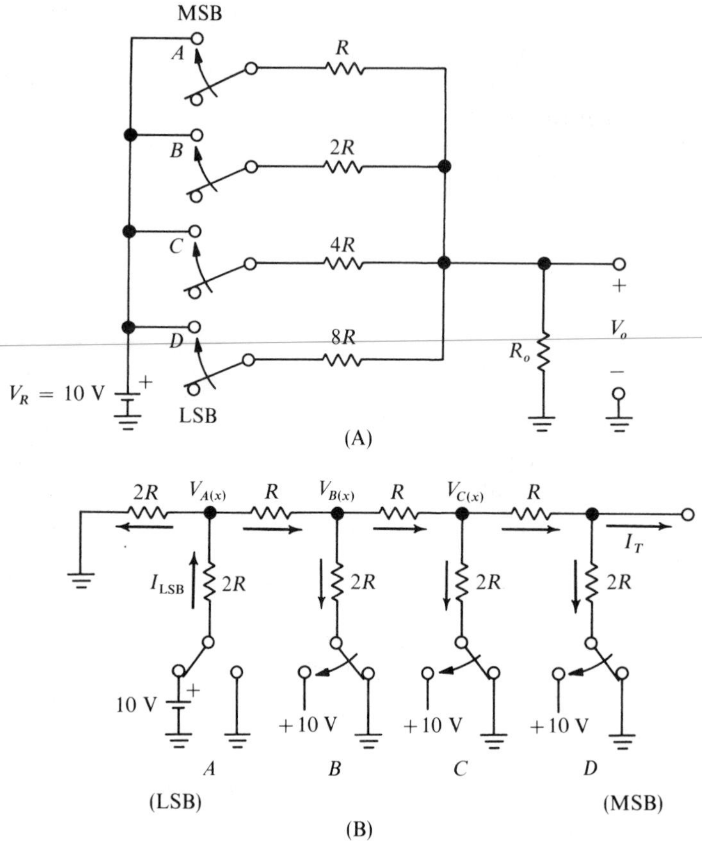

Fig. 23–8. *Resistive divider networks used with D/A converters. (A) Weighted resistor network. (B) R-2R network.*

EXAMPLE 23–2.

For the weighted resistor network of Fig. 23–8A, determine the analog output level corresponding to all possible binary input quantities 0000 through 1111. Assume that $R = 1\,\text{k}\Omega$, $R_o = 2\,\text{k}\Omega$, and the reference level, $V_R = 10\,\text{V}$.

Solution:

For binary 0000, input terminals *A–D* are open. Hence, the output is 0 V.

For binary 0001, the 10-V reference is connected to the LSB terminal, *D*. Terminals *A*, *B*, and *C* are open. By voltage division, the output is

$$V_o = V_R \times \frac{R_o}{R_o + 8R}$$
$$= 10 \times \frac{2}{2 + 8} = 2\,\text{V}$$

For binary 0010, terminal *C* is connected to 10 V; terminals *A*, *B*, and *D* are open. Again, by voltage division,

$$V_o = 10 \times \frac{2}{2 + 4} = \frac{10}{3}\,\text{V}$$

For binary 0011, terminals C and D are connected to 10 V; terminals A and B are open. Hence,

$$V_o = 10 \times \frac{2}{2 + 8\|4} = 4.28 \text{ V}$$

The remaining analog equivalents are obtained in a similar manner and are summarized in Table 23–2.

TABLE 23–2. Results of Example 23–2.

Binary Number	Decimal Equivalent	Analog Output (V)
0 0 0 0	0	0.00
0 0 0 1	1	2.00
0 0 1 0	2	3.33
0 0 1 1	3	4.28
0 1 0 0	4	5.00
0 1 0 1	5	5.55
0 1 1 0	6	6.00
0 1 1 1	7	6.37
1 0 0 0	8	6.67
1 0 0 1	9	6.92
1 0 1 0	10	7.14
1 0 1 1	11	7.33
1 1 0 0	12	7.50
1 1 0 1	13	7.65
1 1 1 0	14	7.78
1 1 1 1	15	7.89

An examination of Table 23–2 reveals that each binary number corresponds to a different voltage level. The voltage differential between numbers, however, is unequal. A circuit that yields an equal increment analog signal is shown in Fig. 23–9. The weighted resistor divider network is con-

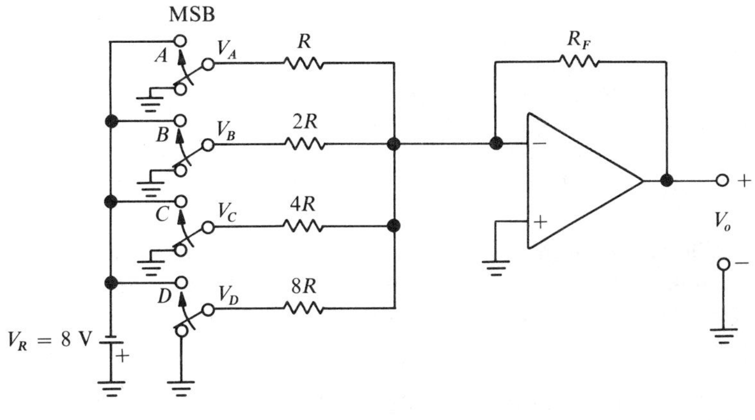

Fig. 23–9. *Weighted resistor D/A converter for Example 23–3.*

nected to an op amp to form a summing amplifier. The operation of the circuit is illustrated in Example 23–3.

EXAMPLE 23–3.

Construct a table similar to Table 23–2 for the circuit of Fig. 23–9. Assume that $R = 10\,\text{k}\Omega$, $R_F = 5\,\text{k}\Omega$, and $V_R = -8$ V. In this circuit, when a bit is present, -8 V are applied to the corresponding input terminal. When the input bit is 0, the terminal is returned to ground.

Solution:

The output voltage for a summing amplifier is given by Eq. (12–9):

$$V_o = -\left(\frac{R_F}{R_1} V_1 + \frac{R_F}{R_2} V_2 + \frac{R_F}{R_3} V_3 + \frac{R_F}{R_4} V_4\right)$$

In our case,

$$\begin{aligned} V_1 &= V_A \\ V_2 &= V_B \\ V_3 &= V_C \\ V_4 &= V_D \\ R_1 &= 10\,\text{k}\Omega \\ R_2 &= 20\,\text{k}\Omega \\ R_3 &= 40\,\text{k}\Omega \\ R_4 &= 80\,\text{k}\Omega \\ R_F &= 5\,\text{k}\Omega \end{aligned}$$

For a binary input of 0000, $V_o = 0$ V. A binary input of 0001 yields

$$\begin{aligned} V_o &= -\left[\frac{5}{80} \times (-8) + 0 + 0 + 0\right] \\ &= 0.5\text{ V} \end{aligned}$$

Binary 0010 corresponds to

$$\begin{aligned} V_o &= -\left[0 + \frac{5}{40} \times (-8) + 0 + 0\right] \\ &= 1.0\text{ V} \end{aligned}$$

For a 0011 input, we obtain

$$\begin{aligned} V_o &= -\left[\frac{5}{80} \times (-8) + \frac{5}{40} \times (-8) + 0 + 0\right] \\ &= 1.5\text{ V} \end{aligned}$$

The results of these and the remaining binary inputs are summarized in Table 23–3. Note that a one-bit change in the binary number results in a half-volt change in the analog output voltage.

The R-$2R$ divider (Fig. 23–8B) is called a *ladder network*. The current contribution of each bit is reduced by the current splitting (dividing) action of the resistors in the ladder. The direction of current flow from a "high" at the

TABLE 23–3. Results of Example 23–3.

Binary Number	Decimal Equivalent	Analog Output (V)
0 0 0 0	0	0.0
0 0 0 1	1	0.5
0 0 1 0	2	1.0
0 0 1 1	3	1.5
0 1 0 0	4	2.0
0 1 0 1	5	2.5
0 1 1 0	6	3.0
0 1 1 1	7	3.5
1 0 0 0	8	4.0
1 0 0 1	9	4.5
1 0 1 0	10	5.0
1 0 1 1	11	5.5
1 1 0 0	12	6.0
1 1 0 1	13	6.5
1 1 1 0	14	7.0
1 1 1 1	15	7.5

LSB terminal is indicated by arrows. Output current I_T is proportional to the digital quantity at the input.

The R-$2R$ D/A converter is desirable because it requires only two values of resistance: R and $2R$. On the other hand, the weighted resistor divider requires the use of a different resistance value for each bit. The ratio between the resistance values of the LSB and MSB can become very large and impractical to realize.

EXAMPLE 23–4.

For the ladder-type converter of Fig. 23–10, determine the output voltage, V_o, if the input is 0100. Resistance values are related to $R = 1\text{ k}\Omega$.

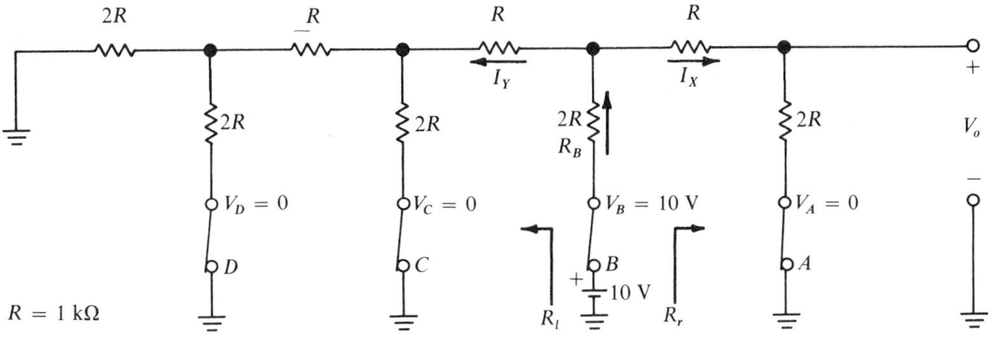

Fig. 23–10. *Ladder-type converter for Example 23–4.*

Solution:

For a binary input of 0100, $V_B = 10\text{ V}$, and $V_A = V_C = V_D = 0\text{ V}$. The resistance seen to the left of R_B, R_l, is $R + 2R\|(R + 2R\|2R) = R + 2R\|2R = 2R$. The resistance seen to the right of R_B, R_r, is $R + 2R = 3R$. Current

I_B flowing in resistance R_B is

$$I_B = \frac{10}{2R + 2R \| 3R} = \frac{50}{16}\,\text{mA}$$

By current division, the current flowing in the resistances to the right of R_B, I_X, is

$$I_X = \frac{50}{16} \times \frac{2R}{5R} = 1.25\,\text{mA}$$

Solving for output voltage V_o,

$$V_o = 1.25 \times 2 = 2.5\,\text{V}$$

23.4 The A/D Converter

Analog-to-digital conversion may be accomplished by several different methods. A commonly used technique is *successive approximation.* A basic element in an A/D converter is the *comparator* (such as the difference amplifier discussed in Chapter 12), which compares the analog input signal with a reference level. The A/D converter is more complex than the D/A type. In fact, a D/A converter is usually a component of the A/D converter.

A block diagram of a successive approximation A/D converter is shown in Fig. 23–11. The analog input signal is fed to one side of the comparator. Its level is compared with the output level of the D/A converter. When the conversion enable line is activated, the output of the D/A converter corresponds to the MSB. This is compared with the unknown input signal. If the analog input is the larger of the two, a 1 is shifted through the shift register to the MSB position of the output register. If the analog input is less than the MSB, a 0 is inserted instead.

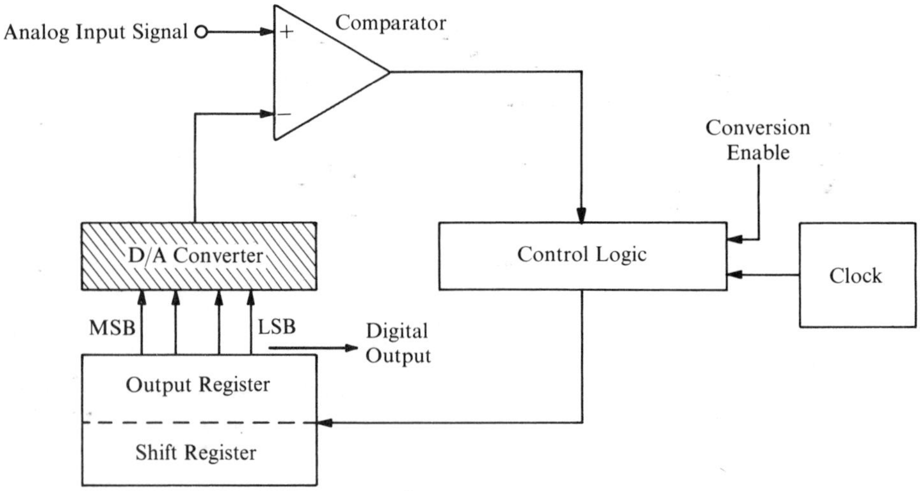

Fig. 23–11. *Successive approximation-type A/D converter.*

The next output from the D/A converter to be compared with the analog input is the corresponding value of the next bit. This is in addition to the value of the MSB stored in the register. The process is continued through the LSB. When the conversion is completed, the digital equivalent signal is available at the output register.

Specifications for D/A and A/D converters are very similar. An important characteristic of a converter is its *resolution.* The resolution of a D/A converter is defined as the difference between two output levels (in millivolts) which correspond to two adjacent binary numbers (for example, 0001 and 0010). In general, it is equal to the maximum voltage range of the converter output divided by 2^n, where n is the maximum number of bits the converter can process. Because its output is binary, the resolution of an A/D converter is the maximum number of bits it can handle.

Accuracy of a D/A or an A/D converter refers to the degree the output tracks with the input signal. A common specification is $\pm\frac{1}{2}$ LSB. This means that at full scale, the output can be off by one-half the value of the least significant bit.

The *speed* of a D/A converter is the time it takes for a full-scale change of the output. This quantity also is called the *maximum speed of conversion.* Speed of an A/D converter is expressed as the *rate of conversion.* It denotes the number of conversions performed per unit time. Examples of commercial D/A and A/D converters are provided in Fig. 23–12.

Fig. 23–12. *Examples of commercial D/A and A/D converters. (Courtesy Burr-Brown Corp.)*

23.5 Introduction to the Microprocessor

The microprocessor (μP) serves as the central processor unit (CPU) of a computer. When ROMs, RAMs, and input/output (I/O) chips are connected to it, the resulting system may function as a special purpose or general purpose computer. When used as a general purpose computer, the system is sometimes called a *microcomputer.* A block diagram of a typical microprocessor system is shown in Fig. 23–13.

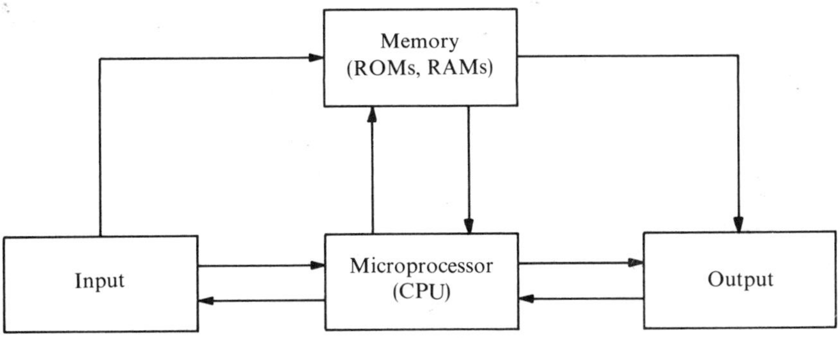

Fig. 23–13. *Block diagram of a generalized microprocessor.*

The microprocessor provides inexpensive computer control of various processes. Virtually every system that exhibits a computerlike organization can be redesigned to use a microprocessor. The device adds flexibility to a system by permitting the execution by software of certain tasks normally performed by wired logic. Applications for the microprocessor include calculators, machine control systems, point-of-sale terminals, automatic typesetting, automotive controllers and diagnostic systems, instrumentation, and traffic controllers.

For example, a calculator may be thought of as a small specialized computer. Manufacturers have developed a single chip which contains, in addition to a microprocessor, its own memory (PROM and a limited-capacity RAM). Interface (I/O) logic is also contained on the chip.

Some numerical control machines employ a microprocessor as their main building block. The processor acquires, manipulates, and processes data from the memory. An output is thereby produced which initiates various machines used in the process. The control program is stored in a PROM, specifically programmed for a given operation. When the process is altered, the original PROM is replaced with one in which a new set of instructions is stored. If a RAM is used for storing instructions, it becomes easy to change the sequence of operations performed by the machine with punched tape, cards, or other input media.

The microprocessor is also found in computer-type terminals. These include TTY (teletype), CRT, and point-of-sale (POS) terminals. The POS terminal is one which replaces the cash register in supermarkets and department stores. The processor controls the transfer of data from the computer to the display terminal. It must be capable of recognizing, storing, and manipulating various types of transaction data, as well as printing out a receipt.

23.6 Characteristics of a Microprocessor

Some of the major characteristics of a microprocessor include speed, word size (bits per word), type of memory, memory size, addressing modes, and software capabilities. The processor is generally slower than wired logic systems. Because most microprocessor chips use MOS logic, their speed is less than that of bipolar logic circuits. For example, the Intel 8080 microprocessor has an instruction time of $2\,\mu s$–$6\,\mu s$. This means that it takes at least $2\,\mu s$ to execute an instruction. This execution time is adequate for most applications.

The word size that is generally processed by a microprocessor is either four or eight bits long. Some chips are capable of processing 16-bit words. Chips that process four-bit words are generally used with systems that perform mainly arithmetic operations, such as a calculator and a cash register. A CRT terminal usually requires eight-bit words for its operation.

When the output of an A/D converter is to be processed, the handling of 12-bit words is usually required. A general-purpose processor can have a fixed or variable word length. A variable word length may be produced by paralleling several processors, each of which has a smaller word length. In such a manner, systems are designed to handle 24- or 32-bit words.

As pointed out earlier, both the ROM and RAM are used in a microprocessor system. The ROM stores fixed and routine instructions. The RAM stores data that are altered during the execution of instructions. Generally, a PROM is used instead of a straight ROM for storing instructions and routines. The amount of storage on the processor chip and its capabilities determine the amount of external memory required.

The instruction set, or *software*, is an important part of a microprocessor system. Programming in machine language (1's and 0's) is very laborious and time consuming. It requires the loading of a program into the processor via switches, bit by bit.

As with other computers, the microprocessor is generally programmed in an *assembly level language*. An assembly level language uses abbreviations of instruction instead of 1's and 0's used in machine language. The assembly language must be translated by an assembler program into machine language.

Direct addressing is the most commonly used method for locating data in a memory. The processor receives the data location directly from the instruction set. A method similar to direct addressing is *relative addressing*. In relative addressing, some of the address data are contained in the instruction set, and the remainder in registers within the processor.

Various *indirect* addressing schemes are also used. In general, indirect addressing refers to the storage of addressing data in a given register of the processor. The address in the instruction set specifies only the register that contains the data.

23.7 Organization of a Microprocessor

A general microprocessor system was shown in Fig. 23–13. To gain a better understanding of the functioning of such a system, we shall examine the Motorola M6800 microprocessor family. This family is typical of what is available from other manufacturers. The M6800 chip set consists of six NMOS units which include the following:

1. The microprocessor (MC6800).
2. A 1024 × 8 ROM (MCM6830).
3. A 128 × 8 RAM (MCM6810).
4. A peripheral interface adapter, or PIA (MC6820).
5. A communication interface adapter, or CIA (MC6850).
6. A MODEM (MC6860). The MODEM is a modulator-demodulator that permits the connection of a microprocessor to telephone lines. Digital data thereby may be transmitted and received over the lines.

A block diagram of a microprocessor system constructed with the Motorola chip set is illustrated in Fig. 23–14. The chip set operates at standard T^2L levels, and the entire system can be powered from a 5-V source.

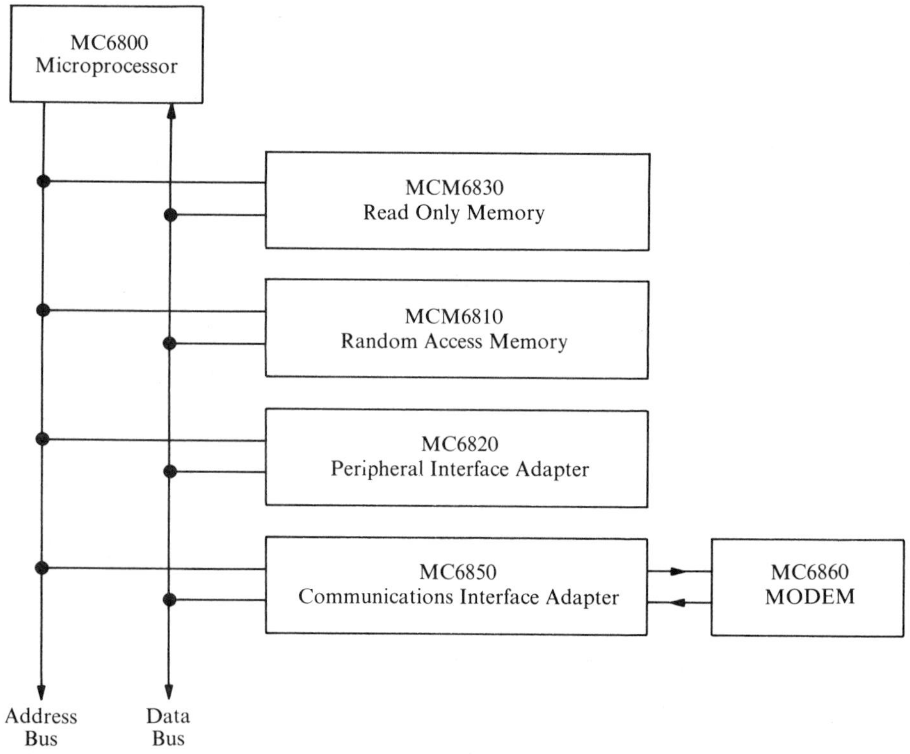

Fig. 23–14. *Block diagram of a microprocessor system constructed from Motorola chips. (Courtesy Motorola Semiconductor Products, Inc.)*

The heart of the system is the MC6800 microprocessor which is packaged in a 40-pin dual in-line package. As shown in Fig. 23–15, it consists of an *arithmetic logic unit* (ALU), control section, data and address registers for a total of six, and data, address, input, and output bus lines.

The data bus (8 bits) is bidirectional, allowing for direct addressing of the memory. A total of seven different ad-

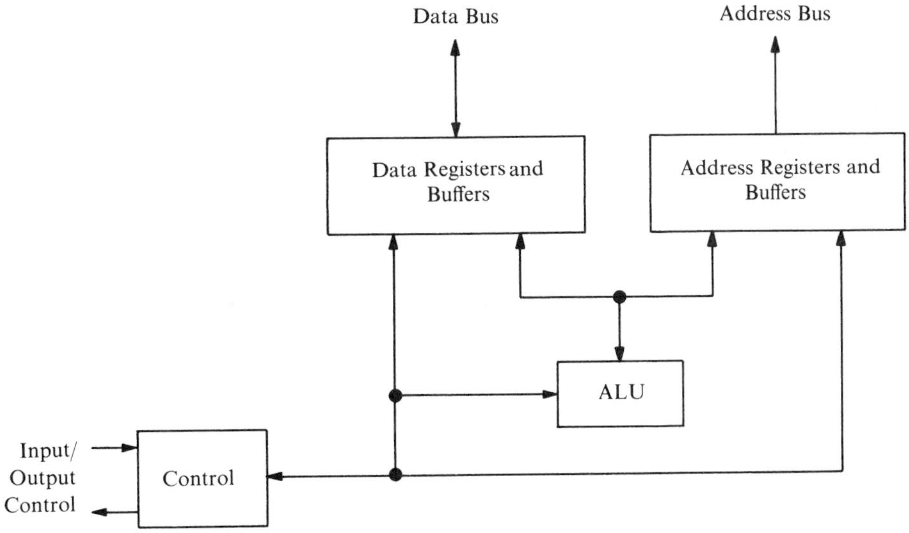

Fig. 23–15. *Block diagram of the MC6800 microprocessor. (Courtesy Motorola Semiconductor Products, Inc.)*

dressing modes is possible. The address bus (16 bits) makes it possible to address up to 64 kilobytes of memory. The system contains 72 instructions for performing decimal and binary arithmetic as well as shift, store, and other instructions. Maximum operating frequency is 1 MHz, and a typical instruction time is less than 5 μs.

The MCM6810 RAM (Fig. 23–16A) is a static NMOS memory with a 128 word $\times$ 8 bit organization. This memory is word organized (as explained in Chapter 22, an entire word is addressed rather than an individual bit). It is an *expandable* memory, meaning that the same type unit can be connected to another to increase storage capacity. The manufacturer specifies a maximum access time of 1 μs for the memory.

The MCM6830 chip (Fig. 23–16B) is a 1024 word $\times$ 8 bit ROM. Like the RAM, the fixed memory is static and therefore needs no clock or refreshing. The ROM is preprogrammed by the manufacturer to the user's specifications. This memory also can be expanded for larger storage capacity.

The peripheral interface adapter MC6820 chip of Fig. 23–16C is used to interface peripheral equipment to the microprocessor. It accomplishes this task through two eight-bit bidirectional peripheral data buses and four control lines. The control signals are provided by the microprocessor. This peripheral interface adapter is designed as a universal chip for interfacing with most peripheral devices with no additional external logic.

The MC6850 chip of Fig. 23–16D serves as a communications interface adapter. It provides the control and formatting for interfacing communications data information with the microprocessor. Together with the MC6860

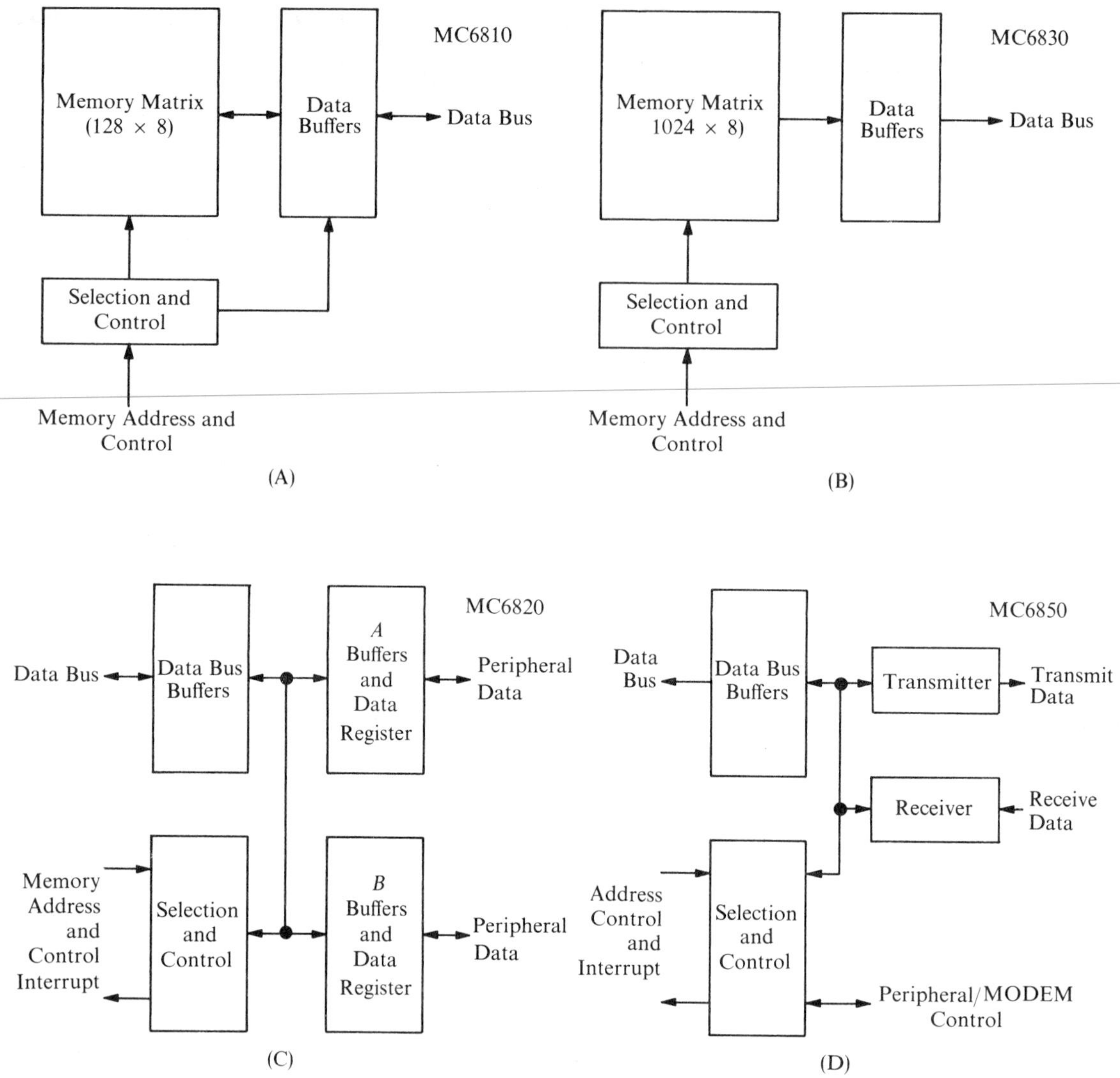

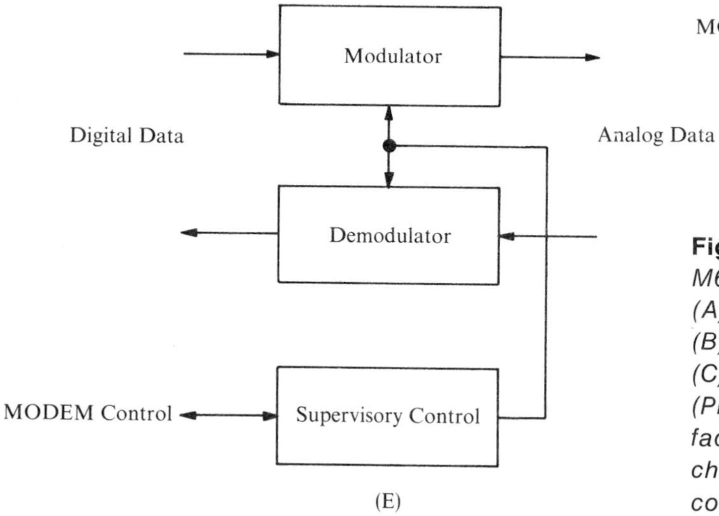

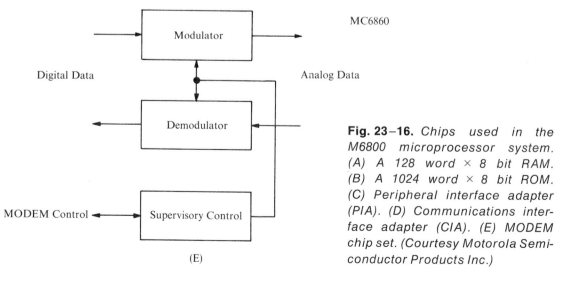

Fig. 23–16. *Chips used in the M6800 microprocessor system. (A) A 128 word × 8 bit RAM. (B) A 1024 word × 8 bit ROM. (C) Peripheral interface adapter (PIA). (D) Communications interface adapter (CIA). (E) MODEM chip set. (Courtesy Motorola Semiconductor Products Inc.)*

MODEM chip (Fig. 23–16E), it is capable of receiving communications data and feeding them to the MC6800 for further processing.

23.8 The Digital Multimeter— An Example of an Electronic System

The last section of this chapter is devoted to an example of an electronic system. The digital multimeter (DMM) was selected because it contains analog, digital, and display circuitry. It is based on the Simpson Model 464 DMM illustrated in Fig. 23–17. A block diagram of the instrument is given in Fig. 23–18.

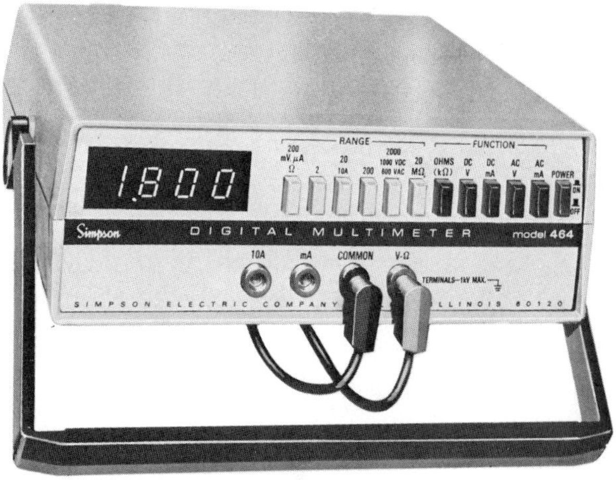

Fig. 23–17. *Example of a digital multimeter (DMM). (Courtesy Simpson Electric Corp.)*

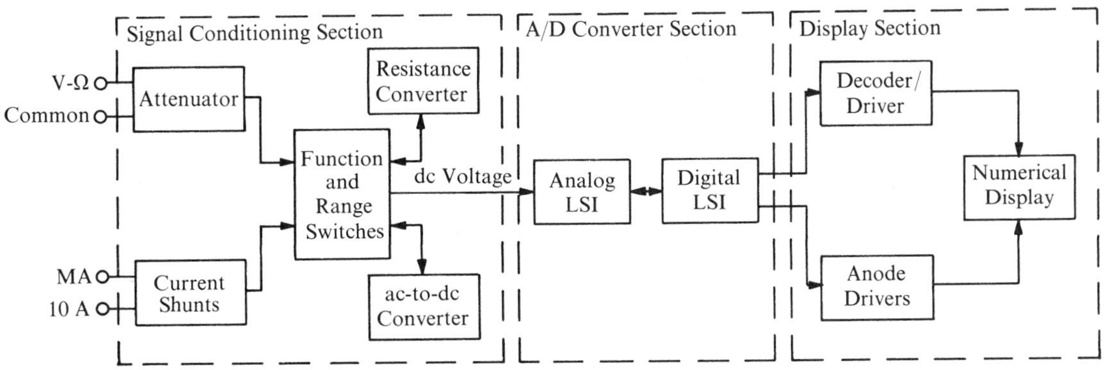

Fig. 23–18. *Block diagram of the Simpson Model 464 DMM. (Courtesy Simpson Electric Corp.)*

The DMM consists of three sections: the input or signal conditioning section, the A/D converter section, and the display section. The signal conditioning section converts the measured input quantity (voltage, current, or resistance) to a proportional voltage level. A corresponding digital signal is obtained from the A/D section. The display section contains decoder and driver circuits, and the numerical display unit. In the Simpson Model 464 DMM, a seven-segment LED display is used.

Measuring dc Voltages

To measure a dc voltage, we apply the unknown voltage to the V-Ω and COMMON jacks of the DMM. Depending on the range selected, the attenuator yields a scaled voltage level which is applied to the A/D converter. The A/D converter has two inputs. At one input, it accepts signals up to 0.2 V, and at the other, up to 2 V. The meter has a 0.2-, 2-, 20-, 200-, and 1000-V dc range. An attenuator is used on all ranges except the 0.2-V and 2-V ranges.

Measuring ac Voltages

The circuit used for ac voltage measurements is illustrated in Fig. 23–19. The ac input to be measured, as for dc voltage measurements, is applied to the V-Ω and COMMON jacks. It is attenuated according to the voltage range selected and fed to an amplifier. The amplifier serves as a buffer between the rectifier and attenuator. A half-wave rectifier converts the ac output of the amplifier to a dc level. The dc level is calibrated to the rms value of a sine wave. A digital readout is obtained from the A/D converter and is fed to the numerical display.

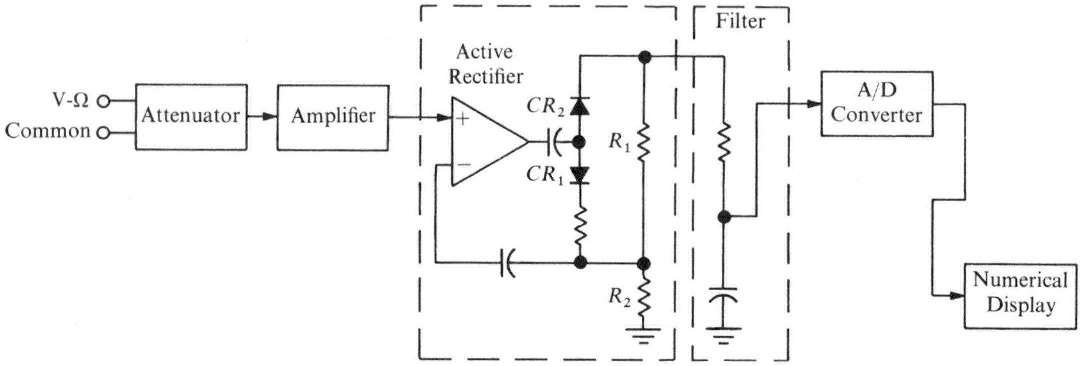

Fig. 23–19. *Circuit for measuring ac voltages. (Courtesy Simpson Electric Corp.)*

Measuring Current

A group of shunt resistors (Fig. 23–20) is used in the measurement of dc current. The voltage developed across the resistors is applied to an A/D converter. For ac current measurements, the same group of shunt resistors is used. The only difference is that the voltage developed across the resistors is fed to the ac voltage-measuring circuit of Fig. 23–19 instead of directly to the A/D converter.

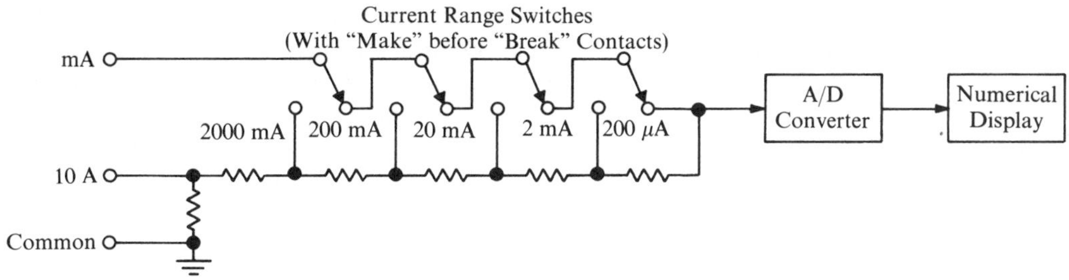

Fig. 23–20. *Circuit for measuring dc currents. (Courtesy Simpson Electric Corp.)*

Measuring Resistance

In Fig. 23–21, an unknown resistance, R_x, is measured by developing a voltage across it which is proportional to its resistance value. This is accomplished by passing a constant current through the unknown resistance. For a selected resistance range, the voltage across resistance R_A remains constant. The voltage across R_x, however, varies with its value of resistance. The voltage to the A/D converter, therefore, is proportional to R_x.

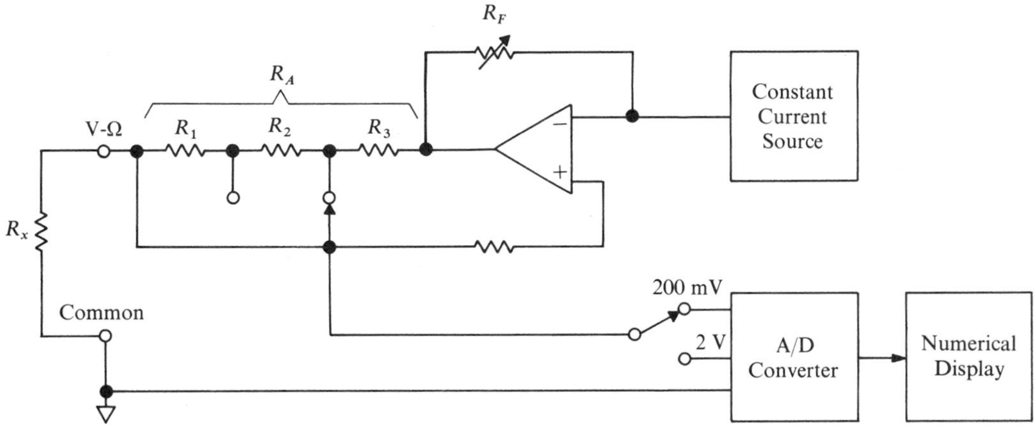

Fig. 23–21. *Resistance measurement circuit. (Courtesy Simpson Electric Corp.)*

The A/D and Display Sections

The A/D converter used in the DMM consists of two LSI chips. An external clock, reference current supply, and an overload protection circuit complement the A/D converter. The numerical display section contains a seven-segment, three and one-half digit LED display with a polarity indicator. It is driven by a BCD-to-seven-segment decoder/driver cricuit.

The half digit may be either unlighted or energized to show a 1. If, for example, the three digits read 999, the half digit permits a reading of 1999. Thus, the voltage range of the DMM is nearly doubled.

SUMMARY

Alphanumeric displays are classified by their operating voltage, number of characters displayed, switching speed, and whether they are segmented or continuous. The LED, LCD, and incandescent lamp are operated from a low voltage supply. They are easily interfaced with standard IC logic. The LED is a segmented device, in which a character is displayed by energizing a number of diodes. The seven-segment version is the most popular type of LED display.

The LCD has the advantage of consuming very little power compared with the LED. It suffers, however, from the need for illumination of its front plate for the characters to be displayed. The LED comes in a variety of colors, with red the brightest. Incandescent lamp displays are much slower than the other devices and have a limited life.

Gas discharge-type displays require high voltages for their operation. An additional power supply is therefore generally required. On the other hand, these devices are capable of displaying up to thousands of characters at a time. The CRT display, commonly used for computer terminals, also is capable of displaying a large number of data.

The D/A converter is used to convert digital to analog signals. In the A/D converter, the reverse process occurs; analog signals are changed to digital signals. An A/D converter generally contains a D/A converter in its system. Both A/D and D/A converters are used in hybrid systems where data are entered in one form and changed to another for processing. An example of such a system is the digital multimeter.

The microprocessor is used in a variety of applications. They include the calculator, machine and process control, automotive systems, and traffic control. Coupled with RAMs, PROMs, and I/O chips, they are capable of performing these and other operations efficiently and economically. The microprocessor generally processes smaller word lengths and is slower than general-purpose minicomputers.

Further Reading

Barna, A., and D. I. Porat. *Introduction to Microcomputers and Microprocessors.* New York: John Wiley and Sons, 1976.

Gilder, J., ed. "Focus on Displays." *Electronic Design,* Sept. 13, 1975, pp. 52–65.

Intel. *8080 Microcomputer Systems User's Manual.* Santa Clara, Calif: Intel Corporation, Sept. 1975.

Motorola. *M6800 Systems Reference and Data Sheets.* Phoenix, Ariz.: Motorola Semiconductor Products, Inc., May 1975.

Sheingold, D., and R. Ferrero. "Understanding A/D and D/A Converters." *IEEE Spectrum*, Sept. 1972, pp. 47–56.

Texas Instruments. *The Microprocessor Handbook*. Dallas, Tex.: Texas Instruments, Inc., 1975.

Tireford, H. *Introduction to Microprocessors*. Phoenix, Ariz.: Motorola Semiconductor Products, Inc., 1975.

REVIEW QUESTIONS

23.1 Identify four types of direct-illumination displays.

23.2 Explain what is meant by electroluminescence.

23.3 What is the efficiency of a typical LED?

23.4 Can all letters of the alphabet be generated with a seven-segment display? Why?

23.5 Compare the advantages and disadvantages of the LCD and LED.

23.6 What is a major drawback of the Nixie tube?

23.7 For what applications are planar gas discharge displays best suited?

23.8 Describe, in your own words, the function of
(a) A D/A converter.
(b) An A/D converter.

23.9 What is the function in a D/A converter of a
(a) Reference supply?
(b) Register?

23.10 What is the advantage of the op amp circuit in Fig. 23–9 over the weighted resistor network of Fig. 23–8A?

23.11 Describe the function of the comparator in Fig. 23–11.

23.12 For a D/A or A/D converter, define
(a) Resolution.
(b) Accuracy.
(c) Rate of conversion.

23.13 Explain how a microprocessor replaces hard-wired logic.

23.14 Discuss the function of each block in Fig. 23–13.

23.15 Discuss the differences between direct and indirect addressing.

23.16 What is the difference between assembly level and machine language?

23.17 Why does a microprocessor have both a ROM and a RAM?

23.18 What is meant by an expandable memory?

23.19 Explain the function of the MODEM chip in the M6800 microprocessor system.

23.20 Why is it necessary to employ an A/D converter in a DMM?

23.21 Describe the operation of the Model 464 Simpson DMM when it is used to measure resistance.

PROBLEMS

P23–1 From the logic diagram of the decoder in Fig. 23–2B, show how number 7 is displayed.

P23–2 Repeat prob. P23–1 for number 4.

P23–3 For the network of Fig. 23–8A, calculate the output voltage for binary input 0101. Assume that $R = 1\,\text{k}\Omega$, $R_o = 10\,\text{k}\Omega$, and $V_R = 12\,\text{V}$.

P23–4 Repeat prob. P23–3 for binary input 1001.

P23–5 For the circuit in prob. P23–3, calculate the binary input if the analog output is 3.33 V.

P23–6 For the D/A converter of Fig. 23–9, $R = R_F = 10\,\text{k}\Omega$, and $V_R = -10\,\text{V}$. Determine the output level for binary input 1010.

P23–7 Repeat prob. P23–6 for binary input 1111.

P23–8 For the circuit in prob. P23–6, determine the binary input that results in an output of 2.5 V.

P23–9 Referring to Fig. 23–8B, determine the output voltage if the input is 1000. Resistance values are based on $R = 1\,\text{k}\Omega$. A logic 1 corresponds to 10 V, and a logic 0 to 0 V.

P23–10 Repeat prob. P23–9 for a binary input of 1011.

P23–11 An op amp and a feedback resistor $R_F = 5\,\text{k}\Omega$ are connected to the the output of the network in prob. P23–9. Calculate the output level of the new circuit if the input is 0010.

Appendix A

A.1 Four-Terminal Linear Networks

In Chapter 6, the small-signal model derived for the BJT was based on its physical operation. We can extend this procedure to other configurations, as well as to the FET. Another approach is to develop these models with the aid of some elementary circuit theory.

When we consider small-signal operation, *linearity* is implied. This means that if the input increases (or decreases) by a given amount, the output increases (or decreases) by a proportional amount. If this is not true, *nonlinear* operation is said to exist. The methods we shall adopt in analyzing small-signal amplifiers apply only to linear operation.

Consider the block diagram of the linear four-terminal network of Fig. A.1–1, which is similar to Fig. 5–1. The network is completely described by two equations: one for the input side and another for the output side of the network. There are a total of six possible sets of equations, only three of which are useful for our purposes.

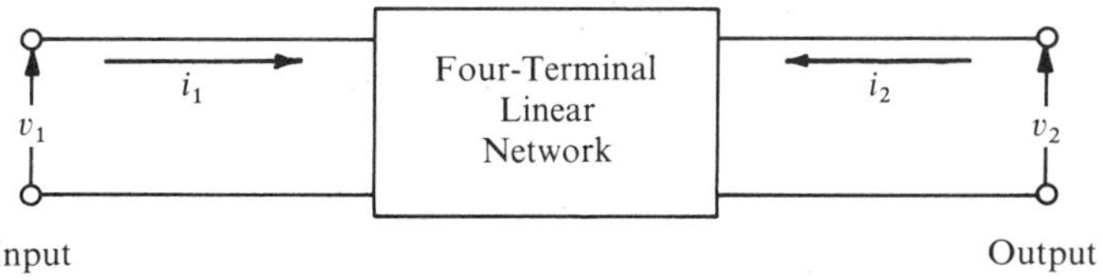

Fig. A.1–1. *Four-terminal linear network.*

If i_1 and v_2 are chosen as independent variables, this may be stated mathematically as

$$v_1 = f_1(i_1, v_2) \qquad \textbf{(A.1–1a)}$$

$$i_2 = f_2(i_1, v_2) \qquad \textbf{(A.1–1b)}$$

Equation (A.1–1a) is read, "Input voltage v_1 is a function of (depends on) input current i_1 and output voltage v_2." Likewise, Eq. (A.1–1b) states that, "Output current i_2 is a function of i_1 and v_2." Equations (A.1–1a) and (A.1–1b) lead to the hybrid parameters. The hybrid parameters are ideal for characterizing the BJT at low and mid frequencies.

In more explicit terms, Eqs. (A.1–1a) and (A.1–1b) can be written as

$$v_1 = h_{11}i_1 + h_{12}v_2 \qquad \textbf{(A.1–2a)}$$

$$i_2 = h_{21}i_1 + h_{22}v_2 \qquad \textbf{(A.1–2b)}$$

These equations were solved in Chapter 6 for the h parameters.

If v_1 and v_2 are selected as independent variables in Eqs. (A.1–1a) and (A.1–1b), we can write

$$i_1 = y_{11}v_1 + y_{12}v_2 \qquad \textbf{(A.1–3a)}$$

$$i_2 = y_{21}v_1 + y_{22}v_2 \qquad \textbf{(A.1–3b)}$$

The *y parameters* are defined by

$$y_{11} = i_1/v_1\Big|_{v_2=0} = \text{input admittance} \tag{A.1–4a}$$

$$y_{12} = i_1/v_2\Big|_{v_1=0} = \text{reverse transfer gain} \tag{A.1–4b}$$

$$y_{21} = i_2/v_1\Big|_{v_2=0} = \text{forward transfer gain} \tag{A.1–4c}$$

$$y_{22} = i_2/v_2\Big|_{v_1=0} = \text{output admittance} \tag{A.1–4d}$$

Because each ratio is a current to a voltage, the unit for the y parameters is the mho (℧). The y parameters also are called *admittance*, and *short-circuit*, parameters. A small-signal y model, based on Eq. (A.1–3a) and Eq. (A.1–3b), is illustrated in Fig. A.1–2.

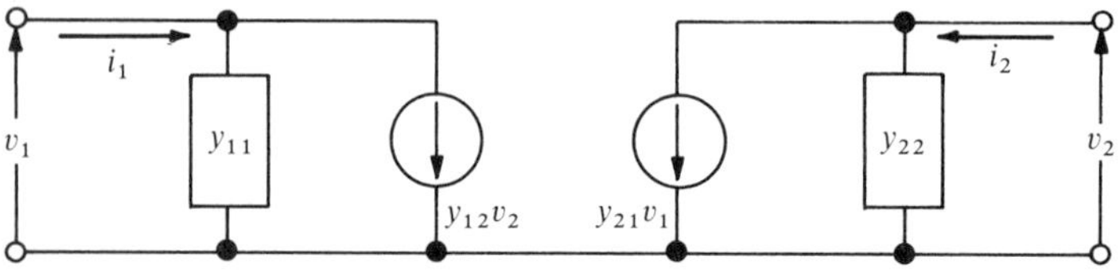

Fig. A.1–2. *Small-signal y model. Sources $y_{12}v_2$ and $y_{21}v_1$ are examples of voltage-controlled (dependent) current sources.*

Another set of useful expressions is produced when i_1 and i_2 are chosen as the independent variables:

$$v_1 = z_{11}i_1 + z_{12}i_2 \tag{A.1–5a}$$

$$v_2 = z_{21}i_1 + z_{22}i_2 \tag{A.1–5b}$$

The *z parameters* are defined by

$$z_{11} = v_1/i_1\Big|_{i_2=0} = \text{input impedance} \tag{A.1–6a}$$

$$z_{12} = v_1/i_2\Big|_{i_1=0} = \text{reverse transfer ratio} \tag{A.1–6b}$$

$$z_{21} = v_2/i_1\Big|_{i_2=0} = \text{forward transfer ratio} \tag{A.1–6c}$$

$$z_{22} = v_2/i_2\Big|_{i_1=0} = \text{output impedance} \tag{A.1–6d}$$

The unit for z parameters is the ohm (Ω). The z parameters are also called *impedance*, and *open-circuit*, parameters. Figure (A.1–3) shows a z model, based on Eqs. (A.1–5a) and (A.1–5b), for small-signal operation.

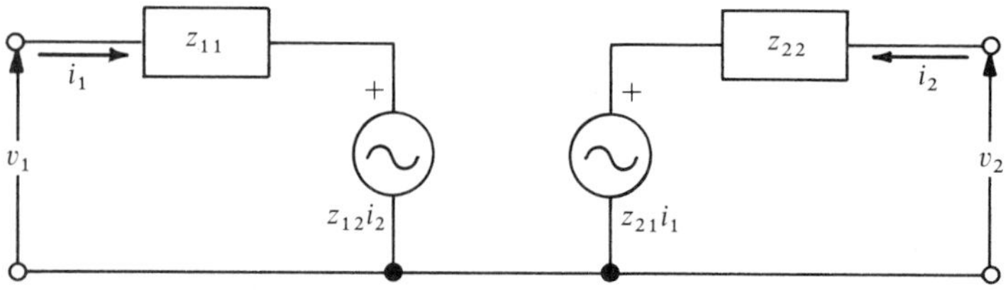

Fig. A.1–3. *Small-signal z model. Sources $z_{12}i_2$ and $z_{21}i_1$ are examples of current-controlled vol-age sources.*

Example A–1.

Determine

(a) The y parameters for the *pi* network of Fig. A.1–4A.

(b) The z parameters for the *tee* network of Fig. A.1–4B.

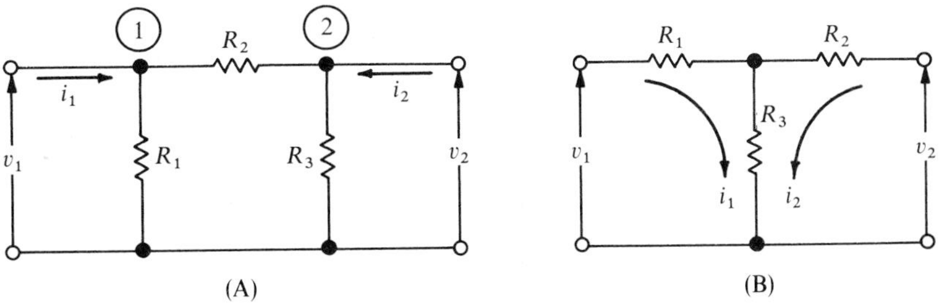

Fig. A.1–4. *Determining the y parameters for (A) a pi network and the z parameters for (B) a tee network. These networks are called "pi" and "tee" because of their configuration. (See Example A–1.)*

Solutions:

(a) Writing nodal equations at nodes 1 and 2 for the pi network, we obtain

$$i_1 = \left(\frac{1}{R_1} + \frac{1}{R_2}\right)v_1 - \frac{v_2}{R_2} \qquad \textbf{(A.1–7a)}$$

$$i_2 = -\frac{v_1}{R_2} + \left(\frac{1}{R_2} + \frac{1}{R_3}\right)v_2 \qquad \textbf{(A.1–7b)}$$

Comparing Eq. (A.1–7) with Eq. (A.1–3), we find that

$$y_{11} = \frac{1}{R_1} + \frac{1}{R_2}$$

$$y_{12} = y_{21} = -\frac{1}{R_2}$$

$$y_{22} = \frac{1}{R_2} + \frac{1}{R_3}$$

Letting

$$\frac{1}{R_1} = G_1 \qquad \frac{1}{R_2} = G_2 \qquad \frac{1}{R_3} = G_3$$

then

$$y_{11} = G_1 + G_2$$
$$y_{12} = y_{21} = -G_2$$
$$y_{22} = G_2 + G_3$$

(b) Writing loop equations for the tee network, we get

$$v_1 = (R_1 + R_3)i_1 + R_3 i_2 \qquad \textbf{(A.1–8a)}$$
$$v_2 = R_3 i_1 + (R_2 + R_3)i_2 \qquad \textbf{(A.1–8b)}$$

Comparing Eq. (A.1–8) with Eq. (A.1–5), we obtain $z_{11} = R_1 + R_3$; $z_{12} = z_{21} = R_3$; and $z_{22} = R_2 + R_3$.

A.2 FET y Model

Applying Kirchhoff's current law at the input and output sides of Fig. A.2–1, we obtain

$$i_1 = v_s g_{11} + g_{12} v_2 \qquad \textbf{(A.2–1a)}$$
$$i_2 = v_s g_{21} + g_{22} v_2 \qquad \textbf{(A.2–1b)}$$

and

$$v_2 = -R_L i_2 \qquad \textbf{(A.2–2)}$$

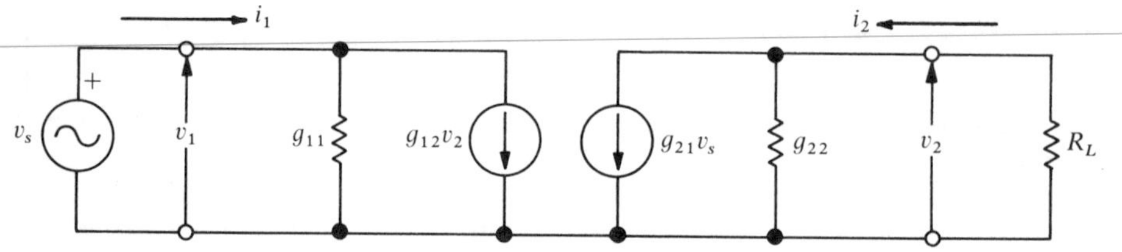

Fig. A.2–1. *Basic small-signal model for a FET amplifier operating at mid and low frequencies.*

By Eq. (A.2–2), $i_2 = -v_2/R_L$; equating this expression to Eq. (A.2–1b) and solving for the voltage gain, we have

$$A_v = \frac{v_2}{v_s} = -\frac{g_{21}}{\dfrac{1}{R_L} + g_{22}} \qquad \textbf{(A.2–3)}$$

To determine the current gain, v_2 in Eq. (A.2–1a) is replaced by Eq. (A.2–2):

$$i_1 = v_s g_{11} - g_{12} R_L i_2 \qquad \textbf{(A.2–4)}$$

By Eq. (A.2–3), $v_s = v_2/A_v$, or

$$v_s = -v_2 \frac{\left(\dfrac{1}{R_L} + g_{22}\right)}{g_{21}}$$

But, by Eq. (A.2–2), $v_2 = -i_2 R_L$; hence,

$$v_s = i_2 R_L \frac{\left(\dfrac{1}{R_L} + g_{22}\right)}{g_{21}} \qquad \textbf{(A.2–5)}$$

Substituting Eq. (A.2–5) in Eq. (A.2–4) and solving for the current gain, we get

$$A_i = \frac{g_{21}}{g_{11} + R_L(g_{11}g_{22} - g_{12}g_{21})} \qquad \textbf{(A.2–6)}$$

To find the input resistance, by Eq. (A.2–3),

$$v_2 = -\frac{g_{21} v_s}{\dfrac{1}{R_L} + g_{22}} \qquad \textbf{(A.2–7)}$$

Substituting Eq. (A.2–7) in Eq. (A.2–1a) and solving for $R_i = v_s/i_1$ yields

$$R_i = \frac{1}{g_{11} - \dfrac{g_{12}g_{21}}{1/R_L + g_{22}}} \qquad \textbf{(A.2–8)}$$

To determine the output resistance, v_s is set to zero. Because $v_s = v_1 = 0$, inspection of Fig. A.2–1 shows that dependent source $g_{21}v_s$ equals zero. Hence,

$$R_o = \frac{1}{g_{22}} \tag{A.2–9}$$

A.3 Indefinite-*y* Matrix

Consider the following *display*, or *array*, of quantities:

$$[y]_i = \begin{array}{c} \begin{matrix} G & D & S \end{matrix} \\ \begin{bmatrix} y_{11} & y_{12} & y_{13} \\ y_{21} & y_{22} & y_{23} \\ y_{31} & y_{32} & y_{33} \end{bmatrix} \end{array} \begin{matrix} G \\ D \\ S \end{matrix} \tag{A.3–1}$$

Equation (A.3–1) defines the *indefinite-y matrix*, where y_{11}, y_{12}, and so on are called the *elements* of the matrix. The first subscript denotes the row, and the second subscript the column, in which an element is located. For example, element y_{23} is located in the second row and third column in the matrix.

The indefinite-y matrix has the following useful property: *The sum of the elements in any row or in any column of the indefinite-y matrix is equal to zero.* This means, for example, that $y_{11} + y_{12} + y_{13} = 0$, $y_{12} + y_{22} + y_{32} = 0$, and so on.

For the *C-S* amplifier, source *S* is common to input *G* and output *D* terminals of the device. If we *cross out* column *S* and row *S* of Eq. (A.3–1), we are left with the following display:

$$[y]_{CS} = \begin{array}{c} \begin{matrix} G & D \end{matrix} \\ \begin{bmatrix} y_{11} & y_{12} \\ y_{21} & y_{22} \end{bmatrix} \end{array} \begin{matrix} G \\ D \end{matrix}$$

$$= \begin{array}{c} \begin{matrix} G & D \end{matrix} \\ \begin{bmatrix} 0 & 0 \\ g_{fs} & g_d \end{bmatrix} \end{array} \begin{matrix} G \\ D \end{matrix} \tag{A.3–2}$$

The elements of Eq. (A.3–2) are for the *C-S* amplifier, where

$$y_{11} = g_{11} = 0$$
$$y_{12} = g_{12} = 0$$
$$y_{21} = g_{21} = g_{fs}$$
$$y_{22} = g_{22} = g_d$$

Using Eq. (A.3–2) and the property of the indefinite-y matrix that the sum of the elements in any row or in any column equals zero, we can construct the indefinite-y matrix in terms of g_{fs} and g_d:

$$[y]_i = \begin{array}{c} \\ \\ \\ \end{array}\begin{matrix} G & D & S & \\ \end{matrix}$$

$$[y]_i = \begin{bmatrix} 0 & 0 & 0 \\ g_{fs} & g_d & -(g_{fs} + g_d) \\ -g_{fs} & -g_d & (g_{fs} + g_d) \end{bmatrix} \begin{matrix} G \\ D \\ S \end{matrix} \quad \text{(columns } G, D, S\text{)} \tag{A.3–3}$$

Note that the sum of the elements in each row and column is equal to zero. For example, in the second row, $g_{fs} + g_d - (g_{fs} + g_d) = 0$.

For the *C-D* (source follower) amplifier, column *D* and row *D* are crossed out. Therefore, Eq. (A.3–3) reduces to

$$[y]_{CD} = \begin{bmatrix} 0 & 0 \\ -g_{fs} & (g_{fs} + g_d) \end{bmatrix} \begin{matrix} G \\ S \end{matrix} \quad \text{(columns } G, S\text{)} \tag{A.3–4}$$

Hence, for the source follower, $g_{11} = g_{12} = 0, g_{21} = -g_{fs}$, and $g_{22} = g_{fs} + g_d$.

For the *C-G* amplifier, we cross out column *G* and row *G*:

$$[y]_{CS'} = \begin{bmatrix} g_d & -(g_{fs} + g_d) \\ -g_d & (g_{fs} + g_d) \end{bmatrix} \begin{matrix} D \\ S \end{matrix} \quad \text{(columns } D, S\text{)} \tag{A.3–5}$$

But *D* is the output terminal, and *S* is the input terminal, in the *C-G* amplifier. The result of Eq. (A.3–5) is for an amplifier where *D* is the input and *S* the output—a useless configuration. To correct this, Eq. (A.3–5) is altered by interchanging the elements along their diagonals, as shown in the following:

$$[y]_{CG} = \begin{bmatrix} (g_{fs} + g_d) & -g_d \\ -(g_{fs} + g_d) & g_d \end{bmatrix} \begin{matrix} S \\ D \end{matrix} \quad \text{(columns } S, D\text{)} \tag{A.3–6}$$

Hence, for the *C-G* amplifier, $g_{11} = (g_{fs} + g_d)$, $g_{12} = -g_d$, $g_{21} = -(g_{fs} + g_d)$, and $g_{22} = g_d$.

Appendix B

B.1 The Miller Effect

In Fig. B.1–1A, current I_1 flowing in Z is

$$I_1 = \frac{V_1 - V_2}{Z} \qquad \textbf{(B.1–1)}$$

If V_1 is factored out, we have

$$I_1 = V_1 \frac{\left(1 - \dfrac{V_2}{V_1}\right)}{Z} \qquad \textbf{(B.1–2)}$$

Ratio V_2/V_1 defines the voltage gain, A_v, of the amplifier in Fig. B.1–1A. Hence,

$$I_1 = \frac{V_1(1 - A_v)}{Z}$$

or

$$I_1 = \frac{V_1}{\dfrac{Z}{1 - A_v}} \qquad \textbf{(B.1–3)}$$

Equation (B.1–3) states that current I_1 is equal to the input voltage, V_1, divided by $Z/(1 - A_v)$.

Now, to determine I_2, from Fig. B.1–1A, we have

$$I_2 = \frac{V_2 - V_1}{Z}$$

$$= V_2 \frac{\left(1 - \dfrac{V_1}{V_2}\right)}{Z}$$

$$= V_2 \frac{\left(1 - \dfrac{1}{A_v}\right)}{Z}$$

or

$$I_2 = \frac{V_2}{\dfrac{Z}{(1 - 1/A_v)}} \qquad \textbf{(B.1–4)}$$

Equation (B.1–4) tells us that I_2 is equal to the output voltage, V_2, divided by $Z/(1 - 1/A_v)$.

Based on Eq. (B.1–3) and Eq. (B.1–4), impedance Z may be removed from its position across terminals 1 and 2, and Fig. B.1–1A may be redrawn as Fig. B.1–1B. In Fig. B.1–1B, the modified impedance $Z/(1 - A_v)$ is placed across the input terminals, and the modified impedance $Z/(1 - 1/A_v)$ is placed across the output terminals. From

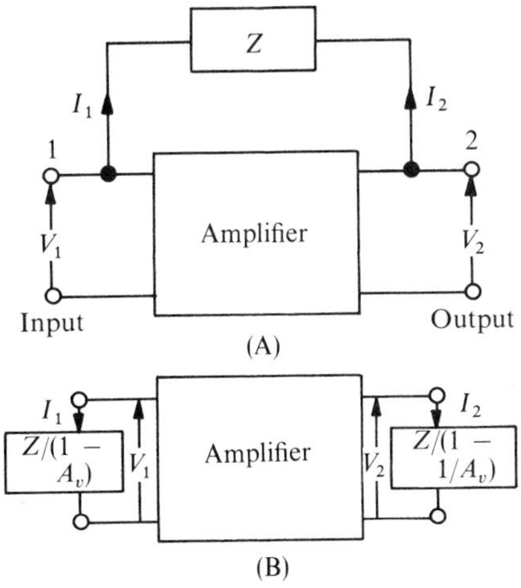

Fig. B.1–1. *Miller effect. Replacing feedback impedance Z in (A) by two modified impedances across the input and output terminals of the amplifier in (B).*

the preceding analysis, currents I_1 and I_2 are the same for this configuration as for that of Fig. B.1–1A. Hence, *both circuits are identical.*

B.2 Figures of Merit

Referring to Fig. B.2–1, assume that the output is short circuited (collector connected to emitter); hence, $R_C = 0$. The resultant model appears in Fig. B.2–2, excited by current source I_s. Because $R_C = 0$, $g_m R'_L = 0$, and by Eq. (8–19), $C_i = C_{b'e} + C_{b'c}$. Voltage $V_{b'e}$ is equal to current I_s divided by the admittance of $1/r_{b'e}$ in parallel with $C_{b'e} + C_{b'c}$:

$$V_{b'e} = \frac{I_s}{\dfrac{1}{r_{b'e}} + j\omega(C_{b'e} + C_{b'c})}$$

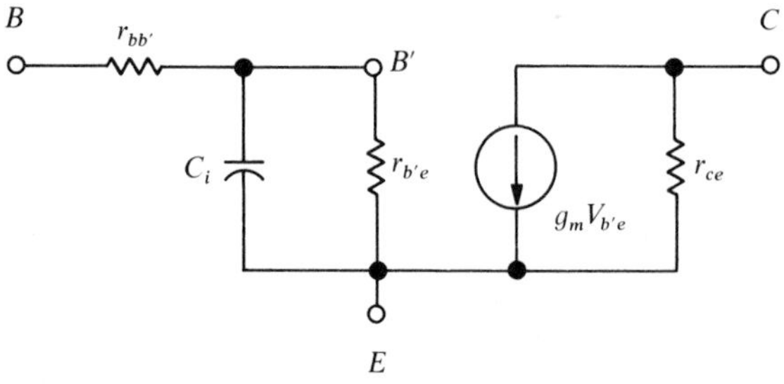

Fig. B.2–1. *Simplified hybrid-pi model of a BJT.*

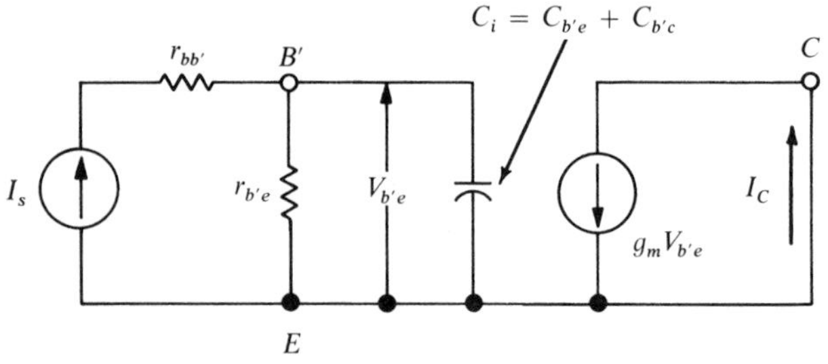

Fig. B.2–2. *Model used for deriving f_β. Collector C is connected to emitter E.*

The short-circuit current flowing in the collector is equal to $g_m V_{b'e}$, or

$$I_c = \frac{g_m I_s}{\dfrac{1}{r_{b'e}} + j\omega(C_{b'e} + C_{b'c})}$$

Multiplying the numerator and denominator by $r_{b'e}$, the short-circuit current gain, $A_{is}(j\omega)$, is

$$A_{is}(j\omega) = \frac{I_c}{I_s} = \frac{g_m r_{b'c}}{1 + j\omega(C_{b'e} + C_{b'c})r_{b'e}}$$

But $g_m r_{b'e} = h_{fe}$; hence,

$$A_{is}(j\omega) = \frac{h_{fe}}{1 + j\omega(C_{b'e} + C_{b'c})r_{b'e}} \qquad \textbf{(B.2-1)}$$

Let

$$\omega_\beta = \frac{1}{(C_{b'e} + C_{b'c})r_{b'e}}$$

or, dividing by 2π,

$$f_\beta = \frac{0.159}{(C_{b'e} + C_{b'c})r_{b'e}} \qquad \textbf{(B.2-2)}$$

Substitution of Eq. (B.2–2) in Eq. (B.2–1) yields, in terms of frequency, f,

$$A_{is}(jf) = \frac{h_{fe}}{1 + \dfrac{jf}{f_\beta}} \qquad \textbf{(B.2-3)}$$

An examination of Eq. (B.2–3) shows that when $f = f_\beta$, the beta cutoff frequency, the magnitude of the short-circuit current gain is $0.707h_{fe}$. For large values of f_β, which are desirable, capacitances $C_{b'e}$ and $C_{b'c}$ and resistance $r_{b'e}$ should be small.

The current gain-bandwidth product, f_T, is defined as the frequency at which the magnitude of the short-circuit current gain is unity. Letting $A_{is}(jf) = 1$ and $f = f_T$ in Eq. (B.2–3), we obtain

$$1 = \frac{h_{fe}}{\sqrt{1 + \left(\dfrac{f_T}{f_\beta}\right)^2}}$$

Squaring both sides and simplifying,

$$\left(\frac{f_T}{f_\beta}\right)^2 = h_{fe}^2 - 1 \simeq h_{fe}^2$$

Hence,

$$f_T = h_{fe} f_\beta \qquad \textbf{(B.2-4)}$$

If Eq. (B.2–4) is substituted in Eq. (B.2–2), and $g_m = h_{fe}/r_{b'e}$, we obtain an alternate expression for f_T:

$$f_T = \frac{0.159 g_m}{C_{b'e} + C_{b'c}} \qquad \textbf{(B.2-5)}$$

B.3 Response of a High-Pass Network

Applying voltage division to the high-pass network of Fig. B.3–1, output voltage, V_o, is

$$V_o = \frac{RV_s}{R + \dfrac{1}{j\omega C}}$$

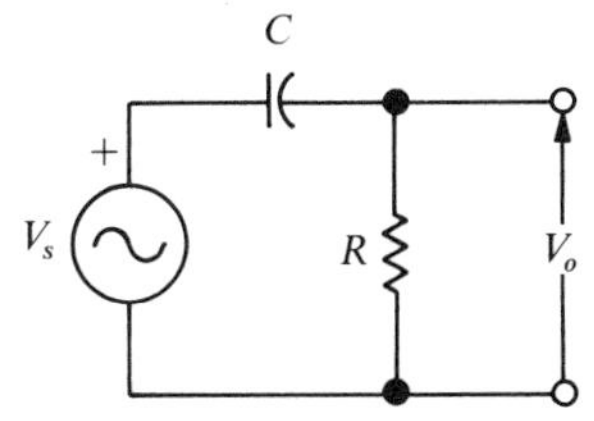

Fig. B.3–1. *Basic high-pass RC network.*

Dividing the numerator and denominator by R and solving for V_o/V_s,

$$\frac{V_o}{V_s} = \frac{1}{1 - \dfrac{j}{\omega RC}} \tag{B.3–1}$$

Let,

$$\omega_L = \frac{1}{RC} \tag{B.3–2}$$

Substitution of Eq. (B.3–2) in Eq. (B.3–1) yields

$$\frac{V_o}{V_s} = \frac{1}{1 - \dfrac{j\omega_L}{\omega}} \tag{B.3–3}$$

Expressing Eq. (B.3–3) in polar form,

$$\left|\frac{V_o}{V_s}\right| = \frac{1}{\sqrt{1 + \left(\dfrac{\omega_L}{\omega}\right)^2}} \tag{B.3–4a}$$

and

$$\theta = \tan^{-1}\left(\frac{\omega_L}{\omega}\right) \tag{B.3–4b}$$

ANSWERS TO SELECTED PROBLEMS

CHAPTER 2:

P2-1. **(a)** 24.06 μA; **(b)** -10 nA.
P2-2. **(a)** 1.205 mA; **(b)** -10 nA.
P2-3. **(a)** 0.6 V; **(b)** 0.5 V.
P2-4. **(a)** $P_{\text{diode}} = 0.04$ W, $P_{R_L} = 0.4$ W; **(b)** $P_{\text{diode}} = 1.06$ W, $P_{R_L} = 10.6$ W.
P2-11. **(a), (b), (c)** 0 V; **(d)** 10 V; **(e)** 5 V.
P2-12. **(a)** 0 V; **(b), (c), (d), (e)** 10 V.

CHAPTER 3:

P3-1. **(a)** 0.975; **(b)** 117; **(c)** 114.
P3-3. **(a)** 49; **(b)** 150 nA.
P3-4. 0.984.
P3-6. **(a)** $I_B = 0.06$ mA, $I_C = 3.6$ mA, $V_{CE} = 12.8$ V.
P3-7. 51.
P3-8. **(a)** -1 V; **(b)** 12 V.
P3-11. **(a)** -3 V; **(b)** -26 V.

CHAPTER 4:

P4-5. **(a)** 100 Ω; **(b)** $222.2\ \Omega \leq R_L \leq \infty$.
P4-7. $40.5\text{ V} \leq V' \leq 60\text{ V}$.
P4-8. $33.8\text{ V} \leq V' \leq 53.3\text{ V}$.
P4-9. $210.5\ \Omega \leq R_L \leq \infty$.
P4-12. 252.8 W.
P4-13. 685.4 W.
P4-16. **(a)** 20.4 pF; **(b)** 15.07 pF; **(c)** 11.9 pF.

CHAPTER 5:

P5-1. **(a)** 200; **(b)** 60; **(c)** 12,000.
P5-2. **(b)** Slope $= -1/1000$, intercept = 20 mA.
P5-4. 57.5 kΩ.
P5-5. **(c)** Q**(a)** $\simeq 8$ V, 12 mA; Q**(b)** $\simeq 6$ V, 11.5 mA.
P5-6. **(a)** $0.091v_s$; **(b)** $0.8v_s$.
P5-7. **(b)** $V_{D_Q} \simeq 17$ V, $I_{D_Q} \simeq 2.5$ mA.
P5-9. **(a)** 66.7 mV; **(b)** -2 V; **(c)** 0.75 mA.
P5-12. **(a)** 30 dB; **(b)** 54 dB; **(c)** 26 dB.
P5-14. **(a)** 300; **(b)** 49.6 dB.

CHAPTER 6:

P6-2. **(a)** 0 V; **(b)** 5.32 V; **(c)** 9.88 V; **(d)** $\simeq 10$ V.
P6-3. **(a)** 10 V; **(b)** 1.57 V; **(c)** 0.318 V; **(d)** 0.159 V.
P6-5. **(a)** -125; **(b)** -41.67.
P6-6. 15.
P6-9. $h_{11} = 1000\ \Omega$, $h_{12} = 10^{-4}$, $h_{21} = 40$, $h_{22} = 10^{-5}$ ℧.
P6-10. $h_{11} = 1500\ \Omega$, $h_{12} = 10^{-3}$, $h_{21} = 30$, $h_{22} = 10^{-4}$ ℧.
P6-11. **(a)** -238.1; **(b)** 95.2; **(c)** $-22{,}667.12$; **(d)** 2000 Ω; **(e)** 100 kΩ.
P6-12. **(a)** 250; **(b)** -0.99; **(c)** -247.5; **(d)** 19.8 Ω; **(e)** 10^7 Ω.
P6-13. **(a)** 0.996; **(b)** -96.2; **(c)** -95.8; **(d)** 483 kΩ; **(e)** 19.8 Ω.
P6-15. **(a)** 50; **(b)** 1 kΩ; **(c)** -25; **(d)** 50 kΩ.
P6-16. **(b)** -100; **(c)** -66.7.
P6-19. **(a)** 19.6; **(b)** 0.95.
P6-20. **(a)** 34.48; **(b)** 0.972.

CHAPTER 7:

P7-2. **(a)** 0.143 mA; **(b)** 1.22 kΩ.
P7-3. **(a)** 0.05 mA; **(b)** 12 kΩ.
P7-5. **(a)** 6 V; **(b)** 0 V.
P7-7. **(a)** 0.046 mA; **(b)** 17 V and 1.84 mA.
P7-9. **(a)** -2.22; **(b)** -156.4.
P7-12. 13.47 μF.
P7-14. **(a)** 1.06 μF; **(c)** -64.26.
P7-16. **(a)** $V_{CE} = 12$ V, $I_C = 200$ mA; **(b)** 12 V; **(c)** 2260 Ω.
P7-18. $R_S = 74\ \Omega$, $R_D = 126\ \Omega$.
P7-20. $R_1 = 1.5$ MΩ, $R_2 = 107.1$ kΩ.
P7-22. **(b)** -13; **(c)** -33.5.
P7-24. **(a)** 0 V; **(b)** -2 V; **(c)** 500 Ω.
P7-25. **(a)** 10 kΩ; **(b)** 450 kΩ.

CHAPTER 8:

P8-1. 6360 Ω.
P8-4. **(b)** -30.5; **(c)** 690 kHz.
P8-5. **(b)** -225.7; **(c)** 116.5 kHz.
P8-8. 9 pF.
P8-9. **(b)** $A_o = -165.6$, $f_H = 11.86$ kHz.
P8-11. 0.318 μF.
P8-14. 0.397 μF.
P8-16. 105.2 dB.
P8-17. 59.2 dB.
P8-19. 64,282 Hz.

CHAPTER 9:

P9-1. 15.7×10^{-3}.
P9-2. 14.7×10^{-3}.
P9-4. **(a)** -11; **(b)** 5.83 Hz.
P9-7. -5.
P9-10. **(a)** 0.976; **(b)** 41 kΩ; **(c)** 12.5 Ω.
P9-12. **(a)** -16.16; **(b)** 1.34 kΩ; **(c)** 22.22 kΩ.
P9-14. **(a)** -166.7 kΩ; **(b)** 0.25×10^{-4}; **(c)** -32.24; **(d)** 386.8 Ω; **(e)** 967.1 Ω.
P9-16. 500 Ω, -24×10^{-3} ℧; **(c)** -3.7; **(d)** 13 kΩ; **(e)** 7.7 kΩ.
P9-17. **(a)** 100 Ω, -28.6×10^{-3} ℧; **(c)** -13.8; **(d)** 3860 Ω; **(e)** 25.9 kΩ.

CHAPTER 10:

P10-6. **(a)** $\simeq 0.54$ h; **(b)** $\simeq 5$ h.
P10-8. 4.61 h.
P10-10. 2.236 μm.
P10-12. $\simeq$1020°C.
P10-14. 160 s.
P10-16. **(a)** 0.7 μm; **(b)** 24 μm; **(c)** 30 μm.
P10-17. **(a)** 1.33; **(b)** 3.99 μm.
P10-18. **(a)** 0.8; **(b)** 2.4 μm.

CHAPTER 11:

P11-1. **(a)** 2 mV; **(b)** 3 mV.
P11-3. 1000, 60 dB.
P11-7. **(a)** -25; **(b)** -28.6; **(c)** 1.144.
P11-9. 0.81 mA.
P11-10. **(a)** $R_{id} = 3$ kΩ, $A_{vd} = -800$; **(b)** $R_{id} = 30$ kΩ, $A_{vd} = -80$.

P11-14. $V_{B_1} = 1.107$ V, $V_{E_1} = 0.407$ V, $V_{C_1} = V_{B_2} = 0.93$ V, $V_{E_2} = 0.23$ V, $V_{C_2} = 2.7$ V.
P11-16. **(a)** $I_{C_1} = I_{C_2} \simeq 0.35$ mA, $I_{C_3} = I_{C_4} \simeq 3.9$ mA, $I_{C_5} = 0.7$ mA, $I_{B_1} = I_{B_2} = 0.0035$ mA, $I_{B_3} = I_{B_4} = 0.39$ mA, $I_{B_5} = 0.007$ mA; **(b)** $V_{C_1} = V_{C_2} = 8.5$ V; **(c)** $V_{E_3} = V_{E_4} = 7.8$ V; **(d)** 102 mW.

CHAPTER 12:

P12-5. 2.33 V.
P12-8. 0 V.
P12-10. **(a)** 10 kΩ; **(b)** 0.013 μF.
P12-12. ±8 mV.
P12-14. −20 mV.
P12-17. **(a)** 30°; **(b)** −50°.

CHAPTER 13:

P13-1. 0.125 W.
P13-3. 0.1 W.
P13-5. **(a)** 12.15 V; **(b)** 0.148 W.
P13-7. **(a)** 25 mW.
P13-9. **(a)** 160 Ω; **(b)** 1 kΩ; **(c)** 100 kΩ.
P13-13. $R_B = 9.65$ kΩ, $N_p/N_s = 5.59$.
P13-16. **(a)** 0%.
P13-17. 8 W.
P13-19. **(a)** 70.65%; **(b)** 50.9%.
P13-23. Transformer: 300-Ω to 4-Ω, center-tapped. Transistor: $I_{C(\max)} = 0.267$ A, $BV_{CEO} = 40$ V.

CHAPTER 14:

P14-1. 0.2 A.
P14-3. $V_{ce} = 14.28$ V.
P14-4. 45 W.
P14-7. **(a)** 3.77 mA; **(b)** 3.34 kΩ.
P14-9. 1.4 A.
P14-12. 20°C/W.
P14-13. **(a)** 3.75 W; **(b)** 1.25 W.
P14-17. 1.8°C/W.
P14-19. 115 in.^{2} for heat sink having flat vertical fins.

CHAPTER 15:

P15-1. 52.61 V.
P15-3. 0.526 A.
P15-4. **(a)** 111.2 V; **(b)** $N_p/N_s = 28/111.2$.
P15-7. **(a)** 330.9 V; **(b)** 210.4 V.
P15-9. **(a)** $R_L = 100$ Ω, $N_p/N_s = 117/111.2$.
P15-11. $R_L = 100$ Ω, $N_p/N_s = 117/111.2$.
P15-13. **(a)** 65.27 V; **(c)** 4.82%.
P15-15. 8.33%.
P15-17. $C > 8488$ μF; use 10,000 μF. $N_p/N_s = 117/7.77$.
P15-19. $C > 6630$ μF. $N_p/N_s = 117/9.22$.
P15-23. 95.24 V.
P15-25. 0.28%
P15-27. 0.088 H.

CHAPTER 16:

P16-1. Output voltage is regulated.
P16-3. $P_Z = 800$ mW; zener diode will be destroyed.
P16-5. $105.3\ \Omega \leq R_L \leq 500\ \Omega$.
P16-7. No voltage regulation; zener diode will be destroyed.
P16-9. 180 Ω.
P16-11. 15.55 V.
P16-17. 28.33 mA.
P16-19. 106.5°C.
P16-20. 16.35 V.

CHAPTER 17:

P17-1. $50° \leq \theta_C \leq 80°$.
P17-3. $40° \leq \theta_C \leq 75°$.
P17-5. 50 A.
P17-7. 162.56 W.
P17-9. **(a)** 50%; **(b)** 120 W.
P17-11. 233.3 Ω.
P17-13. 0.488 Hz.
P17-15. $R_T C_T = 5.457$ s. Use $R_T = 110$ kΩ, $C_T = 50$ μF.
P17-17. 75 ms.

CHAPTER 18:

P18-1. **(a)** 11; **(b)** 53; **(c)** 34.
P18-3. 361 (decimal), 10110100 (binary).
P18-7. 0010.
P18-15. **(a)** $AC + \bar{A}B\bar{C}$; **(b)** $C(\bar{A} + \bar{B}) + AB\bar{C}$; **(c)** $YX + Z$.
P18-20. $\bar{Y}Z + XZ + \bar{X}Y\bar{Z}$.

CHAPTER 19:

P19-1. Not saturated.
P19-3. 7.168 V.
P19-5. Assuming a load current of 10 mA and a base current of 1 mA, $R_C = 480$ Ω and $R_B = 4.3$ kΩ.
P19-7. 2005 ns.
P19-9. 1.367 V.
P19-11. 11.39 kΩ.
P19-17. 3.
P19-20. 2.13 V.

CHAPTER 20:

P20-2. 0.76 V.
P20-5. F.O. = 34; manufacturer specifies an F.O. of 15 for conservative operation.
P20-7. 24 ns.
P20-12. 1 mA.
P20-14. **(a)** $I_{D_1} = I_{D_2} = 1.46$ mA; **(b)** same as **(a)**.

CHAPTER 21:

P21-1. The circuit operates as a bistable MV.
P21-5. **(a)** 6; **(b)** 10.
P21-7. Yes, proper switching occurs.
P21-9. **(a)** 7.87 V; **(b)** 5.96 V; **(c)** 24 V.
P21-11. 0.1739 V.
P21-13. **(a)** 0.0043 μF; **(b)** $R_{C_1} = R_{C_2} > 660$ Ω.
P21-15. 69 μs.
P21-17. 183 Ω.
P21-19. For $C_1 = C_2 = 1$ μF, $R_1 = 289$ Ω and $R_2 = 578$ Ω.
P21-21. 1.14 ms.
P21-23. $C = 0.32$ μF, $R_B = 20$ kΩ.

CHAPTER 23:

P23-3. 10.34 V.
P23-5. Input is noise.
P23-7. 18.75 V.
P23-9. 5 V.
P23-11. −6.25 V.

INDEX